*

AMERICAN WRITERS SERIES
*
HARRY HAYDEN CLARK
General Editor

*

✸ AMERICAN WRITERS SERIES ✸

Volumes of representative selections, prepared by American scholars under the general editorship of Harry Hayden Clark, University of Wisconsin. Volumes now ready are starred.

AMERICAN TRANSCENDENTALISTS, *Raymond Adams, University of North Carolina*

*WILLIAM CULLEN BRYANT, *Tremaine McDowell, University of Minnesota*

*JAMES FENIMORE COOPER, *Robert E. Spiller, Swarthmore College*

*JONATHAN EDWARDS, *Clarence H. Faust, University of Chicago, and Thomas H. Johnson, Lawrenceville School*

*RALPH WALDO EMERSON, *Frederic I. Carpenter, Harvard University*

*BENJAMIN FRANKLIN, *Frank Luther Mott, University of Iowa, and Chester E. Jorgenson, Wayne University*

*ALEXANDER HAMILTON AND THOMAS JEFFERSON, *Frederick C. Prescott, Cornell University*

BRET HARTE, *Joseph B. Harrison, University of Washington*

*NATHANIEL HAWTHORNE, *Austin Warren, Boston University*

OLIVER WENDELL HOLMES, *S. I. Hayakawa, University of Wisconsin, and Howard Mumford Jones, Harvard University*

*WASHINGTON IRVING, *Henry A. Pochmann, Mississippi State College*

HENRY JAMES, *Lyon Richardson, Western Reserve University*

*HENRY WADSWORTH LONGFELLOW, *Odell Shepard, Trinity College*

JAMES RUSSELL LOWELL, *Norman Foerster, University of Iowa, and Harry H. Clark, University of Wisconsin*

*HERMAN MELVILLE, *Willard Thorp, Princeton University*

*JOHN LOTHROP MOTLEY, *Chester P. Higby and B. T. Schantz, University of Wisconsin*

THOMAS PAINE, *Harry H. Clark, University of Wisconsin*

*FRANCIS PARKMAN, *Wilbur L. Schramm, University of Iowa*

*EDGAR ALLAN POE, *Margaret Alterton, University of Iowa, and Hardin Craig, Stanford University*

WILLIAM HICKLING PRESCOTT, *Michael Kraus, College of the City of New York, and William Charvat, New York University*

*SOUTHERN POETS, *Edd Winfield Parks, University of Georgia*

SOUTHERN PROSE, *Gregory Paine, University of North Carolina*

*HENRY DAVID THOREAU, *Bartholow Crawford, University of Iowa*

*MARK TWAIN, *Fred Lewis Pattee, Rollins College*

*WALT WHITMAN, *Floyd Stovall, University of Texas*

JOHN GREENLEAF WHITTIER, *Harry H. Clark, University of Wisconsin, and Bertha M. Stearns, Wellesley College*

Pen drawing by Kerr Eby, after
the painting by J. O. Eaton

HERMAN MELVILLE

ÆT. CA. 50

Herman Melville

REPRESENTATIVE SELECTIONS, WITH
INTRODUCTION, BIBLIOGRAPHY, AND NOTES

BY

WILLARD THORP

*Assistant Professor of English
Princeton University*

AWS

AMERICAN BOOK COMPANY
*New York · Cincinnati · Chicago
Boston · Atlanta*

PREFACE

The time has not yet arrived when a biographer can write definitively about Herman Melville. The grip of the academic tradition of American criticism has only just released him. His reputation still suffers both from neglect and from the extravagancies of his new worshippers. The facts of his life history are not and probably never will be so numerous as those of the other great figures in our literature, but important information about him turns up constantly in the journals. If, then, the Introduction and Notes to this volume in the American Writers Series contain more bald biographical material and indulge in more controversy than is the custom in the other books of the series, this will be excused, I hope, because Melville was born late to fame.

It is the good fortune, however, of one who undertakes to study Melville at this juncture to come upon hitherto unpublished writing of his and new records of episodes in his life. In the following pages will be found, specifically, new biographical material from the Duyckinck Collection of the New York Public Library, an unknown review by Melville, an unpublished poem of considerable personal interest, five unpublished letters, three letters from which only fragments have previously been quoted and nine which have not before been given in a correct and complete text.

It is a pleasant duty to acknowledge the assistance which I have had from various people. Mr. H. H. Clark, the General Editor of the American Writers Series, has been most generous with his counsel at every point in the undertaking. To Mr. F. J. Mather, Jr., first of the modern critics of Melville, I am indebted for information and the loan of first editions. Mrs. Eleanor Melville Metcalf, Melville's granddaughter, has been, as she is when any student seeks her aid, eager to assist in the presentation of a frank and true picture of her grandfather's career.   To Mr. Lewis Mumford, a pioneer in Melville biography, I am under obligation, and also to Mr. Carl Stroven of the University of Hawaii.   Mr. Malcolm Young, Reference Librarian of Princeton University, has procured many rare books for my use.   I have been the recipient of courtesies from Mr. V. H. Paltsits, Curator of Manuscripts at the New York Public Library, and his staff; the librarians of the New York Historical Society; the curators of the Treasure Room of the Harvard College Library; and the library staff of the Berkshire Athenaeum.

W. T.

CONTENTS

HERMAN MELVILLE

I. FORMATIVE INFLUENCES

Among the voluminous business papers of Allan Melville, father of Herman Melville, is a sheet of notes for a speech which he apparently delivered to a group of young men eager to learn his method for getting ahead in the world. He cautioned them against vice; advised them to reverence the religion of their fathers and gain the esteem of the ladies by "uniform politeness and attention." They must remember that "money is the only solid substratum on which man can safely build in this world."[1] Allan was describing his own industriously cultivated virtues.

With the support of his father, Major Thomas Melville, a patriot of the Revolution, with whom he had been in business in Boston, he settled first in Albany. He had been four years married when he removed to New York in 1819, determined to make himself a solid citizen in that thriving metropolis which now held the commercial leadership in the country. In August of this year his third child and second son, Herman, was born at 6 Pearl Street. Allan's business prospered. No establishment in the city displayed more elegant French fabrics, silk vestings, *drap royal*, gloves, hose, or perfumeries. With an increasing income he was able to remove in 1824 to a house in suburban Bleecker Street.

Within two years a business depression halted this upward course. A firm in which he was a silent partner failed. For the expansion of his property he had borrowed from his father to the extent of $22,580.96, honorably, though disastrously for

[1] Gansevoort-Lansing Collection, New York Public Library.

his children, requesting that the debts should be charged against his eventual share in the Major's estate. He was obligated to his uncle-in-law. In 1830 he retreated to Albany where he struggled to re-establish himself. In January, 1832, he died, his mind deranged by worry and overwork.[2]

Allan Melville's career followed the pattern of the life histories of his generation, for which money, deserved and expected as a reward for piety and hard work, was the only "solid substratum." But he was hardly the ridiculous prig he has been painted. He was familiar, from his many Atlantic voyages, with the European scene. He had sat at Governor Clinton's dinner table. Visiting French merchants were commended to his good offices. French societies in the city were honored to have him enrolled in their membership. He was conscious of his distinguished Scotch ancestry, and felt keenly, if self-righteously, the responsibility which rested on him as his father's favorite son after his brother Thomas had disgraced himself in Paris by failing in business and secretly marrying a French wife. Allan's portrait by Ezra Ames, now in the Henry E. Huntington Library, reveals a man of force and a patrician in dress and demeanor.[3]

If Allan had prospered, books and pictures and objects of *virtu* would have multiplied in his house, things which his son later thought indispensable for sustaining life. It is not fantastic to trace his mature longing for the amenities to a feeling that they were part of his lost birthright. But if we read as

[2] Letter of Peter Gansevoort to Thomas Melville, Jr., Jan. 10, 1832, Gansevoort-Lansing Collection, New York Public Library.

[3] This portrait, which was reproduced in the catalogue of the Thomas B. Clarke sale, 1919, should be better known. It is surely a more accurate picture of him than the languid and foppish sketch made in Paris in 1810 and reproduced on p. 56 of Mr. Weaver's biography. Melville may have had the two portraits in mind when he makes Mrs. Glendinning in *Pierre* prefer the large and elegant portrait of her husband to the impromptu sketch of a "gay-hearted, youthful gentleman."

autobiography passages in *Pierre* which describe the filial feeling of the hero we perceive that his son allowed his fancy to
play with the idea of Allan Melville as a *seigneur* and man of
the world to a degree which would have shocked that strict
New Englander whom French and Knickerbocker society had
only partially thawed.

In the absence of material for a picture of Melville's mother,
Maria Gansevoort, biographers have tried to model her features
after Mrs. Glendinning in *Pierre*, a dangerous course since we
know so much about that imperious lady which cannot be true
of Maria Melville. If her son had drawn her picture in *Pierre*
so plainly that all might recognize it she would have been the
first to resent the caricature.[4] What is known is that she was
proud of her patroon and patriot ancestors, a dutiful wife and
ruthless housekeeper and, after her husband's death, a resourceful head of the family. Her parents were conscientious members
of the Dutch Reformed Church. They passed on their piety
to her, and she was strict in her religious observances all her
life. However quickly the young Herman threw off the orthodoxy which descended to him from both sides of the family,
two marks of it remained, a minute knowledge of the Bible
and a speculative interest in the central problem of Calvinism,
the freedom of the will.

Allan Melville regrets, in two letters which survive, that his
second son was a dull boy at his school tasks. He forgave him
this shortcoming, since, at the age of eleven, he seemed "to
have chosen Commerce as a favorite pursuit, whose practical

---

[4]One wishes Mr. Weaver had given the source of the remark
about his mother supposed to have been made by Melville: "She
hated me" (*Herman Melville*, 62). The tone of a letter, written by
him to his mother in 1870 (Paltsits, *Family Correspondence*, 22–23)
indicates the relationship between them when the son was 51 and the
mother 79. He still hastens to do her bidding and say what she will
like to hear, but there are ironic touches which must have escaped
the old lady's eyes.

activity can well dispense with much book knowledge."[5] Like
many a parent Allan Melville saw himself mirrored in his off-
spring. Herman's delight in pictures of Versailles and French
men-of-war, his gazing with wonder at the word "London"
on the title page of the *Spectator*, the eagerness with which
he cross-questioned the family servant who had actually been
in Paris and listened to his father's tales of life in foreign
capitals evidently deceived the merchant ambitious to found
a great importing house and leave it to his heir. This son,
he believed, though "backward in speech and somewhat slow
of comprehension," would be his successor. He little dreamed
these interests betokened an "everlasting itch for things remote" and a love for sailing on forbidden seas and landing on
barbarous coasts.

Two months after Allan's death in 1832, his eldest son
Gansevoort opened in Albany a cap and fur store, with the
backing of his mother and her brother Peter Gansevoort.
Herman attended for a time the excellent Albany Academy.
In 1834, to help the family finances, he worked in his uncle's
bank. The next year he was a clerk in Gansevoort's store.
He spent most of 1836 with his reprobate uncle Thomas Melville as "active assistant" on his Pittsfield farm. To the romantic boy the mild and kindly man with his satinwood snuff
box and French manners, so incongruous with his rustic surroundings, seemed a courtier of Louis XVI reduced as a refugee
to haymaking on a Berkshire hillside.[6]

If we follow the sequence of events in *Redburn*, we infer
that Melville's first sea voyage, under the hard-bargaining
Captain Riga of the *Highlander*, took place between the late
spring and the autumn of 1837. There is no reason to suppose
that Melville was impelled to go to sea for any other reason

---

[5] *Family Correspondence*, 4.

[6] J. E. A. Smith, *Herman Melville*, 7 (quoting Melville's sketch of
his uncle written for *The History of Pittsfield*, Springfield, 1876).

than those which actuated Redburn: "Sad disappointments in several plans which I had sketched for my future life, the necessity of doing something for myself, united to a naturally roving disposition, had now conspired within me, to send me to sea as a sailor."[7]

After making allowance for the fact that Melville was not telling the story of his life in *Redburn* but was seeking to create an atmosphere of pathos mingled with romance, we may suppose that the effect on a boy of seventeen of the brutal experience of fo'c'sle life and of the horrors of the slums and booble-alleys of Liverpool and the steerage on the return trip, must have been as deeply impressive on him as on the character he created. Melville's hatred of man's inhumanity to man originated in the savage thoughts which coursed through his mind as he explored Launcelott's Hey and the waterfront of the Sodom-like city in the days of the Chartists.

The three years which elapsed before the itch for things remote impelled him to sign on for a whaling voyage are the most obscure in his biography. His wife once set down the fact that during this period he taught school at intervals in Pittsfield and in Greenbush (now East Albany), New York.[8] One letter from these days survives, a dutiful, stiff little report to his uncle Peter describing his school under the Washington Mountain in the Sykes district five miles from Pittsfield.[9] Some of his scholars, who numbered thirty, were as old as he, but, contrary to the rumor which has been dug up by S. Foster Damon, Melville on his own testimony quickly gathered them "under a proper organization" and was able to improve

---

[7] *Works*, V, 1. References to Melville's works are to the Standard Edition.

[8] The passage from the Commonplace Book is quoted by Weaver, 113.

[9] Dated Dec. 31, 1837 (*Family Correspondence*, 5–7). The schoolhouse still stands, moved down the road and transformed into a private dwelling.

his leisure time "by occasional writting & reading."[10]   The
experience afforded him plenty of opportunity to study directly
one of the most vaunted of democratic institutions, the free
school.   His conclusions submitted to his uncle in his letter
are the first sign of his dissent from the great American dream:
"Orators may declaim concerning the universally-diffused blessings of education in our Country, and Essayests may exhaust
their magazine of adje[ctives] in extolling our systim of common
school instruction,—but when reduced to practise, the high
and sanguine hopes excited by its imposing appearance in
theory—are a little dashed."

There is no call to make a mystery about the motives which
sent Melville to New Bedford in January, 1841, to sign on for
a whaling voyage.   Ambitious young men in that age went
west or down to the sea unless their careers were already plotted
for them.   A whole literature had come into being describing
the glamorous new world of the South Seas and showing the
way to wealth in a whale ship.   Incredible stories of adventures
like Bligh's account of the mutiny on the *Bounty*, retold by
Sir John Barrow and versified by Lord Byron in "The Island"
(1823), troubled the dreams of romantic boys.   Books like
Kotzebue's *A New Voyage Round the World* (1830) and Captain
Beechey's *Narrative of a Voyage to the Pacific and Beering's
Straits* (1831) lured the imagination to strange places.   For
the more practical minded who wished to master the natural
science and economics of whaling there were such books as
Thomas Beale's *Natural History of the Sperm Whale* (1839)
and Obed Macy's *History of Nantucket* (1836).   A voyage
round the Horn was considered a good cure for wayward boys

[10] *Ibid.*, 5.   The *Boston Museum* for Jan. 31, 1852, asserted that
Melville was driven "out of school by two naughty boys" (S. F.
Damon, "Why Ishmael Went to Sea," *American Literature*, II,
281–283).   J. E. A. Smith's biographical sketch mentions a rebellion
in which some of the bigger boys undertook to "lick" him, but
declares that Melville was the victor.

as well as an opportunity for ambitious ones. Especially after the publication of Dana's *Two Years Before the Mast* (1840), anxious mothers worried lest their sons be infected with a mania to run away to sea.

Melville had no prospects and lacked the training necessary to follow his brothers Gansevoort and Allan into the law. He is telling the truth about himself, without artistic exaggeration, in the first chapter of *Moby-Dick*, when he says there is nothing surprising in his quietly taking ship to cure the spleen and regulate the circulation. It is plain human nature to go to sea. "If they but knew it, almost all men in their degree, some time or other, cherish very nearly the same feelings toward the ocean with me." This famous voyage in the *Acushnet* was not his only departure seaward to drive off the spleen. Three times in later years, after he had settled down to a land-lubberly life, he took ship to drive out the "drizzly November" in his soul. Two of these voyages restored his mental health when poverty and the struggle to fend it off had brought him near the danger line.

What did these years at sea mean to Melville? To those who know *Redburn* and *Moby-Dick* the question is otiose, for the record tells plainly that they meant the fulfillment of the boy's romantic desire to round the world and look in at all its strange ports. It mattered little that the longing to find the earthly paradise was soon replaced with the need to return home. These alternating urges—to be a vagabond on the loose, and to be secure, with books on the table and a good bottle in the sideboard waiting for a friend to crack it with him—are familiar to those who know him well. But for the time he sleeps as contentedly at sea as the Nantucketer who "at nightfall . . . out of sight of land, furls his sails, and lays him to his rest, while under his very pillow rush herds of walruses and whales."[11]

[11] *Works*, VII, 79.

Mr. Lincoln Colcord in his "Notes on Moby-Dick"[12] observed that Melville's nautical psychology was that of the fo'c'sle, the psychology of obeying orders. He evinced little of that professional interest in seamanship which would show in detailed remarks about the ship's position and the orders from the quarter-deck for her maneuvering. He had no ambition to command a ship, like his sailor brother Tom, the captain of the *Meteor*. When he dipped his hand in the tar bucket and shared the kid with his fellow sailors he adopted their point of view and felt the solidarity built up of common grievances, which always holds the oppressed together. He loafed in the maintop as the others did and was not easy to find when ordered aloft. He was never better than his vocation. He showed as "brown a chest and as hard a hand as the tarriest of them all." Life in the fo'c'sle helped to make him a genuine democrat, a passionate hater of all forms of tyranny and shows of authority.

The contrast between Melville and R. H. Dana, Jr., whom he knew and admired, inevitably suggests itself. W. Clark Russell put the difference thus: "Melville is essentially American: Dana writes as a straight-headed Englishman would; he is clear, convincing, utterly unaffected."[13] We should have amended the passage to read: "Dana writes as a straight-headed English gentleman would." For Dana, his two years before the mast were an adventurous interlude before he began the serious pursuit of a profession. No details of the management of the ship or the business she was engaged in escaped his attention, but he spun no yarns out of what he saw, as Melville did. The charm of his narrative lies in its minute and utter truthfulness. Sympathetic as he was with the tribulations of his fellow seamen, one feels all along that Dana is as aloof from them as he

[12] *Freeman*, V, 560.
[13] "A Claim for American Literature," *North American Review,* CLIV, 141.

might be if he were a well-disposed officer watching them from the quarter-deck. The protecting hand of his influence with the owners back in Boston can always rescue him if things become unendurable. At the critical moment when the captain refuses to take him home on the *Alert* he is able to put on a bold front and answer that he has in his chest a letter from the owners permitting him to return on that ship. Dana states frankly that it was this knowledge that he had "friends and interest enough at home to make them suffer for any injustice they might do me" which turned the scale.

How different the case with Melville! Before he sails east of the Horn again he will wake within many a strange fo'c'sle. To escape from cruelty and bad food and boredom he will risk his neck by deserting to the cannibals of the Taipi valley.

When the sailor of twenty-five returned to his mother's home at Lansingburgh in the fall of 1844, he had completed his education in the only Harvard and Yale which were open to him. He brought back far more than any college can afford its undergraduates. He had his stock in trade which would make the bulk of the books he would write and prove as valuable in certain markets as any cargoes his brother Tom ever transported. Of most importance to him at the moment was the confidence in his own powers which came to him with the consciousness that he had seen miracles, and that no one could question his authority when he spoke of whales, missionaries, and cannibals. He could hold his head up because he was somebody. As soon as Melville had proved that he could transmute his Marco Polo adventures into books which England and America would buy, the eminent Judge Lemuel Shaw of Boston would intrust his daughter to him in marriage and the most inaccessible literary coterie in New York would welcome him to their sessions over the punch bowl.

He could not have been altogether aware, in the first excitement of homecoming, of the important changes in outlook he had undergone. Unlike most of the previous voyagers to Tahiti and Honolulu he had nothing to sell and no gospel message to deliver. In consequence he had judged what he saw in the South Seas with impartial eyes. That a citizen of the Taipi valley chose to eat his enemy after conquering him was no presumptive proof that he might not be a good fellow and a loyal friend. That the queens of Kamehameha occasionally doffed the *holokus* made for them by patient missionary wives and reverted to nakedness did not prove them totally depraved. Of the two brands of imperialism which he saw fighting for the privilege of civilizing the Hawaiians he preferred that of the British Paulet to that 'of the American Judd, a preference he did not find fashionable on his return to the Boston of the American Board of Commissioners for Foreign Missions.

His intellectual insurgency did not end when he had put his own evaluation on the experience of those three momentous years. The habit of thinking was fixed, and as soon as he got himself acclimated, savored the praise given *Typee* and *Omoo*, and had digested some of the books in Evert Duyckinck's huge library, he undertook, in his thirtieth year, to review and judge the contemporary scene in Europe and America. It was not long after this was accomplished in *Mardi* that the literary circle in New York, which represented to him four years earlier the acme of wit, elegance, and wisdom, began to seem provincial and earnestly respectable. Before this time came, however, he enjoyed in its midst some of the happiest hours of his life. The world of music, the theater, the fine arts, opened before him, in the city which had become the commercial center of the United States and was justly proud of its numerous cultural institutions.

Poe hit off the character of Evert Duyckinck, Melville's sponsor in this circle, in a brief paragraph in *The Literati:* "[He is] distinguished for the *bonhomie* of his manner, his simplicity and single-mindedness, his active beneficence, his hatred of wrong done even to any enemy, and especially for an almost Quixotic fidelity to his friends. He seems in perpetual good-humor with all things, and I have no doubt that in his secret heart he is an optimist." This charm of personality, which evidently failed to impress Poe, secured him a crowd of companionable literary, artistic, and theatrical friends. His correspondence with men like Emerson, Hawthorne, Longfellow, Melville, and Simms, fortunately preserved (Evert had the Victorian passion for stowing away every scrap of paper which passed over his desk), is voluminous. His punch parties at 20 Clinton Place where the "Knights of the Round Table" (as Melville called them) gathered, were the nearest to Rogers's breakfast parties New York could offer. He entertained European men of letters whenever one could be caught. His own writing, chiefly reviews and books of reference, is dull, but as editor of *Arcturus* (Dec., 1840–May, 1842) and the influential *Literary World* (Feb.–May, 1847; Oct., 1848–Dec., 1853), and as literary adviser to Wiley and Putnam, whose "Library of Choice Reading" he supervised, his interest and favor were valuable.

Melville, when he commenced author, owed Duyckinck for a great deal more than a series of laudatory reviews in the *Literary World*. His sense of the favors he was receiving is betrayed by the "literary" style of his early letters to Duyckinck. It was some time before he ceased to write up to his great new friend who had introduced him among the elect.[14] In Duyckinck's company he met, among others, Bayard Taylor, Cornelius Mathews, editor, poet, and dramatist, Robert Tomes, the military and naval historian, Charles Fenno Hoffman, critic and novelist, William Cullen Bryant, and most certainly Irving,

---

[14] The great importance of Duyckinck's friendship in Melville's life has been made fully evident in Mr. Mansfield's *Herman Melville: Author and New Yorker*. See note 18, p. xxvi.

who was a close friend of Duyckinck.)The occasion of Melville's introduction to Bryant is typical of many glamorous evenings. Duyckinck describes it in his diary (Oct. 6, 1847):

> The Art Union opened its new rooms to night in its Broadway quarters in the rear of Mr. Cram's former dwelling house —a long hall, well lighted, the walls covered with paintings by Cole, Page, Brown, Gignoux, Hicks etc, the floor well sprinkled with good fellows, the artists generally of fine personal appearance, a selection from the Press. Frank Panton brought me a ticket of invitation and Herman Melville dropping in, I carried him along, introducing him to Mr. Bryant and others. One of Sully's bathing nymphs suggested Fayaway. Lanman introduced me to Mount the humorous painter, of a fine and even beautiful countenance. There was supper, and punch, a liquor according to the ordinary in Jonathan Wild nowhere spoken against in Scripture. . . . Mr. George Gibbs in a speech of solid impudence drew out Colton of the Whig Review, as the head of the leading magazine. Colton, whose ordinary estate is that of a crank ship under a pretty heavy press of canvas was in a state of high art. Thumping an inverted wineglass on the table he began and rivalled an infuriated Dutch windmill in the flourishes of his arms. It was a circular speech also, revolving on a single idea or rather half a dozen words loud sounding among which was Platonic. . . . Mount and Melville were delighted with the living tableaus.[15]

Evert Duyckinck was as fully aware as the limitations of his taste permitted of the genius he had helped to discover. His diary and his letters to his brother George are studded with records of Melville's witty yarns and delightful table talk. He is enthusiastic over each new work as he receives it and makes sure that all his friends read it. When the novelist moved to Pittsfield he supplied him with the latest journals and books from his library and occasional gifts of champagne and cigars.

[15] Diary, May 29–Nov. 8, 1847, Duyckinck Collection, New York Public Library.

When George Duyckinck returned from his tour of Europe in 1848, he was added to the crowd of Melville enthusiasts. Their friendship seems incongruous at first, for George was even more orthodox than his brother. In his own *Cyclopædia of American Literature* he was eulogistically described after his death as one who was "by early education and by deliberate choice, warmly attached to the Liturgy and Order of the Episcopal Church, and especially interested in its biographical literature."[16] But as George's biographical specialities among the Anglican clergy were the worthies of the seventeenth century, he and Melville could share their admiration for Jeremy Taylor while on such excursions as the one they made in September, 1858, up the Greenfield valley, to have a look at the Hoosac tunnel, then under construction. In the later years George seems to have been closer to Melville than his brother.

In the company of the Duyckincks and their friends Melville could release his pent-up enthusiasm for the writers he had discovered by himself in his years of wandering. The letters to Evert explode into sudden bursts of excitement over his newest discoveries, for example the rhapsody over Shakespeare, whom he had neglected before February, 1849, because any copy he had previously found was "in a vile small print" undecipherable to his weak eyes. His declaration that the "divine William" is full of "sermons on the Mount" and "gentle, aye, almost as Jesus" shocked Duyckinck so deeply that Melville apologized for his irreverence. In the following month it is Emerson, whose ideas he had previously encountered only once in a casual glance through a book he picked up in Putnam's store. Now, having heard him lecture in Boston, he declares of him: "For the sake of the argument, let us call him a fool; then had I rather be a fool than a wise man," and is off on a eulogy of "the whole corps of thought-divers, that have been diving

16 Edition of 1866, Vol. II, Supplement, 157.

and coming up again with blood-shot eyes since the world began."[17]

Melville was all his life an omnivorous reader (of the kind Dr. Johnson admired) who reads from immediate inclination, led on by looking at the backs of books. The extent of his reading, apparent in the Coleridgean allusiveness of a few pages of *White-Jacket* or *Moby-Dick*, places him among the best read of American writers. A delightful chapter in *White-Jacket*—"A Man-of-War Library"—proves with what eagerness he took the heart out of any new lot of books which happened to lie convenient to his hand.

Who had the selection of these books, I do not know, but some of them must have been selected by our chaplain, who so pranced on Coleridge's *High German horse*.

Mason Good's *Book of Nature*—a very good book, to be sure, but not precisely adapted to tarry tastes—was one of these volumes; and Machiavel's *Art of War*—which was very dry fighting; and a folio of Tillotson's Sermons—the best of reading for divines, indeed, but with little relish for a main-top man; and Locke's Essays—incomparable essays, everybody knows, but miserable reading at sea; and *Plutarch's Lives*—super-excellent biographies, which pit Greek against Roman in beautiful style, but then, in a sailor's estimation, not to be mentioned with the *Lives of the Admirals;* and Blair's Lectures, University Edition—a fine treatise on rhetoric, but having nothing to say about nautical phrases . . . ; besides numerous invaluable but unreadable tomes, that might have been purchased cheap at the auction of some college professor's library.

But I found ample entertainment in a few choice old authors, whom I stumbled upon in various parts of the ship, among the inferior officers. One was Morgan's *History of Algiers*, a famous old quarto, abounding in picturesque narratives of corsairs, captives, dungeons, and sea-fights; and making men-

---

[17] These letters are printed on pp. 370–373, below.

tion of a cruel old Dey, who, toward the latter part of his life, was so filled with remorse for his cruelties and crimes that he could not stay in bed after four o'clock in the morning, but had to rise in great trepidation and walk off his bad feelings till breakfast time. And another venerable octavo, containing a certificate from Sir Christopher Wren to its authenticity, entitled Knox's *Captivity in Ceylon*, 1681—abounding in stories about the Devil, who was superstitiously supposed to tyrannize over that unfortunate land: to mollify him, the priests offered up buttermilk, red cocks, and sausages; and the Devil ran roaring about in the woods, frightening travellers out of their wits. . . .

Then there was Walpole's *Letters*—very witty, pert, and polite—and some old volumes of plays, each of which was a precious casket of jewels of good things, shaming the trash nowadays passed off for dramas, containing "The Jew of Malta," "Old Fortunatus," "The City Madam," "Volpone," "The Alchemist," and other glorious old dramas of the age of Marlowe and Jonson, and that literary Damon and Pythias, the magnificent, mellow old Beaumont and Fletcher, who have sent the long shadow of their reputation, side by side with Shakespeare's, far down the endless vale of posterity. . . .

 My book experiences on board of the frigate proved an example of a fact which every book-lover must have experienced before me, namely, that though public libraries have an imposing air, and doubtless contain invaluable volumes, yet, somehow, the books that prove most agreeable, grateful, and companionable, are those we pick up by chance here and there; those which seem put into our hands by Providence; those which pretend to little, but abound in much.

 In the course of his unsystematic excursions through ships' libraries, the shelves of the New York Society Library, the 17,000 or so volumes on Evert Duyckinck's shelves, and the loot of his own raids on second-hand book stores in London and New York, Melville possessed himself of an intimate knowledge of the English poets and essayists, the Elizabethan dramatists and the seventeenth-century prose writers. Contemporary American writers he read extensively. He reviewed Cooper and Parkman for the *Literary World*. The ancient and modern classics he knew in translation, in particular Homer, Plato, the Roman historians, Rabelais, Montaigne, Voltaire, Goethe, and Richter.[18]

[18] The only comprehensive studies of the development of Melville's ideas through his reading are to be found in two unpublished dissertations, Luther S. Mansfield's *Herman Melville: Author and New Yorker, 1844–1851* (University of Chicago, 1936) and William Braswell's *Herman Melville and Christianity* (University of Chicago, 1932). The latter deals, of course, chiefly with Melville's reading of philosophy and biblical criticism.

The Bible he knew with the precision we should expect of a boy brought up in a house where Calvinistic fundamentalism lingered. His copy of the New Testament is marked and annotated with care. In later life his religious views were particularly affected by Niebuhr and Strauss.

In his early writing the influence of Plato, Hobbes, Spinoza, Rousseau, and Hume is to be seen. In July and August of 1848, I find, by searching the ledgers of the New York Society Library of which he was a member, that he was reading Hartley's *Observations on Man*. His purchase, in April, 1849, of Bayle's *Dictionnaire historique et critique* had momentous results. At this same time he was exploring German metaphysics, over which he had many arguments on his voyage to England (1849) with Professor Adler, a member of the Duyckincks' circle, and Dr. Taylor, a cousin of the translator of *Faust*. As his record of one of these conversations shows, their dryness was relieved by liberal doses of whiskey punch: "I forgot to mention that *last night* about 9:30 P.M., Adler and Taylor came into my room, and it was proposed to have whiskey punches, which we *did* have accordingly. Adler drank about three tablespoons full—Taylor four or five tumblers, etc. We had an extraordinary time and did not break up till after two in the morning. We talked metaphysics continually, and Hegel, Schlegel, Kant, etc., were discussed under the influence of the whiskey. I shall not forget Adler's look when he quoted La Place the French astronomer—'It is not necessary, gentlemen, to account for these worlds by the hypothesis,' etc. After Adler retired, Taylor and I went out on the bowsprit—splendid spectacle." (Quoted by Weaver, *Herman Melville*, 288.) There was much "riding on the German horse" during this voyage.

Mr. Braswell believes that Shelley's Satanism may have had much

The curiosity of the literary source-hunters has effectively destroyed the earlier notion that Melville was a mere chronicler of the wonders he had seen.[19] Even in works like *Typee*, which appear on the surface purely autobiographical, he not only altered the facts to conform to the exigencies of his narrative but made free use of the writings of earlier travelers whenever he needed a fact or a picture. His usual method was to document himself thoroughly in whatever subject was involved in the tale he was constructing. One should never be too dogmatic in declaring that a given passage of even the most circumstantial sort comes straight from Melville's adventures. It is as likely to be found in an unworked state in such a book as Stewart's *A Visit to the South Seas* or Nathaniel Ames's *A Mariner's Sketches*.[20]

to do with the Promethean conception of Ahab. That Melville knew Shelley's essay on Milton's Satan is certain. It is possible that Ahab's contempt for the Deity which ignorantly supposes itself the first cause owes something to the ideas of the gnostics. In the last months of his life Melville was reading Schopenhauer with a particular interest in his separation of morality and religion.

[19] Their most important discoveries are considered in the next section of this Introduction.

[20] As external evidence of what Melville was reading during the most productive period of his life, nothing could be more valuable than the entries which Evert Duyckinck made in the memoranda book in which he kept a list of the books borrowed from his library. This is preserved in the Duyckinck Collection of the New York Public Library. The dates on which books were lent are not often set down but are numerous enough to establish certain limits. The date nearest to the first book which Melville took away is Oct. 13, 1847. Some time thereafter Duyckinck made the following entries by his name (listed here as they are set down in the notebook): "Rabelais vol 2; Barnard's Narrative [*Narrative of the Sufferings and Adventures of Captain Charles H. Barnard . . .* New York, 1829]; Sir Thos Browne, vol 2; Rabelais, vol 3; Frithiolf's Saga [Tegner's translation, 1838]; Sir T. Browne 2 vols; Rabelais vol 4." Some time after July, 1848, he borrowed *Angela* [Anne Marsh's novel of that name]. On April 13, 1849, he took with him Fuller's *The Holy State and the Profane State*, and at other times during the year: " 2 vols Ed.[inburgh] Review [the nearest previous date noted

When Melville crossed to England in the fall of 1849 with the
hope of selling *White-Jacket* more advantageously in person
than by long-distance negotiation, he moved, and by right,
among literary celebrities of the day. The deference with
which he was received and the mere fact of his being in such

is July 20]; Hawthorne's [Twice-Told] Tales; Bergerac Voyage
to the Moon." The list for 1850 is long: "Roderick Random;
Jean Paul's [Richter's] Flower Pieces; Sartor Resartus; Hero Worship; Wilhelmeister 3 vols; Scoggins [*sic*] Jests; Carlyles Germ Rom
2 v; Miss Barretts Poems 2 v; Browne's Brit[annia's] Pastorals;
Tennyson's In Memoriam; Democratic Review 2 v; Arcturus vol 1;
Thoreau's Merrimack; Judd's 'Margaret'; Lazarillo De Tormes."
Scattered entries at a later period show that Melville borrowed seven
volumes of Vasari and Lanzi in November, 1859, and ten volumes of
the *Tatler*, *Observer*, and *Looker On* during January, 1860. The Duyckinck correspondence yields evidence of other books borrowed by
Melville. In February, 1851, a copy of *Leigh Hunt's Journal* was sent
to Pittsfield. In November, 1858, Duyckinck presented Melville with
Chapman's *Homer*, which, Melville remarks, will send Pope's version,
when put beside it, "off shrieking, like the bankrupt deities in Milton's
hymn." When Melville was rheumatism-bound in February, 1862,
he asked for a loan of the Elizabethan dramatists, especially Dekker
and Webster.

Melville jotted down at the end of the journal which he kept on his
European tour of 1849–1850 (see the next note) a list of the books
which he purchased abroad or received as gifts. Aside from guide-
books, of which he secured seven, and copies of the English editions
of *Mardi* and *Redburn*, these books were the following: "Ben
Jonson. folio; Davenant. folio; Beaumont and Fletcher folio;
Hudibras 18mo. [as a gift for Evert Duyckinck; see p. 378]; Bos-
well's Johnson (10 vol. 18mo); Sir Thomas Browne folio; Lavater
[*Essays on Physiognomy*, London, 1789?]; Rousseau Confessions;
Castle of Otranto; 2 plays of Shakspeare; Charles Lamb's works
(octavo): Final Memorials of Lamb [these two a present from
Moxon]; Guzman 3 vol. [the Spanish picaresque romance *Guzman
de Alfarache*]; Chatterton 2 vol.; Anastasius (2 vol) [Thomas
Hope's novel, published in 1819]; Caleb Williams (1 vol); Vathek
(1 vol); Corinne (1 vol) [Madame de Staël's novel]; Frankenstein
(1 vol); Aristocracy of England [Lord Brougham's *Thoughts upon
the Aristocracy of England*?]; Marlowe's Plays; Autobiography of
Goethe; Letters from Italy (Goethe); Confessions of an Opium
Eater: Telemachus [bought in France]; Anastasius (2 vol) [*sic*];
Lays and Legends of the Rhine [Frankfort, 1847]."

surroundings seemed to him slightly unreal. The night before
he landed he wrote in his diary: "This time to-morrow I shall
be on land, and press English earth after the lapse of ten years—
then a *sailor*, now H. M. author of *Peedee*, *Hullabaloo* and
Pog-dog." [21]

When he chanced on the "long story about a short book"—
the fourteen-page notice of *Redburn* in *Blackwood's*—he thought
it comical. Why should the old Tory "waste so many papers
upon a thing which I, the author, know to be trash, and wrote
it to buy some tobacco with?" [22] But if he thought the English
a little silly to make so much of plain H. M., he allowed them
to entertain him as much as they pleased. At Murray's dinner
party, the snobbish "conventionalism" of which offended his
democratic notion of social decency, he met Lockhart, "in a
prodigious white cravat," which he supposed must have been
made from Walter Scott's shroud. As the guest of Bentley,
who struck a bargain (£200) with him over *White-Jacket*, he sat
down to dinner with fourteen, including the humorist "Alfred
Crowquill" who proved a "good fellow—free and easy and no
damned nonsense, as there is about so many of these English."
By his invitation Melville later went to see the pantomime
rehearsed at the Surrey Theatre.

In the intervals between his visits to publishers, manuscript
in hand, he dined and wined himself into many a next day's
headache and indulged in book-buying and theater-going and
sight-seeing. He managed to slip away for two weeks on the
continent, all he could afford of a flying tour he had originally
planned with Evert Duyckinck.

The crowded impressions of these three months reappeared

[21] Weaver, *Herman Melville*, 290. Melville's Journal of this European tour, now in the Harvard College Library, is extremely detailed
in regard to the many interesting and important persons he met and
the places he visited. Only parts of it have been published, by
Weaver, 284–304.

[22] *Ibid.*, 292.

in after years in many passages which he wrote. His medita-
tions as he watched the Thames flowing under London bridge,
as "polluted by continual vicinity to man, [it] curdled on between rotten wharves, one murky sheet of sewage," furnished
the "City of Dis" chapter in *Israel Potter*. In that same book
the experiences of young Israel in his first night's lodging in
Paris borrow from Melville's record of his own arrival there.[23]
The first part of "The Paradise of Bachelors and the Tartarus of
Maids," which he contributed to *Harper's Magazine* in April,
1855, recalls a merry evening spent in the midst of good wine,
good fellows, and good talk in rooms high up within Elm Court,
the Temple, on the invitation of Robert Francis Cooke.

In 1854 Melville submitted to *Putnam's Magazine* a prose
satire entitled "The Two Temples," [24] which was rejected because
the moral of the "Temple First"—that only the rich and well-
dressed were welcome at the newly built Grace Church—would
offend its wealthy congregation.[25] The "Temple Second" is a
fanciful account of a Yankee stranger, destitute in London, who
is treated to a performance of Macready in *Richelieu* in another,
more hospitable "Temple" just off the Strand. It glows with
the memory of those happy nights five years before when he
was foot-loose in London.

I stood within the topmost gallery of the temple. But hardly
alone and silently as before. This time I had company. Not of
the first circles, and certainly not of the dress-circle, but most

[23] Weaver, *Herman Melville*, 297.
[24] *Works*, XIII, 173–191.
[25] Melville's satire would have been applauded in some quarters.
Philip Hone noted in his *Diary* on Feb. 5, 1846, as the church was
ready for consecration: "The pews were sold last week, and brought
extravagant prices . . . so that the word of God, as it came down
to us from fishermen and mechanics, will cost the quality who worship
in this splendid temple about three dollars every Sunday. This
may have a good effect, for many of them, though rich, know how to
calculate, and if they do not go regularly to Church they will not
get the worth of their money."

acceptable, right welcome, cheery company, to otherwise un-companioned me. Quiet, well-pleased working men, and their glad wives and sisters, with here and there an aproned urchin, with all-absorbed, bright face, vermilioned by the excitement and the heated air, hovering like a painted cherub over the vast human firmament below. The height of the gallery was in truth appalling. The rail was low. I thought of deep-sea-leads, and the mariner in the vessel's chains, drawing up the line, with his long-drawn musical accompaniment. And like beds of glittering coral, through the deep sea of azure smoke, there, far down, I saw the jewelled necks and white sparkling arms of crowds of ladies in the semicirque.[26]

Toward the end of his stay a flattering invitation arrived from the Duke of Rutland to visit at Belvoir. Melville was in a quandary. For three hours and a half on Sunday, December 16, he argued the matter with himself. Recurrent waves of home-sickness had assaulted him as they always did when he was away from his family for long. But such a chance would never come again to see what the English aristocracy really is and to store up "material" for future exploitation. His brother Allan would account him a ninny if he did not accept. Finally, at six-thirty, he resolved to bring to an end his progress through English drawing-rooms by taking passage. The next day he made arrangements with the captain of the *Independence*, "took a letter for a Duke to the post office and a pair of pants to be altered to a tailor." On Christmas morning he sailed from Portsmouth.

Six months after his return Melville transported his family from New York to temporary quarters in the roomy old farm-house of his Uncle Thomas, near Pittsfield, which was now transformed into a boardinghouse. This region of broad rich valleys and distant noble hills he had loved as a child, and he had determined to settle here because he might live more

[26] *Works*, XIII, 188.

cheaply than in the city by farming in a small way while he
kept on with his literary work. Early in the fall of 1850 he
found the place he wanted, a central-chimneyed house near
"Broadhall" which had once been a tavern. It was large enough
to hold his numerous female relatives and in-laws who found
it a pleasant place to visit. For his own special pleasure Melville built a wide porch to the north, unconnected with the
rest of the house, where he might pace up and down uninterrupted and keep his eye on the clouds over Greylock twenty
miles away.[27]

The Pittsfield region was at that time a gathering place of
literary men. Doctor Holmes spent his summers there. G. P.
R. James, historical novelist and subsequently a British consul,
was turning out two books each year in Stockbridge. Fanny
Kemble had settled in Lenox after her divorce from Pierce
Butler. About the time Melville came to board at "Broadhall,"
Hawthorne, whom the success of *The Scarlet Letter* had at
last brought into public favor, moved into a little red house
near Lenox. It was inevitable that Melville and Hawthorne
should meet and that friendship should spring up between
them, for each admired the other's genius and had made public
acknowledgment of his admiration.

Hawthorne reviewed *Typee* for the *Salem Advertiser* in 1846,
noting that the narrative is "skilfully managed, and in a literary
point of view, the execution of the work is worthy of the
novelty and interest of its subject."[28] To Evert Duyckinck
he wrote with unwonted enthusiasm of the reality of *Redburn*
and *White-Jacket* and of the depths of *Mardi*, which here and
there "compel a man to swim for his life."[29] Mrs. Hawthorne

[27] For some details of Melville's occupancy of "Arrowhead" see
p. 432 below.
[28] The review is reprinted in Randall Stewart's "Hawthorne's
Contributions to the *Salem Advertiser*," *American Literature*, V,
328–329 (Jan., 1934).
[29] For the complete text of this letter see p. 423 below.

testified to Duyckinck that her husband was reading, on the new hay in the barn during August, 1850, all of Melville's books.[30] They did not know, at the time of the momentous picnic of August 5 when the two authors met, that Melville was engaged in writing a long and most rhapsodic article inspired by Hawthorne's *Mosses* which would appear in the *Literary World* for August 17 and 24. Would he find in Hawthorne the man, as he found in his book, "a humour so spiritually gentle, so high, so deep, and yet so richly relishable, that it were hardly inappropriate in an angel"; a "depth of tenderness, such a boundless sympathy with all forms of being, such an omnipresent love, that we must needs say that this Hawthorne is . . . almost alone in his generation"?

This friendship began propitiously. After the first meeting Hawthorne wrote to Horatio Bridge: "I met Melville the other day, and liked him so much that I have asked him to spend a few days with me before leaving these parts."[31] This visit, in early September, lasted four days. During the next year they saw much of each other, drove or walked along the country roads and talked "about time and eternity, things of this world and of the next, and books, and publishers, and all possible and impossible matters" in sessions that lasted deep into the night.[32] Mrs. Hawthorne, with her usual quick sympathy and penetration of character, felt the power of Melville. She wrote of him to her mother: "I am not quite sure that *I do not think him* a very great man. . . . A man with a true, warm heart, and a soul and an intellect,—with life to his finger-tips; earnest, sincere and reverent; very tender and *modest*. . . . He has very keen perceptive power. . . . Once in a while, his animation gives place to a singularly quiet expression . . . an in-

[30] Her letter is printed on p. 423 below.
[31] Bridge, *Personal Recollections of Nathaniel Hawthorne* (New York, 1893), 123.
[32] Randall Stewart, *The American Notebooks by Nathaniel Hawthorne* (New Haven, 1932), 220.

drawn, dim look, but which at the same time makes you feel
that he is at that moment taking deepest note of what is before
him. It is a strange, lazy glance, but with a power in it quite
unique. It does not seem to penetrate through you, but to
take you into itself."[33] The Hawthorne children adored this
strange man who hailed their papa in Spanish on the streets
of Lenox and told with terrifying gestures such amazing tales
of savages. Julian informed the household that he loved Mr.
Melville as well as his father, and "as mamma, and as Una."[34]

These delightful visits between "Arrowhead" and the red
house in Lenox ceased when the Hawthornes moved away in
November, 1851, and so, apparently, did the wonderful series
of confessional letters which Melville wrote Hawthorne during
the months of their intimacy. But the friendship, which was
so fructifying in Melville's development, did not end. He
visited Hawthorne at Concord in 1852, possibly in September,
when they discussed the literary potentialities in a tale of ship-
wreck, marital desertion, and bigamy which Melville had picked
up from a New Bedford lawyer. Hawthorne did his best to
secure him a consular appointment under President Pierce's
administration[35] and suggested to Commodore Perry, who was
looking for a suitable person to prepare his notes for the publication of an account of his voyage, that Melville might satisfy
his requirements.[36] They met for the last time in November,
1856, when Melville was on a recuperative journey to Europe
and the Holy Land. He came down from Scotland to Liverpool expressly to visit Hawthorne. They were soon, in Hawthorne's words, "on pretty much our former terms of sociability
and confidence."[37] A complex of disasters, in which spiritual
exhaustion was the severest, had brought Melville in the inter-

[33] Rose Hawthorne Lathrop, *Memories of Hawthorne* (Boston, 1897),
135.
[34] Stewart, *American Notebooks*, 232.
[35] Newton Arvin, *The Heart of Hawthorne's Journals* (Boston, 1929),
229.   [36] *Ibid.*, 177.   [37] *Ibid.*, 230.

vening years to the point where he had "pretty much made up his mind to be annihilated." The habit of wandering over the deserts of theological speculation had grown upon him, but Hawthorne found him still of "a very high and noble nature" and "better worth immortality than most of us." Their talks at Southport and Liverpool and their rambles around medieval Chester improved Melville's state of mind, so that when they parted finally he confessed that he "already felt better than in America."

There is no reason to suppose that Hawthorne was insensible to the outpouring of admiration and friendship which Melville offered him, however incapable he may have been of making an equally fervid return.[38] Before Melville encountered him in the flesh he was sure he had found in him those qualities which mark all true candid men, all seekers like himself. The picture that he draws of Hawthorne in "Hawthorne and His Mosses"

[38] The myth that he showed Melville's advances a cool impercipience originated in the biographies of Weaver and Mumford, both of whom in their effort to dramatize the loneliness of Melville and the failure of his contemporaries to take the measure of his greatness have exaggerated the native aloofness of Hawthorne. Weaver supposes that Hawthorne's letter to Melville after receiving a copy of *Moby-Dick*, which was dedicated to him, was merely "some sort of acknowledgment of the tribute" (*Herman Melville*, 329). To Melville, who called the letter "joy-giving and exultation-breeding," it gave actually a sense of unspeakable security because the one man in America whose opinion would be a real touchstone, understood his book. To Evert Duyckinck, Hawthorne sent a rebuke for what he considered the lukewarmness of the review in the *Literary World* which was, as it happened, one of the most penetrating the book received. (See p. 435 for this letter.)

Mumford goes much further than Weaver in accusing Hawthorne of indifference and even malice in his relation with Melville. His hypothesis that Hawthorne mocked at his friend's spiritual dilemmas under the guise of Ethan Brand has been so abundantly proved to be wild that Mumford must be heartily sick of his guess.

The best account of the friendship between the two men is contained in Newton Arvin's *Hawthorne*, 166–173. Arvin concludes that Melville conquered "more territory in Hawthorne's confidence" than Emerson, Thoreau, and Holmes.

is projected from his own mind. The power of blackness which he admired in him, his "great, deep intellect, which drops down into the universe like a plummet," his "short quick probings at the very axes of reality," he discerned in Hawthorne because they were in himself. He had outgrown the New York "literati" and their petty ambitions. London had shown him no heroes. In neither city were there men of letters whose ideals he could admire. Suddenly he recognized in Hawthorne the new self he was seeking.

Hawthorne not only gave him confidence that his own way was right. He inspired him to believe that at last America had a writer fit to represent the nation. Taking Hawthorne's accomplishment for his text Melville preached a sermon to his countrymen, in his article on the *Mosses*, on their neglect of native writers and the foolish bardolatry which inhibited their rise. Shakespeare, he says, has become a "part of our Anglo-Saxon superstition."[39] He was, in his time, only a thriving author like Hawthorne. Our literary genius is not going to arrive "in the costume of Queen Elizabeth's day." He will not be a "writer of dramas founded upon old English history or the tales of Boccaccio."

A superabundance of native material, of the kind which Hawthorne has exploited, awaits American writers. They must foster originality, though at first it be "crabbed and ugly as our own pine knots."[40] This does not mean they are to "cleave to nationality," but they are to write like men and show they are

[39] Cf. Emerson in "The American Scholar": "Genius is always sufficiently the enemy of genius by over-influence. . . . The English dramatic poets have Shakespearized now for two hundred years." Melville's remarks in this passage are not made, of course, in denigration of Shakespeare, for whom his admiration was unbounded and frequently expressed.

[40] *Works*, XIII, 136. Cf. Emerson's hope in 1834 that the "rank rabble party, the Jacksonism of the country . . . may root out the hollow dilettantism of our cultivation in the coarsest way" (Bliss Perry, *Heart of Emerson's Journals* [Boston, 1926], 85).

animated by that "unshackled, democratic spirit of Christianity in all things, which now takes the practical lead in the world"— in which spirit the rest of the world is led by America.[41] Such men America must encourage for the nation's sake. Since we are preparing to take the political supremacy in the world we shall have to be supreme in literature as well.

In her pressing need for genius America has overlooked an "unimitating, and, perhaps, in his way, an inimitable man" of the new and better generation. Hawthorne has evinced the "largest brain with the largest heart" in American literature. The smell of the young hemlocks is upon him and the "broad prairies are in his soul." He shows the course our literature must take.[42]

[41] *Works*, XIII, 136. Melville adumbrates Whitman's main contention in *Democratic Vistas* that a powerful literature, incarnating the "fervid and tremendous Idea" of democracy, is vital to America's future as a democratic country.

[42] Melville's admiration of Hawthorne's work was expressed in many other places besides the article on the *Mosses*. His rapturous letter of thanks on receiving a copy of *The House of the Seven Gables* is printed on pp. 386–389. See also his letter to Duyckinck (Feb. 12, 1851), pp. 385–386.

Melville's views of four other American authors are well defined. Irving he holds up in the paper on the *Mosses* as the type of imitative writer for whom our new literature will have no place. To Duyckinck he wrote, anent Hawthorne: "Irving is a grasshopper to him." (See p. 386.) Parkman's *Oregon Trail* (reviewed in the *Literary World*, March 31, 1849) was a trifle too gentlemanly for him though he liked its "wild game flavor." His strong words directed at Parkman's unhumanitarian contempt for the savages he later repented. (See pp. cii–ciii for excerpts from this review.) Cooper's novels were among the earliest books he could remember. They produced a "vivid and awakening power" upon his mind. (*Memorial of James Fenimore Cooper* [New York, 1852], 30.) He defended Cooper against the fortuitous disfavor which befell him in later years. His review of *Sea-Lions* (*Literary World*, April 28, 1849) praised the depiction of scenes of the lonely and terrible, but expressed amusement at the way in which the hero is rewarded for religious orthodoxy "somewhat in the pleasant spirit of the Mahometan . . . who rewards all the believers with a houri." Emerson he had shied from, fearing his reported

The amazing letters which Melville dispatched to the red house in Lenox prove that the Hawthorne who occasionally roamed the Housatonic valley with him was the man he had detected in the *Mosses*. We may well doubt if *Moby-Dick* would have been the book it is if Melville had not been able to stay himself with the thought that six miles away there dwelt a man who would risk perishing rather than give up his right to treat all powers on an equal basis. Hawthorne, too, could thunder the Everlasting No in the Devil's teeth. When Hawthorne praised the hell-cooked *Whale* an infinite fraternity of feeling pervaded him, as when big hearts strike together. He felt the daemon in him, and the power of growing would never end.

Hawthorne's immediate influence is perceptible in the dark and intense story of intimate human relationships in *Pierre*— a new departure in Melville's literary career. It is to be noted that it appeared in the same year as Hawthorne's *Blithedale Romance*. The heroes of the two books are idealists who fail because of the excessiveness of their idealism. Hawthorne's condemnation of Hollingsworth differs from Melville's partial sympathy with Pierre, who is crushed by the ineluctable fact that man cannot pursue heaven's way on earth. But the moral to be drawn from Hollingsworth's character and errors, as Hawthorne states it, fits likewise the tragedy of Pierre: "an exemplification of the most awful truth in Bunyan's book of such; from the very gate of heaven there is a by-way to the

---

"transcendentalisms, myths and oracular gibberish," but he was at least momentarily enthusiastic about him in March, 1849, and recognized in him "an uncommon man." *Mardi*, especially in the chapter on "Dreams" (*Works*, IV, 52–55), shows Melville's cognizance of the idea of the Over-Soul. Nevertheless he assured the anti-transcendentalist Duyckinck that he did not "oscillate in Emerson's rainbow." His attack on the "compensation" school of philosophy in *Pierre* is not altogether a surprise. See Braswell, "Melville as a Critic of Emerson," *American Literature*, IX, 317–334.

pit!"[43] It is surely no coincidence that Hawthorne's novel, written to express his disapproval of the New England reformers, is contemporary with *Pierre*, which satirizes the "new-light Apostles" who go about "muttering the Kantian Categories through teeth and lips dry and dusty as any miller's, with the crumbs of Graham crackers." Undoubtedly, too, Hawthorne's dislike of Transcendental optimism increased Melville's distrust of Emersonianism, which he voices in *Pierre* in his attack on the "preposterous rabble of Muggletonian Scots and Yankees"—a plain hit at the disciples of Carlyle and Emerson.

The sustaining power of Hawthorne's encouragement vanished with his removal to Concord, for the intensity of friendship rarely survives geographical separation. While it existed between them it brought Melville to the fullness of his powers. It was the last great influence in his life. Thereafter he went his way alone, drawing farther within himself as the years passed. When he saw Hawthorne in England in 1856, he had lost the power to be moved by new adventures, except those of the mind. After 1852 the drama of his life is played on that stage. It little mattered whether, physically, he was in his attic room at "Arrowhead," on a donkey jogging on the road to Bethlehem, behind his desk in the Customs Office at 470 West Street, or smoking among his books and engravings after a long day of checking cargoes.

There were, then, five determining influences in Melville's youth and the years of his greatest creative period: the religious orthodoxy of his home, which left its imprint though he revolted from it; his contact with the brutalities of a sailor's life and with savage societies which impelled him to question the premises of western civilization; his reading in philosophy and

---

[43] For a study of the similarity between the attitudes of the two friends towards the relationship between the ideal of purity and the sense of sin, see F. I. Carpenter, "Puritans Preferred Blondes," *New England Quarterly*, IX, 253–272.

belles-lettres which, though unmethodical, was prodigious between 1846 and 1851; his friendships with artists and men of letters in New York who advanced his interests and educated him in his craft; and the sympathy of Hawthorne, which more than any other factor contributed to the fruition of his genius.

II. MELVILLE AS ARTIST

At the time of Melville's death the fourth-class poet R. H. Stoddard, who had known him in the Customs House, produced a judgment of his work which is easily the most perverse of all the strange opinions which have been ventured about him. Melville was a genius, Stoddard reluctantly admitted, "but he cannot be said to have understood the limitations of genius. . . . He wrote as he felt." His imagination was "unbrained." "He wrote too easily, and at too great length, his pen sometimes running away with him, and from his readers. There were strange, dark, mysterious elements in his nature, as there were in Hawthorne's, but he never learned to control them, as Hawthorne did from the beginning, and never turned them into actualities."[44]

The conception still persists that Melville was a natural genius who never understood the art he practiced, but wrote out of the fullness of experience, and then, when memory and emotion were exhausted, could write no more. As we come to know his books for what they really are, it will have to give way to the truer picture of a writer who from the beginning of his career was occupied with the theme of the artist's problems and brooded over the nature of his own creative powers and their relation to the vital center of his spiritual life, until in much of his finest work this theme is deeply involved in the other mysteries with which he wrestled.[45]

[44] *The Mail and Express*, October 8, 1891, 5.
[45] Especially *Mardi*, *Pierre*, and *The Confidence Man*.

Melville wrote to Hawthorne in 1851 that he felt himself to be like one of "those seeds taken out of the Egyptian Pyramids" which grew to greenness when planted three thousand years later, for until he was twenty-five he had had no development at all. "From my twenty-fifth year I date my life."[46] (This significant moment falls in the year 1844 when he returned from more than three years wandering in the world and settled down to write what he had seen. A new life begins when he commences author. The "unfolding" which has been so rapid since then that he now feels he has come to "the inmost leaf of the bulb," can mean nothing else than the revelation of inward power and of latent possibilities for its expression which followed his amazement at finding himself a writer.

The role of artist he assumed with ease and delight. As has been said earlier,[47] the first years in New York, when he moved as an equal among the circle of his literary peers, were the happiest of his life. But he by no means intended to become a performing lion for publishers and editors and, as his understanding of his own genius deepened, he resisted with increasing firmness their attempts to control him. It is not without significance that when he definitely turns from reviewers, publishers, and editors to explore the truth that is in him and reveal it in his own way, he removes himself from the literary sociabilities of New York to an attic room in the Berkshires where his eyes rest on Greylock.

"All Fame is patronage," he wrote to Hawthorne, and he loathed the idea of going down to posterity as the "man who lived among the cannibals,"[48] the author of "*Typee, Piddledee,* etc." In *Mardi* he allegorized his own position as a public favorite. For years, the philosopher Babbalanja says, "a man may move unnoticed among his fellows; but all at once, by some chance attitude, foreign to his habit, become a trumpetful

[46] The letter is printed on pp. 389–393 below.
[47] See p. xx above.   [48] See p. 392 below.

for fools; though, in himself, the same as ever."[49]   Fame is an accident; merit, a thing absolute.

What might have happened to him, what was happening, he believed, to most successful young writers in America, he suggests in the satiric account of the sudden rush of recognition which overtook Pierre.[50]   As yet the author of only a few fugitive pieces, which the perfunctory reviewers have pronounced to be in perfect taste and of high respectability, the editors and publishers are already in full cry after this juvenile author.   Wonder and Wen, who have recently abandoned the "ignoble pursuit of tailoring for the more honorable trade of the publisher," importune him to allow them to issue his complete works.   Fortunately Pierre realized that his writings could not fill more than a very small duodecimo, and that a Library Edition might seem a little premature.   Nor would he consent to permit a designer to illustrate his meager sonnets.   The young ladies with autograph albums are more difficult to refuse.   The Lyceums, Young Men's Associations, and other literary and scientific societies offer him flattering invitations to lecture before them which he conscientiously and respectfully declines. When an editor of the *Captain Kidd Monthly* begs him to have his daguerreotype taken for use in their next issue, he puts him off with some violence, for Pierre knows that "when everybody has his portrait published, true distinction lies in not having yours published at all."

Pierre's efforts to wrench himself from the embraces of "publishers, engravers, editors, critics, autograph-collectors, portrait-fanciers, biographers, and petitioning and remonstrating literary friends of all sorts," were, in some respects, those of his creator.   Melville's letters to Evert Duyckinck, generally so affable, occasionally reveal him repulsing that industrious promoter of literary enterprises in the amiable but decisive

[49] *Works*, IV, 86.
[50] Book XVII.   *Works*, IX, 341-357.

manner of Pierre. He refuses to review for the *Literary World*
Hart's *Romance of Yachting* because it is too wretched a piece
of botching to deserve notice. Duyckinck, with questionable
honesty, published a review which was concocted out of Melville's amusing remarks meant for his eye alone.[51]

In April, 1851, Duyckinck became the editor of *Holden's
Dollar Magazine*. From jottings, referring to possible articles
and contributors, in a commonplace book in the New York
Public Library, one gathers that he had hoped to persuade
Melville to write for his new venture. Melville declined. He
would be glad, he wrote, to help a friend, "but I am not in the
humor to write the kind of thing you need—and I am not in
the humor to write for Holden's Magazine."[52] Duyckinck
must believe that he has reasons. In the same letter he also
refused to send a daguerreotype of himself to be used in the
magazine. He passes over his refusal with a jest about his
vanity, but the phrases he uses in making his excuses are similar
to those which Pierre employs when he is besought by the
editor of *Captain Kidd's Monthly*.[53]

In spite of his determination to choose a mighty theme and
produce a mighty book Melville recognized his obligation to his
family sufficiently to try to meet part way the public's demand
for the thing it had discovered he could do delightfully. He
knows that those who try to get a living by Truth "go to the
Soup Societies." To avoid this he is willing to dilute his work
"with that prudential worldly element" which conciliates the
conventionalists. The pitiful fact is that though *Typee* and

[51] The letter is printed on pp. 369–370 below.
[52] The letter is printed on pp. 384–386 below.
[53] In the first excitement of his sudden fame Melville, four years
earlier, had been ready to "play the game." Evert Duyckinck notes,
in his diary for Oct. 23, 1847: "With Mathews and Melville, in
the evening discussed a possible weekly newspaper which should
combine the various projects of the kind which he [Mathews] had
entertained for the last few years."

Omoo, and to a lesser extent *Redburn* and *White-Jacket*, were really successes because of these conciliations, the conditions of publication in America at the time made it impossible for him, even though he worked unflaggingly, to make a decent living. Dollars damned him. The harder he worked the deeper he sank into debt to his wife's family.

When at length, with *Mardi*, *Moby-Dick*, and *Pierre*, Melville dared to write the kind of books he thought frank and truthful, he set himself deliberately against the main currents of fiction-writing of his time. We wonder at the obtuseness of the critics, who really thought him mad, because they could not understand the import of his allegory and symbolism.[54] The fact is, of course, that his conception of what constituted reality in fiction was utterly at variance with the dominant attitude of the mid-century, which had yet to be given the name realism, though it had manifested itself abundantly in art and literature and was already accepted as a fixed critical canon.[55] Melville was completely aware of this insurgency. In *The Confidence Man* he devoted three chapters (XIV, XXXIII, XLIV) to an exposition of his matured views on the subject of truth in the representation of life and character. They deserve our close attention.

In the first place, he asks, is it not odd that readers, who by the mere fact that they read novels would seem to wish to escape the dullness of their lives, should demand an exact picture of that dullness? In life the proprieties will not allow one complete freedom, but in fiction the whole truth can be told. There may be "more reality than real life itself can show. . . . It is with fiction as with religion: it should present another world, and yet one to which we feel the tie."[56]

[54] See brief discussion of the critics' difficulties on pp. cxxi–cxxv.

[55] For an account of the first definitions of the concept see the article by Franklin Gary, "Charlotte Brontë and George Henry Lewes," *Publications of the Modern Language Association*, LI, 525–527.

[56] *Works*, XII, 244.

This world will be nature as we know it, but nature "unfettered, exhilarated, in effect transformed."[57]

Another absurd tradition, Melville held, prevented the novel of his day from being true to this superior reality: namely, the convention that every character in fiction must be consistent, whereas in life, as we very well know, a consistent individual is a *rara avis*—"That fiction, where every character can, by reason of its consistency, be comprehended at a glance, either exhibits but sections of character, making them appear for wholes, or else is very untrue to reality."[58] Novelists are popularly commended who "represent human nature not in obscurity, but transparency," and the writers who can exhibit "the tangled web of some character, and then raise admiration . . . at their satisfactory unravelling of it" are considered very great masters indeed. But the sciences which deal with the human mind have "excluded with contempt" such untruthful "sallies of ingenuity."

Upon the whole, it might rather be thought, that he, who, in view of its inconsistencies, says of human nature the same that, in view of its contrasts, is said of the divine nature, that it is past finding out, thereby evinces a better appreciation of it than he who, by always representing it in a clear light, leaves it to be inferred that he already knows all about it.[59]

---

[57] *Loc. cit.*   [58] *Op. cit.*, 90.

[59] *Ibid.*, 91. This chapter in *The Confidence Man* is paralleled by remarks in *Pierre* about the novelists' "false, inverted attempts at systematizing eternally unsystematizable elements; their audacious, intermeddling impotency, in trying to unravel and spread out, and classify, the more thin than gossamer threads which make up the complex web of life" (*Works*, IX, 198). Melville's heterodoxy on the subject of character portrayal is strikingly modern. Cf. D. H. Lawrence's letter to Edward Garnett (quoted by Aldous Huxley, *Letters of D. H. Lawrence* [London, 1932], xxi): "Somehow, that which is physic—non-human in humanity, is more interesting to me than the old-fashioned human element, which causes one to conceive a character in a certain moral scheme and make him consistent. The

The third passage in *The Confidence Man* in which Melville discusses fiction-writing (ch. XLIV) particularly illuminates his reasons, finally, for wishing to create such single Titanic figures as Ahab and Pierre, rather than to people his novels, in the contemporary fashion, with a number of equally developed characters. (Picking up the phrase "quite an original," he develops his view of what makes a character "original." The word, he holds, is too loosely used and made to mean only odd or singular. But a truly original character in literature would be almost as much of a prodigy "as a revolutionizing philosopher or the founder of a new religion)"[60] A Hamlet or Don Quixote or Satan is seldom achieved.

Furthermore, if we consider, what is popularly held to entitle characters in fiction to being deemed original, is but something personal—confined to itself. The character sheds not its characteristic on its surroundings, whereas, the original character, essentially such, is like a revolving Drummond light, raying away from itself all round it—everything is lit by it, everything starts to it (mark how it is with Hamlet), so that, in certain minds, there follows upon the adequate conception of such a character, an effect, in its way, akin to that which in Genesis attends upon the beginnings of things.[61]

---

certain moral scheme is what I object to." Also Huxley's comment (*Eyeless in Gaza* [New York, 1936], 397–398): "Lying by omission turns inevitably into positive lying. The implications of literature are that human beings are controlled, if not by reason, at least by comprehensible, well-organized, avowable sentiments. Whereas the facts are quite different." Huxley earlier broached this idea in describing Lawrence's method (*op. cit.*, xxii): "For ordinary practical purposes we conceive human beings as creatures with characters. But analysis of their behaviour can be carried so far, that they cease to have characters and reveal themselves as collections of psychological atoms."

[60] *Works*, XII, 318.
[61] *Loc. cit.* Melville discusses in other places the question of originality in literature; e.g., *Mardi* (*Works*, IV, 90) and *Pierre* (*Works*, IX, 361).

It was the ambition of Melville's maturity to create "originals" of this stature. His Ahab is such a character and Pierre was intended to be another.[62]

Before he came to the point of defying accepted conventions of fiction with *Moby-Dick*, he had written a number of lesser works. They show how he taught himself the art of writing and reveal that by the time he had fairly well exhausted the great store of adventures of which he had been a part and which could easily be molded into literary form, he had learned how to construct from various kinds of source materials, if not "grand erections" which "ever leave the copestone to posterity," at least workmanlike tales such as *Israel Potter* and "Benito Cereno." It will be illuminating to follow the course of his self-education in the craft.

Typee is as nearly artless as anything Melville wrote. When he had used up the suspense inherent in the predicament by which two American sailors find themselves in the cannibal valley, he had only to describe the life that surrounded him in order to convey a continuous thrill of horror and delight to his audience. Toward the end of the story the element of suspense enters again to hold our attention until Melville is safely aboard the rescuing boat. Yet even in writing *Typee* Melville needed the stimulant of a "source." His actual residence in the valley had been only a month.[63] He had kept no journal, and the adventure was already two years in the past when he began to write. To refresh his memory and authenticate his statements, he kept C. S. Stewart's *A Visit to the South Seas in the U.S. Ship Vincennes* (1831) open beside him.[64]

[62] Cf. *Moby-Dick* (*Works*, VIII, 220): "To produce a mighty book, you must choose a mighty theme. No great and enduring volume can ever be written on the flea, though many there be who have tried it."

[63] R. S. Forsythe, "Herman Melville in the Marquesas," *Philological Quarterly*, XV, 11.

[64] Russell Thomas, "Yarn for Melville's *Typee*," *Philological Quarterly*, XV, 17.

His use of Stewart is apparently not extensive, but one significant fact should be observed about the way in which he transfers
the worthy chaplain's remarks to his own pages. Stewart
generalizes. Melville reports, and, in his effort to give the
effect of reporting, he usually turns Stewart's careful hypotheses
into personal impressions or hearsay evidence. The tone of
the two narratives varies decidedly. Melville's is a yarn; Stewart's a sober treatise. The point is important, because here at
the start we see Melville doing what any skilled writer who
"works up" his sources must do, namely, absorb his material
into his own style so that it leaves no trace of its origin.

Omoo evinces a new versatility. Each picaresque incident
is fully developed and the new one introduced at the right point
to keep interest alive. For the first time Melville explores the
ship-microcosm which is to constitute a large element of the
formal structure of *White-Jacket* and *Moby-Dick*. His essays
in characterization and caricature were so successful that visitors
to the South Seas reported the annoyance of the originals at
the ease with which the portraits had been identified.[65] Melville's reliance on sources in writing *Omoo* was almost wholly
to substantiate the serious charges he wished to make in regard
to the degradation of native life under the white man's rule
and the inefficacy of missionary zeal in accomplishing any real
conversions.

So many details in *Redburn* can definitely be identified as
autobiographical and so many others have that appearance that
Melville's biographers have habitually used it with scant discrimination in reconstructing the years of his young manhood.[66]
But *Redburn*, though it has that tone, is not pure autobiography.
Incidents like the visit which Wellingborough and the soft-
handed Harry Bolton make to the London gaming house are

---

[65] E. Lucett, *Rovings in the Pacific*, 1851, I, 288–297; Lieutenant
Wise, *Los Gringos*, 1849, 357; E. T. Perkins, *Na Motu*, 1854, 322–323.
[66] See, for example, pp. 21–36 of Mumford's *Herman Melville*.

evidently imaginary.[67] The manipulation of his story for artistic ends, however, goes beyond such manifestly fictional passages as this. It has not hitherto been noticed that Melville in *Redburn* makes extensive use of a source book in a way which foreshadows his later method of literary *rifacimento*.

In chapter XXX Redburn describes with humorous comment several guidebooks which he had often pored over as a boy. Among them is a guide to Liverpool which he has brought along on this trip.[68] His father, he declares, had carried it about with him when in England thirty years before, and it contains jottings and accounts in his hand. Whether Allan Melville owned the guidebook no one knows. But it is certain that his son did when he wrote *Redburn*, for he relies upon it not only to replenish his memory but to produce a number of well-calculated effects.

In the chapter in which the guide is first introduced Melville endeavors to extract from it, to flavor his pages, the essence of its antiquated style. It is such a book, of course, as he loved, the sort which, as he wrote to Evert Duyckinck, has the "sovereign virtue of age" about it.[69] Two great things are yet to be discovered, he said in that letter—"The Art of rejuvenating old age in men and oldageifying youth in books." For this latter service the Liverpool guide was admirably adapted. In this chapter, then, and the next ("With his Prosy Old Guide Book He Takes a Prosy Stroll Through the Town") the guide provides him with material for sentimental reflection on the halcyon state of the city as it was when his father walked its streets. With his imagination full of the scenes of old English life suggested by his study of its pictures (there are seventeen

---

[67] The biography of Melville in the Duyckincks' *Cyclopædia of American Literature* (1855, II) 672–676, confirms the London journey.

[68] An article on Melville's use of the guide, with citation of parallel passages, will soon appear in the *Publications of the Modern Language Association*.

[69] See the letter of April 5, 1849, pp. 373–375 below.

plates in the guide) he wanders in the city trying to live in
its pages. "Dear delusion!" The actuality of the modern commercial city shatters the dream.

Without intimating for the benefit of his future biographers
how he had fortified his memory, Melville in later passages
freely cribs descriptions, anecdotes, and bits of geographical
lore from his guide. This sort of thing he had done in his
earlier books. But he had never previously employed his
source to help him invent and expatiate on a situation—in this
instance, the plight of a boy who dreams deliciously of revisiting a foreign city with his father's eyes but who is roughly
awakened from his fantasy by the sordid realities which he
finds there.[70]

In *White-Jacket* Melville shows an increased independence of
the remembered facts of his own nautical adventures and a
firmer reliance on his imagination. It is well known that most
of the important characters, from the Commodore, Captain
Thomas ap Catesby Jones, down to the gunner, Asa Curtis, are
portraits.[71] Jack Chase, the noble first captain of the top,
"better than a hundred common mortals . . . a whole phalanx
. . . an entire army" in himself, whose image would stay in
Melville's mind until he had made Billy Budd out of him forty
years later, was down as John J. Chase, No. 513 on the muster
roll.

But faithful picture as *White-Jacket* is of much that Melville
saw on board the *United States*, one must not forget that by no
means all of it can be taken as autobiography. The ship's
surgeon, Dr. William Johnson, may have performed amputa-

[70] Melville seems to have thought least well of *Redburn* of all his
books. He wrote to Evert Duyckinck: "I hope I shall never write
such a book again—tho' when a poor devil writes with duns all
round him . . . what can you expect of that poor devil? What
but a beggarly 'Redburn.'" The letter is on pp. 375–377 below.
[71] Albert Mordell, "Melville and 'White-Jacket,'" *Saturday Review
of Literature*, VII, 946.

tions for the instruction of his assistants, but his method could not have been that of Melville's Cuticle, for that insatiable operator learned his profession from Dr. Mackshane in Smollett's *Roderick Random*. The two most strikingly circumstantial incidents in the whole book, Melville's murderous intention to pitch the Captain into the sea if the threat of flogging him were carried out, and the marvelous description of his fall from the topgallant yard into the ocean, are, it seems, pure fiction.[72] The second of these two episodes is not recorded in the log book of the frigate, which would not fail to notice such an event. Its source is purely literary—a passage in Nathaniel Ames's *A Mariner's Sketches*.[73] These three most artistically developed sections of the book are so carefully welded into the part which is factual that when an angry admiral of the navy attempted to demolish Melville as a liar and a coward he vented his wrath without discrimination on the "lies" which Melville reported and those which he invented.

Between the writing of *White-Jacket* and *Israel Potter* Melville twice struggled to achieve the sort of book he wanted to write. When the true fit was his in composing *Moby-Dick* and *Pierre*[74] he felt what Babbalanja said poets must feel: "our hearts hot-hissing in us. And ere their fire is revealed, it must burn its way out of us; though it consume us and itself. . . . Know, thou, that the lines that live are turned out of a furrowed brow. Oh! there is a fierce, a cannibal delight, in the grief that shrieks to multiply itself. . . . Some damned spirits would not be otherwise, could they." [75]

But the fit passed. There could not be another *Moby-Dick* or *Pierre*, but there was left the architectural skill which he had

[72]C. R. Anderson, "A Reply to Herman Melville's *White-Jacket*," *American Literature*, VII, 131.

[73]Published at Providence in 1830, pp. 227–230. The passage is given on pp. 415–416 of this book.

[74]These books are discussed at length in the next section, p. lxix ff. below. [75]*Works*, IV, 324.

taught himself, beginning with *Typee*. The loss such as he
suffered after *Pierre*, of fullness and spontaneity, and of the
volition without which the fullness cannot be drained, could
not deprive him of this carefully acquired skill. Melville in
Israel Potter and in some of the *Piazza Tales* convinces one
that, had he wished, he might have gone on doing this sort
of thoroughly competent job. They are worth our attention
since they reveal so plainly, just because the greatness of *Moby-
Dick* and *Pierre* is lacking in them, how thoroughly he had
mastered the technique of his craft.

Melville had by chance stumbled upon a chapbook published
in Providence in 1824 and purporting to tell the *Life and Remarkable Adventures of Israel R. Potter*, (*A Native of Cranston,
Rhode Island*,) *who was a Soldier in the American Revolution*.
As early as 1849 he was meditating serving up "the Revolutionary narrative of the beggar" and had begun, evidently, to think
how it might be done. When he came to write it, in 1854, he
made a charming historical novel out of a bare, unadorned tale.
Of his 276 pages, about 200 are not derived from the *Life*.[76] He
adds "details and incidents to create suspense, or to cause possible complications." He deepens the character of Israel by link-
ing the episodes to his motives and by stressing certain acts of
his which expose dominant traits in his nature. The plausibility
of the sequence of events is strengthened. Subsidiary figures
are made to carry part of the burden of the story. The finest

---

[76] Melville's alterations have been studied by Roger P. McCutcheon,
"The Technique of Melville's Israel Potter," *South Atlantic Quarterly*,
XXVII, 161–174. A more detailed comparison of the novel with
its principal source may be found in W. S. Holden's unpublished
master's thesis, *Some Sources for Herman Melville's "Israel Potter"*
(Columbia University, 1932). Holden also points to many passages
which are derived from Melville's journal of his 1849 trip; from the
Sayings of Poor Richard; *The Life and Correspondence of John Paul
Jones* (New York, 1830); J. H. Sherburn's *Life and Character of the
Chevalier John Paul Jones* (Washington, 1825); and from *The Narrative of Col. Ethan Allen's Captivity* (Burlington, Vt., 1846).

things in the book, the capital satirical portrait of Franklin, the heroic one of John Paul Jones, and the sea-fight between the *Serapis* and the *Bon Homme Richard*, are, in part, free inventions of Melville, though based on authentic materials. And though the end is too hurried and perfunctory, we can see clearly that Melville was aiming at an impressively ironic conclusion.

The culmination of Melville's art of the transmutation of sailors' yarns and travelers' tales into fiction is achieved in "Benito Cereno." It will hardly do to say of it, as Professor Scudder does, that he merely rewrote a chapter in his source,[77] "including a portion of one of the legal documents there appended, suppressing a few items, and making some small additions."[78] The valiant captain's report of his extraordinary rescue of an enfeebled Spanish officer from the grip of his negro captain is unvarnished and straightforward. The events are unusual but he did not attempt to make them seem more than that. We get from his words an impression of a brave, conscientious, and resourceful commander whose nerves are unaffected by experiences aboard the *Tryal* and whose main concern is the capture of the ship as a valuable prize, after Don Benito has given her up for lost. The materials in Delano's chapter furnished, it is true, nearly everything Melville needed for a harrowing tale of terror. The problem was how to manipulate them for a predetermined artistic end.

To effect the transformation Melville had first to build up the atmosphere of horrible suspense and to keep always in the consciousness of the reader the feeling that ghastly things have been done here and that new horrors may at any moment be discovered or committed. Delano is at first made to move among these intimations of frightfulness in a kind of innocent

[77] Chapter XVIII of Captain Amasa Delano's *Narrative of Voyages and Travels, in the Northern and Southern Hemispheres* (Boston, 1817).

[78] H. H. Scudder, "Melville's *Benito Cereno* and Captain Delano's Voyages," *Publications of the Modern Language Association*, XLIII, 502.

extraverted wonder. Gradually he begins to speculate on what he sees, trying to solve the problem according to the logic of life on the high seas. He allows his mind, time and again, to push toward what suddenly seem to him unreal conclusions, as common sense holds him up and purges his imagination. Then a new episode again thrusts him deeper into the mazes of suspicion and fear.

Many of these episodes, such as the shaving of Cereno by Babo, and the luncheon at which the black attends with ironic deference, Melville invents. And their use is not merely contributory to the increasing oppression which Delano feels. They serve the primary purpose of holding him much longer on the ship than, according to his own story, he actually stayed. For this increasing sense of his isolation, of his having got himself fixed in the scene of unmentionable deeds whence there may be, perhaps, no escape, Melville strives to convey by all the art he commands.

Some of the machinery, imported from the Gothic tradition, thumps. We are not likely to be much frightened by the skeleton substituted for the ship's proper figurehead or fascinated by the dangers which hover over Cereno while he is being shaved, although the ironies of the scene are adroitly hinted. But symbolic touches, like the emphasis on the central figure of a "dark satyr in a mask, holding his foot on the prostrate neck of a writhing figure, likewise masked" which adorned the stern-piece of the Spanish ship, lead one's imagination into the story. This particular symbol could have come out of one of Hawthorne's notebooks. If it had been jotted down there, the whole story might have evolved from it. In Melville's case the reverse process seems to be the rule. The story suggests the poetic symbol appropriate to it.

With the composition of *Mardi* Melville first evinced an interest in the use of symbolism in fiction. Under the influence of Hawthorne he explored its possibilities extensively. In the important "Agatha letter" which Melville wrote Hawthorne on August 13, 1852, to turn over to him the scenario of a story which he felt Hawthorne could fashion better than he, one notices that the hints he offers for using the materials are concerned largely with the elaboration of symbolic details which he felt appropriate. Since he could hardly have supposed Hawthorne would overlook any such opportunities, we may assume that such details struck him at this time as indispensable in developing a story of this sort. The text of the letter bears this out. "The narrative from the Diary is instinct with significance.—Consider the mention of *shawls* [as a symbol of concealment] & the inference drawn from it. Ponder the conduct of this Robinson throughout. Mark his trepidation & suspicion when anyone called upon him.—But why prate so— you will mark it all and mark it deeper than I would, perhaps."[79]

The notes for the elaboration of the Agatha story are precious to students of Melville's art, for nowhere else can one so directly see his mind at work upon his material. Since in the lesser books he makes unashamed and often freely acknowledged use of sources, we can infer, by comparison, as we have just been doing, what his methods were. But in this unique instance he stands before his easel, so to speak, and begins the actual sketch.

We notice first that it is a true story, which was furnished him in more than outline form by the New Bedford lawyer who was engaged in the case. In his earliest writing he had depended upon his own true but amazing adventures, which he could supplement with his reading and the introduction of episodes wholly invented by him. Later, as in "Benito Cereno" and *Israel Potter*, the true story furnished him by a source was transformed by his imagination. At no time, except in *Pierre*, did he embark on a wholly fictitious tale. It is to be

[79] S. E. Morison, "Melville's 'Agatha' Letter to Hawthorne," *New England Quarterly*, II, 301.

noticed that in commending his Agatha story to Hawthorne he stresses one fact in particular: "You have a skeleton of actual reality to build about with fulness and veins and beauty."[80]

The lawyer's story related the marital deceptions practiced by a man named Robinson who deserted his Falmouth wife, named Agatha, whom he had married after his ship was wrecked near her home. After this desertion he married two other women. Such a tale of bigamy, involving, possibly, a study of the remorse of the chief character, Melville saw at once should naturally "gravitate" toward Hawthorne. But he was loath to permit him to do with Robinson what he rightly supposed Hawthorne might, use him for a homily on some particular variety of Sin. "In estimating the character of Robinson," he wrote, "Charity should be allowed a liberal play. I take exception to that passage from the Diary which says that *'he must have received a portion of his punishment in this life—'*[81] thus hinting of a future supplemental castigation."

If Melville had written the story, its theme would not have been the remorse of the bigamous Robinson. He sketches enough of the plot to show us where he would have placed the emphasis. In his conversation with the lawyer they had talked of the "great patience, and endurance, and resignedness of the women of the island in submitting so uncomplainingly to the long, long absences of their sailor husbands," and the lawyer had told his story to illustrate their talk. This would have been his "moral," symbolized in the opening scene by the "strange and beautiful contrast" of a sheep on the cliff overlooking the coast where the wreck is to take place, "placidly eyeing the malignity of the sea." The lover is coming in the storms.

---

[80] *Loc. cit.* One notices that the few details which Melville had worked out occurred to him in Nantucket from scenes he beheld "by chance, during my strolls thro the island." Again the "skeleton of actual reality" was articulated from something observed and tangible.

[81] *Op. cit.*, 298.

When he goes he will leave only the prow-bone of his ship projecting above the wreck buried in the sand to remind his wife what the "malignity of the sea" has done to her. *Agatha* would have been another variation of the theme which is manifest in *Moby-Dick*.

(The lesser books of Melville were made from his memories of men and places, from the works he read to stimulate or supplement these memories, and by the skill in literary architecture which increased as he practiced his art.[82] (*Moby-Dick* and *Pierre* came from another place entirely. They were produced in pain, and the mystery of their bringing forth did not cease to fascinate their begetter.) To understand them we must know the state of mind in which Melville created them.

We know that the production of *Moby-Dick* was painful, for the letters to Hawthorne speak of the "hell-fire in which the whole book is broiled" and of the weary slavery which will be necessary to get it to the press.[83] It has been customary to read autobiography out of the desperate picture of Pierre, struggling with his soul, bearing up like a demigod "against the breaking heart, and the bursting head; against all the dismal lassitude, and deathful faintness and sleeplessness, and whirlingness, and craziness."[84] But this does not describe Melville's feeling while composing *Moby-Dick*, because, in spite of the

[82] An amusing instance of Melville's habit of turning to account even fairly unpromising literary material is presented in the sketch called "The Apple-Tree Table" published in *Putnam's*, May, 1856. The "source" for the tale is a story which was going the rounds in New England. Thoreau refers (Conclusion of *Walden*) to this legend "of a strong and beautiful bug which came out of the dry leaf of an old table of apple-tree wood, which had stood in a farmer's kitchen for sixty years, first in Connecticut, and afterward in Massachusetts, —from an egg deposited in the living tree many years earlier still, as appeared by counting the annual layers beyond it; which was heard gnawing out for several weeks, hatched perchance by the heat of an urn."

[83] See the letter on pp. 388–393 below.

[84] *Works*, IX, 471.

pain of creating, he felt in himself Titanic powers and the will to grow. His soul did not yet foresee the inevitable rocks.[85]

When we try to say what caused this heat and torment we approach the crisis of Melville's maturity. The nature of his quest for the truth about the apparent interpenetration of good and evil, which he sought to objectify in Ahab's pursuit of the whale and in Pierre's conduct, we shall consider in the next section of this Introduction. What we need to notice here is that it was the dual effort, both to get at the truth and to communicate it, which produced the pain.

Melville wrote bitterly on many occasions of the impossibility of being frank with the world, but he knew that the trouble was partly within himself, for he makes Lord Media instruct Babbalanja on this matter. "Your own fleeting fancies are too often secrets to yourselves; and sooner may you get another's secret, than your own. Thus with the wisest of you all; you are ever unfixed."[86] To eliminate this strange stuff which in the act of attempting his book was upheaved and upgushed in Pierre's soul, is that youthful author's difficulty. The better book is laid upon his private shelf; the bungled one the world sees.[87] In *Moby-Dick* Melville successfully plumbed the secret and was wholly frank in communicating it. The twofold difficulty of achieving a complete intuition and of communicating it in viable symbols was met. The public and the private book were one. In *Pierre* Melville succeeded in objectifying the secret in symbols which had, we suppose, full meaning for him, but which failed to communicate anything to his readers. He could not, as the reviews of the book showed, go farther in that direction. His last effort to state an important theme ended in a checkmate.

Another and more personal difficulty, as a writer, Melville

[85] See below, in this section, p. lxx.
[86] *Works*, IV, 57.   [87] *Works*, IX, 424.

had to face as he came to the end of the series of *Mardi, Moby-Dick,* and *Pierre:* the possible loss of the creative vitality, the "fullness" which Babbalanja describes as a "full heart:—brimful, bubbling, sparkling; and running over like a flagon."[88] Too few poets, he continued, are whole men, whose brains are "planted on capacious chests, inhaling mighty morning inspirations." The race is made up of dwarfs, "staggering under heads overgrown." There was no lack of "heart"[89] when Melville composed *Mardi.* Then so much fullness was in him that it oppressed him with its power until he would fain "hurl off this Dionysius that rides me."[90]

While he was at work on *Moby-Dick*, too, he was gratifyingly conscious both of the desired fullness and of the power required to induce its overflow into words. To Evert Duyckinck he wrote in December, 1850, asking if he could send him fifty fast-writing youths who were not averse to polishing their labors. He needed them in a hurry because he had planned about that number of future works and had no time to think of them separately.[91] The same exultant feeling of the adequacy of his will to accomplish the task he had set himself pervades

[88]*Works*, IV, 322.

[89]What precisely did Melville mean by "heart?" It is a concept which he refers to constantly during these years, usually in opposition to the bloodlessness which results from too abstract speculative thought. Thus it is Emerson's misfortune that he cannot be convivial because "his brains descend down into his neck." (See letter to Duyckinck, p. 373.) Even in Hawthorne there is something lacking to the natural "plump sphericity" of a man. "He doesn't patronize the butcher—he needs roast-beef, done rare." (See letter to Duyckinck, p. 386.) In a significant passage of commentary on "Ethan Brand" (see p. 392) Melville advanced the opinion to Hawthorne that men who have really "fine brains and work them well" also have hearts that extend "down to the hams." He would in general seem to mean by "heart" a close contact with life, which the "hearty" man evinces, and the romantic virtues of enthusiasm, spontaneity, and humanitarianism.

[90]*Works*, IV, 55.

[91]This letter is printed on pp. 381–384 below.

the letters to Hawthorne at this time. When *Moby-Dick* was done, and Hawthorne had given it his approval, he was in the mood to say: "As long as we have anything more to do, we have done nothing. . . . Leviathan is not the biggest fish;— I have heard of Krakens."[92] In the midst of the chapter on the "Grand Armada" of the whales (LXXXVII), as in his imagination the vast fleet of leviathans hurries forward through the straits, Melville is reminded of his condition while he writes. Even as in all this turmoil the young leviathan amours go on, so, "amid the tornadoed Atlantic of my being," he wrote, "do I myself still forever centrally disport in mute calm; and while ponderous planets of unwaning woe revolve round me, deep down and deep inland there I still bathe me in eternal mildness of joy."[93] As the appalling ocean surrounds the verdant land, so there lies deep in his soul "one insular Tahiti, full of peace and joy, but encompassed by all the horrors of the half-known life."[94]

It was otherwise when *Pierre* was written. The center still persists, but is it creation or destruction which is at work there? While Pierre labors (and Melville labors with *Pierre*) he feels two leeches drain the life from him. One draws out the book the world will see; the other, to fit him "for the highest life," thins his blood and collapses his heart.[95] And what is this leech that draws the blood from his heart? It is evidently the ceaseless speculation about virtue and vice, good and evil, God and man, in which both Pierre and his creator indulged. Melville was evidently fully aware of the danger to his creative life—the first requisite of which is the "full heart"—of his increasing indulgence in metaphysics. If the brain wins over the heart there will be no more novels.

To resume the argument of the last few pages, we may assert that Melville's failure to go on in the vein of *Moby-Dick* and

---

[92] This letter is printed on pp 394–396 below.
[93] *Works*, VIII, 136.   [94] *Works*, VII, 349.   [95] *Works*, IX, 425.

Pierre, aside from the physical exhaustion from which it is known he suffered after 1852, is due to three causes. He knew, from the reception of *Pierre*, that his readers were incapable of understanding a book of that unorthodox kind. Yet such books only did he care to write. He realized, too, one feels, the possibility that if he risked another *Pierre*, his interest in metaphysical speculation might completely inhibit the creative overflow. A third factor must be included. The theme which he had developed in *Mardi* with its political implications, in *Moby-Dick* with reference to the natural world, and in *Pierre* as it applies to the realm of moral values, was now exhausted. He had told the threefold story he had to tell. The fullness of heart and the volition needed to move it lasted just long enough to accomplish the creation of the trilogy.

The prose which Melville schooled himself to write is in the great tradition of the English masters. As Freeman says: "He was not an irregular innovating genius who overthrows idols and breaks up a language in order to build and make anew: he used the things he loved, for they possessed his mind."[96] His literary enthusiasms can be followed successively through his books. Rabelais and Urquhart preside over the visit to the "extraordinary old antiquary" in *Mardi*.[97] Sir Thomas Browne helped to form the chapter (I, 32) on "Xiphius Platypterus" in the same book, and the dissertation on the way "Lombardo produced his great Kostanza" (II, 76) owes him much. The unabashed pedantry of Old Burton furnishes

[96] *Herman Melville*, 170.
[97] *Works*, IV, 67–76. Oh-Oh's collection of ancient and curious manuscripts derives, of course, from the library of St. Victor. The whole voyage of King Media and his companions in search of Yillah suggests the journey of Pantagruel, Panurge, and Friar John in search of the oracle of Bacbuc, "alias the Holy Bottle." W. H. Wells has found close parallels between the chapter on the "Whiteness of the Whale" in *Moby-Dick* and Rabelais I, 10—"Of That Which Is Signified by the Colours White and Blue." (See Bibliography.)

the method for the cetological chapters in *Moby-Dick*. The staccato apostrophes of Carlyle explode in *Moby-Dick* and *Pierre*.[98]

⟨The masterly prose of *Moby-Dick*, in which Melville reached the heights, was the result of the convergence of two styles he had been perfecting since he began to write.⟩ ⟨The one is realistic, rapid, lucid, ~~in the manner of Defoe—as has often been re-marked~~—a style admirably suited to the requirements of narrative, and no doubt owing much to the yarns Melville had listened to and had himself related during three years of wandering.⟩ It relies for its charm on an abundance of picturesque details and appeals to the eye. ⟨The other style depends solely for its effect on the music which its rhythms convey to our ears.⟩ It emerges for the first time in his books in rhapsodic passages in the second half of *Mardi*. The images are usually vague and not co-ordinated, the words used for the beauty of their sound.

How superior Melville's realistic style is to the prose of the travel books contemporary with his early work can be judged by comparing passages in *Typee* or *White-Jacket* with their sources in Stewart and Ames. When, for example, White-Jacket fell from the yardarm, a bloody film was before his eyes through which, "ghostlike, passed and repassed my father, mother and sisters." Ames saw only the "forms of all I hold dear on earth." White-Jacket felt an unutterable nausea; he was conscious of gasping, there was no breath in his body and

---

[98] In *Moby-Dick*, see especially the end of "Knights and Squires" (*Works*, VII, 149–150) and the conclusion of "Fast-fish and Loose-fish" (*Works*, VIII, 146–147). The influence of Carlyle on *Pierre* is treated briefly in the Introduction to Forsythe's edition of the novel (pp. xxxvi–xxxvii). He notes both the use of Carlyle's eccentricities of style and some actual reflection of ideas. "The historian's praises of silence in *Sartor* and in *The French Revolution* are adapted by the novelist. The description of the mood wherein Pierre has his vision of the Titans has its original in *Sartor*. . . ." Forsythe finds echoes of Longfellow's *Hyperion* and De Quincey's *Suspira de Profundis*, also, in *Pierre*.

he went "down, down, with lungs collapsed as in death."
Ames felt merely a "peculiar sickness and distress at the stomach." His mind stored with the wonders he had seen in his
voyages and that store constantly enriched by his reading, his
visits to the theater in New York and abroad, and the works of
art which he delighted in,[99] Melville's prose rapidly acquired
the remarkable cumulative richness which gives a universal
quality to scenes and emotions he describes.

As early as 1839, in "Fragments from a Writing-Desk," [100]
Melville showed that he had an ear. In the elaborate sentences
of these youthful exercises there are signs of later characteristic
movements. The periods are hurried, as if the writer were
afraid of losing breath before the end, but the paragraphs attempt to rise to a suspended moment before the final cadence.
When in *Mardi* he turned to a theme which permitted an emotional treatment, it is not surprising that he should revert to a
musical prose, which he had tried to write in his schoolteaching
days before he went to sea.

The following passage will show how the realistic and musical
styles finally merge in the prose of *Moby-Dick:*

Nor is it, altogether, the remembrance of her cathedral-
toppling earthquakes; nor the stampedoes of her frantic seas;
nor the tearlessness of arid skies that never rain; nor the sight
of her wide field of leaning spires, wrenched cope-stones,
and crosses all adroop (like canted yards of anchored fleets);
and her suburban avenues of house-walls lying over upon each
other, as a tossed pack of cards;—it is not these things alone
which make tearless Lima the strangest, saddest city thou
canst see. For Lima has taken the white veil; and there is a
higher horror in this whiteness of her woe. Old as Pizarro,
this whiteness keeps her ruins forever new; admits not the

[99] Melville's fondness for genre artists like Teniers, Hogarth,
Cruikshank, and Wilkie should be noted in this connection.
[100] Contributed to the *Democratic Press and Lansingburgh Advertiser;* reprinted in *Works*, XIII, 382–399.

cheerful greenness of complete decay; spreads over her broken
ramparts the rigid pallor of an apoplexy that fixes its own
distortions.[101]

The moving quality of such passages as this is not due entirely
to their music. This is not lovely nonsense like the rhythmic
parts of *Mardi*. The mind's eye is impressed as well as the ear.
Each cadence brings with it a new picture. These things Melville has seen—the frantic seas, the canted yards of anchored
fleets and the broken ramparts—but his impressions are put
here to the poetic uses of signifying and symbolizing. As
Freeman says, speaking generally of the quality of this sort
of prose: "The words become more than the words, the meaning
is increased by suggestion and the excitement of the mind at
the touch of so much beauty, and apprehensions come in
crowds, all quickening and intensifying as they come. The
reader's emotion and intelligence co-operate at last with the
writer's."[102]

The passage just quoted will serve to demonstrate another
fact about the prose of Melville's maturity. Among the varied
rhythms of which its "long-breathed sea-like movement" is
composed, three definite and recurrent patterns can often be
observed: a sequence of short phrases or clauses of nearly
equal length, like the long catalogue in *White-Jacket* of the
ships which will appear at the Judgment Day; variations of the
Old Testament antiphonal verse, most familiar to Melville's
pulse in the cadences of his favorite books of the Bible, Ecclesi-
astes and the Song of Solomon; and a tripartite arrangement of
clauses which rise, wave on wave, before dropping to a weighted
close. It is not uncommon to find these three patterns in a

---

[101] *Works*, VII, 241. It should be remembered that in *Moby-Dick*
the realistic style is still used by Melville for the more matter-of-fact
chapters. It is because his musical prose has elsewhere absorbed
the realistic that the two styles do not clash.

[102] *Herman Melville*, 176.

single passage, as we find them in this paragraph, just quoted, from "The Whiteness of the Whale."

III. THE TRILOGY: *Mardi, Moby-Dick, Pierre*

With a slightly malicious smile Melville announced in the preface to *Mardi:* "Having published two narratives of voyages in the Pacific, which, in many quarters, were received with incredulity, the thought occurred to me of indeed writing a romance of Polynesian adventure, and publishing it as such; to see whether the fiction might not, possibly, be received for a verity: in some degree the reverse of my previous experience." But it was not simply a romance he had undertaken. "This thought was the germ of others, which have resulted in *Mardi*," the preface continues. It was for the sake of uttering those "other thoughts" that *Mardi* was really written. It is the first of the three books, *Moby-Dick* and *Pierre* being the other two, where a theme arising from Melville's spiritual quest is merged with the ostensible story.

His ambition to be more than a spinner of yarns was formed, and the time had come to tell his readers, under the necessary guise of romance and allegory, what conclusions he had struggled toward in the realms of social and religious thought. The fictional device was simple but well-adapted to his ends. With a companion he would desert his ship, the *Arcturion,* and take to the open ocean. After a series of adventures not too improbable to be believed in, including the rescue, from a native priest, of Yillah, a mysterious and beautiful girl who supposed she had once lived in Oroolia, the Polynesian paradise, he would land on Odo and be received there as the demigod Taji, as Captain Cook had been received by the Hawaiians as Lono the war-god. To this point Melville introduced nothing which was not credible. He carefully makes Taji doubt the supernatural parts of Yillah's story and seek a natural explanation of her history. After his setting forth on a tour of the islands of Mardi (the world) with King Media, marvelous scenes soon appear, but the accounts of the first three kingdoms visited contain only traces of satire. A reader might have traveled thus far with a growing belief that Melville was forcing him to take for fiction what might indeed be fact.[103]

Melville makes Taji and his companions visit a group of island-states whose names suggest they are modern countries in disguise. Their voyage allows him to give vent to his fermenting ideas on kingship, democracy, social revolution, the new plutocracy in England and America, imperialism, slavery,

---

[103] Actually Melville's fabulous islands do owe much to his memory of definite places in the South Seas, Hawaii in particular, and to his reading of the voyagers. No one seems to have noticed that the description of surfboard-riding in the chapter entitled "Rare Sport at Ohonoo" recalls what Melville had seen at Waikiki beach on Oahu and that the valley where the visitors feasted (Monlova) is really Manoa. There are many other passages which circumstantially refer to Hawaiian geography and history. Chapter XCII—"The God Keevi and the Precipice of Mondo"—describes, for instance, the cliff of the Pali over which, in 1795, the conquering invader Kamehameha drove scores of the defenders to their death on the rocks below. Melville seems also to have made some use of the Hawaiian folk-tales.

Melville's recourse to the voyage literature in writing *Mardi* is discussed in David Jaffé's "Some Sources of Melville's *Mardi*," *American Literature*, IX, 56–69. To indicate the way he transformed his originals, an example from Ellis's *Polynesian Researches* may be cited. In "The Tale of a Traveler" (I, 98) Samoa tells the marvelous story of how he once, in performing a trepanning operation on a wounded friend, replaced a portion of the injured brain with part of a pig's brain. Ellis reports the operation on hearsay: "It is also related, although I confess I can scarcely believe it, that on some occasions, when the brain has been injured as well as the bone, they have opened the skull, taken out the injured portion of the brain, and, having a pig ready, have killed it, taken out the pig's brains, put them in the man's head, and covered them up. They persist in stating that this has been done; but add, that the persons always became furious with madness, and died" (ed. of 1829, II, 277). Melville, with a characteristic twist, makes the patient survive for a time in a perverse-minded, piggish state.

and nationalist war. In none of these nations do the travelers find a perfect commonwealth. The realms which are controlled by the church (Maramma) are no better, and in them, in addition, the ecclesiastical sins prevail. Pilgrims who are humble of heart, poor, and truth-seeking, are not wanted there.

In Serenia, at length, a Utopia is discovered where the ethics of Alma (Christ) form the constitution of the people. Without priests, kings, or statutes to govern them, they dwell in peace under the Master.

The Master's great command is Love; and here do all things wise, and all things good, unite. Love is all in all. The more we love, the more we know; and so reversed. Oro [God] we love; this isle; and our wide arms embrace all Mardi like its reef. How can we err, thus feeling? We hear loved Alma's pleading, prompting voice, in every breeze, in every leaf; we see his earnest eye in every star and flower.[104]

Babbalanja, the philosopher, greatly moved by a mystic vision, elects to stay among the Serenians, and tries to persuade Taji to stay with him. But the phantom of the blue firmament eyes and Golconda locks of Yillah, whose disappearance impelled him first to set out, lures Taji toward his doom of an endless quest.

How are we to interpret Taji's pursuit of the mysterious Yillah and the equally mysterious pursuit of Taji by the dark lady, Hautia? Beneath the symbolism of this myth Melville concealed the dualistic enigma which had begun to wrack his spirit. The theme here first announced is augmented in *Moby-Dick*, *Pierre*, and *Billy Budd*.

Melville, in the days since his homecoming, had wrestled with the chronic problems of philosophy. In *Mardi*, as he had done with his friends in conversation, he threshed over the old arguments for the proof of consciousness, the debate between necessity and free will, the problem of a sinful world and a righteous God, the question of the moral responsibility of the natural man. To us who in the course of a systematic education encounter these dilemmas first in the textbooks and are cognizant of all the traditional answers, these iterative passages in *Mardi* seem a little sophomoric. To Melville the ideas were new and the rehearsal of them helped to purge away the remnants of the Calvinistic orthodoxy of his upbringing.

What troubled him ceaselessly was to know whether a master key to all these teasing questions could ever be found. An urge, deep in his nature, compelled him to "grind away at the nut of the universe" though it crack his jaws. The Penultimate will not satisfy him; he must have the Ultimate. That he might be dragged asunder in the effort to reconcile heaven and earth and find the Absolute, he knew, as well as did his creature Babbalanja. In the conversion of Taji's companions to the way of life of the Serenians, Melville represents the inclination he often felt to content himself with the natural "theology in the grass and the flower," and to follow the promptings of the heart, supplemented by Christ's gospel. "Yet, alas! too often do I swing from these moorings." [105]

When Babbalanja is granted a vision of the Mardian Paradise he dares to ask there the question, "Why create the germs that sin and suffer, but to perish?"

"That," breathed my guide, "is the last mystery which underlieth all the rest. Archangel may not fathom it; that makes of Oro the everlasting mystery he is; that to divulge, were to make equal to himself in knowledge all the souls that are; that mystery Oro guards; and none but him may know." [106]

This evasion contents Babbalanja. Taji it did not content. He would solve the mystery or pull down heaven. Leaving his

[105] *Works*, IV, 126.
[106] *Ibid.*, 376.

companions behind he seizes the helm, eternity in his eye, and steers for the outer ocean.[107]

As with most great books into which the writer has poured his whole thought and energy, the reader can make of *Moby-Dick* pretty much what he pleases. He can read it as the most thrilling of sea stories which at the same time far outranks the sober works of Beale and Cheever in presenting a definitive account of the short-lived whaling industry that brought fabulous wealth to New England in the 1840's. To some it epitomizes the romantic generation's "pursuit of death." For others it records the experience, which Melville was not the only man of the century to endure, of the clash of a transcendental optimism with the new realistic perception of the natural world, which would culminate in the end of the century in the "capricious sub-rational fatalism" of such men as Hardy and Housman. It is also Melville's *Anatomy of Melancholy*, large enough in scope to allow him to include within its covers the strange miscellaneous lore, that he, like the seventeenth-century "Democ-

---

[107] Melville's critics have identified Yillah and Hautia and their supplementary symbols in various ways. They are in fundamental agreement, however, since the general meaning is sufficiently clear. Plainly Yillah stands for the ultimate revelation. If she connotes happiness, as Homans contends ("The Dark Angel," *New England Quarterly*, V, 708), then the identification must mean happiness of a heavenly sort, something like the heavenly beauty of Spenser and the intellectual beauty of Shelley. As for Hautia, the dark charmer who entices Taji to her Circean island with the intimation that there he will find Yillah, the best I can suggest is that to Melville she represents whatever soul-deadening worldly lures impede the search for truth (she offers him "beauty, health, wealth, long life, and the last lost hope of man"). The symbol is given a theological cast from the suggestion of the theme of the fall of man and original sin which Melville introduces into the story of Hautia's ancestry (*Works*, IV, 385–386). We might be led to interpret Yillah's captivity in Hautia's bower as a simple allegory of truth's temporary subservience to evil, did we not know, from Melville's subsequent development of the Yillah-Hautia dualism, that he had in mind the ambiguity of the moral universe and the inextricability of good and evil.

ritus" whom he loved, gathered in from the remotest sources.
These various elements he fused together into an artistic performance whose skill his admirers, though they prized the book
for other excellencies, have been late in recognizing. Even
Van Wyck Brooks had to look a second time before he observed
the "careful disorderliness" of his method and the accelerations
of the rhythm when the voyage begins which portend the fate
that will overwhelm the mad Ahab and his crew.[108]

What we are more particularly concerned with here is the
place of *Moby-Dick* in Melville's quest for the Ultimate. When
Mardi ended, Taji held the prow toward the open sea and the
realm of shades that harbors Yillah. The action of *Moby-Dick*
begins when Ahab, whose "quenchless feud," Melville declares, "seemed mine,"[109] tells the crew that they have signed
on to chase the White Whale "round perdition's flames,"
till he "spouts black blood and rolls fin out." The new voyage
is the continuation of the first, with this great difference, that
the object of the quest has been transformed. Taji still hoped
to recover the lost happiness of the days when Yillah was his
in Odo; Ahab seeks revenge against an inscrutable and apparently capricious foe.

What is this White Whale which swam before the lunatic
captain as the "monomaniac incarnation of all those malicious
agencies which some deep men feel eating in them, till they are
left living on with half a heart and half a lung"?[110] The exegetes
are ready with many answers. Is he, as D. H. Lawrence said,
"the deepest blood-being of the white race" which is hunted by
the "maniacal fanaticism of our white mental consciousness"?
This is close, for Starbuck cried out to Ahab in the third
day's chase, "Moby-Dick seeks thee not. It is thou, thou,
that madly seekest him!"[111] Is Lewis Mumford right in seeing
in him "the brute energies of existence, blind, fatal, overpower-

[108] *Emerson and Others*, 196.   [109] *Works*, VII, 222.
[110] *Ibid.*, 229.   [111] *Works*, VIII, 361.

ing"?[112]   This shoots somewhat wide of the mark, for what
chiefly torments Ahab is to know whether he is fighting against
energies from the void of death which man has himself animated,
or against "some unknown but still reasoning thing."[113]
Whichever guess may be the true one, what Ahab chiefly
hates is the inscrutableness of his enemy who impales him first
on one and then the other of these desperate answers.

The frightfulness of the whale is incarnate in his whiteness,
the "colorless, all-color of atheism," of the universal charnel-
house inhabited by nothingness.   To pursue him is to pursue
death.   If we try to solve the incantation of his whiteness, we
must to the grave to learn it.   Sometimes Ahab, in this mood,
thinks "there's naught beyond" the mask, behind which his
foe fights, but blankness.[114]   But this mood is not frequent.
To whalers who encountered Moby-Dick in times past his
seeming infernal aforethought of ferocity was "not wholly
regarded as having been inflicted by an unintelligent agent."[115]
Their inclination to believe in his demoniac purpose became
at length in Ahab an obsession of certainty.   The beast, whether
agent of a devil-god or the god himself, showed purposeful
malice beneath his outrageous strength.   All the suspected
malice of the universe, all the "subtle demonisms of life and
thought" crazy Ahab saw at last practically assailable in Moby-
Dick.[116]

[112] *Herman Melville*, 184.   [113] *Works*, VII, 204.
[114] *Loc. cit.*   [115] *Works*, VII, 228.
[116] *Ibid.*, 229.   In concentrating here on the symbolism of the White
Whale, I do not infer that Moby-Dick is to be taken only as a symbol.
The book has been read by most—with no harm done—as the story
of a mad sea-captain's pursuit of a vengeful creature whom the
rest of the whaling masters shun.   The whole force of the book is,
of course, directed by Melville to the end of creating in the reader
an impression of the monster's terrible actuality.   The details of the
preparation for the voyage, the operation of the ship, the digressions
on the natural history of the whale, the encounters with other ships,
and the final mighty three-day struggle with Moby-Dick, serve,
chapter by chapter, to convince the reader that he is real, a part of

Before his mind was overthrown by this fatal obsession Ahab
was sensitive to other elements than the demonism of the world.
We are allowed glimpses, as in the words of Ophelia about the
Hamlet of other days, of an Ahab who responds to the clear,
strong, and steadfast mildness of the trade winds. The "long-
drawn virgin vales; the mild blue hillsides" of the ocean have
yet their temporary effect upon him.[117] He can still weep and,
in conversation with Starbuck, remember Nantucket and home
and child. In his calmer moments, such as prevail in this
colloquy with Starbuck in "The Symphony," he looks back
longingly to the world of reason and love which he has put
behind him.[118] But these moods are few and are annihilated
by the remorseless commands of the emperor who rules him.
He feels himself the Fates' lieutenant acting under orders. His
act is immutably decreed and was rehearsed a billion years
before the ocean rolled.[119] He and the crew are turned round
and round like the ship's windlass, and Fate is the handspike.

So Ahab wills to believe. His creator knows this is delusion.
Once when the ship, aglow with the flame and smoke of the
try-works, drove on through the night, Ishmael-Melville dozed
at the helm. The tiller smote his side, and he awoke in fright,
having turned himself about in his sleep. Grateful to have

---

nature like the other whales which have been killed, their blubber
tried out and stowed in the hold. It is by means of the energy in this
external story that its allegorical significance is, in Ahab's word,
"shoved" near us.

In this connection attention should be called to Melville's statement to Mrs. Hawthorne, in a letter of Jan. 8, 1852: "I had some
vague idea while writing it [*Moby-Dick*], that the whole book was
susceptible of an allegorical construction, and also that parts of it
were—but the specialty of many of the particular subordinate
allegories were first revealed to me after reading Mr. Hawthorne's
letter, which, without citing any particular examples, yet intimated
the part-and-parcel allegoricalness of the whole." (See Bibliography:
"An Unpublished Letter from Herman Melville to Mrs. Hawthorne.")

[117]*Works*, VIII, 264.   [118]*Ibid*., 329.   [119]*Ibid*., 352.

escaped the fatal contingency of being brought by the lee, he meditates: "Look not too long in the face of the fire, O man! Never dream with thy hand on the helm! Turn not thy back to the compass; accept the first hint of the hitching tiller; believe not the artificial fire, when its redness makes all things look ghastly." [120]   Such wisdom Ahab trampled on.   He had gazed too long on the unholy fires.   He willed his mind to follow the cursed fiends who beckoned him down among them. In the chapter called "The Chart" Melville represents him as starting from his hammock at night, forced by intolerable dreams.   His explanation of Ahab's anguish is explicit, and we should not pass it by.   The Ahab who rushed from his sleep was not, he says, the crazy Ahab who pursued the whale.   It was the innocent living soul of him that for a moment, in sleep, dissociated itself from and escaped the characterizing mind, which at other times employed it for its outer vehicle or agent.

But as the mind does not exist unless leagued with the soul, therefore it must have been that, in Ahab's case, yielding up all his thoughts and fancies to his one supreme purpose; that purpose, by its own sheer inveteracy of will, forced itself against gods and devils into a kind of self-assumed, independent being of its own.   Nay, could grimly live and burn, while the common vitality to which it was conjoined, fled horror-stricken from the unbidden and unfathered birth.   Therefore, the tormented spirit that glared out of bodily eyes, when what seemed Ahab rushed from his room, was for the time but a vacated thing, a formless somnambulistic being, a ray of living light, to be sure, but without an object to colour, and therefore a blankness in itself.   God help thee, old man, thy thoughts have created a creature in thee; and he whose intense thinking thus makes him a Prometheus; a vulture feeds upon that heart forever;   that vulture the very creature he creates. [121]

[120] *Ibid.*, 181.   [121] *Works*, VII, 252–253.

This significant passage makes plain the symbolic meaning of the mysterious Fedallah, the Parsee whom Ahab smuggles aboard the ship and who led his chase against the whale. Though they never spoke while they kept watch together, a potent spell joined them, "as if in the Parsee Ahab saw his forethrown shadow, in Ahab the Parsee his abandoned substance."[122]   Which is to say, that Ahab brought his own fate on board with him.   This vulture that feeds upon his heart he himself created.[123]

How is *Moby-Dick* to be read as the allegory of Melville's spiritual state in 1851? To what point has he come in his quest for the Ultimate? He invites us to inquire in the passage which admits his sympathy with Ahab's feud.[124] The wall of the mystery had been shoved menacingly near. He was like a prisoner whose only escape was by thrusting through. The ultimate answer, if it could be reached, would be complex, he now realized, and its quest perhaps dangerous to the sanity. He might have to impute the evil omnipresent in the universe to its ruler. But was this evil the work of principal or of agent? He began to suspect even that the intricate subject of all his speculations might dissolve in nothing, that there was, as he wrote to Hawthorne, no secret, "like the Freemason's mighty secret, so terrible to all children," which turns out, at last, "to consist in a triangle, a mallet, and an apron,—nothing more."[125]

[122] *Works*, VIII, 320.

[123] This point has been overlooked or minimized by critics of *Moby-Dick*. It would seem to be of the utmost importance. There are other passages in the book which show even more plainly Melville's feeling at this time that within the lines of necessity which control man's world there is room for the play of free will. In the chapter called "The Mat-Maker," for example, Ishmael weaves a sword-mat, using his own hand for a shuttle, while Queequeg ever and anon with his oaken sword carelessly drives home every yarn. To Ishmael this suggests "the straight warp of necessity"; free will, "still free to ply her shuttle between given threads"; and chance, which has the "last featuring blow at events."

[124] The chapter entitled "Moby-Dick."   [125] See p. 388 below.

In this same illuminating letter he notes that as soon as man begins to objectify the invisible world, to talk of *Me*, a *God*, a *Nature*, he prepares the noose that will hang him, like Ahab who sought to fight the intangible malignities only when he found in the White Whale their tangible incarnation.

Although Ahab was mad, as Melville knew him to be, and though he tried revenge, which is no solution to man's predicament, we must not suppose that Melville, even though defiant, would now choose to follow Ahab into the gulf, as Taji had turned his prow towards the racing tide. It is not merely for the purpose of saving the narrator that Ishmael-Melville survives the White Whale's assault. However much he sympathized with Ahab's Promethean determination to stare down the inscrutableness of the universe, Melville hurled, not himself, but Ahab, his creature, at the injurious gods. Like the mountain eagle, though he had swooped into the blackest gorge, that gorge lay within the lofty mountains.[126] He had written a wicked book for which Ahab was made to suffer vicariously, and he felt as spotless as the lamb.

Melville's contemporaries dismissed *Pierre* as not only a dead failure but as a work so "repulsive, unnatural and indecent"[127] that it might endanger one's mental health to read it. With his admirers of more recent times, enthusiasts over the neglected *Moby-Dick*, it did not fare much better. Only in the past half dozen years has it been studied objectively with the intent of elucidating its mysteries and determining what Melville thought he had accomplished.

Pierre is still a difficult book. To us of this generation who read with ease Meredith and James and Woolf, and think we

---

[126] This position is summed up in the passage from which this figure comes (*Works*, VIII, 182): "There is a wisdom that is woe; but there is a woe that is madness." In other words, the perception of the dualism in the universe brings woe, but man is not fated to allow that woe to pass into madness.

[127] *American Whig Review.*

fathom the expressionism of Joyce's *Ulysses* and Lawrence's *The Rainbow*, Melville's methods are not utterly confusing, as they were to an earlier generation. Our difficulty is not to understand the drift and significance of the story but to know how much of what we think we see was placed there by Melville, and how much we read into the text because we have lived through the Freudian era.[128] So startling is Melville's prescience about such subjects as adolescent psychology and the unconscious[129] and so modern is his literary use of dreams and myths that one has constantly to remind oneself of the date of the novel.

As a barrier to our enjoyment of *Pierre*, and sometimes to comprehension, we cannot overlook the insecurity of its style. In *Moby-Dick* potentially dissonant passages of realism, rhapsody, instruction, humor, and tragedy are modulated to the universally heroic tone of the book. These various elements have one trait in common. In *Pierre* this is not the case. Time and again it is impossible without weighing and comparing to apprehend the intended tone of a particular passage. Two examples will sufficiently demonstrate this. The over-sweet Arcadian opening of the book, disclosing Pierre the Innocent

---

[128] In this connection one may object to some of the terminology in E. L. Grant Watson's "Melville's *Pierre*" (*New England Quarterly*, April, 1930). He is inclined to treat the novel as if it were the work of a contemporary whose symbolism shows him to be thoroughly familiar with the concepts of the Freudian school. In *Pierre* the story takes place in the realm where moral values are paramount, in society that is, and chiefly within the family. But the theme which the story embodies is metaphysical as well as moral and the symbols which Melville invents to add depth to it belong therefore to both orders of thought. When they seem to be startlingly erotic as well, the presumption is that they are often so only by the accident that Melville's plot necessarily involves various sex relationships.

[129] For passages showing Melville's interest in the psychology of childhood and adolescence, see particularly *Works*, IX, 96, 111-114, 123-127, 164, 301. Modern ideas of the unconscious are suggested in pages 97-98, 150-151, 396-397, 407.

in the center of his earthly paradise, is probably intended as satire and is artistically satisfying when read as such.[130]   But it is so near to the style of the "thee-and-thou" school of sentimental fiction contemporary with it that one cannot be quite sure. For a second example consider Plinlimmon's pamphlet on "Chronometricals and Horologicals," advocating a "virtuous expediency" in moral actions, which opens Pierre's eyes though it does not affect his will. So unemphatic is Melville's attitude toward the pamphlet that some critics have been convinced that he sided with Plinlimmon, though if such were the case, the novel would contain insoluble contradictions.

In spite of these difficulties *Pierre* is a fascinating book. It possesses the vigor and promise of greater things to come which any primitive displays. André Gide has said that more interesting than the finished novel itself would be the journal of a great novelist like Stendhal or Dostoevsky showing the progress of the fight to achieve it. In *Pierre* we see Melville struggling, as M. Gide says of his central figure in *Les Faux Monnayeurs*, "entre ce que lui offre le réalité et ce que, lui, prétend en faire." The substance of the book is Melville's struggle to fathom the mystery of Pierre, who in turn is struggling to understand his author-hero Vivia, who is struggling to write a novel about his own "pursuit of the highest health of virtue and truth."

Melville knew that he would have to disrupt the confines of the conventional novel which laboriously spins veils of mystery, "only to complacently clear them up at last." His readers need not expect him to unravel his mysteries, because in human life there are no proper endings, but only "imperfect, unanticipated, and disappointing sequels," which "hurry to

---

[130] Braswell believes that the aberrances of style throughout the book are deliberate on Melville's part and reveal his satiric purpose ("The Satirical Temper of Melville's *Pierre*," *American Literature*, VII, 432–435).

abrupt intermergings with the eternal tides of time and fate."[131]
He was about to descend into the heart of man by a spiral stair
without an end, "where that endlessness is only concealed by
the spiralness of the stair, and the blackness of the shaft."
In two earlier books he had presented the tormenting dualism
which is masked behind the inscrutableness of the universe,
as it is embodied in the political and economic realm (*Mardi*)
and as it may be discovered in the world of nature (*Moby-Dick*).
He wished to work it out anew in the plane of metaphysical
values. His search for the Ultimate here brought him, as it
did Browning, into conflict with the dominant belief of the
nineteenth century fostered by the scientist, that reality is to
be found in the natural world.

Melville wished to show in *Pierre* that there are some men,
"Enthusiasts to Duty," who will obey the highest behest of
their souls, though they lose their worldly felicity and bring
upon themselves a "not-to-be-thought-of-woe." They stake
all on the good faith of God. The world casts them out and
mocks them. Heaven gives no sign, either of having ordained
their fall or of being concerned for it. They are befooled by
Truth, Virtue, and Fate. This theme would be projected through
the story, deliberately Hamletian in outline, of Pierre Glendinning, gently born and reared in innocence and piety. He
reveres the memory of his father as the personification of a
goodness which is almost divine. He adores his haughty,
worldly mother and worships Lucy Tartan, to whom he is
engaged, as if she were almost more than mortal. Suddenly
there invades this heaven on earth a mysterious dark-haired girl
(Isabel) who, he is convinced, is an unacknowledged daughter of
his father. He faces a dilemma. Heaven-decreed Duty com-
pels him to receive Isabel, yet to receive her as his sister will
shame his father's memory and cast down his mother's pride.
He cuts the knot by the fantastic device of a pseudo-marriage

[131] *Works*, IX, 199.

to her.   Lucy nearly dies of the shock and his mother, after disinheriting Pierre, is killed by grief and anger.   In the city whither the couple have gone, Pierre struggles to write a novel, which is a failure.   Lucy follows him to the city, pursued by Glen Stanly, Pierre's cousin and former friend, who wishes to save her.   Pierre is goaded into killing him.   Lucy dies of shock.   Pierre and Isabel end the tragedy with poison.

What Pierre learns in the boundless expansion of his life, how society judges the folly of men like him, what the philosophers have to tell the Pierres of the world about the disparity between heavenly and terrestrial morality, what Melville had concluded about the issue, were all to find a place within the plot of this *Hamlet raisonné*.

A few ludicrously melodramatic scenes in *Pierre* have induced critics to overlook the fact that Melville invented an external plot which could be excellently manipulated to embody his theme and was capable of appropriate symbolic elaboration. There is scarcely a situation in the story which is not sound psychological realism except the pseudo-marriage between Pierre and his half-sister Isabel.   The exception is a large one, but Melville could not avoid the episode.   The incest motive was symbolically indispensable to the development of the idea of the ambiguity and the terrestrial taint of heavenly truth. Yet Pierre, since he represents in the beginning absolute innocence (though he is soon made alarmingly aware of the inversions of Truth) could not be made a deliberate partner in a physically incestuous relationship, however much this might have enhanced the probability of the external plot.   The solution of the pseudo-marriage Melville recognized as a weak link and he devotes most of Book X—"The Unprecedented Final Resolution of Pierre"—to an analysis of the motives which induced his hero to take this way out.   In the course of it he uncovers two psychological facts which nearly convince the reader.   Isabel's mysterious nature had already begun to work

an ambiguous charm upon Pierre so that the performance of his
heaven-appointed duty was not single-motived; nor was the
act, for another reason, entirely unprepared for. The artificial
and ambiguous brother-sister relationship which Pierre and
his mother had established between themselves was the pre-
parative to this "nominal conversion of a sister into a wife."

The characters in *Pierre*, their actions, even objects which
they touch, like Isabel's guitar and Pierre's Terror Stone, have
symbolic value. The whole novel is a "continued allegory or
dark conceit." Pierre is the Demigod whose parentage is
half heavenly and half earthly. Because half his nature is
divine he has a natural and insatiable appetite for God and seeks
to regain his paternal birthright "even by fierce escalade."
Pierre's father symbolizes the Deity; his haughty mother, the
World. His betrothed Lucy, his Good Angel, who seeks to
recapture him in the end, is heavenliness, as Pierre, while still
the innocent and the enthusiast, apprehended it. The mysterious Isabel, whose unjust fate and irresistible charm attract
Pierre into the pseudo-marriage, symbolizes Melville's maturing
intuition of the nature of ultimate truth. She is heaven-born—
Pierre's father is her father—but her mother was earthborn,
and so Isabel's birth was tainted. His love for her grows
imperceptibly warm and earthly, and is finally revealed as such
to Lucy.[132] In the allegory, abstract truth, to follow which a
righteous man has sacrificed his world, proves at last to be
ambiguous, casting two shadows, Virtue and Vice. The tragic
course of Pierre—the Demigod who seeks to recover his lost
heaven—proves the indisputableness of Melville's maxim: "In
those Hyperborean regions, to which enthusiastic Truth, and
Earnestness, and Independence, will invariably lead a mind
fitted by nature for profound and fearless thought, all objects
are seen in a dubious, uncertain, and refracting light. Viewed
through that rarefied atmosphere the most immemorially ad-

[132] *Works*, IX, 465.

mitted maxims of men begin to slide and fluctuate, and finally
become wholly inverted; the very heavens themselves being
not innocent of producing this confounding effect, since it is
mostly in the heavens themselves that these wonderful mirages
are exhibited."[133]

In *Moby-Dick* Melville stood outside the tragedy; though
sympathizing with Ahab's feud, he believed the captain's thirst
for revenge was not fated and that he might have avoided the
woe that is madness. Melville is not Ahab. What is the
circumstance in *Pierre?* Does Melville identify himself with
his hero; are we permitted to suppose Pierre's tragedy is his
also? Actually, Melville, even more directly than in *Moby-
Dick*, cautions us against assuming that hero and author are
one: "But the thoughts we here indite as Pierre's are to be
very carefully discriminated from those we indite concerning
him."[134]

Commenting on the dangerous state to which "enthusiastic
Truth" has brought Pierre, he goes so far as to declare that the
"example of many minds forever lost, like undiscoverable
Arctic explorers, amid those treacherous regions, warns us
entirely away from them; and we learn that it is not for man
to follow the trail of truth too far, since by so doing he entirely
loses the directing compass of his mind; for arrived at the
Pole, to whose barrenness only it points, there, the needle
indifferently respects all points of the horizon alike."[135]

These words do not prove, of course, that when Melville
was at work on *Pierre* he had abandoned his speculations on
the nature of ultimate truth. Though he would stop short of
Ahab's madness and Pierre's self-destruction, he had still much
to say, explicitly and by implication, on the quest initiated in
Mardi.

There can be no doubt, in the first place, of Melville's disgust
with the prudent materialism with which the world, represented

[133] *Ibid.*, 231.   [134] *Ibid.*, 233.   [135] *Ibid.*, 231.

by Mrs. Glendinning, her white-handed pastor, and Pierre's cousin Glen, views Pierre's agony, which these people would be quite incapable of comprehending. The desire to satirize their hypocrisy persisted with Melville until the writing of *The Confidence Man.* But there is another way of viewing the problem which obsesses Pierre, that offered by the transcendentalist philosopher Plotinus Plinlimmon, in his lecture on "Chronometricals and Horologicals." His comfortable doctrine proclaims a "virtuous expediency" as the best way for the heaven-conscious mortal to live on earth. When he goes to heaven it will be quite time enough to live by heaven's chronometrical time.

By introducing Plinlimmon and his pamphlet, which promised a later (unaccomplished) reconciliation of God's truth to man's truth, Melville intended a satire on all shallow and amiable transcendental "reconcilers" of the "Optimist" or "Compensation" school.[136] Their waving away of the problem he found quite as distasteful as the worldly hypocrisy of the Rev. Mr. Falsgrave.

To know at what position Melville had now positively arrived in his quest for the Ultimate, we must study a passage in Book XIV of *Pierre* where he sets down candidly his own conclusions. He testifies there to the conviction of divine origin which the beauty of the Sermon on the Mount carries to the heart of an earnest or enthusiastic youth. When he first looks about him in the world he cannot believe that the professed Christian can live so totally at variance with it. Unless his faith fades, or he fails to see the lying world around him or unless "he can find the talismanic secret, to reconcile this world with his own soul, then there is no peace for him, no slightest truce for him in this life."[137] The talismanic secret has never been found, nor does Melville suppose it will be found. Philoso-

---

[136] *Works*, IX, 385.
[137] *Ibid.*, 290.

phers pretend to have it—"Plato, and Spinoza, and Goethe,[138] and many more belong to this guild of self-imposters, with a preposterous rabble of Muggletonian Scots and Yankees, whose vile brogue still the more bestreaks the stripedness of their Greek or German Neoplatonical originals." They lie when they assert they have received an answer from the "Voice of our God." How can a man "get a Voice out of Silence"?[139]

Here in 1852 ended, for the moment, Melville's quest for the Ultimate. His mood had changed from the reckless high adventure of Taji, not content with Serenia, to partial sympathy with the vengeful Ahab who longed to strike through the mask of whiteness and so lay bare the malice or the blankness which lay beyond, to the desponding and skeptical mood of *Pierre*. There seems to be no answer, least of all a transcendental one, yet for Melville there could be no truce in the war to wrest one from the silent heavens.

If Melville could have continued to objectify his quest in books like *Mardi*, *Moby-Dick*, and *Pierre*, he might have saved himself from the emotional collapse which darkened the next ten years of his life. But the story of his truceless war was told on all possible planes. Chaos was come again, but there was no further possibility of subliming it into another *Moby-Dick*, for the "fullness" was gone. He abandoned himself in private conversation to continued wandering over the deserts of speculation.

---

[138] The inclusion of Goethe here is illuminated by Melville's remark in a letter to Hawthorne (see p. 393, below): "In reading some of Goethe's sayings, so worshipped by his votaries, I came across this, 'Live in the all.' That is to say, your separate identity is but a wretched one,—good; but get out of yourself, spread and expand yourself, and bring to yourself the tinglings of life that are felt in the flowers and the woods, that are felt in the planets Saturn and Venus, and the Fixed Stars. What nonsense! Here is a fellow with a raging toothache, 'My dear boy,' Goethe says to him, 'you are sorely afflicted with that tooth; but you must *live in the all*, and then you will be happy!'" [139] *Loc. cit.*

In the end Melville called the truce. On April 19, 1891—
five months before he died—he put the last words to "Billy
Budd, Foretopman," a story which Mr. Watson has named his
"testament of acceptance." [140] In this tale of an innocent and
beautiful young sailor accused of mutiny by a master-at-arms
in whom breeds "a depravity according to nature," Melville
achieves unsurpassable tragedy. His own passionate rage at
the inscrutableness of the universe is spent. He acquiesces in
the magnanimous Captain Vere's sentence of death on Billy,
for Captain Vere, like Melville, had learned that here below
we have no concern with the "mystery of iniquity." "We fight
at command," but for the "law and the rigor of it, we are not
responsible." This is the blight man was born for, and when
we weep for the undoing of such men as Billy Budd it is for
ourselves we mourn.

IV. MELVILLE'S POETRY

(During the last thirty-five years of his life Melville wrote
little except poetry.) As early as the time of *Mardi* he shows
himself interested, philosophically at least, in its nature. While
Yoomy, the Mardian poet, from time to time recites his own
verses, Babbalanja, the philosopher, gives him sound advice
about the theory and practice of his art. Yoomy's verse, as
we should expect from a poet with a name like his, is sentimental after the manner of Tom Moore, and he is deeply moved
by his own reciting of it.

There is little to show that Melville read much poetry at
this time. The books which he borrowed before 1850 from
Evert Duyckinck were mainly works in prose. Even Shakespeare did not really come within his ken until 1849. [141]

When the full years of his creative life were past, the impulse
to versify manifested itself. Mrs. Melville wrote to her mother

[140] *New England Quarterly*, VI, 319–327.   [141] See p. xxiii above.

in 1859: "Herman has taken to writing poetry. You need not tell any one, for you know how such things get around."[142] Possibly she wished to prepare the minds of the Chief Justice of Massachusetts and his wife for the shock of discovering their son-in-law's newest perversity. Whatever this remark was supposed to convey, it is a fact that Mrs. Melville undertook to see through the press the volume he had prepared, when, in June, 1860, he hurriedly sailed for San Francisco on his brother's ship, the *Meteor*. Melville suggests that she was the one who chiefly desired the book's publication. In writing to Evert Duyckinck, on the point of sailing, he said: "As my wife has interested herself a good deal in this matter, and in fact seems to know more about it than I do—at least about the *merits* of the performance—I must therefore refer you to her."[143] In her own letters to Duyckinck about the book, she rejoices in having, as she says, "my own prejudice in its favor confirmed by someone in whose appreciation we can feel confidence."[144] If the book were to be withdrawn by Herman in case it did not find a publisher at once, it would greatly disappoint her.

But the book found no publisher. We do not even know for certain what these first poems of Melville's were. They cannot be the long poem *Clarel*, as Minnigerode supposed,[145] for the "Memoranda for Allan concerning the publication of my verses" which Melville sent his brother, prove them to have been a collection of short poems. There is reason to suppose the book contained some if not all of that little group of poems which were printed in *Timoleon* (1891) under the caption "Fruit of Travel Long Ago." The themes treated in these poems can all be traced to impressions of the 1856–1857 journey and many of them are foreshadowed in the diary which he kept at that time.

---

[142] Weaver, *Herman Melville*, 360.
[143] Minnigerode, *Some Personal Letters of Herman Melville*, 80.
[144] *Ibid.*, 87.   [145] *Ibid.*, 77.

Melville had hoped to make a little money with his book of verses. He regarded them highly enough to enjoin Allan very strictly to see to their careful printing and assured him that though the publication of an author's first volume of verses is a most insignificant matter to the world, to him it is "still of some concern." If he was sadly disappointed by the failure of his book to find a hospitable publisher, he showed it only in the half-rueful, half-jocular way in which he wrote his brother Tom (May 25, 1862) that the trunk-maker had taken the whole lot of his doggerel off his hands at ten cents the pound. If Tom were not "such a devil of a ways off" he would send him a trunk lined with stanzas as a presentation copy.[146]

This depreciatory tone became habitual with him when referring to his poetry. *Clarel* he described to his English correspondent Mr. Billson as "a metrical affair, a pilgrimage or what not, of several thousand lines, eminently adapted for unpopularity."[147] To his brother-in-law John Hoadley he remarks, on sending him a copy of "The Age of the Antonines,"[148] that he has just turned it up among a lot of papers and has no idea what it means. His real feeling toward his verses we can infer from the fact that, as the extant manuscripts show, he labored at rewriting them until they came somewhere near satisfying him. Biographers who have called him incapable of self-criticism as a poet should be set to work deciphering the significant alterations he made in such a poem as "Art."[149]

We can attach some significance, also, to the anguish with which the completion and the printing of *Clarel* were accomplished. In an affecting letter of Mrs. Melville's to her cousin-in-law Catherine Lansing—which she wrote secretly (February 2, 1876)—she speaks of his "frightfully nervous state," which

[146] Minnigerode, *Some Personal Letters of Herman Melville*, 89.

[147] The letter is dated Oct. 10, 1884. See Bibliography: "Some Melville Letters."

[148] See p. 366.

[149] A transcript of the MS. of the poem is printed on pp. 427–428.

has produced such a strain on his mind that she feels the greatest anxiety for him. The crisis which the preparation of the book brought on has undermined all their happiness.[150]

⟨ After the disappointment of 1860 the desire to write verse seems not to have returned until, on the news of the fall of Richmond (April, 1865), the preceding years of strife came vividly before his imagination. The *Battle-Pieces* which this impulse produced range over the geographical area covered by the war and present themes which, as Melville said, "for any cause chanced to imprint themselves upon the mind."[151] The poems memorialize the events of the war days from the first Manassas to the murder of Lincoln.⟩ But the book possesses unity, in spite of the fact that, as Melville says, it displays "moods variable, and at times widely at variance." To him the glory of the war fell short of its pathos. The sacrifice and slaughter could be endured only if one could be sure that by this laying bare of the "slimed foundations" of the gulf a happier world might be built on them. "The Conflict of Convictions," the second poem in the book, embodies the intuition of the inextricable interweaving of Good and Evil which is central in Melville's thinking. It shows that he became reconciled to the war only because he saw in it again a manifestation of the universal scheme of things, as revealed in *Moby-Dick* in the external world and in *Pierre* in the inner life of man. He appears finally to have viewed the struggle between the North and South as an event predestined.

> The rebel at Port Royal felt
> The Unity overawe,
> And rued the spell. A type was here,
> And victory of Law.[152]

---

[150] Paltsits, *Family Correspondence of Herman Melville*, 35–36.
[151] Prefatory note to *Battle-Pieces*. Melville states that a few of the pieces were composed before this time.
[152] "Dupont's Round Fight."

It may well be, as Mumford suggests,[153] that this conviction of the inexorability of the conflict relieved for a time the mood of extreme skepticism which had prevailed with him during and after the writing of *The Confidence Man* (1857) and gave for the moment a sense of purpose and integration to his life.

Many of the poems deal so specifically with personalities and incidents of the war that the reader wonders naturally where the poet, who of course witnessed no battles, went for material to feed his imagination. Melville, characteristically, gives us a clue. In his note to "Rebel Color-Bearers at Shiloh" he remarks that the incident on which this piece was based is narrated in a newspaper account in the *Rebellion Record*.[154] A glance through some of the documents and journalistic reports in the volumes of this work which relate to episodes turned into poetry by Melville, shows at once that the *Rebellion Record* was exploited extensively by him. Either he turned at once to its pages when the impulse to write verse again was imparted to him or he happened to be going through them when Richmond fell. His use of this monumental record of the war varies from the close paralleling and mere "versified journalism" derived from the New York *Times* account of the capture of Fort Donelson[155] in his "Donelson" to the remarkable reconstruction of the character of the brave General Lyon from the matter-of-fact report of the battle of Springfield as he found it in two newspaper accounts in the *Record*.[156]

Clarel, A Poem and Pilgrimage in the Holy Land, which had lain for some time unpublished, was finally put before the public on June 3, 1876, through the generosity of his uncle Peter Gansevoort. Melville dismissed it, "content beforehand with

---

[153] *Herman Melville*, 299.

[154] *The Rebellion Record: A Diary of American Events, with Documents, Narratives, Illustrative Incidents, Poetry, Etc.*, ed. by Frank Moore (New York: 1861–1869, 12 vols.).

[155] *Rebellion Record*, IV, 170–176.

[156] See "Lyon," p. 348 below, and the notes to this poem, p. 425.

whatever future awaits it."[157] It had no future, and it remains today the least read of his works. The casual reader is sure to be hopelessly bewildered by it. The slight story of Clarel, a theological student, who, after becoming engaged to a young Jewess, leaves on a pilgrimage to the Dead Sea and Bethlehem when, following her father's death, he is forbidden by Jewish custom to visit her, melts away into a description of places and a record of abortive conversations on science, faith, and the modern age. When the story reappears with the sudden discovery of Ruth's death, we miss the poignancy of this moment, as Mumford says, because we have forgotten her.[158]

And yet Melville's partisans will ponder over no work of his for a longer time, for it is the key to his thought in the later years. Here he has it out with himself and comes at last to a fixed place where he can stand for the rest of his days. One should not attempt to read *Clarel* until one has grown familiar with the genesis and development of the dominant moods of Melville's life, for he makes nothing easy for the reader. The overtones of innumerable allusions to books which influenced him profoundly, to events in history, philosophical ideas, even works of painting and architecture, would be quite lost on one who had not met them before in Melville's biography and felt some of their symbolic significance for him. What, for example, could a novice make of the impressive comparison of the enigmatic pilgrim Ungar to Ethan Allen, if he could not recall the eulogistic Ethan Allen scenes in *Israel Potter* which were gratuitously introduced into that story by Melville? *Clarel* possesses all the faults of a "private" poem, but these faults are of the utmost interest to the biographer. One hears the poet converse as with a friend who is intimately familiar with all the details of his life and thought.

The innumerable arguments which make up the substance of the poem move round the circle of science *vs*. religion, paganism

[157] Author's note.   [158] *Herman Melville*, 322.

vs. Christianity, Rome *vs.* modernism, aristocracy *vs.* democracy, and the grounds for debate shift so constantly and
the conclusion is so often indeterminate that a biographer can
make of *Clarel* nearly anything he wishes. It has been plundered
for Melville's views on all these matters. But one must not
lose sight of the fact that *Clarel*, though its tone is incidentally
skeptical, disillusioned, at times cynical, is essentially a religious
poem, though marked by the agnosticism of the century, like
"In Memoriam," or "Stanzas from the Grande Chartreuse," or
Dr. Holmes's "Wind-Clouds and Star-Drifts." All the pilgrims
(including Melville himself) have made this journey to holy
places with the hope that what they will see will affect in some
way their religious intuitions. Not even the most frivolous of
the company can resist the magnetism which has drawn them
hither.

A clue to Melville's purpose in the poem is furnished by the
large amount of space he allows in it to two characters, Derwent
and Ungar. These men, the first a young Church of England
clergyman of latitudinarian views, the second an American of
Catholic lineage from the ravaged South, who is tortured by the
loss of his heritage in country and religion, stand opposed in
the latter half of the pilgrimage. The feud between what they
represent becomes its dominant theme.

On Derwent's easy optimism, his urbane refusal even to be
drawn into serious debate, his satisfaction with the dregs and
remnants of a once glorious faith, Melville allows his pilgrims
to pour their scorn. Mortmain rebukes him in this wise:

> 'Twas Shaftesbury first assumed your tone,
> Trying to cheerfulise Christ's moan.[159]

Clarel fiercely answers him, when Derwent says that the spiritual
anguish of men like Shelley and Hamlet is now considered
perverse, indecorous even:

[159] *Works*, XV, 31.

> Forbear!
> Ah, wherefore not at once name Job,
> In whom these Hamlets all conglobe.
> Own, own with me, and spare to feign,
> Doubt bleeds, nor Faith is free from pain![160]

Derwent refuses to assent and accuses Clarel of being one who
dives too deep. One hears the echo, in this accusation, of
Melville's reverence before all men who dive,[161] and one understands his evident dislike of the shallow cleric.

It is otherwise with his attitude towards Ungar. To the
bias and bitterness of this pilgrim, tormented by his will to
disbelieve, the others are constantly sympathetic. In the last
section of the poem he usurps the scene. And though he
talks chiefly of democracy and the class-war and demagoguery
and the impieties of progress, the ultimate source of his disillusionment is spiritual.

> What shall bind these seas
> Of rival sharp communities
> Unchristianised?[162]

The brute element, he feels, will overwhelm and the years of
internecine war are inevitable. The world has never been
capable of comprehending "Christ's pastoral parables divine."
The heart of man has never changed even with its change of
allegiance to the gods.

The tortured state of all the Ungars in this world, who in
their heart of hearts revere the Lord, though their tongues
mock and revile, is beautifully objectified in the thirteenth
division of Part I of the poem, "The Arch," which contains
one of its most moving passages. Celio, who appears later as
one of the pilgrims, has gone to gaze upon the gallery where
Christ was shown to the populace by Pilate. As he meditates
there, the spectral face, the purple robe, the crown of thorns,

[160] *Ibid.*, 109.   [161] See p. 372.   [162] *Works*, XV, 249.

rise before him, but pity and reverence are eclipsed by bitterness. Before Christ came, heart hoped not; men lived by the natural law. The unwarranted dream no one had dreamt. Eighteen centuries have passed and man cannot find Christ out; yet all the evil done in his name has not weakened the power of the Christian dream. It is the Medusa shield. In beauty and in terror it still paralyzes the race. The tortured Christ proves still a torturer.

> Whatever ribald Future be,
> Thee shall these heed, amaze their hearts with Thee—
> Thy white, Thy red, Thy fairness and Thy tragedy.

Melville was one of the few American poets who walked the road that Tennyson and Arnold and all the perceptive men of his generation in Europe took, but he did not turn aside as most of them did, into materialism or naturalism or positivism or the subtle compromises which the age invented. He wrestled with the angel, but the Epilogue to *Clarel* was an affirmation of faith. What the struggle that reaped this achievement had cost him, the Epilogue reveals.

This struggle toward the light, here achieved, bids comparison particularly with the efforts of Meredith and Hardy to find the place of man in the natural world as pictured by evolution, in which his tragedies are so insignificant. Meredith reaches only the level of "Meditation under Stars" in which a momentary glow of nature mysticism warms the uninvigorating fact that we are distantly allied to the forces of the universe. The final choruses of *The Dynasts* assert no more than a possibility: the Impercipient shows signs of awakening and Consciousness may yet inform the Will. The comfort which Melville offers is profounder. Unless God makes a sign the old struggle to wrest the secret of His nature from Him may go on forever; science only aggravates the feud. But so many illusions does man pass through in the struggle that death may prove

unreal at last—"and stoics be astounded into heaven." The
Epilogue concludes on a triumphant note:

> Then keep thy heart, though yet but ill-resigned—
> Clarel, thy heart, the issues there but mind;
> That like the crocus budding through the snow—
> That like a swimmer rising from the deep—
> That like a burning secret which doth go
> Even from the bosom that would hoard and keep;
> Emerge thou mayst from the last whelming sea,
> And prove that death but routs life into victory.

Though Melville occasionally repulsed visitors who tried to
make him talk of his South Sea adventures,[163] nostalgia for his
life before the mast at times recurred. On the voyage to England in 1849 he took the keenest delight in recalling the "old
emotions of being at the masthead." His occasional feats in
the rigging were regarded as a species of tight-rope dancing by
passengers astonished to see a bearded civilian climbing the
shrouds. The journey to San Francisco in 1860 on his brother
Tom's ship gave him the keenest pleasure. When he became
famous, letters from his former shipmates, written in stiff
copybook English by hands little used to the pen, arrived in
the mail. He kept them and apparently answered them. With
Toby, his fellow Typee-truant, he maintained an intermittent
correspondence. During the Civil War the naval battles,
particularly those in Hampton Roads, fired his imagination.

In 1888 he gathered together under the title *John Marr and
Other Sailors* the verses which his memory of the sea had
prompted him to write, dedicating the volume to a younger
lover of the sea, W. Clark Russell, whose *Wreck of the
Grosvenor* (1877) entitled him, Melville believed, "to the naval
crown in current literature."[164]

[163] See Weaver, *Herman Melville*, 351, for Titus Munson Coan's
description of his futile attempt to draw him out on the Marquesas.

[164] Russell dedicated his *An Ocean Tragedy* (1881) to Melville and

The title-poem suggests a submerged autobiographical theme: John Marr, an old seaman, now dwelling inland and cut off from his past life, invokes the phantoms of his former companions and strives to establish communion with them. The second poem, "Bridegroom Dick," is related to the first. In it a Northern sailor recalls the battles he has known, the commanders he has served under and the mates who have endured shot and storm with him. The other poems touch such themes as the fate of lost crews never heard of and the ship that strikes an iceberg and goes down. But the subjects are not all concerned with ships and men sunk in unfathomable sleep. Melville's sailor brother Tom is affectionately addressed [165] and also Toby, who once with him "breathed primeval balm from Edens ere yet over-run." [166] The final note is reconciliatory. Healed of his hurt, he lauds the inhuman sea and blesses the Four Angels who there convene and whose pitiless breath is distilled in the wholesome dew named rosmarine. [167]

In *Timoleon* (1891), his last published book, the fundamental tone is again one of tranquillity and peace. One's ear catches an insistent harmonic, however, of aloneness which is not lonesomeness. Timoleon, whose righteousness made him slay his tyrant brother and caused his exile, refuses to return to his native Corinth even when the city absolves him and calls him back. The memory of his estrangement from "common membership in the mart" makes him prefer perpetual exile to a reconciliation with the society which had once rejected him. In "The Enthusiast" and "Lone Founts" the overtone is heard again. Shall the heart, which never retreated in youth, he asks in the first, finally conform? The answer is that the torch must be put to the dear ties which bind us to the world, if they are

---

wrote, in 1892, a discriminating article on Melville's contribution to the literature of the sea. See Bibliography.

[165] "To the Master of the *Meteor*."
[166] "To Ned."   [167] "Pebbles."

tempters. The valiant man must stand alone until the end, if he would stand finally with Posterity.

What value can one put on Melville's poetry? Does the recent interest in its resurrection indicate that time may lift from it the pall of incomprehension, as *Moby-Dick* and *Pierre* have slowly won for themselves appreciative readers? Only a few of the poems, it must be admitted, achieve the artistic unity of rhythmical exactness, propriety of image and melodic beauty which the best poetry possesses. One stumbles on imperfections in these artistic elements in nearly every poem, and the slightest jar may be enough, as one knows, to upset the perfect equilibrium which is indispensable in the best art.

To the modern sensibility the weight and didacticism of his verses is an impediment to pleasure. Melville delighted in historical subjects, and fashion has tended to exclude them from poetry. Many of his themes are so personal and so little capable of universalization, that the poems made from them are mere occasional verse.

Melville worked at poetry in a somewhat unpoetic way. He revised repeatedly but not always in the poet's manner. He coveted chiefly the clarity of expression and concision of thought which prose cannot so well attain. If the meter and rime were approximate, that seems to have satisfied him, though he would toil over a passage endlessly to achieve the exact proportion of ideas, as the manuscripts show.[168] To the extent that the patterns of its thought can give artistic form to poetry, his verse can be said to possess the qualities of art.

He seems to have troubled himself little to explore the possibilities of the many verse forms in English, remaining content with variations of the ballad stanza, the four-stress couplet, and an occasional use of *rime-couée*. In *Clarel* he did make an

---

[168] The MSS. of *John Marr and Other Sailors*, *Timoleon*, and the poems unpublished in Melville's lifetime are now owned by the Harvard College Library.

effort to relieve the monotonous tramp-tramp of the ill-chosen
Hudibrastic verse by the use of longer lines and intercalated
lyrics. Blank verse he tried scarcely at all. One prosodic device he was especially fond of, a two-stress line to give a sharp,
cryptic effect in a stanza which is made up of longer lines.
The idea of the stanza often turns on this line. A good example
of its use is seen in "Lyon" (p. 348 below), which also illus-
trates Melville's fancy for double rimes. He often employs
several different stanzas in a single poem or deliberately alters
in succeeding stanzas the pattern which he sets at the beginning
(*e.g.* "Sheridan at Cedar Creek"). This tendency is curiously
in line with the modern preference for organic rhythms, that
is, verse in which the mood of the poem   ther than a fixed
traditional lyric form determines the movement. Though he
showed none of the Victorian tendency to idealize his subjects
by the use of a special poetic diction and made no bones about
the use of colloquial language, he did not eliminate from his
poetry the rags of eighteenth-century and romantic diction.
The juxtaposition of the "neaths," "pelfs," and "fanes" with
hard sailor-words is often ludicrous.

To those who admire Landor and Hardy and Housman
Melville will be congenial. The strength, sobriety, and almost
embarrassing sincerity of his verse should be as invigorating
as the sea air to any American who has been reared patriotically
on the pale prettiness of the "Vision of Sir Launfal" and the
Eagle-Scout morality of "Excelsior." A few of his poems,
among them surely, "The Portent," "Malvern Hill," and the
Epilogue to *Clarel*, must be included with the best we have to
contribute to the world's store of memorable verse.

V. MELVILLE'S SOCIAL IDEAS[169]

Melville possessed, as possibly the fundamental bias of his nature, the inclination to say "No" in an age which demanded that all good citizens should say "Yes." "All men who say *yes*, lie," he wrote to Hawthorne, "and all men who say *no*,— why, they are in the happy condition of judicious, unincumbered travellers in Europe; they cross the frontiers into Eternity with nothing but a carpetbag,—that is to say, the Ego. Whereas those *yes*-gentry, they travel with heaps of baggage, and, damn them! they will never get through the Custom House."[170]

When one contemplates the number of matters on which the age had come to a final opinion, to which Melville offered a challenging negative, and the number of subjects which the age, for its safety, refused to discuss at all, but which Melville insisted on dragging up to the light, one is astonished that he was tolerated as long as he was. He seems, indeed, to be unique among his contemporaries in his freedom from zeal and prejudice. Even the most sacred tabus he insisted on examining with a cool dispassionateness. Not only did he question the inalienable right to property, the dogmas of democracy, the righteousness of imperialist wars and Christian missions, but he dared to discuss in a voice louder than a whisper such horrific subjects as cannibalism, venereal disease, and polygamy. At the moment when young men in America, imbued with transcendentalism, were giving eloquent support to the doctrine of the manifest destiny of the nation and defied the world to show any civilization which could equal ours, Melville was studying with habitually clear eyes a savage society in the South Seas which had achieved an admirable social equilibrium. While American orators scolded the Old World as corrupt and decayed, the home of tyranny and oppression, he measured

---

[169] In preparing this section I have been aided by an unpublished paper by Mr. Robert T. Oliver.   [170] See p. 388 below.

against their glorious American standards the attainment of the naked Polynesians. Equipped as no man in his day was by his contact with all sorts and conditions of men, having crossed many social frontiers without the baggage of the "yes-gentry," he returned to the America of 1845 to record what he had observed. He could report that he had seen happy savages who could live together in charity, and this had made him form a higher "estimate of human nature than [he] had ever before entertained";[171] he could also report that he had lived on an American man-of-war where unbelievable human vileness that made the heart sick nearly overturned any previous theories of the perfectibility of man he may have had.

Though the business of navigating a ship never interested Melville, he felt a deep concern for the destination of the inhabitants of the world which the ship enclosed. He pondered the social relationships, the code of life and manners, the clash of individual on individual, which determined the nature of this compact, artificial society, and endeavored to relate what he saw there to the larger society which dispatched the ship on its errands of commerce or war. Every serious book or article which Melville wrote is a variation on the social theme.

In *Typee* what mainly engages his attention is the small but perfectly poised Taipi state. In *Omoo* his mind turns over the fascinating problem of the impinging of the white man's ideals (and vices) on another such equipoised society. In *White-Jacket* what keeps the book together is Melville's steady pressure on the pulse-beat of society in a ship of war. *Mardi* holds up an allegorical mirror in which society in the western world may see its own face. In the latter part of *Redburn* the main concern is the class-contrast between the horrors in the immigrants' black hole below decks and the selfish fear of the cabin passengers. In *Moby-Dick* we are not allowed to forget the crime Captain Ahab commits when his monomania drives the

[171] *Works*, I, 273.

helpless crew of the *Pequod* with him to destruction. In his mad pursuit of death he has slipped all ties of responsibility which bind man to man. Pierre goes down defeated because he chooses to live by heaven's chronometrical standard and defies the horological measure by which conventional society exists. Finally, in *The Confidence Man*, in bitterness and indecision, Melville for the moment gives up in despair, doubting whether there is enough of the indispensable stuff of confidence in the hearts of men to make it possible for them to fuse into a decent social order.

In attempting an exposition of Melville's social philosophy it would be fatal to proceed in the fashion of the "reconcilers" of scripture who used to set passage against passage and explain away all contradictions tropologically. One must remember that consistency in Melville's thought can be found only in his early work, that is, through *Moby-Dick*. *Pierre* was a desperate attempt to avoid the ultimate skepticism, but the hopelessness of his position had already been borne in upon him. *The Confidence Man* marks the nadir of disillusionment to which he had sunk in 1857. The poetry and prose of the lean years thereafter reveal his slow ascent to another certainty. One needs to be cautious, too, in venturing to assert, as Melville's conclusions, ideas which are expressed by his characters and have relevance only in the setting in which they are expressed.

We must begin by trying to discover what Melville thought in general of his fellow men during his less disillusioned early years (1845–1851), for one's hopefulness or skepticism about society is inevitably determined by what one believes man is capable of as a social animal. For those who recall the two eloquent chapters entitled "Knights and Squires" in *Moby-Dick* there can be no doubt of his confidence in mankind at the time of the book's composition. Speaking of the calamity which will overtake the valorous mate, Starbuck, he says, "Men may seem detestable as joint-stock companies and na-

tions; knaves, fools, and murderers there may be; men may
have mean and meagre faces; but man, in the ideal, is so noble
and so sparkling, such a grand and glowing creature, that over
any ignominious blemish in him all his fellows should run to
throw their costliest robes." [172]   The just Spirit of Equality has
spread one royal mantle over all humankind. The great democratic god culls his selectest champions from the kingly commons. The poetic pearl was given to Bunyan the convict;
Andrew Jackson, hurled upon his war horse, was thundered
higher than a throne.

(From this sense of our common humanity came Melville's
passion for social justice and his hatred of all the tyrannies by
which man enslaves and brutalizes his fellows. When he saw
men flogged aboard a man-of-war, he felt the shame of belonging to the race.) Yet even such brutality, though it may scar
the body for life, cannot touch the innate dignity of the human
being who is scourged, for that is "one of the hushed things,
buried among the holiest privacies of the soul." [173]

The invisible process by which the ordered life of the Typees
was regulated had convinced Melville that a tacit common-sense
law has graven its precepts of virtue and honor on every
heart. [174]   These grand principles are innate and are the same
the world over so that the "right or wrong of any action appears the same to the uncultivated as to the enlightened mind."
This by no means implies that man ever achieves perfection or
that any institution he erects can be flawless. Even in Serenia,
the ideal state which the wanderers visit at the end of *Mardi*,
no one believes this. The old man who receives them declares,
however, that against good, man is not absolutely set. "In his
heart, there is a germ. *That* we seek to foster. To *that* we
cling; else, all were hopeless!" [175]

[172] *Works*, VII, 143.   [173] *Works*, VI, 177.   [174] *Works*, I, 270.
[175] *Works*, IV, 366–367. Melville never settled in his mind just
how extensive social regulation must be in order that this "germ"

He was well aware of the ardor and the radical nature of his democracy during these years, and the extent to which it went beyond the limits to which qualified democrats like Cooper and Hawthorne were willing to go.[176]   In a most revealing passage in a letter to Hawthorne, the friend and biographer of a democratic president, he prepares him for contact with the "ruthlessness" and the unconditional nature of the Melvillean brand of democracy which declares that "a thief in jail is as honorable a personage as Gen. George Washington."[177]

Melville was on the point of continuing with this theme when he broke off impulsively with the words: "It seems an inconsistency to assert unconditional democracy in all things, and yet confess a dislike to all mankind—in the mass. But not so."[178]   How would he have explained the seeming paradox, if he had thought Hawthorne would have listened attentively to an "endless sermon," that man who is individually a "wonder, a grandeur, and a woe," when he associates himself with other men produces a "civilization" which is worse than barbarism?

---

may be fostered. He suggests in *Mardi* that the people may need a ruler, if not a king, to assist them in reform (*op. cit.*, 380). By the time of the writing of *Clarel* he speaks as a nineteenth-century liberal, holding that reform is a kind of natural process:

> Mark the advance: creed drops the hate;
> Events still liberalize the state. (*Works*, XV, 244.)

[176] This is not to say that he found the American democracy an ideal state. On the contrary, he excoriated its many faults, as the discussion below (pp. cvi–cxvi) will show.

[177] The letter is printed on pp. 389–393 below. For a discussion of Hawthorne's "politics," see Austin Warren, *Nathaniel Hawthorne* (New York, 1934), pp. xlvii–lvi.

[178] Oliver (*op. cit.*, 31) cites a dialogue in *White-Jacket* between Jack Chase and Lemsford in which the latter calls the public a monster. To this Jack takes exception because on shore he is a part of the public. Lemsford satisfies him, with dubious logic, by asserting that the "public is one thing . . . and the people another" (*Works*, VI, 239).

The answer is not to be found by supposing that Melville was a naïve Rousseauist, though many have attempted to make him appear so.[179] His reasoned attitude toward the savage was fully set forth in his review in the *Literary World* (March 31, 1849) of Parkman's *Oregon Trail*, where he objects to the historian's contempt for the America Indian, but by no means suggests that he believes the savage is superior to the civilized man:

It is too often the case, that civilized beings sojourning among savages soon come to regard them with disdain and contempt. But though in many cases this feeling is almost natural, it is not defensible; and it is wholly wrong. Why should we contemn them? Because we are better than they? Assuredly not; for herein we are rebuked by the story of the Publican and the Pharisee. Because, then, that in many things we are happier? But this should be ground for commiseration, not disdain. Xavier and Elliot despised not the savages; and had Newton or Milton dwelt among them they would not have done so. When we affect to contemn savages, we should remember that by so doing we asperse our own progenitors; for they were savages also.) Who can swear, that among the naked British barbarians sent to Rome to be stared at more than 1500 years ago, the ancestor of Bacon might not have been found? Why, among the very Thugs of India, or the bloody Dyaks of Borneo, exists the germ of all that is intellectually elevated and grand. We are all of us—Anglo-Saxons, Dyaks, and Indians—sprung from one head, and made in one image. And if we regret this brotherhood now, we shall be forced to join hands hereafter.

[179] D. H. Lawrence declared: "Here at last is Rousseau's Child of Nature" (*Studies in Classic American Literature*, 199). Blankenship follows this conventional view: "The South Seas were Melville's Utopia" (*American Literature* [New York, 1931], 379). Melville's nearest approach to pure Rousseauism is found in a passage in *Omoo* which describes the natives in the interior of Tahiti (*Works*, II, 77), but it should be noticed that he is there recording the effect which the beauty of the island has exercised on European travelers ever since it was discovered.

A misfortune is not a fault; and good luck is not meritorious. The savage is born a savage; and the civilized being but inherits his civilization, nothing more.

Let us not disdain, then, but pity. And wherever we recognize the image of God, let us reverence it, though it hung from the gallows.

Melville did not suppose that there is something inherent in the "social contract" which inevitably "produces" the evils of civilization and that the individual in the state of nature habitually behaves himself and in the social state becomes contemptible. The beauty of life in the Typee valley he recognized as a function of the social order which the Typees had evolved, and he was eager to determine for himself why two civilizations, the savage's and the white man's, as he saw them side by side in Tahiti, could be so different. The institutions which he disliked and which Anglo-American society in his time supported —property, missionary Christianity, slavery, imperialist war, and the factory system—do not grow spontaneously wherever men gather themselves into a society.

He observed that nature had been bountiful to the Typees, so that their natural wants could be supplied with a minimum of labor. Where all might easily have what any might desire, the thousand sources of irritation that the ingenuity of civilized man has created in his attempt to maintain the institution of property, simply did not exist. The plentiful supply of breadfruit and coconuts, he suggests with a Marxian derision, has even rendered the natives remiss in the performance of their religious obligations. [180]

Melville felt no urge, it should be observed, to settle in the Utopia he had found and "go native." He saw, with a clarity remarkable for the time, that the delicate balance of these island societies could be disrupted by a mere contact with another order. Here lay the source of his quarrel with the missionaries;

[180] *Works*, I, 241.

they were ignorantly, if sincerely, aiding in the destruction of a
social order which was in some respects more admirable than
the one they were vainly attempting to impose.[181]

⟨The fundamental problem of social organization, in Melville's
view, is so to arrange the form of government and distribute
the economic goods as to afford the better instincts of man's
nature a proper outlet and give the least possible opportunity
for the base ones to operate.⟩ He says this in effect, through
the mouth of the old man who describes to the voyagers the
Christian socialism which obtains among the Serenians.[182] ⟨Even
in this best of Mardian states, perfection, it is true, has not been
achieved, nor can it be. But they recognize there two indispensable truths: if the miserable many are made to support
the happy few, the state will not prosper; on the other hand,
reason is not to be defied by supposing there can be equality
among men—equality of intelligence and talents, that is to say.⟩
Though there must be differences, no man starves in Serenia
while others feast. The citizens do not live in common, for
Melville does not envisage Serenia as a Fourierist society. The
vicious are made to dwell apart until reclaimed, but they are
not punished vengefully, and everything invites their return to
society. The cohesive force which maintains order in Serenia
is partly the half-dormant "dictates" which tell the Serenians
this is the way to live and partly their faith in the Christian
principles.

When Melville looked about among the nations of the world
he saw none which practiced the Serenian principles of government. He believed, as any good American of his day was
bound to, that the monarchies of Europe could scarcely be

---

[181] Cf., among numerous passages which might be cited, *Works*, I,
263, satirizing missionary "tea-party excitements" under the influence of which funds are raised "the object of which is to ameliorate
the spiritual condition of the Polynesians, but whose end has almost
invariably been to accomplish their temporal destruction!"

[182] *Works*, IV, 364–372.

reformed, so sunk were they under absolutist tyranny. The prospect of the end of the rule by kings delighted him as a nineteenth-century liberal, but the revolutions of '48 in France and Germany he viewed with none of the rapture felt by his fellow countrymen. Let them not suppose that the mere casting down of kings means that the people will stand firmer. "Some victories revert to the vanquished."[183] Apparently there were times, however, when Melville felt strongly that America had a Serenian destiny allotted it, chiefly because it is the melting pot of the world. He particularly rejoiced because "we are not a narrow tribe of men with a bigoted Hebrew nationality— whose blood has been debased in the attempt to ennoble it, by maintaining an exclusive succession among ourselves. No: our blood is as the flood of the Amazon, made up of a thousand noble currents all pouring into one."[184] All tribes and people are forming here a federated whole. The foreign poor have God's right to come to our shores though they bring all the miseries of the Old World with them. "For the whole world is the patrimony of the whole world; there is no telling who does not own a stone in the Great Wall of China."[185] When we realize that we are what the commingling of races makes us, the prejudice of national dislikes should be extinguished in us. In the fullness and mellowness of time we shall then make here a Paradise. Even now we have some right to be proud of the effect our experiment in democracy has had on the other nations. Were not American whalemen the liberators who broke down the power of Spain in her South American colonies and helped to establish eternal democracy in those parts?[186]

In such passages we find Melville speaking with what seems to be a chauvinism scarcely exceeded by that of his most

---

[183]*Ibid.*, 236.   [184]*Works*, V, 216.   [185]*Ibid.*, 378.
[186]*Works*, VII, 137. Melville suggests in *Mardi* (*Works*, IV, 260) that these South American republics, lacking the Anglo-Saxon traditions of self-rule, may not be long-lived.

nationalistic contemporaries. One is not a little startled to
hear him express himself in the extravagant language of the
following passage:

> Seventy years ago we escaped from thrall; and, besides our
> first birthright—embracing one continent of earth—God has
> given to us, for a future inheritance, the broad domains of the
> political pagans, that shall yet come and lie down under the
> shade of our ark, without bloody hands being lifted. God has
> predestinated, mankind expects, great things from our race;
> and great things we feel in our souls. The rest of the nations
> must soon be in our rear. We are the pioneers of the world;
> the advance-guard, sent on through the wilderness of untried
> things, to break a new path in the New World that is ours. In
> our youth is our strength; in our inexperience, our wisdom.
> At a period when other nations have but lisped, our deep voice
> is heard afar. Long enough have we been sceptics with regard
> to ourselves, and doubted whether, indeed, the political Messiah
> had come. But he has come in *us*, if we would but give utter-
> ance to his promptings. And let us always remember that with
> ourselves, almost for the first time in the history of earth,
> national selfishness is unbounded philanthropy; for we cannot
> do a good to America, but we give alms to the world.[187]

One must keep in mind, in reading such bursts of rhetoric,
not only that they are balanced by sober criticism, but that
they are not isolated, being predicated generally upon some
statement of what course America must pursue to make this
dream a reality. In this instance Melville has just been assailing
with all the passion and logic he can command, the undemocratic naval code which allows the terrible evil of flogging.
While this evil exists the American Revolution was fought in
vain as far as the seaman is concerned. As long as it is permitted, the Declaration of Independence is a lie. America, as a
young nation, has a great responsibility in matters of this sort.

[187] *Works*, VI, 189.

She is not bound by the past and so can teach posterity. If she does show the way, then the destiny described in the passage above may be hers.

The average American in 1848 recognized three shibboleths by which true Americanism could be tested. (1) He swore allegiance to the belief that our political system, created by the founding fathers, had made us great. Our limitless natural resources were merely an incidental factor in our rapid advance among the nations of the world.[188] (2) The Constitution had become for him the "reality behind all government" and was no longer regarded as a pact which could be altered or abolished in any generation. (3) Of the three revolutionary passwords, Liberty, Equality, Fraternity, the first only was now the key to the future. Liberty had finally been achieved and Americans were at last a free people. The notion of equality had become, for most citizens of the republic, transmuted into the belief that in this land of opportunity all men may become equal at the higher level. Among the Transcendentalists equality was indeed placed "upon a superhuman plane."

Melville's impulsive response to this national creed was to deny each article in it. The America he envisaged could not be realized out of any such false faiths. In *Mardi*, after their visit to the Congress of Vivenza (the United States), the voyagers listen to the reading of a mysterious scroll whose author is not known. The satire, being interpreted, means that Melville, anonymously, is offering his countrymen a bitter pill to purge their windy patriotism. The reader of the scroll bids the crowd remember that happiness in Vivenza does not come, as they believe, from their noble sires who fought in their behalf, but was necessitated by the fact that they are descended from a freedom-loving people (the English), that their nation is young and

---

[188] This paragraph leans heavily on the first chapter—"New Winds" —of Professor C. R. Fish's *The Rise of the Common Man* (New York, 1935).

strong and that vast economic wealth, due to the accident of their geographical location, has fallen into their possession. It is also folly to suppose, as all Vivenzans assert, that "a universal and permanent Republic" is, necessarily, the final form of government. Of the nature of Liberty and Freedom the anonymous scroll-maker had such startling things as this to say: "It is not the prime end, and chief blessing, to be politically free. And freedom is only good as a means; is no end in itself." [189] It is more social than political and its real felicity cannot be shared. Taji (Melville) had already discovered that slaves toiled in the southern region of the country, and that there is much bowing and cringing even among the sovereign Kings of Vivenza.

As for the sacredness of the Constitution, Melville would call it later, while brooding over the horrors of a civil war which had been fought to preserve it:

> A paper pact, with points abstruse
> As theologic ones—profuse
> In matter for an honest doubt.[190]

In a passage in *White-Jacket* Melville confuted the American version of the dogma of equality as the generation of the 1840's interpreted it. After ridiculing the undemocratic ceremonies which the naval code requires in order to impress "the people" with the exalted superiority of their officers, he comments:

That saying about *levelling upward, and not downward,* may seem very fine to those who cannot see its self-involved absurdity. But the truth is, that, to gain the true level, in some things, we *must* cut downward; for how can you make every sailor a commodore? or how raise the valleys, without filling them up with the superfluous tops of the hills? [191]

Melville was in no danger of falling into the superstitions of the extreme Jacksonian democrats.

[189] *Works,* IV, 242.   [190] *Works,* XV, 177.   [191] *Works,* VI, 206.

This idea is central in his social philosophy. Feeling, as he did most ardently, that in their essential manliness (and this only) men are equal, what he hoped for democratic America was that those who have talents and power should wish to use these gifts for the common good. Leveling downward need not mean that excellence would be despised. Legitimate dignity and authority need not be affected. It is with this idea in mind that he implied, in a letter to Hawthorne, that even the aristocracy of the intellectual estates is selfish and unjustified. A man who is gifted beyond his fellows has no more right to shrink at their touch than they have reason to assert that they possess his gifts or have no need of them.

Several political and social trends and many institutions of mid-century America Melville spoke of with particular scorn. The expansionist movement, blessed with the emotive phrase Manifest Destiny, dismayed him. The Mexican War, which troubled him as it did Thoreau and Lowell, is alluded to in *Mardi* when the travelers enter the southwest of Vivenza and discover the freemen extending their dominions by digging up their neighbors' land, "holding the spear in one hand, and striking the bargain with the other." Melville makes an extended attack on the advocates of imperialist conquest in the Oregon Territory in his satire on the followers of Senator Allan of Ohio[192] who would risk war with Great Britain rather than yield one jot of the land they claimed was ours. Though Melville did not share his countrymen's bellicose attitude towards England, he speaks with barbed words of English imperialism. "Thou Bello [England], and thy locust armies, are the present curse of Orienda [the Orient]. Down ancient streams, from holy plains, in rafts thy murdered float. The pestilence that thins thy armies here is bred of corpses made by thee."[193] Melville's democracy, his pacifism, and his experiences on the seven seas, made him an internationalist. He rejoiced that the currents of a thousand nations flowed into us. "We are not a nation, so much as a world."[194]

Melville's attitude toward slavery was not that of the dogmatic Abolitionists, yet the travelers in Vivenza are aware from the moment of their arrival of the country's scourge. On the central temple itself stands a "man with a collar round his neck, and the red marks of stripes upon his back" hoisting a standard likewise striped.[195]   As the party journeys into the south, they see all the horrors of slavery and talk with the hardhearted Nulli (Calhoun) who holds these slaves have no souls. Souls have been bred out of them, as the instinct of scent is killed in pointers.[196]   The travelers, horror-struck by what they have seen in the savannahs of the south, cannot agree on the cure. Yoomy would risk civil war to free these slaves. Babbalanja counsels, "Better present woes for some, than future woes for all." The conclusion of this chapter apparently presents Melville's own opinion in 1849. Humanity cries out against this wrong; the North cannot be blamed for her zeal and the South must be judged wisely in the light of history. Yet when all is said which charity demands, slavery is a sin, no less, a blot, foul as the crater-pool of hell.   "The great laggard Time must now march up apace, and somehow befriend these thralls. It cannot be, that misery is perpetually entailed; though in a land proscribing primogeniture, the first-born and last of Hamo's tribe must still succeed to all their sires' wrongs." These are not the words of an Abolitionist. The herb-doctor in *The Confidence Man* seems to voice Melville's view a decade later: "If by abolitionist you mean a zealot, I am none; but if you mean a man, who, being a man, feels for all men, slaves included, and by any lawful act . . . would willingly abolish suffering . . . from among mankind, irrespective of colour, then am I what you say."[197]

---

[194] *Works*, V, 216.   [195] *Works*, IV, 226.   [196] *Ibid.*, 248.
[197] *Works*, XII, 149. Melville has little to say about the reform

Melville's disgust with the moneygrubbing plutocracy of his day, which was rapidly dividing America into a nation of those who owned and those who were owned, is frequently stated. One calls to mind the passage in *Typee* describing the joys of a society where there are no hardhearted nabobs and no money,[198] the begging sermon of the missionary in *Omoo*, the paragraphs in *Mardi* on the gold rush of '49, in which the starving miners are pictured as robbed by the merchants "who toiled not, dug not, slaved not," but loaded their caravans with gold and departed. One remembers, too, the cowardice and inhumanity of the cabin passengers in *Redburn* and the deliberate contrasting of the lots of the poor and the rich in "Poor Man's Pudding and Rich Man's Crumbs." Melville's portrait of a capitalist in *Redburn* rivals the conceptions of Eisenstein and Art Young:

One of them was an old fellow in a robust-looking coat, with broad skirts; he had a nose like a bottle of port wine; and would stand for a whole hour, with his legs straddling apart, and his hands deep down in his breeches pockets, as if he had two mints at work there, coining guineas. He was an abominable-looking old fellow, with cold, fat, jelly-like eyes; and avarice, heartlessness, and sensuality stamped all over him. He seemed all the time going through some process of mental arithmetic; doing sums with dollars and cents: his very mouth, wrinkled and drawn up at the corners, looked like a purse.

movements of the generation, save the one of which he was a part, the movement to abolish flogging and other abuses in the navy (see pp. 413). In Book XXII of *Pierre*, he indulges in some delightful fooling at the expense of the dietetic reformers like Lewis Hough, who maintained that fruit is man's natural food, and Sylvester Graham, who advocated his grit-like bread, fruit, and cheerfulness at meals. The craze over hydropathy he satirizes in the connoisseurship of the Apostles who hold that Croton water is "the most potent, Fairmount a gentle tonic, and Cochituate the mildest and least inebriating of all." Melville had the reformers in mind when he remarked to Duyckinck: "These men are all cracked right across the brow" (see p. 372).   [198] *Works*, I, 168.

When he dies, his skull ought to be turned into a savings' box, with the till-hole between his teeth.[199]

Melville's dislike of the new competitive society was not limited to commerce and capitalists. In the mordant second part of "The Paradise of Bachelors and the Tartarus of Maids" (1855), anticipating Samuel Butler's *Erewhon* by twenty years, he symbolizes the industrial slavery of those who tend machines. Apparently the benevolence and piety which greased the machinery of the Lowell Mills, that prize exhibit of American industrialism, would not have moved him to acquiesce. For him the factory system is simply a new form of bondage, the more inhumane because the man who profits by the machine has no direct responsibility towards the laborers in his factory. In his essay Melville visits a paper mill in the Devil's Dungeon on Blood River. Though the girls who feed the machine are as pale as the paper they are making, the guide who shows visitors through the mill has grown usage-hardened and quite indifferent to the scene. As Melville watches the ponderous machinery, a strange dread of this monster and its unbudging fatality strikes his heart.

Though, here and there, I could not follow the thin, gauzy veil of pulp in the course of its more mysterious or entirely invisible advance, yet it was indubitable that, at those points where it eluded me, it still marched on in unvarying docility to the autocratic cunning of the machine. A fascination fastened on me. I stood spell-bound and wandering in my soul. Before my eyes—there, passing in slow procession along the wheeling cylinders, I seemed to see, glued to the pallid incipience of the pulp, the yet more pallid faces of all the pallid girls I had eyed that heavy day. Slowly, mournfully, beseechingly, yet unresistingly, they gleamed along, their agony dimly outlined on the imperfect paper, like the print of the tormented face on the handkerchief of Saint Veronica.[200]

[199] *Works*, V, 338.   [200] *Works*, XIII, 252–253.

On no social problem did Melville think so clearly and express himself so cogently as on the nature of war. So modern are his ideas on the subject that one remembers with surprise that he is writing twenty years before *War and Peace* and half a century before *The Red Badge of Courage*. In one place or another he attacked by argument or satire all the sophistries by which men have convinced themselves that their particular war is a holy war. In *Typee* he notes that though the white man may view with horror the savage's custom of eating his enemy after battle, the savage may look with equal amazement at the death-dealing engines of the white man and the vindictiveness with which he carries on his wars.[201] In *Mardi* he ridicules the scientists who, on Malthusian principles, suppose that war games are needed to keep the population of Diranda, ruled over by those resourceful war-lords Hello and Piko, from eating up the island.[202] In the satiric chapters on King Bello of Dominora (England) he attacks the instigators of imperialist war who justify their methods of conquest of "inferior" peoples and the anxiety they cause the other nations of the world, by the specious contention that they are spreading the benefits of "civilization." Melville leaves no arguments to the sentimentalists who believe that war arouses the primitive virtue of courage. Commenting on Section IV of the *Articles of War*, he remarks in *White-Jacket:* "Courage is the most common and vulgar of the virtues; the only one shared with us by the beasts of the field; the one most apt, by excess, to run into viciousness."[203] To him the hero-spell which generals and naval commanders cast over the imaginations of men is one of the great superstitions of mankind. Of Napoleon, "the Mars and Moloch of our times," he says: "One drop of hero-blood will deify a fool."[204]

Melville's experiences aboard an American man-of-war opened

[201] *Works*, I, 166.   [202] *Works*, IV, 140.   [203] *Works*, VI, 395.
[204] *Works*, IV, 273; see also *Works*, VI, 396.

his eyes to the utter irrationality of the little world within those
wooden walls. The degradation of the seamen who were his
shipmates could never, from the nature of their occupation,
be alleviated. There is no cure for a man-of-war. Its very
object is to fight the battles which are "so naturally averse to
the seamen"; to accomplish its business, "it must ever remain
a picture of much that is tyrannical and repelling in human
nature."[205] He was struck by the sorry irony of the presence
on board of a chaplain, whose right it was to receive two-
twentieths of the bounty for sinking ships, and by his attempts
to practice Christ's religion in such a place. The omission of
the rite of Holy Communion aboard a warship showed that
some faint notion of propriety glimmered even in the minds
of admirals.

Melville concluded in *White-Jacket* that everything connected
with war is "utterly foolish, unchristian, barbarous, brutal, and
savouring of the Feejee Islands, cannibalism, saltpetre, and the
devil."[206] But he did not stop with merely hating war. In
the concluding paragraphs of chapter LXXV ("Sink, Burn, and
Destroy") he turns inside out the arguments of those who
always say to a pacifist, as a final clincher: Must the national
honor be trampled under foot by an insolent foe? War is
inevitable, for Fate everlastingly sustains an armed neutrality.
To the first of these Melville answers: If you are a Christian,
you cannot, even if you are a war-voting bishop, get by the
fact that Christ enjoins us to turn the cheek. No war, not even
a war of defense, is more righteous than another. To the
military fatalist he replies: "I have a voice that helps to shape
eternity; and my volitions stir the orbits of the furthest suns.
In two senses, we are precisely what we worship. Ourselves
are Fate."[207]

[205] *Works*, VI, 260.   [206] *Ibid.*, 396.
[207] *Ibid.*, 404. Melville likewise saw through the "preparedness"
argument. He says (*ibid.*, 260): "Standing navies, as well as stand-

It may seem strange that a man who hated war, and especially civil war, as Melville did, could have reconciled himself to the war between the North and South, could even make poetry of the heroism and idealism which it called forth on both sides. He did not view the conflict, we may be sure, as most of his countrymen did, even under the stress of the war years. The "Battle Pieces" are, most certainly, unique among war poems. Their peculiar tone was vaguely sensed by the reviewer in the *Atlantic Monthly*.[208] "In some respects," he said, "we find his poems admirable. He treats events as realistically as one can to whom they seem to have presented themselves as dreams; but at last they remain vagaries, and are none the more substantial because they have a modern speech and motion." Speaking of "The Scout towards Aldie" the critic continued: "If all the Rebels were as pleasingly impalpable as those the poet portrays, we could forgive them without a pang, and admit them to Congress without a test oath of any kind." These remarks show the significant difference between the war-deluded mentality of the time and Melville's desire to see beyond the moment to the issues the war had raised. The rebels were to him, what they had been before and during the war, men who supported bravely a delusory ideal. He had not hated them or supposed them fiends. He pictures the Northern and Southern soldiers as possessed equally of courage and patience in suffering. In a way they seem in his verses to be fighting on the same side because a like valor animates them.

Force had not convinced the rebels of their false faith; all it had done was to destroy slavery. Melville foresaw clearly that, as in all wars where an unjust peace is enforced, victory must eventuate in defeat, defeat, it may be in this case, for

ing armies, serve to keep alive the spirit of war even in the meek heart of peace. In its very embers and smoulderings they nourish that fatal fire, and half-pay officers, as the priests of Mars, yet guard the temple, though no god be there."

[208] February, 1867, pp. 252–253.

democracy itself. It is no accident, in this connection, that the misanthropic Ungar, in *Clarel*, for whom the democratic ideal has become "a civic barbarism," is a refugee from the conquered South. Melville spoke in the "Supplement" to *Battle Pieces* in defense of a magnanimous re-establishment as the only way to make secure what the idealists in the North supposed they were fighting for.[209] He called on the North not to alienate the great qualities of the South, attested by the War, not to turn victory into oppression for the vanquished. With Johnson and the shade of Lincoln he was defeated, but he was right.

Between 1851 and 1856 Melville apparently passed through the bitterest days of his life.[210] Rejected by critics and public, unable to find an answer to his spiritual problems, he deserted the qualified democracy of his earlier years and became the misanthrope of *The Confidence Man* (1857). Yet his mood is not Timonism, as it has been named, for he does not rail at mankind as Shakespeare's Athenian did. He exhibits his sorry examples of fraudulent humanity with a grim detachment that is more harrowing than a diatribe.

Ostensibly the book is an account of the conversations among the passengers of a Mississippi steamboat; really it is an allegory of man's life journey, like *Pilgrim's Progress* or Hawthorne's "The Celestial Railroad." The story opens symbolically with the appearance in the crowd on deck of a deaf-mute who displays on a slate the words "Charity believeth all things," while at the same moment the ship's barber puts out his sign inscribed "No

[209] "Emancipation has ridded the country of the reproach, but not wholly of the calamity" (*Works*, XVI, 187).

[210] He told Hawthorne in England in November, 1856, "that he had 'pretty much made up his mind to be annihilated'" (*Heart of Hawthorne's Journals*, 230). The evidence, that is, had nearly persuaded him to the materialist position. When one remembers that his trilogy was written out of his aspiration to achieve a kind of idealism which would satisfy both his reason and his religious imagination, one comprehends to what depths of disillusionment he had now sunk.

Trust." Then the confidence man appears in his first guise, as a negro beggar. He subsequently re-enters in protean forms: as a benevolent man soliciting for the Seminole Widow and Orphan Asylum; as the rubicund president of a dubious mining company; as an herb-doctor whose cures are nature's own; and as various private gentlemen working little con-games of great ingenuity.[211]

Though Melville does not speak through any of the persons in the book, the moral is evident. It is most clearly hinted when the confidence man, in his masquerade as a cosmopolitan, reads from the Apocrypha the words, which he was amazed to discover in the Bible: "Believe not his many words—an enemy speaketh sweetly with his lips."[212] For Melville there were now only three kinds of men in the world: the enemies who speak sweetly; the fools who listen; and the misanthropes and pragmatists who awake from sleep in time. Melville, who feared in 1851 lest Hawthorne might shrink from his ruthless democracy, who called man, in the ideal, a "grand and glowing creature," noble and sparkling,[213] with deliberate irony now gives a lying rogue sentiments to utter which he himself might once have expressed: "I candidly admit, with some random exceptions, I have . . . found that mankind . . . presents as pure a moral spectacle as the purest angel could wish."[214] The lesson of *The Confidence Man* teaches the reverse.

[211] The confidence man appears in eight main guises. The negro beggar fortunately enumerates them, else we should have difficulty in distinguishing them, so involuted is the story. (*Works*, XII, 14.)

The book is not great satire, but it is by no means a "posthumous" work, as it has been called. Some of the passages in which Melville ridicules missionaries, transcendentalists, puritans, nature-worshippers, men who despise savages, and those who hail the machine as a benefit to the race, surpass the satire in *Mardi* and *Pierre*. But the reiterated device of the confidence man's pursuit of his game becomes monotonous. The book might never have ended if Melville had not halted it abruptly, promising a second part which he never wrote. [212] Ecclesiasticus 12:16.

[213] *Works*, VII, 143.   [214] *Works*, XII, 158.

After *The Confidence Man* Melville spoke only once on social questions. Scattered through the dialogues of *Clarel* (1876) are many bitter judgments on the Gilded Age, which prophesy a dark future for these states. The Civil War, which Melville mistakenly hoped might permit, with treason thrown, "freedom's larger play," [215] he now saw as the "sad arch between contrasted eras." [216] The country now sinks to the dead level of rank commonplace. A hundred thousand demagogues mislead the people. Democracy spurns the past, "though 'tis the Past from which she gets her saving part." [217]

> Behold her whom the panders crown,
> Harlot on horseback, riding down
> The very Ephesians who acclaim
> This great Diana of ill fame! [218]

The Anglo-Saxon freebooters, hated by myriads dispossessed of rights, deflower the world's last sylvan glade in the name of Christ.[219] Since industry has made human beings the slaves of the machines they tend, the free men of America have again an overlord. One reason only America has for rejoicing. The inevitable class-war, which threatens the western world, may for a time be fended from our shores.

> Those waste-weirs which the New World yields
> To inland freshets—the free vents
> Supplied to turbid elements;
> The vast reserves—the untried fields;
> These long shall keep off and delay
> The class-war, rich-and-poor-man fray
> Of history.[220]

Yet even here the day may come when our "sanguine country's wonted claim," our birthright, may be destroyed. The band

[215] *Works*, XVI, 99.   [216] *Works*, XV, 177.   [217] *Ibid.*, 240.
[218] *Loc. cit.* It must be remembered that the speaker here is Ungar, an expatriate Southerner, whom the war has ruined in spirit and in estate.   [219] *Op. cit.*, 192.   [220] *Op. cit.*, 248.

of pilgrims in *Clarel* are reluctant to admit the truth of Ungar's predictions, yet, looking into the future,

> They felt how far beyond the scope
> Of elder Europe's saddest thought
> Might be the New World's sudden brought
> In youth to share old age's pains—
> To feel the arrest of hope's advance,
> And squandered lost inheritance;
> And cry—"To Terminus build fanes!
> Columbus ended earth's romance;
> No New World to mankind remains!" [221]

VI. MELVILLE'S REPUTATION

The "recovery" of Melville from oblivion is a most interesting chapter in the history of taste. When one asks, however, the apparently simple question why it is that he sank below the attention of the general reading public more than thirty years before his death and then suddenly, about twenty years ago, became the object of a cult, one finds that the answer is not obvious.

Before passing first to consider the reception which critics and public gave Melville's work between 1846 and 1857, it will be wise to recall the state of periodical criticism at that time. We should remember that the tradition of absolutism had not entirely disappeared, so that Melville was disciplined by certain reviewers with the same sternness meted out to Keats and Tennyson by the *Quarterly Review*. Much of the reviewing in American magazines was, on the other hand, of the most perfunctory sort, the object of many notices being merely to inform the reader, by a synopsis, of what he might expect if he bought the book. We need also to keep in mind

[221] *Op. cit.*, 250.

constantly, when we are inclined to be impatient with the obtuseness of these early critics of *Moby-Dick* and *Pierre*, that
these books are still debated by modern students. Melville is
not easy to "place" today with a definiteness which will receive
general assent.

Typee delighted its first readers as few American books have.
A composite of the favorable notices suggests that it was liked
chiefly because it struck the reviewers as thrilling, original, and
racy. Those who shared the era's love of books of travel could
find additional satisfaction in *Typee's* apparent authenticity.
Only the *Harbinger*, organ of the Brook Farm experiment,
saw in *Typee* its importance as a first-hand account, by an
unbiassed witness, of a savage society whose economic and
religious institutions were as yet undisturbed by the intrusion
of the traders and missionaries.[222] The evangelical press naturally advanced to attack. Most severe was the *New York
Evangelist*. (Its review was the one which Melville's friend
Toby saw and so learned Melville had escaped to civilization.)
Typee was written, it maintained, to delight the voluptuaries
of the corrupt London society. It had no place in a library of
American books.

With *Omoo* the chorus of praise was augmented, while the
few dissonant voices grew shriller. It especially delighted the
emancipated who exulted, as did the critic in the *Dublin Review*,
in his sly pictures of missionary ineptitude. The *People's
Journal* gives us a further clue to *Omoo's* popularity. It belongs, the reviewer shrewdly observed, to a new kind of literature written by men who have made danger their daily
companion, who have really experienced the crudest life and
are yet articulate about what they have seen. A new class of
men have found their spokesmen at last. As Melville fully
expected when he pondered the inclusion of the chapters on

---

[222] The reviewer was C. A. Dana. All the reviews cited in this
section are listed, with their dates, in the Bibliography.

the missionaries,[223] the church periodicals leveled their fire
at him. They were joined by others more particularly concerned over the book's "profligacy." [224] G. W. Peck, for instance, in the *American Review: A Whig Journal*, holds no
brief for the missionaries, but he is badly disturbed by "the
cool sneering wit and the perfect want of *heart* everywhere
manifested" in *Omoo*. The book is only one of recent works
which prove that the "manliness of our light literature is cur-
dling into licentiousness on the one hand and imbecility on the
other." Yet even the conscience of Mr. Peck cannot restrain him
from liking *Omoo*, though he reads it with a "perpetual recoil."
It is dangerous for a popular writer to alter the picture his
public has formed of him. This is what Melville, possibly
with some malice, dared to do in *Mardi*. His critics were
puzzled. The English had more trouble with it than the
Americans, as one might expect since the satirical portions are
distinctly American in their point of view. The *Athenaeum*,
for instance, suspected the presence of allegory, but fumbled
to find the key.

In America the tone of the reviews is generally favorable,
Graham's going so far as to say *Mardi* is the most striking
thing Melville has produced. A penetrating article appeared
in the *United States Magazine and Democratic Review*. It
notices that the opening chapters will appeal widely as *Typee*
and *Omoo* did, which they resemble. But they were written
for the multitude; *Mardi* is unique, "and like all new things
must take the chance of being considered ugly, because it is
uncommon." Melville had, it seems, survived his first attempt
to be "frank" with his public. It is an eloquent fact that two-
thirds of the reviewers, remembering what promise he had
shown, are willing to take *Mardi* on faith without very well
understanding what he intends by it.

[223] See p. 407.
[224] Especially the *New Englander* and the *Eclectic Review*.

With *Redburn*, it was agreed, he had found his *métier*. The *Literary Gazette* in England and the *Southern Literary Messenger* in America are glad to behold a sinner saved. The anxious attempts to rate Melville above or below Marryat, Dana, and Cooper begin with *Redburn*. He seemed at last to have brought himself within the range of a well-known critical measure.

A torrent of praise followed the appearance of *White-Jacket*. Scarcely a caviling voice was raised, and even the more lordly reviews, like the *Athenaeum*, thought it needless to point out any minor faults. It fairly let itself go, in fact, venturing that Mr. Melville possesses "more vivacity, fancy, colour and energy than ninety-nine out of the hundred who undertake to poetize or prate about sea monsters." [225]

Part of the enthusiasm which the book aroused can be set down to the element of propaganda in it. The chapters on the abuse of flogging in the navy are commended by the reviewers. It is now well known that Melville's book arrived at the time when the reforming zeal of the age would soon force Congress to act to alter the naval code.[226] It played its part in the last act of the movement, but did not initiate it. But readers found their sentiments eloquently stated in *White-Jacket*.[227]

(Those who felt they had finally discovered the course Melville would follow as a writer received a bad jolt from *Moby-Dick*. There is, indeed, in some of the irritation it caused an intimation that the critics felt themselves badly cheated.) The legend that the reviewers demolished *Moby-Dick* is now so well es-

---

[225] The *Knickerbocker, Holden's*, and the *Southern Literary Messenger* were especially delighted. The last points out that now the English have been awakened through *White-Jacket* to the fact that we have a literature which is "distinctive, national, peculiar," perhaps Melville's countrymen will be willing to believe this has been demonstrated.   [226] See p. 413.

[227] *Littell's Living Age*, in a notice copied from the *Tribune*, observed: "His remarks on the discipline of our *public* vessels are entitled to great consideration, and coincide with the prevailing tendencies of the public mind."

tablished that one despairs of doing anything to modify the picture of Melville, defeated and defiant, sitting down to work on *Pierre* with a mad desire to revenge himself on the critics who derided his best efforts.[228] Enough was said which was obtuse and narrow-minded but as much was said which should have enheartened any author, and even the most adverse judgments were in many instances uttered with a show of respect for Melville's talents.[229] (The reviewers who tried to justify their dislike of the book show in common their dismay in trying to make it fit into any category of fiction-writing then acknowledged.) In particular is this true of the writers in the *Spectator*, the *Dublin University Magazine*, and the *Examiner*.

Three reviews were not only friendly but penetrating. The *Literary World*, edited by Evert Duyckinck, gave *Moby-Dick* a very long notice.[230] It warned readers not to attempt to

[228] Mumford's account of the reception of *Moby-Dick* (*Herman Melville*, 198–199) ignores all of the favorable notices except the one in the *Literary World* and belittles that. Freeman's paragraph on the subject (*Herman Melville*, 130) is even less comprehensive. To speak, as Braswell does, of "the meager praise and the disfavor accorded *Mardi* and *Moby Dick*" ("The Satirical Temper of Melville's *Pierre*," *American Literature*, VII, 428) without adding that in certain quarters both books were highly commended by men whose praise Melville could be proud of, distorts the situation. Braswell's contention that Melville's bitter satire of the world, of authors and publishers in *Pierre* was in part caused by the critical reception of *Moby-Dick* is not shaken by admitting the fact that Melville had really no great cause for complaint.

[229] The *Athenaeum*, which was displeased, admits gruffly that Melville has tantalized "us with indications of genius." The most abusive notice appeared in the *Democratic Review*. Its scorn of *Moby-Dick* retrospectively colors its judgment of the earlier books. They are now seen by it to be licentious or dull or stupid, whereas it had been, on their appearance, enthusiastic about *Mardi*, *Redburn*, and *White-Jacket*.

[230] Undoubtedly written by Duyckinck himself. He had discussed the book with Melville during its composition. Much of its "free-thinking" was too much for his Episcopalian orthodoxy and he says so frankly at the end of the review.

classify it and to be equally cautious of condemning Ahab and his quest until they understand that the pursuit of the whale weaves in a deep allegory of man's destiny. The same point is stressed in the remarkably acute review in *Harper's*,[231] the most discriminating which was published of any of his books in his lifetime. The reviewer saw that it was at once a "romance, a tragedy, and a natural history" and appreciated the skill with which the transitions from one mood to another are made. He perceived the reason for the increased intensity as the denouement approaches and saw beneath the story "a pregnant allegory, intended to illustrate the mystery of human life." It goes deep into the heart of things and shows that Melville's genius for "moral analysis is scarcely surpassed by his wizard power of description"—a judgment a modern enthusiast could hardly wish to modify.

The third important notice of *Moby-Dick* which discovered its greatness appeared in the London *Leader*. It places the book with the most original of American works and asks the question, which it answers to our satisfaction, "Who knows the terrors of the seas like Herman Melville? . . . The ghostly terrors which [he] so skilfully evokes, have a strange fascination. In vain Reason rebels. . . . Imagination has a credulity of its own respondent to power. So it is with Melville's superstitions: we believe in them imaginatively." [232]

Melville could have expected nothing but abuse for his *Pierre*. It is still a mystery why the house of Harper accepted it, unless their reader took it innocently as a sensation novel with a deep transcendental meaning which might appeal to the

[231] Hetherington (*The Reputation of Herman Melville*) plausibly suggests that George Ripley, the Transcendentalist, was the reviewer.
[232] If Melville saw the long summary of *Moby-Dick* by E. D. Forgues in the *Revue des deux Mondes* he should have been flattered, in spite of the reviewer's cautioning him against injuring "sa verve incontestable" by "Emersonian" extravagances. Forgues did not object, incidentally, to the allegory, which he comprehended.

readers of Judd's *Margaret*, or as a novel of psychological horror in the style of Charles Brockden Brown, or the house wished to please an author who they thought was still an asset. The response of the reviews was unanimous. Those who dared mention the theme of incest alluded to it as that "fearfullest of human crimes" (*Albion*) and shuddered. Even the *Literary World* deserted its old friend. It could only ask why he allows his mind to "run riot amid remote analogies." How thoroughly the profession believed him unworthy henceforth of their consideration is proved by the fact that only two journals, so far as one can discover, noticed *Israel Potter* in 1855. *The Piazza Tales* in 1856 inspired a renewed confidence in three periodicals, including his sometime enemy the *Democratic Review*. When *The Confidence Man* appeared, Melville regained in England, surprisingly enough, much of the favor he had lost. Apparently no American journal discussed it. A good deal of the pleasure which it gave the English is derived from their conviction that here was an *exposé* of Yankee shams and hypocrisies. But it would not be fair to leave it at that. The tone of all the reviews except that of the *Spectator*, which did not completely condemn, surprises one by revealing the fact that Melville had been accepted as one of the most important authors of the day writing in English.

Four extended appraisals of Melville's work were published between 1853 and 1857, one in England and three in America. Though the writers do him the compliment of begging him to fulfill his earlier promise of becoming what they wish him to be, their articles must have made very clear to him the impossibility of placating them with anything he cared himself to write. Fitz-James O'Brien in 1853 and again in 1857 beseeches him to abandon his speculative fancies which will be his undoing.[233] The article in the *New Monthly Magazine* for July, 1853— one of a series which considered Dana, Hawthorne, and Curtis

[233] *Putnam's Monthly Magazine.*

as well—is far less penetrative than O'Brien's two papers, but the tenor is the same. It returns to the notion put forward by the reviewers of *White-Jacket*, that "the superstition of life on the waves has no abler interpreter, unequal and undisciplined as he is." The author of the paper on Cooper, Dana, and Melville in the *Dublin University Magazine* reiterates this conviction. *White-Jacket* is still Melville's best book.

Such was Melville's fame when he ceased writing prose in 1857. He had been dropped in America from the heights of an uncommon popularity with public and critics to almost total oblivion. In England the conviction nevertheless grew that whatever new extravagance he might produce, he was at any rate worthy of the greatest respect. He had been told on both sides of the water that he stood on the edge of a precipice.

When we try to offer an adequate solution for the extinction of Melville's name in the subsequent thirty years, the curious critical impasse at the time he ceased writing professionally must be given its due weight. When a popular writer passes off the scene, his posthumous reputation is likely to be for a while the esteem he won in his lifetime. In a sense the critics had required of Melville to earn his reputation over again. Instead he did nothing to regain it. Had he died, handsome things might have been said of him which could be passed down to posterity. As is well known, Melville refused to indulge in any of the innocent self-exploitations by which literary men maintain a legend about themselves. He did not show himself among authors or cultivate the society of anyone who could advance the sale of his books. When deliberately sought out, as on the occasion when the Authors' Club (which he refused to join) gave him a dinner toward the end of his life, men were surprised to find how companionable he was. He acted very much as if he were dead, so far as the business of literature was concerned.

Who were there to foster his posthumous fame after his

literary death? The hegemony in letters had passed to New England, and the Brahmins had no use for him. Lowell mentions him twice.[234] The others, save Longfellow, mention him not at all.[235]

In New York such men as R. H. Stoddard and E. C. Stedman, like their New England colleagues quite incapable of enduring Melville's Rabelaisianism or Timonism, ruled the roast. Both men were his professed friends but it is evident that they really considered Melville a minor writer. Stoddard, at the time of his death, said of the early books, for instance, that they made him "famous among his countrymen, who, less literary in their tastes and demands than at present, were easily captivated by stories of maritime life."[236]

Though Boston and New York forgot him and the makers of textbooks begrudged him more than a line, Melville has always attracted a variegated crowd of admirers. His subterranean reputation resembles that of Blake and Peacock and Borrow, to whom he has been repeatedly compared. In England enthusiasm for Melville became a cult.[237] H. S. Salt shows in his *Company I Have Kept* how the circle of Melville's admirers constantly widened. Dobell induced him to read Melville. Salt passed on his enthusiasm to William Morris who read *Moby-Dick:* "A week or two afterwards I heard him quoting it with huge gusto and delight." Another group, composed of young secularists in Leicester, was fired by James Thomson's

---

[234] *Letters* (Boston, 1914), I, 193. The other reference, a remark about "The Encantadas," may be found in the Standard Edition of Melville's *Works*, XIII, 173.

[235] Melville was asked, in 1857, to contribute to the newly founded *Atlantic Monthly*. See J. H. Birss, "Melville and the *Atlantic Monthly*."

[236] "Herman Melville," *Mail and Express*, October 8, 1891, p. 5.

[237] In reviewing Weaver's biography in 1922, J. St. L. Strachey tasked him with not allowing enough for Melville's reputation in England, which has been continuous (*Spectator*, May 6, 1922, pp. 559–560).

zeal. Other English admirers were Edward Carpenter, Theo-
dore Watts, Louis Becke, and Robert Buchanan. Stevenson's
slangy words of praise are well known.[238] Later Barrie and
Masefield joined this company. Augustine Birrell was made
to read Melville by Sir Alfred Lyall who was, Birrell says,
"shocked at my ignorance." [239]

In America E. L. White, John La Farge, T. M. Coan, and
Arthur Stedman (his literary executor) remembered Melville
while he lived. Charles Warren Stoddard, another adventurer
in Polynesia, had traced the ramblings of Melville and Long
Ghost over Tahiti with the devotion of a pilgrim.[240] These
admirers, even before Melville died, made some efforts to secure
for his work the position they felt it deserved.[241]

Following his death in 1891 something like a genuine revival
of his fame took place. The New York newspapers, when
reminded of his death, published long obituary notices contributed by his friends. New editions of his more popular
works, undertaken in England by H. S. Salt and in America
by Arthur Stedman, were well noticed. But Melville had still
to wait another thirty years to come into his own. By a happy
chance the centenary of his birth in 1919, the publication of
Weaver's biography which partly drew aside the veil of mystery about his life, the assertion of his artistic greatness by
a new group of English admirers, and the movement among

[238] Writing to Charles Baxter in 1888, he promised him a better
book on the South Seas than "any other writer has done—except
Herman Melville perhaps, who is a howling cheese." (*Letters*, III
[New York, 1911], 78.)

[239] On June 20, 1890, Havelock Ellis wrote Melville for genealogical
information to assist him in research he was making in the ancestry
of distinguished English and American writers.

[240] *South Sea Idyls* (New York, 1892), 338–339.

[241] Riegel exaggerates the effect of their articles in his attempt to
prove that there were "at least four or five movements which sought
to reawaken a general interest in Melville" ("The Anatomy of Melville's Fame," *American Literature*, III, 198).

scholars over here to reinterpret our literary history, provided a series of co-ordinated impulses which have succeeded in placing him in the company he should have been keeping.

Melville has had to wait this long because the world has only recently caught up with him. His personal vision was largely at variance with his age for whom, as Sullivan says, the "material world was a perfectly clear-cut and comprehensible affair, and everything that was not material was merely moral." [242] We are aware once more, as Melville was, of the mystery of man. "We feel that Melville's oceans and leviathans are credible symbols. That man hunts through a great deep who looks into himself." [243]

The Bostonians, for whom he had a Knickerbocker's dislike, will be made uncomfortable by Melville's arrival among the immortals. Whitman, who thought *Omoo* "most readable sort of reading," [244] will be glad to see him, and Hawthorne will welcome him. Did Melville not once prophesy their meeting hereafter?

You and I shall sit down in Paradise, in some little shady corner by ourselves . . . and . . . we shall then cross our celestial legs in the celestial grass that is forever tropical, and strike our glasses and our heads together, till both musically ring in concert,—then, O my dear fellow-mortal, how shall we pleasantly discourse of all the things manifold which now so distress us,—when all the earth shall be but a reminiscence, yea, its final dissolution an antiquity.

---

[242] *Times Literary Supplement,* July 26, 1923, p. 493.   [243] *Ibid.*
[244] *Uncollected Poetry and Prose* (New York, 1921), I, 134.

1819. Herman Melville born August 1 at No. 6 Pearl Street, New York City, to Allan and Maria Gansevoort Melville.

1830. Family removed to Albany. Herman became a student at the Albany Academy.

1832. Allan Melville died in debt.

1834–1836. Clerked it in Albany.

1837. Shipped as a sailor on a merchantman bound for Liverpool.

1837–1841. Taught school at Greenbush, N.Y., and Pittsfield, Mass. Other activities unknown.

1839. "Fragments from a Writing Desk" published in the *Democratic Press and Lansingburgh Advertiser*, May 4 and 18.

1841. January 3, shipped at Fairhaven (New Bedford) on the *Acushnet*, a whaler, for the South Seas.

1842. July 9, left ship at Nukuhiva, Marquesas Islands. After a month among the cannibals in the Taipi valley, escaped and reached Tahiti aboard an Australian whaler in September. Left Tahiti on the whaler *Leviathan* in which he (perhaps) touched the shores of Japan.

1843. August 17, mustered into service on the U.S. frigate *United States* at Honolulu, where he had lived for several months.

1844. October 14, discharged at Boston.

1846. *Typee* published by Murray in London and Wiley and Putnam in New York.

1847. March, *Omoo* published in London; New York in April. Attempted to secure a post in the U.S. Treasury Department. August 4, married Elizabeth Shaw, daughter of Chief Justice Lemuel Shaw of Boston. Settled at 103 Fourth Avenue, New York.

1847–1850. Wrote occasional reviews for the *Literary World*, conducted by his friends, Evert and George Duyckinck.

1849. February, his son Malcolm born. March, *Mardi* published by Bentley in London; in April by Harper and Brothers in New York. September, *Redburn* published in London; November, in New York. October 11, sailed for London to arrange for publication of *White-Jacket*. Brief visit in Paris, Brussels, Cologne, and Coblenz. Set out for home December 25, sailing from Portsmouth.

1850. January, *White-Jacket* published in London; March, in New York. Removed to "Arrowhead," two miles from Pittsfield, Mass. Hawthorne his neighbor at Lenox until November, 1851.

1851. His son Stanwix born. October, *The Whale* published by Bentley in London; November, by Harper and Brothers as *Moby-Dick*.

1852. Signed petition to Congress for change in copyright law, with Irving, Putnam, Bryant, *et al.* August, *Pierre* published in New York; November, in London.

1853. His daughter Elizabeth born. Attempted to secure a consular appointment. December 10, the stock of his books destroyed in the Harper fire.

1853–1856. Contributed essays and stories to *Putnam's Monthly Magazine* and *Harper's New Monthly Magazine*.

1855. April, *Israel Potter* published after its serialization in *Putnam's*. His daughter Frances born.

1856. *The Piazza Tales* published. Sailed from New York, October 11, for Glasgow. Visited Hawthorne at Liverpool in November, on his way to the Holy Land and Italy.

1857. April, *The Confidence Man* published. Sailed for America from Liverpool, May 5.

1857–1860. Lectured on "Statuary in Rome," "The South Seas," and "Travelling."

1860. Sailed to San Francisco with his brother Thomas, captain of the clipper-ship *Meteor*. Returned by way of Panama.

1861. Attempted to obtain a consulship under the Lincoln administration.

1863. Moved to 104 East 26th Street, New York, in the autumn.

1866. *Battle-Pieces and Aspects of the War* published; some of these poems had already appeared in *Harper's New Monthly Magazine*. Appointed District Inspector of Customs in New York, December 6.

1867. September 11, Malcolm accidentally shot and killed himself.

1876. *Clarel* published at the expense of his uncle Peter Gansevoort.

1885. December 31, resigned Inspectorship.

1888. *John Marr and Other Sailors* published.

1891. *Timoleon* published. Melville died September 28.

1924. *Billy Budd* published.

SELECTED BIBLIOGRAPHY

I. BIBLIOGRAPHY

Minnigerode, Meade. *Some Personal Letters of Herman Melville and a Bibliography*. New York: 1922, pp. 101–195.

Sadleir, Michael. "Herman Melville," in *Excursions in Victorian Bibliography*. London: 1922, pp. 217–234. (Books only. No articles or reviews. Contains a brief essay on Melville.)

Weaver, R. M. *Herman Melville, Mariner and Mystic*. New York: 1921, pp. 385–388.

II. TEXT

The Works of Herman Melville. Standard Edition. 12 vols. Constable and Company, London: 1922–1923. Four volumes added in 1924 containing: (XIII) *Billy Buda and Other Prose Pieces*, ed. by R. W. [*sic*] Weaver; (XIV, XV) *Clarel;* (XVI) *Poems* (*Battle-Pieces*, *John Marr and Other Sailors*, *Timoleon*, "Miscellaneous Poems").

Pierre or the Ambiguities. Ed. by R. S. Forsythe. New York: 1930. (A carefully edited text with a sane and scholarly introduction.)

Shorter Novels of Herman Melville. Introduction by Raymond Weaver. New York: 1928. (Includes *Billy Budd*.)

Birss, J. H. "Herman Melville and the *Atlantic Monthly*," *Notes and Queries*, CLXVII, 223–224 (September 29, 1934). (Letter from Melville, August 19, 1857, agreeing to contribute to the *Atlantic Monthly*.)

Birss, J. H. "An Obscure Melville Letter," *Notes and Queries*, CLXIII, 275 (October 15, 1932). (A letter to George McLaughlin to be sold at a Sanitary Fair in 1864.)

Birss, J. H. " 'Travelling,' A New Lecture by Herman Melville," *New England Quarterly*, VII, 725–728 (December, 1934). (Report of a lecture, probably Melville's last, from the *Cambridge Chronicle* of February 25, 1860.)

Hawthorne, Julian. *Nathaniel Hawthorne and His Wife.* 2 vols. Boston: 1885. (Contains, Vol. I, 385–389, 398–407, 475, four letters of Melville to Hawthorne.)

"Journal of Melville's Voyage in a Clipper Ship," *New England Quarterly*, II, 120–125 (January, 1929). (Melville's trip to California in 1860 in his brother's ship.)

Lathrop, Rose Hawthorne. *Memories of Hawthorne.* Boston: 1897. (Contains, pp. 156–160, two letters to Hawthorne.)

Mabbott, T. O. "Herman Melville," *Notes and Queries*, CLXII, 151–152 (February 27, 1932). (A letter, addressed to Dr. William Sprague, from Dauber and Pine's Catalogue No. 100, p. 47.)

Mabbott, T. O. "Poem by Herman Melville," *Notes and Queries*, CXLIX, 42–43 (July 18, 1925). ("Inscription for the Slain at Fredericksburg." Not included by Melville in *Battle-Pieces*.)

Memorial of James Fenimore Cooper. New York: 1852. (On p. 30 is printed Melville's letter of tribute. This was reprinted in *Notes and Queries*, CLXII, 39 [January 16, 1932], by J. H. Birss.)

Metcalf, E. M. "A Pilgrim by Land and Sea," *Horn Book*, III, 3–11 (February, 1927). (Contains two letters to Melville's children printed in this children's magazine by his granddaughter Mrs. Eleanor Melville Metcalf.)

Minnigerode, Meade. *Some Personal Letters of Herman Melville and a Bibliography.* New York: 1922. (Gives an inaccurately transcribed text of portions of seventeen of the forty letters in the Duyckinck Collection of the New York Public Library. Extremely untrustworthy.)

Morison, S. E., ed. "Melville's 'Agatha' Letter to Hawthorne," *New England Quarterly*, II, 296–307 (April, 1929). (Melville gave Hawthorne memoranda of a true story of bigamy given him by a New Bedford lawyer. In the accompanying letter he suggested to Hawthorne how the story ought to be worked up into fiction. These suggestions are of the greatest importance to anyone studying Melville's literary method.)

Paltsits, V. H., ed. *Family Correspondence of Herman Melville, 1830–1904.* New York Public Library, New York: 1929. Reprinted from the *Bulletin of the New York Public Library*, July, August, 1929. (Letters by Melville in the Gansevoort-Lansing Collection of the New York Public Library with a selection from the letters of Mrs. Melville, Catherine Gansevoort Lansing, Melville's cousin, and other members of the family. Notes, pp. 14–16, by Henry Gansevoort, of Melville's lecture on "Statuary in Rome." Excellently edited, with useful genealogical notes.)

Smith, J. E. A. *The History of Pittsfield, Massachusetts, from 1800 to 1876.* C. W. Bryan and Co., Springfield, Mass.: 1876. (Pp. 399–400 contain an account of Major Thomas Melville written by Herman Melville but not attributed to him.)

"Some Melville Letters," *Nation and Athenaeum*, XXIX, 712–713 (August 13, 1921). (Eight letters written by Melville to James Billson between October, 1884, and December, 1888. Important for Melville's thought and occupation during his last years.)

"An Unpublished Letter from Herman Melville to Mrs. Hawthorne in Explanation of 'Moby-Dick,'" *American Art Association–Anderson Galleries Catalogue of Sale*, No. 3911, p. 9. New York: 1931. (A portion of a four-page letter dated January 8, 1852.)

Weaver, R. M. *Herman Melville, Mariner and Mystic.* New York: 1921. (Letters of Melville and, pp. 284–304, a portion of a journal kept by him on his journey to England in 1849–1850. Account, from the Boston *Journal* of December 3, 1857, of Melville's lecture on "Statuary in Rome," pp. 371–372; also a report from the same paper, January 31, 1859, of the lecture on "The South Seas," pp. 373–375.)

Weaver, R. M., ed. *Journal up the Straits, October 11, 1856–May 5, 1857.* The Colophon, New York: 1935. (Important not only as a minute account of Melville's trip, but also as an index to his state of mind and as a background for *Clarel*.

See the review by R. S. Forsythe, *American Literature*, VIII, 85–96, for a list of many errors in the notes and in the transcription of the text.)

III. BIOGRAPHY

Aaron, Daniel. "An English Enemy of Melville," *New England Quarterly*, VIII, 561–567 (December, 1935). (The "enemy" is Lucett [see below], whose *Rovings in the Pacific* attacked Melville as a brute and a liar. Lucett claimed to have encountered him in Tahiti.)

Birss, J. H. "Herman Melville Lectures in Yonkers," *American Book Collector*, V, 50–52 (February, 1934).

Brooks, Van Wyck. "Herman Melville," in *Dictionary of American Biography*. New York: 1933. XII, 522–526.

Buchanan, Robert. "Imperial Cockneydom," *Universal Review*, IV, 71–91 (May–August, 1889). (On p. 78 Buchanan reproaches America for her neglect of Melville and suggests, preposterously, that E. C. Stedman did not know his place of residence.)

Coan, T. M. "Herman Melville," *Literary World*, XXII, 492–493 (December 19, 1891). (Accurate brief biography. Interesting glimpse of Melville's later years.)

Damon, S. F. "Why Ishmael Went to Sea," *American Literature*, II, 281–283 (November, 1930). (Melville possibly a failure as a schoolmaster. This, rather than reading *Two Years before the Mast*, may have determined his adventure.)

Duyckinck, E. A. and G. L., eds. "Herman Melville," in *Cyclopædia of American Literature*. New York: 1855. II, 672–676. (In a sense, a brief "official" biography, since the Duyckincks were close friends of Melville.)

Field, M. B. *Memories of Many Men and of Some Women*. New York: 1874. (On pp. 201–202 is an account of a call on Melville and Dr. Holmes made by Darley, the artist, and Field.)

Forsythe, R. S. "Herman Melville in Honolulu," *New England Quarterly*, VIII, 99–105 (March, 1935). (Establishes important facts about Melville's stay in Honolulu. The indenture between him and Isaac Montgomery, in whose store he was to serve as a clerk, is given in full.)

Forsythe, R. S. "Herman Melville in the Marquesas," *Philological Quarterly*, XV, 1–15 (January, 1936). (Important examination of the chronology of Melville's stay in the South Seas as presented in *Typee* and *Omoo*.)

Franklin, S. R. *Memories of a Rear-Admiral Who Has Served for More than Half a Century in the Navy of the United States*. New York: 1898. (Particular reference to Melville, pp. 64–66. Franklin is wrong in asserting that *White-Jacket* was placed on the desk of every member of Congress and induced the abolition of corporal punishment.)

Freeman, John. *Herman Melville*. English Men of Letters series. London: 1926. (See below, under "Criticism and Scholarship.")

Gohdes, Clarence. "Gossip about Melville in the South Seas," *New England Quarterly*, X, 526–531 (September, 1937). (A letter of one "R. S." who visited the scenes of *Typee* after the book appeared.)

Hart, J. D. "Melville and Dana," *American Literature*, IX, 49–55 (March, 1937).

Hudson, H. H. "The Mystery of Herman Melville," *Freeman*, III, 156–157 (April 27, 1921). ("He gave up the struggle for literary greatness in which he was already fairly successful to enter upon a quest for abstract truth, foredoomed to failure.")

Josephson, Matthew. "Libertarians and Others," in *Portrait of the Artist as American*. New York: 1930, pp. 26–36. (A condensation of his *Outlook* article; see below.)

Josephson, Matthew. "The Transfiguration of Herman Melville," *Outlook*, CL, 809–811, 832, 836 (September 19, 1928).

Kummer, George. "Herman Melville and the Ohio Press," *Ohio State Archæological and Historical Quarterly*, XLV, 34–36 (January, 1936). (Notices which appeared in six Ohio newspapers concerning Melville's lecture tour of 1858.)

Larrabee, H. A. "Herman Melville's Early Years in Albany," *New York History*, XV, 144–159 (April, 1934). (Title misleading, for this is mainly an account of the Gansevoort genealogy and the condition of Albany in the 1830's.)

Lathers, Richard. *The Reminiscences of Richard Lathers.* The Grafton Press, New York: 1907. (References to Melville on pp. 51, 328–329, 406–407.)

Lathrop, Rose Hawthorne. *Memories of Hawthorne.* Boston: 1897. (References to Melville, pp. 143, 145, 155–161, 200.)

Lucett, [?]E. *Rovings in the Pacific, from 1837 to 1849. . . .* London: 1851. I, 288–297. (Attack on Melville's veracity and decency by an English merchant who claims to have encountered him in Tahiti. See above under Aaron, Daniel.)

Mansfield, L. S. "Glimpses of Herman Melville's Life in Pittsfield, 1850–1851," *American Literature*, IX, 26–48 (March, 1937). (Letters of Evert Duyckinck describing his visits to Melville in 1850 and 1851. Important.)

Mansfield, L. S. "Melville's Comic Articles on Zachary Taylor," *American Literature*, IX, 411–418 (January, 1938).

Mordell, Albert. "Melville and 'White-Jacket,'" *Saturday Review of Literature*, VII, 946 (July 4, 1931). (Identifies some characters in *White-Jacket* from the frigate's muster-roll.)

Morris, Lloyd. "Melville: Promethean," *Open Court*, XLV, 513–526 (September, 1931), 621–635 (October, 1931). (Freudian. Goes farther than Mumford in creating a picture of a thwarted, neglected, lonely genius. Repeats "Ethan Brand" theory.)

Mumford, Lewis. *Herman Melville.* New York: 1929. (An admirable attempt at an "integrated interpretation" of Melville's life and work. Professor F. J. Mather said of it [*Saturday Review of Literature*, April 27, 1929] that its chief merit will be to "dispel the legend of misanthropy and even of insanity that has gathered about Melville's hidden years." Though Mumford has gone to the sources, the biography is undocumented and many of his statements and conclusions have been questioned. See below under "Criticism": Forsythe, "Mr. Lewis Mumford and Melville's *Pierre*"; Brown, "Hawthorne, Melville and 'Ethan Brand'"; Starke, "A Note on Lewis Mumford's Life of Herman Melville."

Mumford, Lewis. "The Significance of Herman Melville," *New Republic*, LVI, 212–214 (October 10, 1928). (The "Epilogue" of his biography very slightly cut down.)

Mumford, Lewis. "The Writing of 'Moby-Dick,'" *American Mercury*, XV, 482–490 (December, 1928). (Substantially chapter VI of his biography.)

Mumford, Lewis. "The Young Olympian," *Saturday Review of Literature*, V, 514–515 (December 15, 1928). (Part of chapter III of his biography.)

Perkins, E. T. *Na Motu: or, Reef Rovings in the South Seas. A Narrative of Adventures at the Hawaiian, Georgian and Society Islands.* New York: 1854. (Chapter XXI contains the account of the author's meeting, in Tahiti, the ship's carpenter whom Melville describes in *Omoo*, chapter LXXVI.

Simon, Jean. "Recherches australiennes sur Hermann [*sic*] Melville," *Revue Anglo-Américaine*, XIII, 114–129 (December, 1935). (Abstract of the researches of an Australian, J. W. Earnshaw, into the background of *Omoo*.)

Smith, J. E. A. *Herman Melville. Written for the Evening Journal.* Pittsfield: 1891. (A thirty-page biographical sketch by an old friend of Melville who intended to make this a longer work. Smith is disappointingly vague at points where precision would be useful, and occasionally inaccurate, but the sketch has value as a friendly contemporary view.)

[Smith, J. E. A.] *Taghconic, the Romance and Beauty of the Hills, by Godfrey Greylock.* Boston: 1879. (References to Melville, pp. 198–199, 318.)

Stedman, Arthur. "Herman Melville's Funeral," *New York Daily Tribune*, October 1, 1891. Reprinted in *Critic* (New York), N.S. XVI, 190 (October 10, 1891).

Stedman, Arthur. " 'Marquesan Melville.' A South Sea Prospero who Lived and Died in New York," *New York World*, October 11, 1891, p. 26. (Reprinted, in part, in *Critic*, N.S. XVI, 222–223 [October 24, 1891]. Stedman had charge of Melville's literary affairs after his death. This long biographical sketch contains Dr. Coan's letter describing his visit, when a student at Williams, to Melville; Clark Russell's letter

to Melville, July 21, 1886; and information about the publication arrangements of several of the novels. Portions of this
article and the one above were used by Stedman in the introduction to his edition of *Typee* in 1892.)

Stedman, Arthur. "Melville of Marquesas," *Review of Reviews*,
IV, 428–430 (November, 1891). (Useful information on
Melville's business arrangements with publishers.)

Stoddard, R. H. "My Life in the Custom-House," chapter X
in *Recollections Personal and Literary*. New York: 1903,
pp. 142–144. (Melville as an Inspector of Customs.)

Thorp, Willard. "Herman Melville's Silent Years," *University
Review*, III, 254–262 (Summer, 1937).

Wainger, B. M. "Herman Melville: a Study in Disillusion,"
Union College Bulletin, XXV, 35–62 (January, 1932). (Melville's life a "story of disillusionment and defeat in man's
struggle with society and in his struggle with nature.")

Weaver, R. M. "Herman Melville," *Bookman* (New York),
LIV, 318–326 (December, 1921). (Nearly the whole of the
first chapter of his biography.)

Weaver, R. M. *Herman Melville, Mariner and Mystic.* New
York: 1921. (The first full-length biography. Weaver had
access to Melville's manuscripts, correspondence, and business
papers, and published for the first time a great deal of valuable
source material. He made no use of the Melville correspondence in the Duyckinck Collection of the New York
Public Library. Only a tenth of the book is devoted to the
years from 1857–1891. Of necessity the picture he gives of
Melville has been altered by the large amount of subsequent
research.)

Wegelin, Oscar. "Herman Melville As I Recall Him," *Colophon*, N.S. I, 21–24 (Summer, 1935). (Account of the sale of
Melville's library.)

Wise, [H. A.] Lieutenant, U.S.N. *Los Gringos: or an Inside
View of Mexico and California, with Wanderings in Peru,
Chili, and Polynesia.* London: 1849. (In a note to chapter
XLVIII, p. 357, Wise praises Melville's sketches of Polynesia
and verifies, from enquiries he made, scenes and persons de-

scribed by Melville. The pertinent passage was published by J. H. Birss under the title "Melville's Marquesas," *Saturday Review of Literature*, VIII, 429 [January 2, 1932].)

IV. CONTEMPORARY REVIEWS AND CRITICISM

TYPEE

American Review, III, 415–424 (April, 1846).

Anglo-American, VI, 523 (March 21, 1846); 555–557 (April 4, 1846); 580–582 (April 11, 1846).

Athenaeum, No. 956, pp. 189–191 (February 21, 1846); No. 957, pp. 218–220 (February 28, 1846); No. 980, p. 819 (August 8, 1846); No. 988, pp. 1014–1015 (October 3, 1846).

Chambers's Edinburgh Journal, V, 265–269 (April 25, 1846); 282 (May 2, 1846).

Dublin University Magazine, XXVIII, 135–139 (August, 1846).

Eclectic Review, N.S. XIX, 448–459 (April, 1846).

Examiner, No. 1988, pp. 147–148 (March 7, 1846).

Graham's Magazine, XXVIII, 240 (May, 1846).

Harbinger, II, 263–266 (April 4, 1846), by C. A. Dana.

Journal des Débats, "Feuilleton" for June 22 and 25, 1846. (Portions of these articles were used by their author Philarète Chasles in his *Études sur la littérature et les mœurs des Anglo-Américains au XIXᵉ siècle*. See below, under "General Criticism.")

Knickerbocker Magazine, XXVII, 450 (May, 1846).

New Englander, IV, 449–450 (July, 1846).

New York Evangelist, XVII, 60 (April 9, 1846).

Spectator, XIX, 209–210 (February 28, 1846).

United States Catholic Magazine and Monthly Review, VI, 580–583 (November, 1847).

Brief Notices

Albion, V, 168 (April 4, 1846).

Douglas Jerrold's Shilling Magazine, III, 380–383 (April, 1846).

Gentleman's Magazine, N.S. XXVI, 66 (July, 1846).

Godey's Magazine, XXII, 238 (May, 1846).

John Bull, XXVI, 156 (March 7, 1846).
Merchants' Magazine, XIV, 491 (May, 1846).
National Anti-Slavery Standard, April 2, 1846, p. 175.
New-York Mirror, III, 416 (April 4, 1846).
Sartain's Union Magazine, V, 320 (November, 1849).
Southern Literary Messenger, XII, 256 (April, 1846).
Tait's Edinburgh Magazine, XIII, 268 (April, 1846).
United States Magazine and Democratic Review, XVIII, 399 (May, 1846).

OMOO

Albion, N.S. VI, 228 (May 8, 1847).
American Review, VI, 36–46 (July, 1847), by G. W. Peck.
Anglo-American, IX, 69 (May 8, 1847).
Athenaeum, No. 1015, pp. 382–384 (April 10, 1847).
Blackwood's Edinburgh Magazine, LXI, 754–767 (June, 1847). Reprinted in *Littell's Living Age*, XIV, 145–153 (July 24, 1847).
Chambers's Edinburgh Journal, VII, 338–341 (May 29, 1847).
Columbian Magazine, VII, 283 (June, 1847).
Dublin Review, XXIII, 341–363 (December, 1847).
Eclectic Review, N.S. XXVIII, 425–436 (October, 1850). Reprinted in *Littell's Living Age*, XXVII, 325–330 (November 16, 1850); *Eclectic Magazine*, XXI, 553–559 (December, 1850).
Godey's Magazine, XXV, 56 (July, 1847).
John Bull, XXVII, 248 (April 17, 1847).
Knickerbocker Magazine, XXIX, 562 (June, 1847).
Literary World, I, 319–321 (May 8, 1847).
Littell's Living Age, XIII, 426–427 (May 29, 1847).
Merchants' Magazine, XVI, 641 (June, 1847).
New Englander, VI, 41–58 (January, 1848), by W. D. Bourne.
New York Evangelist, XVIII, 84 (May 27, 1847).
People's Journal, III, 223–224 (April 17, 1847).
Southern and Western Literary Messenger and Review, XIII, 383 (June, 1847).
Spectator, XX, 351–352 (April 10, 1847).

MARDI

Athenaeum, No. 1117, pp. 296–298 (March 24, 1849).
Bentley's Miscellany, XXV, 439–442 (April, 1849).
Blackwood's Edinburgh Magazine, LXVI, 172–173 (August, 1849).
Examiner, No. 2148, pp. 195–196 (March 31, 1849).
Graham's Magazine, XXXIV, 385 (June, 1849).
Holden's Dollar Magazine, III, 370–373 (June, 1849).
Literary Gazette, No. 1679, pp. 202–203 (March 24, 1849).
Literary World, IV, 309–310 (April 7, 1849); 333–336 (April 14, 1849); 351–353 (April 21, 1849).
Spectator, XXII, 374–375 (April 21, 1849).
United States Magazine and Democratic Review, XXV, 44–50 (July, 1849).

Brief Notices

Albion, N.S. VIII, 189 (April 21, 1849); also contains extracts from *Mardi*, pp. 182–183.
American Review, X, 329 (September, 1849).
Graham's Magazine, XXXIV, 385 (June, 1849).
John Bull, XXIX, 247 (April 21, 1849).
Merchants' Magazine, XX, 572 (May, 1849).
Sartain's Union Magazine, V, 126 (August, 1849).
Southern Quarterly Review, XVI, 260–261 (October, 1849).

REDBURN

Albion, N.S. VIII, 561 (November 24, 1849).
Athenaeum, No. 1150, pp. 1131–1133 (November 10, 1849).
Bentley's Miscellany, XXXI, 528–530 (November, 1849).
Blackwood's Edinburgh Magazine, LXVI, 567–580 (November, 1849).
Graham's Magazine, XXXVI, 94–95 (January, 1850).
Holden's Dollar Magazine, V, 55–56 (January, 1850).
Home Journal, No. 198 (November 24, 1849).
Literary Gazette, No. 1709, pp. 766–778 (October 20, 1849).
Literary World, V, 395–397 (November 10, 1849); 418–420 (November 17, 1849).

Southern Literary Messenger, XV, 760–762 (December, 1849).
Spectator, XXII, 1020–1021 (October 27, 1849).   Reprinted in
    Littell's Living Age, XXIII, 580–583 (December 29, 1849).

Brief Notices

John Bull, XXIX, 679 (October 27, 1849).
Merchants' Magazine, XXII, 252 (February, 1850).
Sartain's Union Magazine, VI, 174 (February, 1850).
Southern Quarterly Review, N.S. I, 259–260 (April, 1850).
United States Magazine and Democratic Review, XXV, 575
    (December, 1849).

WHITE-JACKET

Albion, N.S. IX, 153 (March 30, 1850).
Athenaeum, No. 1162, pp. 123–125 (February 2, 1850).
Bentley's Miscellany, XXVII, 309–310 (March, 1850).
Holden's Dollar Magazine, V, 314–315 (May, 1850).
Knickerbocker Magazine, XXXV, 448 (May, 1850).
Literary World, VI, 271–272 (March 16, 1850).
Littell's Living Age, XXV, 230–232 (May 4, 1850).
Southern Literary Messenger, XVI, 250–252 (April, 1850).
Southern Quarterly Review, N.S. I, 514–520 (July, 1850).
Spectator, XXIII, Supplement to No. 1127, pp. 3–4 (February 2,
    1850).

Brief Notices

American Review, XI, 442 (April, 1850).
Sartain's Union Magazine, VI, 434 (June, 1850).
United States Magazine and Democratic Review, XXVI, 384
    (April, 1850).

MOBY-DICK

Albion, N.S. X, 561 (November 22, 1851).
Athenaeum, No. 1252, pp. 1112–1113 (October 25, 1851).
Bentley's Miscellany, XXXI, 104–105 (January, 1852).
Democratic Review, XXX, 93 (January, 1852).
Dublin University Magazine, XXXIX, 221–223 (February, 1852).

Examiner, No. 2284, p. 709 (November 8, 1851).

Harper's New Monthly Magazine, IV, 137 (December, 1851).

International Monthly Magazine of Literature, Science, and Art, IV, 602–604 (December, 1851). (Reprinted from the *Spectator*. See below.)

Leader, II, 1067–1069 (November 8, 1851).

Literary Gazette, No. 1820, p. 841 (December 6, 1851).

Literary World, IX, 381–383 (November 15, 1851); 403–404 (November 22, 1851). Reprinted in *Holden's Dollar Magazine*, VIII, 267–272 (December, 1851).

Revue des deux Mondes, February 1, 1853, pp. 491–515, by E.-D. Forgues.

Spectator, XXIV, 1026 (October 25, 1851).

To-Day, A Boston Literary Journal, I, 20–21 (January 10, 1852).

Brief Notices

Graham's Magazine, XL, 219 (February, 1852).

Southern Quarterly Review, n.s. V, 262 (January, 1852).

PIERRE

Albion, n.s. XI, 405 (August 21, 1852).

American Whig Review, XVI, 446–454 (November, 1852).

Athenaeum, No. 1308, pp. 1265–1266 (November 20, 1852).

Literary World, XI, 118–120 (August 21, 1852).

Southern Literary Messenger, XVIII, 574–575 (September, 1852).

Southern Quarterly Review, n.s. VI, 532 (October, 1852).

ISRAEL POTTER

Athenaeum, No. 1440, p. 643 (June 2, 1855).

Leader, VI, 428 (May 5, 1855).

THE PIAZZA TALES

Athenaeum, No. 1500, p. 929 (July 26, 1856).

Southern Literary Messenger, XXII, 480 (June, 1856).

United States Democratic Review, n.s. VII, 172 (September, 1856).

THE CONFIDENCE MAN

Athenaeum, No. 1537, pp. 462–463 (April 11, 1857).
Critic (London), XVI, 174–175 (April 15, 1857).
Leader, VIII, 356 (April 11, 1857).
Literary Gazette, No. 2099, pp. 348–349 (April 11, 1857).
Saturday Review, III, 484 (May 23, 1857).
Spectator, XXX, 398–399 (April 11, 1857).
Westminster and Foreign Quarterly Review, LXVIII, 310–311 (July, 1857).

BATTLE-PIECES

Atlantic Monthly, XIX, 252–253 (February, 1867).
Harper's New Monthly Magazine, XXXIV, 265 (January, 1867).

GENERAL CRITICISM

Chasles, Philarète. "Herman Melville," Section III in *Études sur la littérature et les mœurs des Anglo-Américains au XIXe siècle*. Paris: 1851, pp. 185–235. Translated by Donald MacLeod as *Anglo-American Literature and Manners*. New York: 1852. (In this section on Melville in his book Chasles used his article from the *Revue des deux Mondes* [see the next item] and the two notices of *Typee* which he had written for the *Journal des Débats* [see above, under "*Typee*"]. (Chasles sees in Melville the typical American, reckless and thirsty for sensation. A savor of unknown and primitive nature in him. *Typee* shows him to be the most truthful of the writers about the South Seas.)"*Mardi* has all the defects of the infant Anglo-American literature.")

Chasles, Philarète. "Voyages réels et fantastiques d'Herman Melville," *Revue des deux Mondes*, May 15, 1849, pp. 541–570. (Begins as a notice of *Mardi*, but the main substance of the chapters in his book are here. A translation of this article appeared in the *Literary World*, V, 89–90 [August 4, 1840]; 101–103 [August 11, 1849].)

[O'Brien, F.-J.] "Our Young Authors—Melville," *Putnam's Monthly Magazine*, I, 155–164 (February, 1853). (Melville came forward with his books to relieve the well-informed dullness of the travel literature of the day. But now he "totters on the edge of a precipice, over which all his hard-earned fame may tumble with such another weight as Pierre attached to it.")

[O'Brien, F.-J.] "Our Authors and Authorship—Melville and Curtis," *Putnam's Monthly Magazine*, IX, 384–393 (April, 1857). (Melville needs a critic to set him straight. He is a man "born to create, who resolves to anatomize; a man born to see, who insists upon speculation. . . . He has almost perverted his fine mind from its healthy productive tendencies.")

"Sir Nathaniel." "American Authorship. No. IV—Herman Melville," *New Monthly Magazine*, XCVIII, 300–308 (July, 1853). Reprinted in *Littell's Living Age*, XXXVIII, 481–486 (August 20, 1853); *Eclectic Magazine*, XXX, 46–52 (September, 1853). (Melville is a "Doppelgänger." "The superstition of life on the waves has no abler interpreter," yet he can write such a spasmodic and convulsive book as *The Whale*. *Pierre* is his last "and worst production." Melville urged to put off his worser self.)

"A Trio of American Sailor-Authors," *Dublin University Magazine*, XLVII, 47–54 (January, 1856). Reprinted in *Littell's Living Age*, XLVIII, 560–566 (March 1, 1856). (Cooper, Dana, Melville. *White-Jacket* Melville's best book.)

V. CRITICISM AND SCHOLARSHIP
TYPEE

Adkins, N. F. "A Note on Herman Melville's *Typee*," *New England Quarterly*, V, 348–351 (April, 1932). (Thomas Nichols's claim to having suggested the publishing of *Typee* in England.)

Anderson, C. R. "Contemporary American Opinions of *Typee* and *Omoo*," *American Literature*, IX, 1–25 (March, 1937). (Of fifteen reviews of *Typee* and *Omoo* consulted, only three were hostile to *Typee* and two to *Omoo*. Anderson cites other friendly references to Melville by his contemporaries.)

De Voto, Bernard. "Editions of 'Typee,'" *Saturday Review of Literature*, V, 406 (November 24, 1928). (Variants among copies of the "first" edition of *Typee*.)

Thomas, Russell. "Yarn for Melville's *Typee*," *Philological Quarterly*, XV, 16–29 (January, 1936). (Melville's use of C. S. Stewart's *A Visit to the South Seas*, 1831.)

Thorp, Willard. "'Grace Greenwood' Parodies *Typee*," *American Literature*, IX, 455–457 (January, 1938).

OMOO

Forsythe, R. S. "Herman Melville in Tahiti," *Philological Quarterly*, XVI, 344–357 (October, 1937).

Forsythe, R. S. "Herman Melville's Father Murphy," *Notes and Queries*, CLXXII, 254–258 (April 10, 1937); 272–276 (April 17, 1937).

Frear, W. F. *Anti-Missionary Criticism with Reference to Hawaii*. Honolulu: 1935. (Melville considered, pp. 25–28.)

MARDI

Birss, J. H. "A Note on Melville's 'Mardi,'" *Notes and Queries*, CLXII, 404 (June 4, 1932). (Possible source of Hautia's name.)

Jaffé, David. "Some Sources of Melville's *Mardi*," *American Literature*, IX, 56–69 (March, 1937).

Larrabee, S. A. "Melville against the World," *South Atlantic Quarterly*, XXXIV, 410–418 (October, 1935). (In *Mardi* all the "aspirations, vanities, injustices, and failings" of the mid-nineteenth century are analyzed.)

WHITE–JACKET

Anderson, C. R. "A Reply to Herman Melville's *White-Jacket* by Rear-Admiral Thomas O. Selfridge, Sr.," *American Literature*, VII, 123–144 (May, 1935). (An hitherto unpublished attack on *White-Jacket*. Anderson's notes illuminate the origin and method of *White-Jacket*.)

Anderson, C. R., ed. *Journal of a Cruise to the Pacific Ocean,
1842–1844, in the Frigate United States.* Durham, 1937.
(Firsthand evidence of life on board Melville's *Neversink*.)

Hunt, Livingston. "Herman Melville as a Naval Historian,"
Harvard Graduates' Magazine, XXXIX, 22–30 (September,
1930.) (Objects to the satire in *White-Jacket*.)

Mordell, Albert. "Melville and 'White-Jacket.'" (See above,
under "Biography.")

Van Doren, Carl. "Melville before the Mast," *Century Magazine*, CVIII, 272–277 (June, 1924).

MOBY–DICK

Adams, F. B., Jr. "The Crow's Nest," *Colophon*, N.S. II, 148–
154 (Autumn, 1936). (Satire of Scoresby's *An Account of
the Arctic Regions* in "The Mast-head" chapter of *Moby-
Dick*.)

Ament, W. S. "Bowdler and the Whale. Some Notes on the
First English and American Editions of *Moby-Dick*," *American Literature*, IV, 39–46 (March, 1932). (The English text
"an uninspired revision of the proof [sheets] of the American"
with considerable bowdlerization of passages referring to the
deity, religion, and sex.)

Ament, W. S. "Some Americanisms in Moby Dick," *American
Speech*, VII, 365–367 (June, 1932). (Americanisms eliminated
in the English edition.)

Birrell, Augustine. "The Great White Whale," *Athenaeum*,
No. 4735, pp. 99–100 (January 28, 1921). Reprinted in
Living Age, CCCVIII, 659–661 (March 12, 1921). (A de-
lightful personal appreciation.)

Birss, J. H. " 'Moby-Dick' under Another Name," *Notes and
Queries*, CLXIV, 206 (March 25, 1933). (Use made of
Moby-Dick by C. M. Newell in writing *Péhe Nú-e, the Tiger
Whale of the Pacific*, Boston, 1877.)

Colcord, Lincoln. "Notes on Moby Dick," *Freeman*, V, 559–
562 (August 23, 1922); 585–587 (August 30, 1922). (Melville
shows generally no professional interest in seamanship.

Moby-Dick is not the allegory of Ahab's struggle with destiny, but of Melville's struggle with art and life—to wish the conflict away would be "to wish away the book's divinity." An important article.)

Colum, Padraic. "Epic of the Sea," in *A Half-Day's Ride*. New York: 1932, pp. 175–179. (Reprinted from the *Measure*. See below. *Moby-Dick* an epic rather than a novel. Passages in rhythmical, even polyphonic prose.)

Colum, Padraic. "*Moby Dick* as an Epic: A Note," *Measure*, No. 13, pp. 16–18 (March, 1922). (See above.)

Erskine, John. "Moby-Dick" (chapter X in *The Delight of Great Books*). Indianapolis: 1928, pp. 223–240. (Considers the "poetical" effects used by Melville so that "at the end there will be a powerful catharsis.")

Erskine, John. "A Whale of a Story," *Delineator*, CXV, 15, 68, 71, 72 (October, 1929). (Reprinted from *The Delight of Great Books*. See above.)

Forsythe, R. S. "Herman Melville's 'The Town-Ho's Story,'" *Notes and Queries*, CLXVIII, 314 (May 4, 1935). (This extract from *Moby-Dick* was published in *Harper's New Monthly Magazine* for October, 1851, before the book appeared. Also in the *Baltimore Weekly Sun*, November 8, 1851.)

Galland, René. "Herman Melville et 'Moby-Dick,'" *Revue Anglo-Américaine*, V, 1–9 (October, 1927). (The *Pequod* is the microcosm. Ahab is the conscience of humanity haunted by the idea of destroying evil and piercing the mystery. The whale is seen as "une malice inscrutable." Ahab is damned for his perception, but accomplishes what he must accomplish, proudly aware of the grandeur which arises from his misery.)

Garnett, R. S. "Moby-Dick and Mocha-Dick," *Blackwood's Magazine*, CCXXVI, 841–858 (December, 1929). (Reprints a large part of J. N. Reynolds's "Mocha Dick." See below.)

Gleim, W. S. "A Theory of *Moby Dick*," *New England Quarterly*, II, 402–419 (July, 1929). (An amazing allegorical interpretation, on Swedenborgian lines, which can explain even Ahab's ivory leg.)

Gleim, W. S. *The Meaning of Moby Dick*. New York, 1938. (An expansion of the preceding article.)

Howard, Leon. "A Predecessor of Moby-Dick," *Modern Language Notes*, XLIX, 310–311 (May, 1934). (Suggests that Melville made use of J. C. Hart's *Miriam Coffin, or the Whale-Fisherman*.)

"Moby-Dick," *Critic*, N.S. XIX, 232 (April 15, 1893). (Review of the new edition published by the United States Book Co. Remarkable appreciation of the book for this date.)

Quennell, Peter. "The Author of *Moby Dick*," *New Statesman*, XXXIII, 604 (August 24, 1929). (A review of A. S. W. Rosenbach's edition of *Moby-Dick*, New York, 1929. Melville has a trick of sliding into the center of his theme when the reader is most at sea. This quiet center also in his life.)

Reynolds, J. N. *Mocha Dick or the White Whale of the Pacific*. New York: 1932. With Introduction by L. L. Balcolm. (Reprinted from *Knickerbocker Magazine*, May, 1839. A possible "source" for *Moby-Dick*.)

Tomlinson, H. M. "A Clue to 'Moby Dick,'" *Literary Review, New York Evening Post*, II, 141–142 (November 5, 1921). (An enthusiastic personal appreciation.)

Tomlinson, H. M. "Two Americans and a Whale," *Harper's Monthly Magazine*, CLII, 618–621 (April, 1926). (A rebuke to Americans who do not appreciate their literary heritage.)

Van Doren, Carl. "Lucifer from Nantucket. An Introduction to 'Moby Dick,'" *Century Magazine*, CX, 494–501 (August, 1925). (Transcendentalism in Melville.)

Watson, E. L. G. "Moby Dick," *London Mercury*, III, 180–186 (December, 1920). (A sensible interpretation. "The *Pequod* with her monomaniac captain and all her crew, is representative of his own genius, and in this particular sense that each character is deliberately symbolic of a complete and separate element.")

Wells, W. H. "*Moby Dick* and Rabelais," *Modern Language Notes*, XXXVIII, 123 (February, 1923). (Five passages from the chapter "The Whiteness of the Whale" with close parallels from Rabelais, I, chapter X, "Of That Which is Signified by the Colours White and Blue.")

PIERRE

Bennett, Arnold. *The Savour of Life*. London: 1928, pp. 248–249. (A defense of *Pierre*. Melville "essays feats which the most advanced novelists of to-day imagine to be quite new.")

Braswell, William. "The Satirical Temper of Melville's *Pierre*," *American Literature*, VII, 424–438 (January, 1936). (Melville in *Pierre* recorded his "own sad spiritual history" and "gratified the satirical element in his nature by mocking his too idealistic self and especially by defying the literary conventions of a world that fêted its clever authors and starved its geniuses.")

Damon, S. F. "Pierre the Ambiguous," *Hound and Horn*, II, 107–118 (January–March, 1929). (Melville the first writer to treat the incest theme psychologically rather than merely dramatically. "Melville had learned that the problems of the soul are not to be analyzed horizontally in the conscious, but vertically in the subconscious.")

Forsythe, R. S. "Mr. Lewis Mumford and Melville's *Pierre*," *American Literature*, II, 286–289 (November, 1930). ("It is evident . . . that in relating the plot of *Pierre*, Mr. Mumford has twisted it badly. No further comment seems necessary.")

"Herman Melville's 'Pierre,' " *Times Literary Supplement*, No. 1500, p. 884 (October 30, 1930). (The clue to Melville's thinking is perhaps that the "angelic quality, of 'divine' and universal love, cannot be implicated in action." The Hamlet parallel discussed. Text of the Standard Edition.)

Tomlinson, H. M. Preface to *Pierre*. New York: 1929, pp. vii–xvii. (This edition contains an Introduction by J. B. Moore, pp. xxi–xxvii.)

Watson, E. L. G. "Melville's *Pierre*," *New England Quarterly*, III, 195–234 (April, 1930). (An able and sensible defense of the perfection of the symbols and of the artistry of *Pierre*.)

ISRAEL POTTER

McCutcheon, R. P. "The Technique of Melville's Israel Potter," *South Atlantic Quarterly*, XXVII, 161–174 (April, 1928). (A revealing comparison of Melville's novel with its principal source.)

THE PIAZZA TALES

Howard, Leon. "Melville and Spenser—A Note on Criticism," *Modern Language Notes*, XLVI, 291–292 (May, 1931). (Each of the sections of "The Encantadas" preceded by a quotation or series of quotations in verse, most of them from Spenser. The selections are given to present in verse a parallel to what is to follow in prose. Melville changed the lines slightly to make the parallels closer.)

Scudder, H. H. "Melville's *Benito Cereno* and Captain Delano's Voyages," *Publications of the Modern Language Association*, XLIII, 502–532 (June, 1928). (Reprints chapter XVIII of Amasa Delano's *A Narrative of Voyages and Travels in the Northern and Southern Hemispheres*, Boston, 1817—Melville's source—and comments on his use of the *Narrative*.)

Thomas, Russell. "Melville's Use of Some Sources in *The Encantadas*," *American Literature*, III, 432–456 (January, 1932). (Melville's use of Spenserian quotations and of various journals of South Sea adventure directed toward his dominant purpose of surrounding these Isles with a peculiar atmosphere, consisting of a mixture of enchantment, desolation, and inhospitality.)

GENERAL CRITICISM

Aaron, Daniel. "Melville and the Missionaries," *New England Quarterly*, VIII, 404–408 (September, 1935). (Attacks on Melville in the South Sea journals, the *Polynesian* and the *Friend*.)

Birss, J. H. "A Satire on Melville in Verse," *Notes and Queries*, CLXV, 402 (December 9, 1933). (The 25 lines quoted from

Putnam Portraits [New York, 1855] are complimentary
rather than satirical.)

Boynton, Percy. "Herman Melville," in *More Contemporary
Americans*. Chicago: 1927, pp. 29–50.

Braswell, William. "Melville as a Critic of Emerson," *American Literature*, IX, 317–334 (November, 1937).

Braswell, William. "A Note on 'The Anatomy of Melville's
Fame,' " *American Literature*, V, 360–364 (January, 1934).
("Corrects and extends" article by O. W. Riegel, *American
Literature*, III, 195–203 [May, 1931]. See below.)

Brooks, Van Wyck. "Notes on Herman Melville" in *Emerson
and Others*. New York: 1927, pp. 171–205. (Influence of
Rabelais, Thomas Moore, Butler, Carlyle on Melville. Valuable analysis of the art of *Moby-Dick*.)

Brooks, Van Wyck. "A Reviewer's Notebook," *Freeman*, VI,
550–551 (February 14, 1923); VII, 214–215 (May 9, 1923);
238–239 (May 16, 1923); 262–263 (May 23, 1923); 286–287
(May 30, 1923). (These articles were substantially reprinted,
in a different sequence, in *Emerson and Others*. See above.)

Brown, E. K. "Hawthorne, Melville and 'Ethan Brand,' "
American Literature, III, 72–75 (March, 1931). (Disproving
Mumford's idea—also suggested by F.-J. O'Brien and Newton Arvin—that Hawthorne pictures Melville as Ethan
Brand.)

Canby, H. S. "Hawthorne and Melville," in *Classic Americans*.
New York: 1931, pp. 226–262. (Melville "had neither Hawthorne's respect for the order from which he came, nor the
historian's instinct." Hawthorne closer to the American
mind than Melville "though the latter was so much more
modern in his psychology.")

Canby, H. S. "Conrad and Melville," in *Definitions*, First Series.
New York: 1922, pp. 257–268. (Conrad views nature as a
"modern." To Melville it is still greater and more terrible
than man.)

Carpenter, F. I. "Puritans Preferred Blondes. The Heroines
of Melville and Hawthorne," *New England Quarterly*, IX,
253–272 (June, 1936). ("Much of the literature of modern

America owes the violence of its revolt to the failure" of Hawthorne, Melville, and others to accept their "dark ladies of experience" and "free themselves from the old ideal of purity.")

Cournos, John. "Herman Melville—the Seeker" and "The Comparison of Melville with Rimbaud and Doughty," in *A Modern Plutarch*. Indianapolis: 1928, pp. 78–95, 127–134. (The first of these is a fictionized study in the psychoanalytic manner. Of little value. The second asserts that America produced Melville by reaction from itself. The comparisons are far-fetched.)

Curl, Vega. *Pasteboard Masks. Fact as Spiritual Symbol in the Novels of Hawthorne and Melville*. Cambridge: 1931. (Radcliffe Honors Thesis in English. Hawthorne is concerned with the psychological and moral, Melville with the metaphysical. The attitude toward Transcendentalism of the two men. The problem of sin.)

Edgar, Pelham. "Herman Melville and *Moby Dick*." (Chapter XII in *The Art of the Novel*.) New York: 1933, pp. 130–135. ("A dehumanized hate and defiance are pitted against an implacable impersonal malignity.")

Fagin, N. B. "Herman Melville and the Interior Monologue," *American Literature*, VI, 433–434 (January, 1935). (Refutes Mary Colum's statement that the "interior monologue" first appears in modern literature in Edouard Dujardin's *Les Lauriers sont coupés*, 1886. Melville used it in *Moby-Dick*, chapters XXXVII, XXXVIII, XXXIX.)

Ferris, M. L. D. "Herman Melville," *Bulletin of the Society of American Authors*, VI, 289–293 (September, 1901). (Slight.)

Forster, E. M. *Aspects of the Novel*. London: 1927, pp. 178–190. (Discussion of *Moby-Dick* and *Billy Budd*. "Melville —after the initial roughness of his realism—reaches straight back into the universal, to a blackness and sadness so transcending our own that they are indistinguishable from glory.")

Freeman, John. *Herman Melville*. English Men of Letters series. London: 1926. (A well-balanced biographical and critical study, written before the recent important scholarly work on Melville had appeared. Though Freeman failed to see the importance of *Pierre*, he deals fully with *Moby-Dick* and devotes a chapter to the poetry. The biographical material is mainly taken from Weaver.)

Hawthorne, Hildegarde. "Hawthorne and Melville," *Literary Review, New York Evening Post*, II, 406 (February 4, 1922). (Objections to the picture of the relationship between the two men given in Weaver's *Herman Melville*.)

"Herman Melville's Silence," *Times Literary Supplement*, No. 1173, p. 433 (July 10, 1924). (*Billy Budd* deals again, as does *Pierre*, with the central problem of the Christian religion.)

Homans, G. C. "The Dark Angel: The Tragedy of Herman Melville," *New England Quarterly*, V, 699–730 (October, 1932). (Important study of symbolism in Melville's work. *Mardi*, *Moby-Dick*, and *Pierre* dramatize the tragedy of the "refusal to be satisfied with the penultimate truth.")

Hughes, R. G. "Melville and Shakespeare," *Shakespeare Association Bulletin*, VII, 103–112 (July, 1932). (Insufficient treatment of an important subject.)

Jacoby, J. E. "Herman Melville, Gentleman and Scholar" (chapter IV in *Le Mysticisme dans la pensée américaine*. Paris: 1931, pp. 206–240. (Melville "un mystique non réalisé," who helped clear the air for a new faith. His triumph to have seized "à la vraie manière mystique, l'état d'esprit qui concentrait toute l'incroyance, non considérée, inconsciente peut-être pour une large part, que ne contrecarrait aucune foi religieuse de son temps—un état d'esprit qui s'étend jusqu'à nos jours.")

Johnson, Arthur. "A Comparison of Manners," *New Republic*, XX, 113–115 (August 27, 1919). (A jeu d'esprit, comparing the "later-manner" of the "master," Henry James, with Melville's style in *Pierre*.)

Lawrence, D. H. "Herman Melville's 'Typee' and 'Omoo'" (chapter X) and "Herman Melville's 'Moby Dick'" (chapter XI), in *Studies in Classic American Literature*. New York: 1923, pp. 193–213, 214–240. (Melville hated the world and was mad for paradise. Unhappy in his Paradise, he pined for

Home and Mother. He pined for perfection but was happy when he had something to revolt against.)

Lewisohn, Ludwig. *Expression in America.* New York: 1932, pp. 186–193. ("Melville is not even a minor master." "The final image that arises from all of Melville's work is that of a big bearded violently excited man trying to shout down the whimpering, lonely child in his soul.")

Lucas, F. L. "Herman Melville," in *Authors Dead and Living.* New York: 1935, pp. 105–114. Reprinted from the *New Statesman*, XVIII, 730–731 (April 1, 1922). (*Moby-Dick* "not an allegory spun into a story, but a story strong enough to shoulder a dozen allegories." Melville's life lived in the grand manner.)

MacMechan, A. McK. "The Best Sea-Story Ever Written," in *The Life of a Little College and Other Papers.* Boston: 1914, pp. 181–197. (This article was published in the *Queen's Quarterly*, VII, 120–130 (October, 1899), and in the *Humane Review*, No. 7, pp. 242–252 (October, 1901). (One of the few articles in the lean years of Melville's reputation.)

Marshall, H. P. "Herman Melville," *London Mercury*, XI, 56–70 (November, 1924). (A highly personal evaluation. Marshall refuses to grapple with the symbolism of *Pierre* and *Moby-Dick*.)

Mather, F. J., Jr. "Herman Melville," *Review*, I, 276–278 (August 9, 1919); 298–301 (August 16, 1919). (Many slight errors of fact but the first comprehensive survey of the whole of Melville's literary work. A turning point in Melville criticism.)

Mather, F. J., Jr. "Herman Melville," *Saturday Review of Literature*, V, 945–946 (April 27, 1929). (Review of Mumford's biography.)

Meynell, Viola. "Herman Melville," *Dublin Review*, CLXVI, 96–105 (January–March, 1920). Reprinted in *Living Age*, CCCIV, 715–720 (March 20, 1920). (*Moby-Dick* possesses the kind of fancy which begins in Truth and grows out of it.)

Mumford, Lewis. *The Golden Day.* New York: 1926, pp. 142–

153. ("The White Whale is the external force of Nature and Destiny.")

Nash, J. V. "Herman Melville, 'Ishmael' of American Literature," *Open Court*, XL, 734–742 (December, 1926). (Abounds in dubious inferences.)

Owlett, F. C. "Herman Melville (1819–1891): A Centenary Tribute," *Bookman* (London), LVI, 164–167 (August, 1919). (Comparisons with Borrow.)

Parrington, V. L. "Herman Melville" in *The Romantic Revolution in America, 1800–1860.* (*Main Currents in American Thought*, II.) New York: 1927, pp. 258–267. (An exaggerated, because concentrated, presentation of Melville as the greatest tragedy in American letters. Parrington's discussion of Melville's democracy is valuable.)

Pattee, F. L. "Herman Melville," *American Mercury*, X, 33–43 (January, 1927). Reprinted, with a few changes, in *The New American Literature*. New York: 1930, pp. 359–383. (Melville is Taji, in *Mardi;* he is Jack Chase, Jackson, Paul Jones, Ahab.)

Pavese, Cesare. "Herman Melville," *La Cultura*, XI, 83–93 (January–March, 1932). (Americans like Melville, Thoreau, and Anderson have known how to pass culture through real and primitive experience. "Un greco veramente è Melville." Suggests influence of Giordano Bruno.)

Quinn, A. H. *American Fiction*. New York: 1936, pp. 149–157.

Riegel, O. W. "The Anatomy of Melville's Fame," *American Literature*, III, 195–203 (May, 1931). (Surveys Melville's reputation from his own day to the present. Some of the generalizations are perilous. Corrections made by Braswell. "A Note on 'The Anatomy of Melville's Fame,'" *q.v.*)

Ritchie, M. C. "Herman Melville," *Queen's Quarterly*, XXXVII, 36–61 (Winter, 1930). (Derivative.)

Roberts, Morley. "The Sea in Fiction," *Queen's Quarterly*, XXXVII, 18–35 (Winter, 1930). (Praises Melville as the greatest novelist of the sea.)

Russell, W. C. "A Claim for American Literature," *North American Review*, CLIV, 138–149 (February, 1892). (The commercial sailor without representation in literature till Dana and Melville wrote. They "created a world, not by the discovery, but by the interpretation of it.")

Salt, H. S. "Herman Melville," *Scottish Art Review*, II, 186–190 (June–December, 1889). (The chief characteristic of Melville's books is the "attempted union of the practical with the ideal." Mr. Salt, who has done much to keep Melville's fame alive in England, did not earlier share the modern enthusiasm for *Moby-Dick*. In reviewing Weaver's *Herman Melville* [*Literary Guide*, May, 1922] he declares, however, that "in *The Whale* we find him at the climax of his genius in his extraordinary power of mingling reality with phantasy.")

Salt, H. S. "Marquesan Melville," *Gentleman's Magazine*, CCLXXII, 248–257 (March, 1892). Reprinted in *Eclectic Magazine*, N.S. LV, 517–523 (April, 1892). (*Typee* "may most surely count on lasting popularity." *Pierre* an "unfortunate book"—a "well-merited failure." Much of the material in this essay was used by Salt in his editions of *Typee* and *Omoo* in 1893.)

Starke, A. H. "A Note on Lewis Mumford's Life of Herman Melville," *American Literature*, I, 304–305 (November, 1929). (Mumford's misconception of the meeting between Melville and Hawthorne in 1856.)

Stedman, Arthur. "Poems by Herman Melville," *Century Magazine*, N.S. XXII, 104–105 (May, 1892). (Five of the poems with a note by Stedman.)

Stoddard, R. H. "Herman Melville," *Mail and Express* (New York), XX, 5 (October 8, 1891). Reprinted in part in the *Critic*, N.S. XVI, 272–273 (November 14, 1891). (Melville a great but undisciplined genius. Significant judgment by a contemporary *littérateur*.)

[Strachey, J. St. L.] "Herman Melville," *Spectator*, LXX, 858–859 (June 24, 1893). (Melville has not the literary power of Stevenson, yet *Typee* is the document of all others of savage life. Strachey was an early enthusiast for *Moby-Dick*.)

Strachey, J. St. L. "Herman Melville: Mariner and Mystic," *Spectator*, CXXVIII, 559–560 (May 6, 1922). (A review of

Weaver's biography. Suggests influence of Balzac on Melville. Notes that Melville's reputation in England has been continuous.)

Sullivan, J. W. N. "Herman Melville," in *Aspects of Science*, Second Series. New York: 1926, pp. 190–205. (Reprinted from *Times Literary Supplement*. See below. Important analysis of the failure of *Moby-Dick* as a popular work. A shift in values has made it possible for a later age to appreciate it. Foreshadowings in it of *Pierre*.)

[Sullivan, J. W. N.] "Herman Melville," *Times Literary Supplement*, No. 1123, pp. 493–494 (July 26, 1923). (Reprinted in *Aspects of Science*. See above.)

Sundermann, K. H. *Herman Melvilles Gedankengut*. Berlin, 1937. (Useful attempt to systematize Melville's religious, philosophical, aesthetic, and political ideas.)

Van Doren, Carl. *The American Novel*. New York: 1921, pp. 68–76. (Substantially the same as the section on Melville in the *Cambridge History of American Literature*. See below.)

Van Doren, Carl. "Contemporaries of Cooper," in *Cambridge History of American Literature*. New York: 1917. I, 320–323. Bibliography of Melville, pp. 536–537. (Melville to be compared to Borrow rather than Dana. *Pierre* is "hopelessly frantic.")

Van Doren, Carl. "A Note of Confession," *Nation* (New York), CXXVII, 622 (December 5, 1928). (A review of *Shorter Novels of Herman Melville*, 1928, by way of recantation for his earlier lack of appreciation of *The Piazza Tales*.)

Van Vechten, Carl. "The Later Work of Herman Melville," in *Excavations*. New York: 1926, pp. 65–88. Reprinted from the *Double Dealer*, III, 9–20 (January, 1922). (A defense of the later works.)

Watson, E. L. G. "Melville's Testament of Acceptance," *New England Quarterly*, VI, 319–327 (June, 1933). (Admirable discussion of the symbolism in *Billy Budd*.)

Weaver, R. M. "The Centennial of Herman Melville," *Nation* (New York), CIX, 145–146 (August 2, 1919).

Weaver, R. M. "Herman Melville," in *American Writers on*

American Literature. New York: 1931, pp. 190–206. (Substantially the same as Weaver's Introduction to *Shorter Novels of Herman Melville*, New York, 1928, pp. vii–li.)

Woolf, Leonard. "Herman Melville," *Nation and Athenaeum*, XXXIII, 688 (September 1, 1923). ("He writes most execrable English," yet half-way through *Moby-Dick* there is a change. Woolf confesses himself baffled by the symbolism in *Mardi* and *Moby-Dick*.)

A number of important studies of Melville are still in manuscript or in the course of preparation. Mr. J. H. Birss and Mr. R. S. Forsythe are compiling an extensive bibliography which will contain a calendar of letters and manuscripts. Dr. Henry A. Murray is at work on a psychological study of Melville. Mr. Charles Anderson's *In the South Seas with Herman Melville* is completed but not yet in print. M. Jean Simon is preparing a biography. Mr. Charles Olson promises a book about Melville. Four significant doctoral dissertations are unpublished: William Braswell, *Herman Melville and Christianity* (University of Chicago, 1932); H. W. Hetherington, *The Reputation of Herman Melville in America* (University of Michigan, 1933); Viola Chittenden White, *Symbolism in the Writings of Herman Melville* (University of North Carolina, 1934); Luther S. Mansfield, *Herman Melville: Author and New Yorker* (University of Chicago, 1936). W. S. Holden's master's thesis, *Some Sources of Herman Melville's Israel Potter* (Columbia University, 1932) is also important.

Students should consult the current bibliographies in the *Publications of the Modern Language Association* and in *American Literature*.

★

Selections from

HERMAN MELVILLE

★

From TYPEE

CHAPTER X

*The Head of the Valley—Cautious Advance—A Path—Fruit
—Discovery of two of the Natives—Their Singular Conduct—
Approach towards the Inhabited Parts of the Vale—Sensation
Produced by our Appearance—Reception at the House of one of
the Natives*

How to obtain the fruit which we felt convinced must grow
near at hand was our first thought.

Typee or Happar[1]? A frightful death at the hands of the
fiercest of cannibals, or a kindly reception from a gentler race
of savages? Which? But it was too late now to discuss a
question which would so soon be answered.

The part of the valley in which we found ourselves appeared
to be altogether uninhabited. An almost impenetrable thicket
extended from side to side, without presenting a single plant
affording the nourishment we had confidently calculated upon;
and with this object, we followed the course of the stream,
casting quick glances as we proceeded into the thick jungles
on either hand.

My companion—to whose solicitations I had yielded in descending into the valley—now that the step was taken, began
to manifest a degree of caution I had little expected from him.
He proposed that in the event of our finding an adequate supply

[1] Superior figures through the text refer to Notes in pp. 405 ff.
The text of the selections from *Typee, Omoo, Mardi, White-Jacket,*
and *Moby-Dick* is derived, in each instance, from a copy of the first
American edition. Obvious typographical errors and misspellings
have been corrected, but peculiarities of punctuation and capitaliza-
tion have been retained. The texts of the selections from *Battle-
Pieces, John Marr and Other Sailors,* and *Timoleon* are derived from
the first editions, these volumes not being published in England until
the appearance of the Standard Edition in 1924.

of fruit, we should remain in this unfrequented portion of the country—where we should run little chance of being surprised by its occupants, whoever they might be—until sufficiently recruited to resume our journey; when laying in a store of food equal to our wants, we might easily regain the bay of Nukuheva, after the lapse of a sufficient interval to ensure the departure of our vessel.

I objected strongly to this proposition, plausible as it was, as the difficulties of the route would be almost insurmountable, unacquainted as we were with the general bearings of the country, and I reminded my companion of the hardships which we had already encountered in our uncertain wanderings; in a word, I said that since we had deemed it advisable to enter the valley, we ought manfully to face the consequences, whatever they might be; the more especially as I was convinced there was no alternative left us but to fall in with the natives at once, and boldly risk the reception they might give us: and that as to myself, I felt the necessity of rest and shelter, and that until I had obtained them, I should be wholly unable to encounter such sufferings as we had lately passed through. To the justice of these observations Toby somewhat reluctantly assented.

We were surprised that, after moving as far as we had along the valley, we should still meet with the same impervious thickets; and thinking that although the borders of the stream might be lined for some distance with them, yet beyond there might be more open ground, I requested Toby to keep a bright look-out upon one side, while I did the same on the other, in order to discover some opening in the bushes, and especially to watch for the slightest appearance of a path or anything else that might indicate the vicinity of the islanders.

What furtive and anxious glances we cast into those dim-looking shades! With what apprehensions we proceeded, ignorant at what moment we might be greeted by the javelin of some ambushed savage! At last my companion paused, and directed my attention to a narrow opening in the foliage. We struck into it, and it soon brought us by an indistinctly traced path to a comparatively clear space, at the further end of which we descried a number of the trees, the native name of which is "annuee," and which bear a most delicious fruit.

What a race! I hobbling over the ground like some decrepit wretch,[2] and Toby leaping forward like a greyhound. He quickly cleared one of the trees on which there were two or three of the fruit, but to our chagrin they proved to be much decayed; the rinds partly opened by the birds, and their hearts half devoured. However, we quickly despatched them, and no ambrosia could have been more delicious.

We looked about us uncertain whither to direct our steps, since the path we had so far followed appeared to be lost in the open space around us. At last we resolved to enter a grove near at hand, and had advanced a few rods, when, just upon its skirts, I picked up a slender bread-fruit shoot perfectly green, and with the tender bark freshly stripped from it. It was slippery with moisture, and appeared as if it had been but that moment thrown aside. I said nothing, but merely held it up to Toby, who started at this undeniable evidence of the vicinity of the savages.

The plot was now thickening.—A short distance further lay a little faggot of the same shoots bound together with a strip of bark. Could it have been thrown down by some solitary native, who, alarmed at seeing us, had hurried forward to carry the tidings of our approach to his countrymen?—Typee or Happar?—But it was too late to recede, so we moved on slowly, my companion in advance casting eager glances under the trees on either side, until all at once I saw him recoil as if stung by an adder. Sinking on his knee, he waved me off with one hand, while with the other he held aside some intervening leaves, and gazed intently at some object.

Disregarding his injunction, I quickly approached him and caught a glimpse of two figures partly hidden by the dense foliage; they were standing close together, and were perfectly motionless. They must have previously perceived us, and withdrawn into the depths of the wood to elude our observation.

My mind was at once made up. Dropping my staff, and tearing open the package of things we had brought from the ship,

I unrolled the cotton cloth, and holding it in one hand plucked with the other a twig from the bushes beside me, and telling Toby to follow my example, I broke through the covert and advanced, waving the branch in token of peace towards the shrinking forms before me.

They were a boy and a girl, slender and graceful, and completely naked, with the exception of a slight girdle of bark, from which depended at opposite points two of the russet leaves of the bread fruit tree. An arm of the boy, half screened from sight by her wild tresses, was thrown about the neck of the girl, while with the other he held one of her hands in his; and thus they stood together, their heads inclined forward, catching the faint noise we made in our progress, and with one foot in advance, as if half inclined to fly from our presence.

As we drew near, their alarm evidently increased. Apprehensive that they might fly from us altogether, I stopped short and motioned them to advance and receive the gift I extended towards them, but they would not; I then uttered a few words of their language with which I was acquainted, scarcely expecting that they would understand me, but to show that we had not dropped from the clouds upon them. This appeared to give them a little confidence, so I approached nearer, presenting the cloth with one hand, and holding the bough with the other, while they slowly retreated. At last they suffered us to approach so near to them that we were enabled to throw the cotton cloth across their shoulders, giving them to understand that it was theirs, and by a variety of gestures endeavoring to make them understand that we entertained the highest possible regard for them.

The frightened pair now stood still, whilst we endeavored to make them comprehend the nature of our wants. In doing this Toby went through with a complete series of pantomimic illustrations—opening his mouth from ear to ear, and thrusting his fingers down his throat, gnashing his teeth and rolling his eyes about, till I verily believe the poor creatures took us for a couple of white cannibals who were about to make a meal of them. When, however, they understood us, they showed no inclination to relieve our wants. At this juncture it began to rain violently, and we motioned them to lead us to some place of shelter. With this request they appeared willing to comply, but nothing could evince more strongly the apprehension with which they regarded us, than the way in which, whilst walking before us, they kept their eyes constantly turned back to watch every movement we made, and even our very looks.

"Typee or Happar, Toby?" asked I as we walked after them.

"Of course Happar," he replied, with a show of confidence which was intended to disguise his doubts.

"We shall soon know," I exclaimed; and at the same moment I stepped forward towards our guides, and pronouncing the two names interrogatively and pointing to the lowest part of the valley, endeavored to come to the point at once. They repeated the words after me again and again, but without giving any peculiar emphasis to either, so that I was completely at a loss to understand them; for a couple of wilier young things than we afterwards found them to have been on this particular occasion never probably fell in any traveller's way.

More and more curious to ascertain our fate, I now threw together in the form of a question the words "Happar" and "Mortarkee," the latter being equivalent to the word "good." The two natives interchanged glances of peculiar meaning with one another at this, and manifested no little surprise; but on the repetition of the question, after some consultation together, to the great joy of Toby, they answered in the affirmative. Toby was now in ecstasies, especially as the young savages continued to reiterate their answer with great energy, as though desirous of impressing us with the idea that being among the Happars, we ought to consider ourselves perfectly secure.

Although I had some lingering doubts, I feigned great delight with Toby at this announcement, while my companion broke out into a pantomimic abhorrence of Typee, and immeasurable love for the particular valley in which we were; our guides all the while gazing uneasily at one another as if at a loss to account for our conduct.

They hurried on, and we followed them; until suddenly they

set up a strange halloo, which was answered from beyond the grove through which we were passing, and the next moment we entered upon some open ground, at the extremity of which we descried a long, low hut, and in front of it were several young girls. As soon as they perceived us they fled with wild screams into the adjoining thickets, like so many startled fawns. A few moments after the whole valley resounded with savage outcries, and the natives came running towards us from every direction.

Had an army of invaders made an irruption into their territory they could not have evinced greater excitement. We were soon completely encircled by a dense throng, and in their eager desire to behold us they almost arrested our progress; an equal number surrounding our youthful guides, who with amazing volubility appeared to be detailing the circumstances which had attended their meeting with us. Every item of intelligence appeared to redouble the astonishment of the islanders, and they gazed at us with inquiring looks.

At last we reached a large and handsome building of bamboos, and were by signs told to enter it, the natives opening a lane for us through which to pass; on entering without ceremony, we threw our exhausted frames upon the mats that covered the floor. In a moment the slight tenement was completely full of people, whilst those who were unable to obtain admittance gazed at us through its open cane-work.

It was now evening, and by the dim light we could just discern the savage countenances around us, gleaming with wild curiosity and wonder; the naked forms and tattooed limbs of brawny warriors, with here and there the slighter figures of young girls, all engaged in a perfect storm of conversation, of which we were of course the one only theme; whilst our recent guides were fully occupied in answering the innumerable questions which every one put to them. Nothing can exceed the fierce gesticulation of these people when animated in conversation, and on this occasion they gave loose to all their natural vivacity, shouting and dancing about in a manner that wellnigh intimidated us.

Close to where we lay, squatting upon their haunches, were

some eight or ten noble-looking chiefs—for such they subsequently proved to be—who, more reserved than the rest, regarded us with a fixed and stern attention, which not a little discomposed our equanimity. One of them in particular, who appeared to be the highest in rank, placed himself directly facing me; looking at me with a rigidity of aspect under which I absolutely quailed. He never once opened his lips, but maintained his severe expression of countenance, without turning his face aside for a single moment. Never before had I been subjected to so strange and steady a glance; it revealed nothing of the mind of the savage, but it appeared to be reading my own.

After undergoing this scrutiny till I grew absolutely nervous, with a view of diverting it if possible, and conciliating the good opinion of the warrior, I took some tobacco from the bosom of my frock and offered it to him. He quietly rejected the proffered gift, and, without speaking, motioned me to return it to its place.

In my previous intercourse with the natives of Nukuheva and Tior,[3] I had found that the present of a small piece of tobacco would have rendered any of them devoted to my service. Was this act of the chief a token of his enmity? Typee or Happar? I asked within myself. I started, for at the same moment this identical question was asked by the strange being before me. I turned to Toby; the flickering light of a native taper showed me his countenance pale with trepidation at this fatal question. I paused for a second, and I know not by what impulse it was that I answered "Typee." The piece of dusky statuary nodded in approval, and then murmured "Mortarkee!" "Mortarkee," said I, without further hesitation—"Typee mortarkee."

What a transition! The dark figures around us leaped to their feet, clapped their hands in transport, and shouted again and again the talismanic syllables, the utterance of which appeared to have settled everything.

When this commotion had a little subsided, the principal chief squatted once more before me, and throwing himself into a sudden rage, poured forth a string of philippics, which I was at

no loss to understand, from the frequent recurrence of the word
Happar, as being directed against the natives of the adjoining
valley. In all these denunciations my companion and I acquiesced, while we extolled the character of the warlike Typees.
To be sure our panegyrics were somewhat laconic, consisting
in the repetition of that name, united with the potent adjective
"mortarkee." But this was sufficient, and served to conciliate
the good will of the natives, with whom our congeniality of
sentiment on this point did more towards inspiring a friendly
feeling than anything else that could have happened.

At last the wrath of the chief evaporated, and in a few moments he was as placid as ever. Laying his hand upon his
breast, he gave me to understand that his name was "Mehevi,"
and that, in return, he wished me to communicate my appellation. I hesitated for an instant, thinking that it might be difficult
for him to pronounce my real name, and then with the most
praiseworthy intentions intimated that I was known as "Tom."
But I could not have made a worse selection; the chief could
not master it: "Tommo," "Tomma," "Tommee," everything
but plain "Tom." As he persisted in garnishing the word
with an additional syllable, I compromised the matter with him
at the word "Tommo"; and by that name I went during the
entire period of my stay in the valley. The same proceeding
was gone through with Toby, whose mellifluous appellation
was more easily caught.

An exchange of names is equivalent to a ratification of good-
will and amity among these simple people; and as we were
aware of this fact, we were delighted that it had taken place
on the present occasion.

Reclining upon our mats, we now held a kind of levee, giving
audience to successive troops of the natives, who introduced
themselves to us by pronouncing their respective names, and
retired in high good humor on receiving ours in return. During
this ceremony the greatest merriment prevailed, nearly every
announcement on the part of the islanders being followed by
a fresh sally of gaiety, which induced me to believe that some
of them at least were innocently diverting the company at our

expense, by bestowing upon themselves a string of absurd titles, of the humor of which we were of course entirely ignorant.

All this occupied about an hour, when the throng having a little diminished, I turned to Mehevi and gave him to understand that we were in need of food and sleep. Immediately the attentive chief addressed a few words to one of the crowd, who disappeared, and returned in a few moments with a calabash of "poee-poee," and two or three young cocoa-nuts stripped of their husks, and with their shells partly broken. We both of us forthwith placed one of these natural goblets to our lips, and drained it in a moment of the refreshing draught it contained. The poee-poee was then placed before us, and even famished as I was, I paused to consider in what manner to convey it to my mouth.

This staple article of food among the Marquese islanders is manufactured from the produce of the bread-fruit tree. It somewhat resembles in its plastic nature our bookbinders' paste, is of a yellow color, and somewhat tart to the taste.

Such was the dish, the merits of which I was now eager to discuss. I eyed it wistfully for a moment, and then, unable any longer to stand on ceremony, plunged my hand into the yielding mass, and to the boisterous mirth of the natives drew it forth laden with the poee-poee, which adhered in lengthy strings to every finger. So stubborn was its consistency, that in conveying my heavily-freighted hand to my mouth, the connecting links almost raised the calabash from the mats on which it had been placed. This display of awkwardness—in which, by the by, Toby kept me company—convulsed the bystanders with uncontrollable laughter.

As soon as their merriment had somewhat subsided, Mehevi, motioning us to be attentive, dipped the fore-finger of his right hand in the dish, and giving it a rapid and scientific twirl, drew it out coated smoothly with the preparation. With a second peculiar flourish he prevented the poee-poee from dropping to the ground as he raised it to his mouth, into which the finger was inserted, and drawn forth perfectly free from any adhesive matter. This performance was evidently intended for our instruction; so I again essayed the feat on the principles inculcated, but with very ill success.

A starving man, however, little heeds conventional proprieties, especially on a South-Sea island, and accordingly Toby and I partook of the dish after our own clumsy fashion, beplastering our faces all over with the glutinous compound, and daubing our hands nearly to the wrist. This kind of food is by no means disagreeable to the palate of a European, though at first the mode of eating it may be. For my own part, after the lapse of a few days I became accustomed to its singular flavor, and grew remarkably fond of it.

So much for the first course; several other dishes followed it, some of which were positively delicious. We concluded our banquet by tossing off the contents of two more young cocoa-nuts, after which we regaled ourselves with the soothing fumes of tobacco, inhaled from a quaintly carved pipe which passed round the circle.

During the repast, the natives eyed us with intense curiosity, observing our minutest motions, and appearing to discover abundant matter for comment in the most trifling occurrence. Their surprise mounted the highest, when we began to remove our uncomfortable garments, which were saturated with rain. They scanned the whiteness of our limbs, and seemed utterly unable to account for the contrast they presented to the swarthy hue of our faces, embrowned from a six months' exposure to the scorching sun of the Line. They felt our skin, much in the same way that a silk mercer would handle a remarkably fine piece of satin; and some of them went so far in their investigation as to apply the olfactory organ.

Their singular behavior almost led me to imagine that they never before had beheld a white man; but a few moments' reflection convinced me that this could not have been the case; and a more satisfactory reason for their conduct has since suggested itself to my mind.

Deterred by the frightful stories related of its inhabitants, ships never enter this bay, while their hostile relations with the tribes in the adjoining valleys prevent the Typees from visiting that section of the island where vessels occasionally lie. At long intervals, however, some intrepid captain will touch on the skirts of the bay, with two or three armed boats' crews, and accompanied by an interpreter. The natives who live near the sea descry the strangers long before they reach their waters, and aware of the purpose for which they come, proclaim loudly the news of their approach. By a species of vocal telegraph the intelligence reaches the inmost recesses of the vale in an inconceivably short space of time, drawing nearly its whole population down to the beach laden with every variety of fruit. The interpreter, who is invariably a "tabooed Kannaka,"[4] leaps ashore with the goods intended for barter, while the boats, with their oars shipped, and every man on his thwart, lie just outside the surf, heading off from the shore, in readiness at the first untoward event to escape to the open sea. As soon as the traffic is concluded, one of the boats pulls in under cover of the muskets of the others, the fruit is quickly thrown into her, and the transient visitors precipitately retire from what they justly consider so dangerous a vicinity.

The intercourse occurring with Europeans being so restricted, no wonder that the inhabitants of the valley manifested so much curiosity with regard to us, appearing as we did among them under such singular circumstances. I have no doubt that we were the first white men who ever penetrated thus far back into their territories, or at least the first who had ever descended from the head of the vale. What had brought us thither must have appeared a complete mystery to them, and from our ignorance of the language it was impossible for us to enlighten them. In answer to inquiries which the eloquence of their gestures enabled us to comprehend, all that we could reply was, that we had come from Nukuheva, a place, be it remembered, with which they were at open war. This intelligence appeared to affect them with the most lively emotions. "Nukuheva mortarkee?" they asked. Of course we replied most energetically in the negative.

They then plied us with a thousand questions, of which we could understand nothing more than that they had reference to the recent movements of the French,[5] against whom they seemed to cherish the most fierce hatred. So eager were they to obtain information on this point, that they still continued to propound their queries long after we had shown that we were utterly unable to answer them. Occasionally we caught some indistinct idea of their meaning, when we would endeavor by every method in our power to communicate the desired intelligence. At such times their gratification was boundless, and they would redouble their efforts to make us comprehend them more perfectly. But all in vain; and in the end they looked at us despairingly, as if we were the receptacles of invaluable information, but how to come at it they knew not.

After a while the group around us gradually dispersed, and we were left about midnight (as we conjectured) with those who appeared to be permanent residents of the house. These individuals now provided us with fresh mats to lie upon, covered us with several folds of tappa, and then, extinguishing the tapers that had been burning, threw themselves down beside us, and after a little desultory conversation were soon sound asleep.

· CHAPTER XVII

Improvement in health and spirits—Felicity of the Typees—Their enjoyments compared with those of more enlightened communities—Comparative wickedness of civilized and unenlightened people—A skirmish in the mountain with the warriors of Happar

Day after day wore on, and still there was no perceptible change in the conduct of the Islanders towards me.[6] Gradually I lost all knowledge of the regular recurrence of the days of the week, and sunk insensibly into that kind of apathy which ensues after some violent outbreak of despair. My limb suddenly healed, the swelling went down, the pain subsided, and I had every reason to suppose I should soon completely recover from the affliction that had so long tormented me.

As soon as I was enabled to ramble about the valley in company with the natives, troops of whom followed me whenever

I sallied out of the house, I began to experience an elasticity of mind which placed me beyond the reach of those dismal forebodings to which I had so lately been a prey. Received wherever I went with the most deferential kindness; regaled perpetually with the most delightful fruits; ministered to by dark-eyed nymphs; and enjoying besides all the services of the devoted Kory-Kory,[7] I thought that, for a sojourn among cannibals, no man could have well made a more agreeable one.

To be sure there were limits set to my wanderings. Toward the sea my progress was barred by an express prohibition of the savages; and after having made two or three ineffectual attempts to reach it, as much to gratify my curiosity as anything else, I gave up the idea. It was in vain to think of reaching it by stealth, since the natives escorted me in numbers wherever I went, and not for one single moment that I can recall to mind was I ever permitted to be alone.

The green and precipitous elevations that stood ranged around the head of the vale where Marheyo's habitation was situated effectually precluded all hope of escape in that quarter, even if I could have stolen away from the thousand eyes of the savages.

But these reflections now seldom obtruded upon me; I gave myself up to the passing hour, and if ever disagreeable thoughts arose in my mind, I drove them away. When I looked around the verdant recess in which I was buried, and gazed up to the summits of the lofty eminence that hemmed me in, I was well disposed to think that I was in the "Happy Valley," and that beyond those heights there was naught but a world of care and anxiety.

As I extended my wanderings in the valley and grew more familiar with the habits of its inmates, I was fain to confess that, despite the disadvantages of his condition, the Polynesian savage, surrounded by all the luxurious provisions of nature, enjoyed an infinitely happier, though certainly a less intellectual existence, than the self-complacent European.

The naked wretch who shivers beneath the bleak skies, and starves among the inhospitable wilds of Terra-del-Fuego, might indeed be made happier by civilisation, for it would alleviate his physical wants. But the voluptuous Indian, with every desire supplied, whom Providence has bountifully provided with all the sources of pure and natural enjoyment, and from whom are removed so many of the ills and pains of life—what has he to desire at the hands of Civilisation? She may "cultivate his mind," may "elevate his thoughts,"—these I believe are the established phrases—but will he be the happier? Let the once smiling and populous Hawaiian islands, with their now diseased, starving, and dying natives, answer the question. The missionaries may seek to disguise the matter as they will, but the facts are incontrovertible; and the devoutest Christian who visits that group with an unbiased mind, must go away mournfully asking—"Are these, alas! the fruits of twenty-five years of enlightening?"

In a primitive state of society, the enjoyments of life, though few and simple, are spread over a great extent, and are unalloyed; but Civilisation, for every advantage she imparts, holds a hundred evil in reserve;—the heart-burnings, the jealousies, the social rivalries, the family dissensions, and the thousand self-inflicted discomforts of refined life, which make up in units the swelling aggregate of human misery, are unknown among these unsophisticated people.

But it will be urged that these shocking unprincipled wretches are cannibals. Very true; and a rather bad trait in their character it must be allowed. But they are such only when they seek to gratify the passion of revenge upon their enemies; and I ask whether the mere eating of human flesh so very far exceeds in barbarity that custom which only a few years since was practised in enlightened England:—a convicted traitor, perhaps a man found guilty of honesty, patriotism, and suchlike heinous crimes, had his head lopped off with a huge axe, his bowels dragged out and thrown into a fire; while his body, carved into four quarters, was with his head exposed upon pikes, and permitted to rot and fester among the public haunts of men!

The fiend-like skill we display in the invention of all manner of death-dealing engines, the vindictiveness with which we carry on our wars, and the misery and desolation that follow in their train, are enough of themselves to distinguish the white civilized man as the most ferocious animal on the face of the earth.

His remorseless cruelty is seen in many of the institutions of our own favored land. There is one in particular lately adopted in one of the States of the Union, which purports to have been dictated by the most merciful considerations. To destroy our malefactors piece-meal, drying up in their veins, drop by drop, the blood we are too chicken-hearted to shed by a single blow which would at once put a period to their sufferings, is deemed to be infinitely preferable to the old-fashioned punishment of gibbeting—much less annoying to the victim, and more in accordance with the refined spirit of the age; and yet how feeble is all language to describe the horrors we inflict upon these wretches, whom we mason up in the cells of our prisons, and condemn to perpetual solitude in the very heart of our population!

But it is needless to multiply the examples of civilized barbarity; they far exceed in the amount of misery they cause the crimes which we regard with such abhorrence in our less enlightened fellow-creatures.

The term "Savage" is, I conceive, often misapplied, and indeed, when I consider the vices, cruelties, and enormities of every kind that spring up in the tainted atmosphere of a feverish civilisation, I am inclined to think that so far as the relative wickedness of the parties is concerned, four or five Marquesan Islanders sent to the United States as Missionaries, might be quite as useful as an equal number of Americans despatched to the Islands in a similar capacity.

I once heard it given as an instance of the frightful depravity of a certain tribe in the Pacific, that they had no word in their language to express the idea of virtue. The assertion was unfounded; but were it otherwise, it might be met by stating that their language is almost entirely destitute of terms to express the delightful ideas conveyed by our endless catalogue of civilized crimes.

In the altered frame of mind to which I have referred, every object that presented itself to my notice in the valley struck me in a new light, and the opportunities I now enjoyed of observing the manners of its inmates, tended to strengthen my favorable impressions. One peculiarity that fixed my admiration was the perpetual hilarity reigning through the whole extent of the vale. There seemed to be no cares, griefs, troubles, or vexations, in all Typee. The hours tripped along as gaily as the laughing couples down a country dance.

There were none of those thousand sources of irritation that the ingenuity of civilized man has created to mar his own felicity. There were no foreclosures of mortgages, no protested notes, no bills payable, no debts of honor in Typee; no unreasonable tailors and shoemakers, perversely bent on being paid; no duns of any description; no assault and battery attorneys, to foment discord, backing their clients up to a quarrel, and then knocking their heads together; no poor relations, everlastingly occupying the spare bed-chamber, and diminishing the elbow room at the family table; no destitute widows with their children starving on the cold charities of the world; no beggars; no debtors' prisons; no proud and hard-hearted nabobs in Typee; or to sum up all in one word—no Money! "That root of all evil" was not to be found in the valley.

In this secluded abode of happiness there were no cross old women, no cruel step-dames, no withered spinsters, no love-sick maidens, no sour old bachelors, no inattentive husbands, no melancholy young men, no blubbering youngsters, and no squalling brats. All was mirth, fun, and high good humor. Blue devils, hypochondria, and doleful dumps, went and hid themselves among the nooks and crannies of the rocks.

Here you would see a parcel of children frolicking together the live-long day, and no quarrelling, no contention, among them. The same number in our own land could not have played together for the space of an hour without biting or scratching one another. There you might have seen a throng of young females, not filled with envyings of each other's charms, nor displaying the ridiculous affectations of gentility, nor yet moving in whalebone corsets, like so many automatons, but free, inartificially happy, and unconstrained.

There were some spots in that sunny vale where they would frequently resort to decorate themselves with garlands of flowers. To have seen them reclining beneath the shadows of one of the beautiful groves; the ground about them strewn with freshly gathered buds and blossoms, employed in weaving chaplets and necklaces, one would have thought that all the train of Flora had gathered together to keep a festival in honor of their mistress.

With the young men there seemed almost always some matter of diversion or business on hand that afforded a constant variety of enjoyment. But whether fishing, or carving canoes, or polishing their ornaments, never was there exhibited the least sign of strife or contention among them.

As for the warriors, they maintained a tranquil dignity of demeanor, journeying occasionally from house to house, where they were always sure to be received with the attention bestowed upon distinguished guests. The old men, of whom there were many in the vale, seldom stirred from their mats, where they would recline for hours and hours, smoking and talking to one another with all the garrulity of age.

But the continual happiness, which so far as I was able to judge appeared to prevail in the valley, sprung principally from that all-pervading sensation which Rousseau has told us he at one time experienced, the mere buoyant sense of a healthful physical existence. And indeed in this particular the Typees had ample reason to felicitate themselves, for sickness was almost unknown. During the whole period of my stay I saw but one invalid among them; and on their smooth clear skins you observed no blemish or mark of disease.

The general repose, however, upon which I have just been descanting, was broken in upon about this time by an event which proved that the islanders were not entirely exempt from those occurrences which disturb the quiet of more civilized communities.

Having now been a considerable time in the valley, I began

to feel surprised that the violent hostility subsisting between its inhabitants, and those of the adjoining bay of Happar, should never have manifested itself in any warlike encounter. Although the valiant Typees would often by gesticulations declare their undying hatred against their enemies, and the disgust they felt at their cannibal propensities; although they dilated upon the manifold injuries they had received at their hands, yet with a forbearance truly commendable, they appeared patiently to sit down under their grievances, and to refrain from making any reprisals. The Happars, entrenched behind their mountains, and never even showing themselves on their summits, did not appear to me to furnish adequate cause for that excess of animosity evinced towards them by the heroic tenants of our vale, and I was inclined to believe that the deeds of blood attributed to them had been greatly exaggerated.

On the other hand, as the clamors of war had not up to this period disturbed the serenity of the tribe, I began to distrust the truth of those reports which ascribed so fierce and belligerent a character to the Typee nation. Surely, thought I, all these terrible stories I have heard about the inveteracy with which they carried on the feud, their deadly intensity of hatred, and the diabolical malice with which they glutted their revenge upon the inanimate forms of the slain, are nothing more than fables, and I must confess that I experienced something like a sense of regret at having my hideous anticipations thus disappointed. I felt in some sort like a 'prentice boy who, going to the play in the expectation of being delighted with a cut-and-thrust tragedy, is almost moved to tears of disappointment at the exhibition of a genteel comedy.

I could not avoid thinking that I had fallen in with a greatly traduced people, and I moralized not a little upon the disadvantage of having a bad name, which in this instance had given a tribe of savages, who were as pacific as so many lambkins, the reputation of a confederacy of giant-killers.

But subsequent events proved that I had been a little too premature in coming to this conclusion. One day about noon, happening to be at the Ti,[8] I had lain down on the mats with

several of the chiefs, and had gradually sunk into a most luxurious siesta, when I was awakened by a tremendous outcry, and
starting up beheld the natives seizing their spears and hurrying
out, while the most puissant of the chiefs, grasping the six
muskets which were ranged against the bamboos, followed after, and soon disappeared in the groves. These movements
were accompanied by wild shouts, in which "Happar, Happar,"
greatly predominated. The islanders were now to be seen
running past the Ti, and striking across the valley to the Happar
side. Presently I heard the sharp report of a musket from the
adjoining hills, and then a burst of voices in the same direction.
At this the women, who had congregated in the groves, set
up the most violent clamors, as they invariably do here as
elsewhere on every occasion of excitement and alarm, with a
view of tranquillizing their own minds and disturbing other
people. On this particular occasion they made such an outrageous noise, and continued it with such perseverance, that
for awhile, had entire volleys of musketry been fired off in the
neighboring mountains, I should not have been able to have
heard them.

When this female commotion had a little subsided I listened
eagerly for further information. At last bang went another
shot, and then a second volley of yells from the hills. Again
all was quiet, and continued so for such a length of time that I
began to think the contending armies had agreed upon a suspension of hostilities; when pop went a third gun, followed as
before with a yell. After this, for nearly two hours nothing
occurred worthy of comment, save some straggling shouts from
the hill-side, sounding like the halloos of a parcel of truant boys
who had lost themselves in the woods.

During this interval I had remained standing on the piazza
of the "Ti," which directly fronted the Happar mountain, and
with no one near me but Kory-Kory and the old superannuated
savages I have before described. These latter never stirred
from their mats, and seemed altogether unconscious that anything unusual was going on.

As for Kory-Kory, he appeared to think that we were in the

midst of great events, and sought most zealously to impress me with a due sense of their importance. Every sound that reached us conveyed some momentous item of intelligence to him. At such times, as if he were gifted with second sight, he would go through a variety of pantomimic illustrations, show-ing me the precise manner in which the redoubtable Typees were at that very moment chastising the insolence of the enemy. "Mehevi hanna pippee nuee Happar," he exclaimed every five minutes, giving me to understand that under that distinguished captain the warriors of his nation were performing prodigies of valor.

Having heard only four reports from the muskets, I was led to believe that they were worked by the islanders in the same manner as the Sultan Solyman's ponderous artillery at the siege of Byzantium, one of them taking an hour or two to load and train. At last, no sound whatever proceeding from the mountains, I concluded that the contest had been determined one way or the other. Such appeared, indeed, to be the case, for in a little while a courier arrived at the "Ti," almost breath-less with his exertions, and communicated the news of a great victory having been achieved by his countrymen: "Happar poo arva!—Happar poo arva!" (the cowards had fled). Kory-Kory was in ecstasies, and commenced a vehement harangue, which, so far as I understood it, implied that the result exactly agreed with his expectations, and which, moreover, was intended to convince me that it would be a perfectly useless undertaking, even for an army of fire-eaters, to offer battle to the irresistible heroes of our valley. In all this I of course acquiesced, and looked forward with no little interest to the return of the conquerors, whose victory I feared might not have been pur-chased without cost to themselves.

But here I was again mistaken; for Mehevi, in conducting his warlike operations, rather inclined to the Fabian than to the Bonapartean tactics, husbanding his resources and exposing his troops to no unnecessary hazards. The total loss of the victors in this obstinately contested affair was, in killed, wounded, and missing—one forefinger and part of a thumb-nail (which the late proprietor brought along with him in his hand), a severely contused arm, and a considerable effusion of blood flowing from the thigh of a chief, who had received an ugly thrust from a Happar spear. What the enemy had suffered I could not discover, but I presume they had succeeded in taking off with them the bodies of their slain.

Such was the issue of the battle, as far as its results came under my observation; and as it appeared to be considered an event of prodigious importance, I reasonably concluded that the wars of the natives were marked by no very sanguinary traits. I afterwards learned how the skirmish had originated. A number of the Happars had been discovered prowling for no good purpose on the Typee side of the mountain; the alarm sounded, and the invaders, after a protracted resistance, had been chased over the frontier. But why had not the intrepid Mehevi carried the war into Happar? Why had he not made a descent into the hostile vale, and brought away some trophy of his victory—some materials for the cannibal entertainment which I had heard usually terminated every engagement? After all, I was much inclined to believe that these shocking festivals must occur very rarely among the islanders, if, indeed, they ever take place.

For two or three days the late event was the theme of general comment; after which the excitement gradually wore away, and the valley resumed its accustomed tranquillity.

CHAPTER XX

History of a day as usually spent in the Typee Valley— Dances of the Marquesan Girls

Nothing can be more uniform and undiversified than the life of the Typees; one tranquil day of ease and happiness follows another in quiet succession; and with these unsophisticated savages the history of a day is the history of a life. I will, therefore, as briefly as I can, describe one of our days in the valley.

To begin with the morning. We were not very early risers—the sun would be shooting his golden spikes above the Happar mountain, ere I threw aside my tappa robe, and girding my long tunic about my waist, sallied out with Fayaway and Kory-Kory, and the rest of the household, and bent my steps towards the stream. Here we found congregated all those who dwelt in our section of the valley; and here we bathed with them. The fresh morning air and the cool flowing waters put both soul and body in a glow, and after a half hour employed in this recreation, we sauntered back to the house—Tinor and Marheyo gathering dry sticks by the way for fire-wood; some of the young men laying the cocoa-nut trees under contribution as they passed beneath them; while Kory-Kory played his outlandish pranks for my particular diversion, and Fayaway and I, not arm in arm to be sure, but sometimes hand in hand, strolled along, with feelings of perfect charity for all the world, and especial goodwill towards each other.

Our morning meal was soon prepared. The islanders are somewhat abstemious at this repast; reserving the more powerful efforts of their appetite to a later period of the day. For my own part, with the assistance of my valet, who, as I have before stated, always officiated as spoon on these occasions, I ate sparingly from one of Tinor's trenchers of poee-poee; which was devoted exclusively for my own use, being mixed with the milky meat of ripe cocoa-nut. A section of a roasted bread-fruit, a small cake of "Amar," or a mess of "Cokoo," two or three bananas, or a Mammee apple; an annuee, or some other agreeable and nutritious fruit served from day to day to diversify the meal, which was finished by tossing off the liquid contents of a young cocoa-nut or two.

While partaking of this simple repast, the inmates of Marheyo's house, after the style of the indolent Romans, reclined in sociable groups upon the divan of mats, and digestion was promoted by cheerful conversation.

After the morning meal was concluded, pipes were lighted; and among them my own especial pipe, a present from the noble Mehevi. The islanders, who only smoke a whiff or two at a time, and at long intervals, and who keep their pipes going from hand to hand continually, regarded my systematic smoking of four or five pipefuls of tobacco in succession, as something quite wonderful. When two or three pipes had circulated freely, the company gradually broke up. Marheyo went to the little hut he was for ever building. Tinor began to inspect her rolls of tappa, or employed her busy fingers in plaiting grass-mats. The girls anointed themselves with their fragrant oils, dressed their hair, or looked over their curious finery, and compared together their ivory trinkets, fashioned out of boar's tusks or whale's teeth. The young men and warriors produced their spears, paddles, canoe-gear, battle-clubs, and war-conchs, and occupied themselves in carving all sorts of figures upon them with pointed bits of shell or flint, and adorning them, especially the war-conchs, with tassels of braided bark and tufts of human hair. Some, immediately after eating, threw themselves once more upon the inviting mats, and resumed the employment of the previous night, sleeping as soundly as if they had not closed their eyes for a week. Others sallied out into the groves, for the purpose of gathering fruit or fibres of bark and leaves; the last two being in constant requisition, and applied to a hundred uses. A few, perhaps, among the girls, would slip into the woods after flowers, or repair to the stream with small calabashes and cocoa-nut shells, in order to polish them by friction with a smooth stone in the water. In truth these innocent people seemed to be at no loss for something to occupy their time; and it would be no light task to enumerate all their employments, or rather pleasures.

My own mornings I spent in a variety of ways. Sometimes I rambled about from house to house, sure of receiving a cordial welcome wherever I went; or from grove to grove, and from one shady place to another, in company with Kory-Kory and Fayaway, and a rabble rout of merry young idlers. Sometimes I was too indolent for exercise, and accepting one of the many invitations I was continually receiving, stretched myself out on the mats of some hospitable dwelling, and occupied myself pleasantly either in watching the proceedings of those around me or taking part in them myself. Whenever I chose to do the latter, the delight of the islanders was boundless; and there was always a throng of competitors for the honor of instructing me in any particular craft. I soon became quite an accomplished hand at making tappa—could braid a grass sling as well as the best of them—and once, with my knife, carved the handle of a javelin so exquisitely, that I have no doubt, to this day, Karnoonoo, its owner, preserves it as a surprising specimen of my skill. As noon approached, all those who had wandered forth from our habitation, began to return; and when mid-day was fairly come scarcely a sound was to be heard in the valley: a deep sleep fell upon all. The luxurious siesta was hardly ever omitted, except by old Marheyo, who was so eccentric a character, that he seemed to be governed by no fixed principles whatever; but, acting just according to the humor of the moment, slept, ate, or tinkered away at his little hut, without regard to the proprieties of time or place. Frequently he might have been seen taking a nap in the sun at noon-day, or a bath in the stream at midnight. Once I beheld him perched eighty feet from the ground, in the tuft of a cocoa-nut tree, smoking; and often I saw him standing up to the waist in water, engaged in plucking out the stray hairs of his beard, using a piece of mussel-shell for tweezers.

The noon-tide slumber lasted generally an hour and a half; very often longer; and after the sleepers had arisen from their mats they again had recourse to their pipes, and then made preparations for the most important meal of the day.

I, however, like those gentlemen of leisure who breakfast at home and dine at their club, almost invariably, during my intervals of health, enjoyed the afternoon repast with the bachelor chiefs of the Ti, who were always rejoiced to see me, and lavishly spread before me all the good things which their larder afforded. Mevehi generally produced among other dainties a baked pig, an article which I have every reason to suppose was provided for my sole gratification.

The Ti was a right jovial place. It did my heart, as well as my body, good to visit it. Secure from female intrusion, there was no restraint upon the hilarity of the warriors, who, like the gentlemen of Europe after the cloth is drawn and the ladies retire, freely indulged their mirth.

After spending a considerable portion of the afternoon at the Ti, I usually found myself, as the cool of the evening came on, either sailing on the little lake with Fayaway, or bathing in the waters of the stream with a number of the savages, who, at this hour, always repaired thither. As the shadows of night approached, Marheyo's household were once more assembled under his roof: tapers were lit, long and curious chants were raised, interminable stories were told (for which one present was little the wiser), and all sorts of social festivities served to while away the time.

The young girls very often danced by moonlight in front of their dwellings. There are a great variety of these dances, in which, however, I never saw the men take part. They all consist of active, romping, mischievous evolutions, in which every limb is brought into requisition. Indeed, the Marquesan girls dance all over, as it were; not only do their feet dance, but their arms, hands, fingers, ay, their very eyes, seem to dance in their heads. [In good sooth, they so sway their floating forms, arch their necks, toss aloft their naked arms, and glide, and swim, and whirl, that it was almost too much for a quiet, sober-minded, modest young man like myself.][9]

The damsels wear nothing but flowers and their compendious gala tunics; and when they plume themselves for the dance, they look like a band of olive-colored Sylphides on the point of taking wing.

Unless some particular festivity was going forward, the inmates of Marheyo's house retired to their mats rather early in the evening; but not for the night, since, after slumbering lightly for a while, they rose again, relit their tapers, partook of the third and last meal of the day, at which poee-poee alone was eaten, and then, after inhaling a narcotic whiff from a pipe of tobacco, disposed themselves for the great business of night, sleep. With the Marquesans it might almost be styled the great business of life, for they pass a large portion of their time in the arms of Somnus. The native strength of their constitution is no way shown more emphatically than in the quantity of sleep they can endure. To many of them, indeed, life is little else than an often interrupted and luxurious nap.

CHAPTER XXII

Preparations for a Grand Festival in the Valley—Strange doings in the Taboo Groves—Monument of Calabashes—Gala costume of the Typee Damsels—Departure for the Festival

From the time that my lameness had decreased I had made a daily practice of visiting Mehevi at the Ti, who invariably gave me a most cordial reception. I was always accompanied in these excursions by Fayaway and the ever-present Kory-Kory. The former, as soon as we reached the vicinity of the Ti—which was rigorously tabooed to the whole female sex—withdrew to a neighboring hut, as if her feminine delicacy restrained her from approaching a habitation which might be regarded as a sort of Bachelor's Hall.

And in good truth it might well have been so considered. Although it was the permanent residence of several distinguished chiefs, and of the noble Mehevi in particular, it was still at certain seasons the favorite haunt of all the jolly, talkative, and elderly savages of the vale, who resorted thither in the same way that similar characters frequent a tavern in civilized countries. There they would remain hour after hour, chatting, smoking, eating poee-poee, or busily engaged in sleeping for the good of their constitutions.

This building appeared to be the head-quarters of the valley, where all flying rumors concentrated; and to have seen it filled with a crowd of the natives, all males, conversing in animated clusters, while multitudes were continually coming and going, one would have thought it a kind of savage Exchange, where the rise and fall of Polynesian Stock was discussed.

Mehevi acted as supreme lord over the place, spending the greater portion of his time there: and often when, at particular hours of the day, it was deserted by nearly every one else except the verd-antique looking centenarians, who were fixtures in the building, the chief himself was sure to be found enjoying his "otium cum dignitate" upon the luxurious mats which covered the floor. Whenever I made my appearance he invariably rose, and, like a gentleman doing the honors of his mansion, invited me to repose myself wherever I pleased, and calling out "tam-maree!" (boy), a little fellow would appear, and then retiring for an instant, return with some savory mess, from which the chief would press me to regale myself. To tell the truth, Mehevi was indebted to the excellence of his viands for the honor of my repeated visits,—a matter which cannot appear singular when it is borne in mind that bachelors, all the world over, are famous for serving up unexceptionable repasts.

One day, on drawing near to the Ti, I observed that extensive preparations were going forward, plainly betokening some ap-proaching festival. Some of the symptoms reminded me of the stir produced among the scullions of a large hotel, where a grand jubilee dinner is about to be given. The natives were hurrying about hither and thither, engaged in various duties; some lugging off to the stream enormous hollow bamboos, for the purpose of filling them with water; others chasing furious-looking hogs through the bushes, in their endeavors to capture them; and numbers employed in kneading great moun-tains of poee-poee heaped up in huge wooden vessels.

After observing these lively indications for a while, I was attracted to a neighboring grove by a prodigious squeaking which I heard there. On reaching the spot I found it proceeded from a large hog which a number of natives were forcibly holding to the earth, while a muscular fellow, armed with a bludgeon, was ineffectually aiming murderous blows at the skull of the unfortunate porker. Again and again he missed his writhing and struggling victim, but though puffing and panting with his exertions, he still continued them; and after striking a sufficient number of blows to have demolished an entire drove of oxen, with one crashing stroke he laid him dead at his feet.

Without letting any blood from the body, it was immediately carried to a fire which had been kindled near at hand, and four savages taking hold of the carcass by its legs, passed it rapidly to and fro in the flames. In a moment the smell of burning bristles betrayed the object of this procedure. Having got thus far in the matter, the body was removed to a little distance; and, being disembowelled, the entrails were laid aside as choice parts, and the whole carcass thoroughly washed with water. An ample thick green cloth, composed of the long thick leaves of a species of palm-tree, ingeniously tacked together with little pins of bamboo, was now spread upon the ground, in which the body being carefully rolled, it was borne to an oven previously prepared to receive it. Here it was at once laid upon the heated stones at the bottom, and covered with thick layers of leaves, the whole being quickly hidden from sight by a mound of earth raised over it.

Such is the summary style in which the Typees convert perverse-minded and rebellious hogs into the most docile and amiable pork; a morsel of which placed on the tongue melts like a soft smile from the lips of Beauty.

I commend their peculiar mode of proceeding to the consideration of all butchers, cooks, and housewives. The hapless porker whose fate I have just rehearsed, was not the only one who suffered on that memorable day. Many a dismal grunt, many an imploring squeak, proclaimed what was going on throughout the whole extent of the valley; and I verily believe the first-born of every litter perished before the setting of that fatal sun.

The scene around the Ti was now most animated. Hogs and poee-poee were baking in numerous ovens, which, heaped up with fresh earth into slight elevations, looked like so many ant-hills. Scores of the savages were vigorously plying their stone pestles in preparing masses of poee-poee, and numbers were gathering green bread-fruit and young cocoa-nuts in the surrounding groves; while an exceeding great multitude, with a view of encouraging the rest in their labors, stood still, and kept shouting most lustily without intermission.

It is a peculiarity among these people, that when engaged in any employment they always make a prodigious fuss about it. So seldom do they ever exert themselves, that when they do work they seem determined that so meritorious an action shall not escape the observation of those around. If, for example, they have occasion to remove a stone to a little distance, which perhaps might be carried by two able-bodied men, a whole swarm gather about it, and, after a vast deal of palavering, lift it up among them, every one struggling to get hold of it, and bear it off yelling and panting as if accomplishing some mighty achievement. Seeing them on these occasions, one is reminded of an infinity of black ants clustering about and dragging away to some hole the leg of a deceased fly.

Having for some time attentively observed these demonstrations of good cheer, I entered the Ti, where Mehevi sat complacently looking out upon the busy scene, and occasionally issuing his orders. The chief appeared to be in an extraordinary flow of spirits, and gave me to understand that on the morrow there would be grand doings in the Groves generally, and at the Ti in particular; and urged me by no means to absent myself. In commemoration of what event, however, or in honor of what distinguished personage, the feast was to be given, altogether passed my comprehension. Mehevi sought to enlighten my ignorance, but he failed as signally as when he had endeavored to initiate me into the perplexing arcana of the taboo.

On leaving the Ti, Kory-Kory, who had as a matter of course accompanied me, observing that my curiosity remained unabated, resolved to make everything plain and satisfactory. With this intent, he escorted me through the Taboo Groves, pointing out to my notice a variety of objects, and endeavored to explain them in such an indescribable jargon of words, that it almost put me in bodily pain to listen to him. In particular, he led me to a remarkable pyramidical structure some three yards square at the base, and perhaps ten feet in height, which had lately been thrown up, and occupied a very conspicuous position. It was composed principally of large empty calabashes, with a few polished cocoa-nut shells, and looked not unlike a cenotaph of skulls. My cicerone perceived the astonishment with which I gazed at this monument of savage crockery, and immediately addressed himself to the task of enlightening me: but all in vain; and to this hour the nature of the monument remains a complete mystery to me. As, however, it formed so prominent a feature in the approaching revels, I bestowed upon the latter, in my own mind, the title of the "Feast of Calabashes."

The following morning, awaking rather late, I perceived the whole of Marheyo's family busily engaged in preparing for the festival. The old warrior himself was arranging in round balls the two grey locks of hair that were suffered to grow from the crown of his head; his earrings and spear, both well polished, lay beside him, while the highly decorative pair of shoes hung suspended from a projecting cane against the side of the house. The young men were similarly employed; and the fair damsels, including Fayaway, were anointing themselves with "aka," arranging their long tresses, and performing other matters connected with the duties of the toilet.

Having completed their preparations, the girls now exhibited themselves in gala costume; the most conspicuous feature of which was a necklace of beautiful white flowers, with the stems removed, and strung closely together upon a single fibre of tappa. Corresponding ornaments were inserted in their ears, and woven garlands upon their heads. About their waist they wore a short tunic of spotless white tappa, and some of them superadded to this a mantle of the same material, tied in an elaborate bow upon the left shoulder, and falling about the figure in picturesque folds.

Thus arrayed, I would have matched the charming Fayaway against any beauty in the world.

People may say what they will about the taste evinced by our fashionable ladies in dress. Their jewels, their feathers, their silks, and their furbelows, would have sunk into utter insignificance beside the exquisite simplicity of attire adopted by the nymphs of the vale on this festive occasion. I should like to have seen a gallery of coronation beauties, at Westminster Abbey, confronted for a moment by this band of Island girls;

their stiffness, formality, and affectation, contrasted with the artless vivacity and unconcealed natural graces of these savage maidens. It would be the Venus de' Medici placed beside a milliner's doll.

It was not long before Kory-Kory and myself were left alone in the house, the rest of its inmates having departed for the Taboo Groves. My valet was all impatience to follow them; and was as fidgety about my dilatory movements as a diner out waiting hat in hand at the bottom of the stairs for some lagging companion. At last, yielding to his importunities, I set out for the Ti. As we passed the houses peeping out from the groves through which our route lay, I noticed that they were entirely deserted by their inhabitants.

When we reached the rock that abruptly terminated the path, and concealed from us the festive scene, wild shouts and a confused blending of voices assured me that the occasion, whatever it might be, had drawn together a great multitude. Kory-Kory, previous to mounting the elevation, paused for a moment, like a dandy at a ball-room door, to put a hasty finish to his toilet. During this short interval, the thought struck me that I ought myself perhaps to be taking some little pains with my appearance. But as I had no holiday raiment, I was not a little puzzled to devise some means of decorating myself. However, as I felt desirous to create a sensation, I determined to do all that lay in my power; and knowing that I could not delight the savages more than by conforming to their style of dress, I removed from my person the large robe of tappa which I was accustomed to wear over my shoulders whenever I sallied into the open air, and remained merely girt about with a short tunic descending from my waist to my knees.

My quick-witted attendant fully appreciated the compliment I was paying to the costume of his race, and began more sedulously to arrange the folds of the one only garment which remained to me. Whilst he was doing this, I caught sight of a knot of young lasses, who were sitting near us on the grass surrounded by heaps of flowers, which they were forming into garlands. I motioned to them to bring some of their handiwork

to me; and in an instant a dozen wreaths were at my disposal.
One of them I put round the apology for a hat which I had
been forced to construct for myself out of palmetto-leaves,
and some of the others I converted into a splendid girdle. These
operations finished, with the slow and dignified step of a full-
dressed beau I ascended the rock.

CHAPTER XXIII

The Feast of Calabashes

The whole population of the valley seemed to be gathered
within the precincts of the grove. In the distance could be
seen the long front of the Ti, its immense piazza swarming with
men, arrayed in every variety of fantastic costume, and all
vociferating with animated gestures; while the whole interval
between it and the place where I stood was enlivened by groups
of females fancifully decorated, dancing, capering, and uttering
wild exclamations. As soon as they descried me they set up a
shout of welcome; and a band of them came dancing towards
me, chanting as they approached some wild recitative. The
change in my garb seemed to transport them with delight, and
clustering about me on all sides, they accompanied me towards
the Ti. When however we drew near it these joyous nymphs
paused in their career, and parting on either side, permitted
me to pass on to the now densely thronged building.

So soon as I mounted to the pi-pi I saw at a glance that the
revels were fairly under way.

What lavish plenty reigned around!—Warwick feasting his
retainers with beef and ale, was a niggard to the noble Mehevi!
—All along the piazza of the Ti were arranged elaborately
carved canoe-shaped vessels, some twenty feet in length, filled
with newly made poee-poee, and sheltered from the sun by the
broad leaves of the banana. At intervals were heaps of green
bread-fruit, raised in pyramidical stacks, resembling the regular
piles of heavy shot to be seen in the yard of an arsenal. Inserted into the interstices of the huge stones which formed the

pi-pi were large boughs of trees; hanging from the branches of which, and screened from the sun by their foliage, were innumerable little packages with leafy coverings, containing the meat of the numerous hogs which had been slain, done up in this manner to make it more accessible to the crowd. Leaning against the railing of the piazza were an immense number of long, heavy bamboos, plugged at the lower end, and with their projecting muzzles stuffed with a wad of leaves. These were filled with water from the stream, and each of them might hold from four to five gallons.

The banquet being thus spread, naught remained but for every one to help himself at his pleasure. Accordingly not a moment passed but the transplanted boughs I have mentioned were rifled by the throng of the fruit they certainly had never borne before. Calabashes of poee-poee were continually being replenished from the extensive receptacle in which that article was stored, and multitudes of little fires were kindled about the Ti for the purpose of roasting the bread-fruit.

Within the building itself was presented a most extraordinary scene. The immense lounge of mats lying between the parallel rows of the trunks of cocoa-nut trees, and extending the entire length of the house, at least two hundred feet, was covered by the reclining forms of a host of chiefs and warriors, who were eating at a great rate, or soothing the cares of Polynesian life in the sedative fumes of tobacco. The smoke was inhaled from large pipes, the bowls of which, made out of small cocoa-nut shells, were curiously carved in strange heathenish devices. These were passed from mouth to mouth by the recumbent smokers, each of whom, taking two or three prodigious whiffs, handed the pipe to his neighbor; sometimes for that purpose stretching indolently across the body of some dozing individual whose exertions at the dinner-table had already induced sleep.

The tobacco used among the Typees was of a very mild and pleasing flavor, and as I always saw it in leaves, and the natives appeared pretty well supplied with it, I was led to believe that it must have been the growth of the valley. Indeed Kory-Kory gave me to understand that this was the case; but I never saw a single plant growing on the island. At Nukuheva, and, I believe, in all the other valleys, the weed is very scarce, being only obtained in small quantities from foreigners, and smoking is consequently with the inhabitants of these places a very great luxury. How it was that the Typees were so well furnished with it I cannot divine. I should think them too indolent to devote any attention to its culture; and, indeed, as far as my observation extended, not a single atom of the soil was under any other cultivation than that of shower and sunshine. The tobacco-plant, however, like the sugar-cane, may grow wild in some remote part of the vale.

There were many in the Ti for whom the tobacco did not furnish a sufficient stimulus, and who accordingly had recourse to "arva," as a more powerful agent in producing the desired effect.

"Arva" is a root very generally dispersed over the South Seas, and from it is extracted a juice, the effects of which upon the system are at first stimulating in a moderate degree; but it soon relaxes the muscles, and exerting a narcotic influence produces a luxurious sleep. In the valley this beverage was universally prepared in the following way:—Some half-dozen young boys seated themselves in a circle around an empty wooden vessel, each one of them being supplied with a certain quantity of the roots of the "arva," broken into small bits and laid by his side. A cocoa-nut goblet of water was passed around the juvenile company, who rinsing their mouths with its contents, proceeded to the business before them. This merely consisted in thoroughly masticating the "arva," and throwing it mouthful after mouthful into the receptacle provided. When a sufficient quantity had been thus obtained water was poured upon the mass, and being stirred about with the forefinger of the right-hand, the preparation was soon in readiness for use. The "arva" has medicinal qualities.

Upon the Sandwich Islands it has been employed with no small success in the treatment of scrofulous affections, and in combating the ravages of a disease for whose frightful inroads the ill-starred inhabitants of that group are indebted to their foreign benefactors. But the tenants of the Typee valley, as yet exempt from these inflictions, generally employ the "arva" as a minister to social enjoyment, and a calabash of the liquid circulates among them as the bottle with us.

Mehevi, who was greatly delighted with the change in my costume, gave me a cordial welcome. He had reserved for me a most delectable mess of "cockoo," well knowing my partiality for that dish; and had likewise selected three or four young cocoa-nuts, several roasted bread-fruit, and a magnificent bunch of bananas, for my especial comfort and gratification. These various matters were at once placed before me; but Kory-Kory deemed the banquet entirely insufficient for my wants until he had supplied me with one of the leafy packages of pork, which, notwithstanding the somewhat hasty manner in which it had been prepared, possessed a most excellent flavor, and was surprisingly sweet and tender.

Pork is not a staple article of food among the people of the Marquesas, consequently they pay little attention to the *breeding* of the swine. The hogs are permitted to roam at large in the groves, where they obtain no small portion of their nourishment from the cocoa-nuts which continually fall from the trees. But it is only after infinite labor and difficulty, that the hungry animal can pierce the husk and shell so as to get at the meat. I have frequently been amused at seeing one of them, after crunching the obstinate nut with his teeth for a long time unsuccessfully, get into a violent passion with it. He would then root furiously under the cocoa-nut, and, with a fling of his snout, toss it before him on the ground. Following it up, he would crunch at it again savagely for a moment, and the next knock it on one side, pausing immediately after, as if wondering how it could so suddenly have disappeared. In this way the persecuted cocoa-nuts were often chased half across the valley.

The second day of the Feast of Calabashes was ushered in by still more uproarious noises than the first. The skins of innumerable sheep seemed to be resounding to the blows of an army of drummers. Startled from my slumbers by the din, I leaped up, and found the whole household engaged in making preparations for immediate departure. Curious to discover of what strange events these novel sounds might be the precursors, and not a little desirous to catch a sight of the instruments which produced the terrific noise, I accompanied the natives as soon as they were in readiness to depart for the Taboo Groves.

The comparatively open space that extended from the Ti toward the rock, to which I have before alluded as forming the ascent to the place, was, with the building itself, now altogether deserted by the men; the whole distance being filled by bands of females, shouting and dancing under the influence of some strange excitement.

I was amused at the appearance of four or five old women who, in a state of utter nudity, with their arms extended flatly down their sides, and holding themselves perfectly erect, were leaping stiffly into the air, like so many sticks bobbing to the surface, after being pressed perpendicularly into the water. They preserved the utmost gravity of countenance, and continued their extraordinary movements without a single moment's cessation. They did not appear to attract the observation of the crowd around them, but I must candidly confess that, for my own part, I stared at them most pertinaciously.

Desirous of being enlightened with regard to the meaning of this peculiar diversion, I turned inquiringly to Kory-Kory; that learned Typee immediately proceeded to explain the whole matter thoroughly. But all that I could comprehend from what he said was, that the leaping figures before me were bereaved widows, whose partners had been slain in battle many moons previously; and who, at every festival, gave public evidence in this manner of their calamities. It was evident that Kory-Kory considered this an all-sufficient reason for so indecorous a custom; but I must say that it did not satisfy me as to its propriety.

Leaving these afflicted females, we passed on to the Hoolah Hoolah ground. Within the spacious quadrangle, the whole population of the valley seemed to be assembled, and the sight presented was truly remarkable. Beneath the sheds of bamboo which opened towards the interior of the square, reclined the principal chiefs and warriors, while a miscellaneous throng lay at their ease under the enormous trees which spread a majestic canopy overhead. Upon the terraces of the gigantic altars, at either end, were deposited green bread-fruit in baskets of cocoa-nut leaves, large rolls of tappa, bunches of white bananas, clusters of mammee-apples, the golden-hued fruit of the artu-tree, and baked hogs, laid out in large wooden trenches, fancifully decorated with freshly plucked leaves, whilst a variety of rude implements of war were piled in confused heaps before the ranks of hideous idols. Fruits of various kinds were likewise suspended in leafen baskets, from the tops of poles planted uprightly, and at regular intervals, along the lower terraces of both altars. At their base were arranged two parallel rows of cumbersome drums, standing at least fifteen feet in height, and formed from the hollow trunks of large trees. Their heads were covered with shark skins, and their barrels were elaborately carved with various quaint figures and devices. At regular intervals they were bound round by a species of sinnate of various colors, and strips of native cloth flattened upon them here and there. Behind these instruments were built slight platforms, upon which stood a number of young men who, beating violently with the palms of their hands upon the drum-heads, produced those outrageous sounds which had awakened me in the morning. Every few minutes these musical performers hopped down from their elevation into the crowd below, and their places were immediately supplied by fresh recruits. Thus an incessant din was kept up that might have startled Pandemonium.

Precisely in the middle of the quadrangle were placed perpendicularly in the ground, a hundred or more slender, fresh-cut poles, stripped of their bark, and decorated at the end with a floating pennon of white tappa; the whole being fenced about with a little picket of canes. For what purpose these singular ornaments were intended I in vain endeavored to discover.

Another most striking feature of the performance was exhibited by a score of old men, who sat cross-legged in the little pulpits, which encircled the trunks of the immense trees growing in the middle of the enclosure. These venerable gentlemen, who I presume were the priests, kept up an uninterrupted monotonous chant, which was nearly drowned in the roar of drums. In the right hand they held a finely woven grass fan, with a heavy black wooden handle curiously chased: these fans they kept in continual motion.

But no attention whatever seemed to be paid to the drummers or to the old priests; the individuals who composed the vast crowd present being entirely taken up in chatting and laughing with one another, smoking, drinking arva, and eating. For all the observation it attracted, or the good it achieved, the whole savage orchestra might, with great advantage to its own members and the company in general, have ceased the prodigious uproar they were making.

In vain I questioned Kory-Kory and others of the natives, as to the meaning of the strange things that were going on; all their explanations were conveyed in such a mass of outlandish gibberish and gesticulation that I gave up the attempt in despair. All that day the drums resounded, the priests chanted, and the multitude feasted and roared till sunset, when the throng dispersed, and the Taboo Groves were again abandoned to quiet and repose. The next day the same scene was repeated until night, when this singular festival terminated.

CHAPTER XXVII

The Social Condition and general Character of the Typees

I have already mentioned that the influence exerted over the people of the valley by their chiefs was mild in the extreme; and as to any general rule or standard of conduct by which the commonalty were governed in their intercourse with each other, so far as my observation extended, I should be almost tempted to say, that none existed on the island, except, indeed, the mysterious "Taboo" be considered as such. During the time I lived among the Typees, no one was ever put upon his trial for any offence against the public. To all appearance there were no courts of law or equity. There was no municipal police for the purpose of apprehending vagrants and disorderly characters. In short, there were no legal provisions whatever for the well-being and conservation of society, the enlightened end of civilized legislation. And yet everything went on in the valley with a harmony and smoothness unparalleled, I will venture to assert, in the most select, refined, and pious associations of mortals in Christendom. How are we to explain this enigma? These islanders were heathens! savages! ay, cannibals! and how came they, without the aid of established law, to exhibit, in so eminent a degree, that social order which is the greatest blessing and highest pride of the social state?

It may reasonably be inquired, how were these people governed? How were their passions controlled in their everyday transactions? It must have been by an inherent principle of honesty and charity towards each other. They seemed to be governed by that sort of tacit common-sense law which, say what they will of the inborn lawlessness of the human race, has its precepts graven on every breast. The grand principles of virtue and honor, however they may be distorted by arbitrary codes, are the same all the world over: and where these principles are concerned, the right or wrong of any action appears the same to the uncultivated as to the enlightened mind. It is to this indwelling, this universally diffused perception of what is *just* and *noble*, that the integrity of the Marquesans in their intercourse with each other is to be attributed. In the darkest nights they slept securely, with all their worldly wealth around them, in houses the doors of which were never fastened. The disquieting ideas of theft or assassination never disturbed them. Each islander reposed beneath his own palmetto thatching, or sat under his own bread-fruit tree, with none to molest or alarm him. There was not a padlock in the valley, nor anything that answered the purpose of one: still there was no community of goods. This long spear, so elegantly carved and highly polished, belongs to Wormoonoo: it is far handsomer than the one which old Marheyo so greatly prizes; it is the most valuable article belonging to its owner. And yet I have seen it leaning against a cocoa-nut tree in the grove, and there it was found when sought for. Here is a sperm-whale tooth, graven all over with cunning devices: it is the property of Karluna: it is the most precious of the damsel's ornaments. In her estimation its price is far above rubies—and yet there hangs the dental jewel by its cord of braided bark, in the girl's house, which is far back in the valley; the door is left open, and all the inmates have gone off to bathe in the stream.[10]

So much for the respect in which "personal property" is held in Typee; how secure an investment of "real property" may be, I cannot take upon me to say. Whether the land of the valley was the joint property of its inhabitants, or whether it was parcelled out among a certain number of landed proprietors who allowed everybody to "squat" and "poach" as much as he or she pleased, I never could ascertain. At any rate, musty parchments and title-deeds there were none on the island; and I am half inclined to believe that its inhabitants hold their broad valleys in fee simple from nature herself; to have and to hold, so long as grass grows and water runs; or until their French visitors, by a summary mode of conveyance, shall appropriate them to their own benefit and behoof.

Yesterday I saw Kory-Kory hie him away, armed with a long pole, with which, standing on the ground, he knocked down the fruit from the topmost boughs of the trees, and brought them home in his basket of cocoa-nut leaves. To-day I see an islander, whom I know to reside in a distant part of the valley, doing the self-same thing. On the sloping bank of the stream are a number of banana-trees. I have often seen a score or two of young people making a merry foray on the great golden clusters, and bearing them off, one after another, to different parts of the vale, shouting and tramping as they went. No churlish old curmudgeon could have been the owner of that grove of bread-fruit trees, or of these gloriously yellow bunches of bananas.

From what I have said it will be perceived that there is a vast difference between "personal property" and "real estate" in the valley of Typee. Some individuals, of course, are more wealthy than others. For example: the ridge-pole of Marheyo's house bends under the weight of many a huge package of tappa; his long couch is laid with mats placed one upon the other seven deep. Outside, Tinor has ranged along in her bamboo cupboard—or whatever the place may be called—a goodly array of calabashes and wooden trenchers. Now, the house just beyond the grove, and next to Marheyo's, occupied by Ruaruga, is not quite so well furnished. There are only three moderate-sized packages swinging overhead: there are only two layers of mats beneath; and the calabashes and trenchers are not so numerous, nor so tastefully stained and carved. But then, Ruaruga has a house—not so pretty a one, to be sure—but just as commodious as Marheyo's; and, I suppose, if he wished to vie with his neighbor's establishment, he could do so with very little trouble. These, in short, constituted the chief differences perceivable in the relative wealth of the people in Typee.

Civilisation does not engross all the virtues of humanity: she has not even her full share of them. They flourish in greater abundance and attain greater strength among many barbarous people. The hospitality of the wild Arab, the courage of the North American Indian; and the faithful friendships of some of the Polynesian nations, far surpass any thing of a similar kind among the polished communities of Europe. If truth and justice, and the better principles of our nature, cannot exist unless enforced by the statute-book, how are we to account for the social condition of the Typees? So pure and upright were they in all the relations of life, that entering their valley, as I did, under the most erroneous impressions of their character, I was soon led to exclaim in amazement: "Are these the ferocious savages, the blood-thirsty cannibals of whom I have heard such frightful tales! They deal more kindly with each other, and are more humane than many who study essays on virtue and benevolence, and who repeat every night that beautiful prayer breathed first by the lips of the divine and gentle Jesus." I will frankly declare, that after passing a few weeks in this valley of the Marquesas, I formed a higher estimate of human nature than I had ever before entertained. But alas! since then I have been one of the crew of a man-of-war, and the pent-up wickedness of five hundred men has nearly overturned all my previous theories.

There was one admirable trait in the general character of the Typees which, more than any thing else, secured my admiration: it was the unanimity of feeling they displayed on every occasion. With them there hardly appeared to be any difference of opinion upon any subject whatever. They all thought and acted alike. I do not conceive that they could support a debating society for a single night: there would be nothing to dispute about; and were they to call a convention to take into consideration the state of the tribe, its session would be a remarkably short one. They showed this spirit of unanimity in every action of life, everything was done in concert and good fellowship. I will give an instance of this fraternal feeling.

One day, in returning with Kory-Kory from my accustomed visit to the Ti, we passed by a little opening in the grove; on one side of which, my attendant informed me, was that afternoon to be built a dwelling of bamboo. At least a hundred of the natives were bringing materials to the ground, some carrying in their hands one or two of the canes which were to form the sides, others slender rods of the hibiscus, strung with palmetto leaves, for the roof. Every one contributed something to the work; and by the united, but easy, and even indolent, labors of all, the entire work was completed before sunset. The islanders, while employed in erecting this tenement, reminded me of a colony of beavers at work. To be sure, they were hardly as silent and demure as those wonderful creatures, nor were they by any means as diligent. To tell the truth, they were somewhat inclined to be lazy, but a perfect tumult of hilarity prevailed; and they worked together so unitedly, and seemed actuated by such an instinct of friendliness, that it was truly beautiful to behold.

Not a single female took part in this employment: and if the degree of consideration in which the ever-adorable sex is held by the men be—as the philosophers affirm—a just criterion of the degree of refinement among a people, then I may truly pronounce the Typees to be as polished a community as ever the sun shone upon. The religious restrictions of the taboo alone excepted, the women of the valley were allowed every possible indulgence. Nowhere are the ladies more assiduously courted; nowhere are they better appreciated as the contributors to our highest enjoyments; and nowhere are they more sensible of their power. Far different from their condition among many rude nations, where the women are made to perform all the work while their ungallant lords and masters lie buried in sloth, the gentle sex in the valley of Typee were exempt from toil, if toil it might be called that, even in the tropical climate, never distilled one drop of perspiration. Their light household occupations, together with the manufacture of tappa, the platting of mats, and the polishing of drinking-vessels, were the only employments pertaining to the women. And even these resembled those pleasant avocations which fill up the elegant morning leisure of our fashionable ladies at home. But in these occupations, slight and agreeable though they were, the giddy young girls very seldom engaged. Indeed these wilful, care-killing damsels were averse to all useful employment. Like so many spoiled beauties, they ranged through the groves—bathed in the stream—danced—flirted—played all manner of mischievous pranks, and passed their days in one merry round of thoughtless happiness.

During my whole stay on the island I never witnessed a single quarrel, nor anything that in the slightest degree approached even to a dispute. The natives appeared to form one household, whose members were bound together by the ties of strong affection. The love of kindred I did not so much perceive, for it seemed blended in the general love; and where all were treated as brothers and sisters, it was hard to tell who were actually related to each other by blood.

Let it not be supposed that I have overdrawn this picture. I have not done so. Nor let it be urged, that the hostility of this tribe to foreigners, and the hereditary feuds they carry on against their fellow-islanders beyond the mountains, are facts which contradict me. Not so; these apparent discrepancies are easily reconciled. By many a legendary tale of violence and wrong, as well as by events which have passed before their eyes, these people have been taught to look upon white men with abhorrence. The cruel invasion of their country by Porter has alone furnished them with ample provocation; and I can sympathize in the spirit which prompts the Typee warrior to guard all the passes to his valley with the point of his levelled spear, and, standing upon the beach, with his back turned upon his green home, to hold at bay the intruding European.

As to the origin of the enmity of this particular clan towards the neighboring tribes, I cannot so confidently speak. I will not say that their foes are the aggressors, nor will I endeavor to palliate their conduct. But surely, if our evil passions must find vent, it is far better to expend them on strangers and aliens, than in the bosom of the community in which we dwell. In many polished countries civil contentions, as well as domestic enmities, are prevalent, at the same time that the most atrocious foreign wars are waged. How much less guilty, then, are our islanders, who of these three sins are only chargeable with one, and that the least criminal!

The reader will erelong have reason to suspect that the Typees are not free from the guilt of cannibalism; and he will then, perhaps, charge me with admiring a people against whom so odious a crime is chargeable. But this only enormity in their character is not half so horrible as it is usually described. According to the popular fictions, the crews of vessels, shipwrecked on some barbarous coast, are eaten alive like so many dainty joints by the uncivil inhabitants; and unfortunate voyagers are lured into smiling and treacherous bays; knocked on the head with outlandish war-clubs; and served up without any preliminary dressing. In truth, so horrific and improbable are these accounts, that many sensible and well-informed people will not believe that any cannibals exist; and place every book of voyages which purports to give any account of them, on the same shelf with Blue Beard and Jack the Giant-Killer. While others, implicitly crediting the most extravagant fictions, firmly believe that there are people in the world with tastes so depraved that they would infinitely prefer a single mouthful of material humanity to a good dinner of roast beef and plum pudding. But here, Truth, who loves to be centrally located, is again found between the two extremes; for cannibalism to a certain moderate extent is practised among several of the primitive tribes in the Pacific, but it is upon the bodies of slain enemies alone; and horrible and fearful as the custom is, immeasurably as it is to be abhorred and condemned, still I assert that those who indulge in it are in other respects humane and virtuous.

CHAPTER XXX

A Professor of the Fine Arts—His Persecutions—Something about Tatooing and Tabooing—Two Anecdotes in illustration of the latter—A few thoughts on the Typee Dialect

In one of my strolls with Kory-Kory, in passing along the border of a thick growth of bushes, my attention was arrested by a singular noise. On entering the thicket I witnessed for the first time the operation of tattooing as performed by these islanders.

I beheld a man extended flat upon his back on the ground, and, despite the forced composure of his countenance, it was evident that he was suffering agony. His tormentor bent over him, working away for all the world like a stone-cutter with mallet and chisel. In one hand he held a short slender stick, pointed with a shark's tooth, on the upright end of which he tapped with a small hammer-like piece of wood, thus puncturing the skin, and charging it with the coloring matter in which the instrument was dipped. A cocoa-nut shell containing this fluid was placed upon the ground. It is prepared by mixing with a vegetable juice the ashes of the "armor," or candle-nut, always preserved for the purpose. Beside the savage, and spread out upon a piece of soiled tappa, were a great number of curious black-looking little implements of bone and wood, used in the various divisions of his art. A few terminated in a single fine point, and, like very delicate pencils, were employed in giving the finishing touches, or in operating upon the more sensitive portions of the body, as was the case in the present instance. Others presented several points distributed in a line, somewhat resembling the teeth of a saw. These were employed in the coarser parts of the work, and particularly in pricking in straight marks. Some presented their points disposed in small figures, and being placed upon the body, were, by a single blow of the hammer, made to leave their indelible impression. I observed a few the handles of which were mysteriously curved, as if intended to be introduced into the orifice of the ear, with a view perhaps of beating the tattoo upon the tympanum. Altogether, the sight of these strange instruments recalled to mind that display of cruel-looking mother-of-pearl-handled things which one sees in their velvet-lined cases at the elbow of a dentist.

The artist was not at this time engaged on an original sketch, his subject being a venerable savage, whose tattooing had become somewhat faded with age and needed a few repairs, and accordingly he was merely employed in touching up the works of some of the old masters of the Typee school, as delineated upon the human canvas before him. The parts operated upon were the eyelids, where a longitudinal streak, like the one which adorned Kory-Kory, crossed the countenance of the victim.

In spite of all the efforts of the poor old man, sundry twitchings and screwings of the muscles of the face denoted the exquisite sensibility of these shutters to the windows of his soul, which he was now having repainted. But the artist, with a heart as callous as that of an army surgeon, continued his performance, enlivening his labors with a wild chant, tapping away the while as merrily as a woodpecker.

So deeply engaged was he in his work, that he had not observed our approach, until, after having enjoyed an unmolested view of the operation, I chose to attract his attention. As soon as he perceived me, supposing that I sought him in his professional capacity, he seized hold of me in a paroxysm of delight, and was all eagerness to begin the work. When, however,

I gave him to understand that he had altogether mistaken my views, nothing could exceed his grief and disappointment. But recovering from this, he seemed determined not to credit my assertion, and grasping his implements, he flourished them about in fearful vicinity to my face, going through an imaginary performance of his art, and every moment bursting into some admiring exclamation at the beauty of his designs.

Horrified at the bare thought of being rendered hideous for life if the wretch were to execute his purpose upon me, I struggled to get away from him, while Kory-Kory, turning traitor, stood by, and besought me to comply with the outrageous request. On my reiterated refusals the excited artist got half beside himself, and was overwhelmed with sorrow at losing so noble an opportunity of distinguishing himself in his profession.

The idea of engrafting his tattooing upon my white skin filled him with all a painter's enthusiasm: again and again he gazed into my countenance, and every fresh glimpse seemed to add to the vehemence of his ambition. Not knowing to what extremities he might proceed, and shuddering at the ruin he might inflict upon my figure-head, I now endeavored to draw off his attention from it, and holding out my arm in a fit of desperation, signed to him to commence operations. But he rejected the compromise indignantly, and still continued his attack on my face, as though nothing short of that would satisfy him. When his fore-finger swept across my features, in laying out the borders of those parallel bands which were to encircle my countenance, the flesh fairly crawled upon my bones. At last, half wild with terror and indignation, I succeeded in breaking away from the three savages, and fled towards old Marheyo's house, pursued by the indomitable artist, who ran after me, implements in hand. Kory-Kory, however, at last interfered, and drew him off from the chase.

This incident opened my eyes to a new danger; and I now felt convinced that in some luckless hour I should be disfigured in such a manner as never more to have the *face* to return to my countrymen, even should an opportunity offer.

These apprehensions were greatly increased by the desire which King Mehevi and several of the inferior chiefs now manifested that I should be tattooed. The pleasure of the king was first signified to me some three days after my casual encounter with Karky the artist. Heavens! what imprecations I showered upon that Karky! Doubtless he had plotted a conspiracy against me and my countenance, and would never rest until his diabolical purpose was accomplished. Several times I met him in various parts of the valley, and, invariably, whenever he descried me, he came running after me with his mallet and chisel, flourishing them about my face as if he longed to begin. What an object he would have made of me!

When the king first expressed his wish to me, I made known to him my utter abhorrence of the measure, and worked myself into such a state of excitement, that he absolutely stared at me in amazement. It evidently surpassed his majesty's comprehension how any sober-minded and sensible individual could entertain the least possible objection to so beautifying an operation.

Soon afterwards he repeated his suggestion, and meeting with a like repulse, showed some symptoms of displeasure at my obduracy. On his a third time renewing his request, I plainly perceived that something must be done, or my visage was ruined for ever; I therefore screwed up my courage to the sticking point, and declared my willingness to have both arms tattooed from just above the wrist to the shoulder. His majesty was greatly pleased at the proposition, and I was congratulating myself with having thus compromised the matter, when he intimated that as a thing of course my face was first to undergo the operation. I was fairly driven to despair; nothing but the utter ruin of my "face divine," as the poets call it, would, I perceived, satisfy the inexorable Mehevi and his chiefs, or rather, that infernal Karky, for he was at the bottom of it all.

The only consolation afforded me was a choice of patterns: I was at perfect liberty to have my face spanned by three horizontal bars, after the fashion of my serving-man's; or to have as many oblique stripes slanting across it; or if, like a true courtier, I chose to model my style on that of royalty, I might wear a sort of freemason badge upon my countenance in the shape of a mystic triangle. However, I would have none of these, though the king most earnestly impressed upon my mind that my choice was wholly unrestricted. At last, seeing my unconquerable repugnance, he ceased to importune me.

But not so some other of the savages. Hardly a day passed but I was subjected to their annoying requests, until at last my existence became a burden to me; the pleasures I had previously enjoyed no longer afforded me delight, and all my former desire to escape from the valley now revived with additional force.

A fact which I soon afterwards learned augmented my apprehension. The whole system of tattooing was, I found, connected with their religion; and it was evident, therefore, that they were resolved to make a convert of me.

In the decoration of the chiefs it seems to be necessary to exercise the most elaborate pencilling; while some of the inferior natives looked as if they had been daubed over indiscriminately with a house-painter's brush. I remember one fellow who prided himself hugely upon a great oblong patch, placed high upon his back, and who always reminded me of a man with a blister of Spanish flies stuck between his shoulders. Another whom I frequently met had the hollow of his eyes tattooed in two regular squares, and his visual organs being remarkably brilliant, they gleamed forth from out this setting like a couple of diamonds inserted in ebony.

Although convinced that tattooing was a religious observance, still the nature of the connexion between it and the superstitious idolatry of the people was a point upon which I could never obtain any information. Like the still more important system of the "Taboo," it always appeared inexplicable to me.

There is a marked similarity, almost an identity, between the religious institutions of most of the Polynesian islands, and in all exists the mysterious "Taboo," restricted in its uses to a greater or less extent. So strange and complex in its arrangements is this remarkable system, that I have in several cases met with individuals who, after residing for years among the islands in the Pacific, and acquiring a considerable knowledge of the language, have nevertheless been altogether unable to give any satisfactory account of its operations. Situated as I was in the Typee valley, I perceived every hour the effects of this all-controlling power, without in the least comprehending it. Those effects were, indeed, wide-spread and universal, pervading the most important as well as the minutest transactions of life. The savage, in short, lives in the continual observance of its dictates, which guide and control every action of his being.

For several days after entering the valley I had been saluted at least fifty times in the twenty-four hours with the talismanic word "Taboo" shrieked in my ears, at some gross violation of its provisions, of which I had unconsciously been guilty. The day after our arrival I happened to hand some tobacco to Toby over the head of a native who sat between us. He started up, as if stung by an adder; while the whole company, manifesting an equal degree of horror, simultaneously screamed out "taboo!" I never again perpetrated a similar piece of ill-manners, which, indeed, was forbidden by the canons of good breeding, as well as by the mandates of the taboo. But it was not always so easy to perceive wherein you had contravened the spirit of this institution. I was many times called to order, if I may use the phrase, when I could not for the life of me conjecture what particular offence I had committed.

One day I was strolling through a secluded portion of the valley, and hearing the musical sound of the cloth-mallet at a little distance, I turned down a path that conducted me in a few moments to a house where there were some half-dozen girls employed in making tappa. This was an operation I had frequently witnessed, and had handled the bark in all the various stages of its preparation. On the present occasion the females were intent upon their occupation, and after looking up and talking gaily to me for a few moments, they resumed their employment. I regarded them for awhile in silence, and then carelessly picking up a handful of the material that lay around, proceeded unconsciously to pick it apart. While thus engaged, I was suddenly startled by a scream, like that of a whole boarding-school of young ladies just on the point of going into hysterics. Leaping up with the idea of seeing a score of Happar warriors about to perform anew the Sabine atrocity, I found myself confronted by the company of girls, who, having dropped their work, stood before me with starting eyes, swelling bosoms, and fingers pointed in horror towards me.

Thinking that some venomous reptile must be concealed in the bark which I held in my hand, I began cautiously to separate and examine it. Whilst I did so the horrified girls redoubled their shrieks. Their wild cries and frightened motions actually alarmed me, and throwing down the tappa, I was about to rush from the house, when in the same instant their clamors ceased, and one of them seizing me by the arm, pointed to the broken fibres that had just fallen from my grasp, and screamed in my ears the fatal word Taboo!

I subsequently found out that the fabric they were engaged in making was of a peculiar kind, destined to be worn on the heads of the females, and through every stage of its manufacture was guarded by a vigorous taboo, which interdicted the whole masculine gender from even so much as touching it.

Frequently in walking through the groves I observed bread-fruit and cocoa-nut trees, with a wreath of leaves twined in a peculiar fashion about their trunks. This was the mark of the taboo. The trees themselves, their fruit, and even the shadows they cast upon the ground, were consecrated by its presence. In the same way a pipe, which the king had bestowed upon me, was rendered sacred in the eyes of the natives, none of whom could I ever prevail upon to smoke from it. The bowl was encircled by a woven band of grass, somewhat resembling those Turks' heads occasionally worked in the handles of our whip-stalks.

A similar badge was once braided about my wrist by the royal hand of Mehevi himself, who, as soon as he had concluded the operation, pronounced me "Taboo." This occurred shortly after Toby's disappearance; and were it not that from the first moment I had entered the valley the natives had treated me with uniform kindness, I should have supposed that their conduct afterwards was to be ascribed to the fact that I had received this sacred investiture.

The capricious operations of the taboo are not its least remarkable feature: to enumerate them all would be impossible. Black hogs—infants to a certain age—women in an interesting situation—young men while the operation of tattooing their faces is going on—and certain parts of the valley during the continuance of a shower—are alike fenced about by the operation of the taboo.

I witnessed a striking instance of its effects in the bay of Tior, my visit to which place has been alluded to in a former part of this narrative. On that occasion our worthy captain formed one of the party. He was a most insatiable sportsman. Outward bound, and off the pitch of Cape Horn, he used to sit on the taffrail, and keep the steward loading three or four old fowling-pieces, with which he would bring down albatrosses, Cape pigeons, jays, petrels, and divers other marine fowl, who followed chattering in our wake. The sailors were struck aghast at his impiety, and one and all attributed our forty days' beating about that horrid headland to his sacrilegious slaughter of these inoffensive birds.

At Tior he evinced the same disregard for the religious prejudices of the islanders, as he had previously shown for the superstitions of the sailors. Having heard that there were a considerable number of fowls in the valley—the progeny of some cocks and hens accidentally left there by an English vessel, and which, being strictly tabooed, flew about almost in a wild state—he determined to break through all restraints, and be the death of them. Accordingly, he provided himself with a most formidable looking gun, and announced his landing on the beach by shooting down a noble cock that was crowing what proved to be his own funeral dirge, on the limb of an adjoining tree. "Taboo," shrieked the affrighted savages. "Oh, hang your taboo," says the nautical sportsman; "talk taboo to the marines"; and bang went the piece again, and down came another victim. At this the natives ran scampering through the groves, horror-struck at the enormity of the act.

All that afternoon the rocky sides of the valley rang with successive reports, and the superb plumage of many a beautiful fowl was ruffled by the fatal bullet. Had it not been that the French admiral, with a large party, was then in the glen, I have no doubt that the natives, although their tribe was small and dispirited, would have inflicted summary vengeance upon the man who thus outraged their most sacred institutions; as it was, they contrived to annoy him not a little.

Thirsting with his exertions, the skipper directed his steps to a stream; but the savages, who had followed at a little distance, perceiving his object, rushed towards him and forced him away from its bank—his lips would have polluted it. Wearied at last, he sought to enter a house, that he might rest for a while on the mats; its inmates gathered tumultuously about the door and denied him admittance. He coaxed and blustered by turns, but in vain; the natives were neither to be intimidated nor appeased, and as a final resort he was obliged to call together his boat's crew, and pull away from what he termed the most infernal place he ever stepped upon.

Lucky was it for him and for us that we were not honored on our departure by a salute of stones from the hands of the exasperated Tiors. In this way, on the neighboring island of Ropo, were killed, but a few weeks previously, and for a nearly similar offence, the master and three of the crew of the K——.

I cannot determine with anything approaching to certainty, what power it is that imposes the taboo. When I consider the slight disparity of condition among the islanders—the very limited and inconsiderable prerogatives of the king and chiefs—and the loose and indefinite functions of the priesthood, most of whom were hardly to be distinguished from the rest of their countrymen, I am wholly at a loss where to look for the authority which regulates this potent institution. It is imposed upon something to-day, and withdrawn to-morrow; while its operations in other cases are perpetual. Sometimes its restrictions only affect a single individual—sometimes a particular family—sometimes a whole tribe; and in a few instances they extend not merely over the various clans on a single island, but over all the inhabitants of an entire group. In illustration of this latter peculiarity, I may cite the law which forbids a female to enter a canoe—a prohibition which prevails upon all the northern Marquesas Islands.

The word itself (taboo) is used in more than one signification. It is sometimes used by a parent to his child, when in the exercise of parental authority he forbids it to perform a particular action. Anything opposed to the ordinary customs of the islanders, although not expressly prohibited, is said to be "taboo."

The Typee language is one very difficult to be acquired; it bears a close resemblance to the other Polynesian dialects, all of which show a common origin. The duplication of words, as "lumee lumee," "poee poee" "muee muee," is one of their peculiar features. But another, and a more annoying one, is the different senses in which one and the same word is employed; its various meanings all have a certain connexion, which only makes the matter more puzzling. So one brisk, lively little word is obliged, like a servant in a poor family, to perform all sorts of duties; for instance, one particular combination of syllables expresses the ideas of sleep, rest, reclining, sitting, leaning, and all other things anyways analogous thereto, the particular meaning being shown chiefly by a variety of gestures and the eloquent expression of the countenance.

The intricacy of these dialects is another peculiarity. In the Missionary College at Lahainaluna, [on] Mawee, one of the Sandwich Islands, I saw a tabular exhibition of a Hawaiian verb, conjugated through all its moods and tenses. It covered the side of a considerable apartment, and I doubt whether Sir William Jones[11] himself would not have despaired of mastering it.

CHAPTER XXXIV

The Escape

Nearly three weeks had elapsed since the second visit of Marnoo,[12] and it must have been more than four months since I entered the valley,[13] when one day about noon, and whilst everything was in profound silence, Mow-Mow, the one-eyed chief, suddenly appeared at the door, and leaning forward towards me as I lay directly facing him, said in a low tone, "Toby pemi ena" (Toby has arrived here). Gracious heaven! What a tumult of emotions rushed upon me at this startling intelligence! Insensible to the pain that had before distracted me, I leaped to my feet, and called wildly to Kory-Kory who was reposing by my side. The startled islanders sprang from their mats; the news was quickly communicated to them; and the next moment I was making my way to the Ti on the back of Kory-Kory, and surrounded by the excited savages.

All that I could comprehend of the particulars which Mow-Mow rehearsed to his auditors as we proceeded, was that my long-lost companion had arrived in a boat which had just entered the bay. These tidings made me most anxious to be carried at once to the sea, lest some untoward circumstance should prevent our meeting; but to this they would not consent, and continued their course towards the royal abode. As we approached it, Mehevi and several chiefs showed themselves from the piazza, and called upon us loudly to come to them.

As soon as we had approached, I endeavored to make them understand that I was going down to the sea to meet Toby. To this the king objected, and motioned Kory-Kory to bring me into the house. It was in vain to resist; and in a few moments I found myself within the Ti, surrounded by a noisy group engaged in discussing the recent intelligence. Toby's name was frequently repeated, coupled with violent exclamations of astonishment. It seemed as if they yet remained in doubt with regard to the fact of his arrival, and at every fresh report that was brought from the shore they betrayed the liveliest emotions.

Almost frenzied at being held in this state of suspense, I passionately besought Mehevi to permit me to proceed. Whether my companion had arrived or not, I felt a presentiment that my own fate was about to be decided. Again and again I renewed my petition to Mehevi. He regarded me with a fixed and serious eye, but at length yielding to my importunity, reluctantly granted my request.

Accompanied by some fifty of the natives, I now rapidly

continued my journey; every few moments being transferred from the back of one to another, and urging my bearer forward all the while with earnest entreaties. As I thus hurried forward, no doubt as to the truth of the information I had received ever crossed my mind. I was alive only to the one overwhelming idea, that a chance of deliverance was now afforded me, if the jealous opposition of the savages could be overcome.

Having been prohibited from approaching the sea during the whole of my stay in the valley, I had always associated with it the idea of escape. Toby too—if indeed he had ever voluntarily deserted me[14]—must have effected his flight by the sea; and now that I was drawing near to it myself, I indulged in hopes which I had never felt before. It was evident that a boat had entered the bay, and I saw little reason to doubt the truth of the report that it had brought my companion. Every time therefore that we gained an elevation, I looked eagerly around, hoping to behold him.

In the midst of an excited throng, who by their violent gestures and wild cries appeared to be under the influence of some excitement as strong as my own, I was now borne along at a rapid trot, frequently stooping my head to avoid the branches which crossed the path, and never ceasing to implore those who carried me to accelerate their already swift pace.

In this manner we had proceeded about four or five miles, when we were met by a party of some twenty islanders, between whom and those who accompanied me ensued an animated conference. Impatient of the delay occasioned by this interruption, I was beseeching the man who carried me to proceed without his loitering companions, when Kory-Kory, running to my side, informed me, in three fatal words, that the news had all proved false—that Toby had not arrived—"Toby owlee permi." Heaven only knows how, in the state of mind and body I then was, I ever sustained the agony which this intelligence caused me; not that the news was altogether unexpected; but I had trusted that the fact might not have been made known until we should have arrived upon the beach. As it was, I at once foresaw the course the savages would pursue. They had only yielded thus far to my entreaties, that I might give a joyful welcome to my long-lost comrade; but now that it was known he had not arrived, they would at once oblige me to turn back.

My anticipations were but too correct. In spite of the resistance I made, they carried me into a house which was near the spot, and left me upon the mats. Shortly afterwards several of those who had accompanied me from the Ti, detaching themselves from the others, proceeded in the direction of the sea. Those who remained—among whom were Marheyo, Mow-Mow, Kory-Kory, and Tinor—gathered about the dwelling, and appeared to be awaiting their return.

This convinced me that strangers—perhaps some of my own countrymen—had for some cause or other entered the bay. Distracted at the idea of their vicinity, and reckless of the pain which I suffered, I heeded not the assurances of the islanders, that there were no boats at the beach, but starting to my feet endeavored to gain the door. Instantly the passage was blocked up by several men, who commanded me to resume my seat. The fierce looks of the irritated savages admonished me that I could gain nothing by force, and that it was by entreaty alone that I could hope to compass my object.

Guided by this consideration, I turned to Mow-Mow, the only chief present whom I had been much in the habit of seeing, and carefully concealing my real design, tried to make him comprehend that I still believed Toby to have arrived on the shore, and besought him to allow me to go forward to welcome him. To all his repeated assertions, that my companion had not been seen, I pretended to turn a deaf ear: while I urged my solicitations with an eloquence of gesture which the one-eyed chief appeared unable to resist. He seemed indeed to regard me as a froward child, to whose wishes he had not the heart to oppose force, and whom he must consequently humor. He spoke a few words to the natives, who at once retreated from the door, and I immediately passed out of the house.

Here I looked earnestly round for Kory-Kory; but that hitherto faithful servitor was nowhere to be seen. Unwilling to linger even for a single instant when every moment might

be so important, I motioned to a muscular fellow near me to
take me upon his back: to my surprise he angrily refused. I
turned to another, but with a like result. A third attempt was
as unsuccessful and I immediately perceived what had induced
Mow-Mow to grant my request, and why the other natives
conducted themselves in so strange a manner. It was evident
that the chief had only given me liberty to continue my progress
towards the sea, because he supposed that I was deprived of the
means of reaching it.

Convinced by this of their determination to retain me a captive, I became desperate; and almost insensible to the pain
which I suffered I seized a spear which was leaning against the
projecting eaves of the house, and supporting myself with it,
resumed the path that swept by the dwelling. To my surprise
I was suffered to proceed alone; all the natives remaining in
front of the house, and engaging in earnest conversation, which
every moment became more loud and vehement; and to my
unspeakable delight I perceived that some difference of opinion
had arisen between them; that two parties, in short, were formed,
and consequently that in their divided counsels there was some
chance of my deliverance.

Before I had proceeded a hundred yards I was again surrounded by the savages, who were still in all the heat of argument, and appeared every moment as if they would come to
blows. In the midst of this tumult old Marheyo came to my
side, and I shall never forget the benevolent expression of his
countenance. He placed his arm upon my shoulder, and emphatically pronounced the only two English words I had taught
him—"Home" and "Mother." I at once understood what he
meant, and eagerly expressed my thanks to him. Fayaway and
Kory-Kory were by his side, both weeping violently; and it
was not until the old man had twice repeated the command
that his son could bring himself to obey him, and take me
again upon his back. The one-eyed chief opposed his doing
so, but he was overruled, and, as it seemed to me, by some of
his own party.

We proceeded onwards, and never shall I forget the ecstasy

I felt when I first heard the roar of the surf breaking upon the beach. Before long I saw the flashing billows themselves through the opening between the trees. Oh glorious sight and sound of ocean! with what rapture did I hail you as familiar friends! By this time the shouts of the crowd upon the beach were distinctly audible, and in the blended confusion of sounds I almost fancied I could distinguish the voices of my own countrymen.

When we reached the open space which lay between the groves and the sea, the first object that met my view was an English whale-boat, lying with her bow pointed from the shore, and only a few fathoms distant from it. It was manned by five islanders, dressed in short tunics of calico. My first impression was that they were in the very act of pulling out from the bay; and that, after all my exertions, I had come too late. My soul sunk within me: but a second glance convinced me that the boat was only hanging off to keep out of the surf; and the next moment I heard my own name shouted out by a voice from the midst of the crowd.

Looking in the direction of the sound, I perceived, to my indescribable joy, the tall figure of Karakoee, an Oahu Kannaka, who had often been aboard the "Dolly," [15] while she lay in Nukuheva. He wore the green shooting-jacket with gilt buttons, which had been given to him by an officer of the Reine Blanche —the French flag-ship—and in which I had always seen him dressed. I now remembered the Kannaka had frequently told me that his person was tabooed in all the valleys of the island, and the sight of him at such a moment as this filled my heart with a tumult of delight.

Karakoee stood near the edge of the water with a large roll of cotton-cloth thrown over one arm, and holding two or three canvas bags of powder; while with the other hand he grasped a musket, which he appeared to be proffering to several of the chiefs around him. But they turned with disgust from his offers, and seemed to be impatient at his presence, with vehement gestures waving him off to his boat, and commanding him to depart.

The Kannaka, however, still maintained his ground, and I at once perceived that he was seeking to purchase my freedom. Animated by the idea, I called upon him loudly to come to me; but he replied, in broken English, that the islanders had threatened to pierce him with their spears, if he stirred a foot towards me. At this time I was still advancing, surrounded by a dense throng of the natives, several of whom had their hands upon me, and more than one javelin was threateningly pointed at me. Still I perceived clearly that many of those least friendly towards me looked irresolute and anxious.

I was still some thirty yards from Karakoee when my further progress was prevented by the natives, who compelled me to sit down upon the ground, while they still retained their hold upon my arms. The din and tumult now became tenfold, and I perceived that several of the priests were on the spot, all of whom were evidently urging Mow-Mow and the other chiefs to prevent my departure; and the detestable word "Roo-ne! Roo-ne!" which I had heard repeated a thousand times during the day, was now shouted out on every side of me. Still I saw that the Kannaka continued his exertions in my favor— that he was boldly debating the matter with the savages, and was striving to entice them by displaying his cloth and powder, and snapping the lock of his musket. But all he said or did appeared only to augment the clamors of those around him, who seemed bent upon driving him into the sea.

When I remembered the extravagant value placed by these people upon the articles which were offered to them in exchange for me, and which were so indignantly rejected, I saw a new proof of the same fixed determination of purpose they had all along manifested with regard to me, and in despair, and reckless of consequences, I exerted all my strength, and shaking myself free from the grasp of those who held me, I sprang upon my feet and rushed towards Karakoee.

The rash attempt nearly decided my fate; for, fearful that I might slip from them, several of the islanders now raised a simultaneous shout, and pressing upon Karakoee, they menaced him with furious gestures, and actually forced him into the sea.

Appalled at their violence, the poor fellow, standing nearly to the waist in the surf, endeavored to pacify them; but at length, fearful that they would do him some fatal violence, he beckoned to his comrades to pull in at once, and take him into the boat.

It was at this agonizing moment, when I thought all hope was ended, that a new contest arose between the two parties who had accompanied me to the shore; blows were struck, wounds were given, and blood flowed. In the interest excited by the fray, every one had left me except Marheyo, Kory-Kory, and poor dear Fayaway, who clung to me, sobbing indignantly. I saw that now or never was the moment. Clasping my hands together, I looked imploringly at Marheyo, and moved towards the now almost deserted beach. The tears were in the old man's eyes, but neither he nor Kory-Kory attempted to hold me, and I soon reached the Kannaka, who had anxiously watched my movements; the rowers pulled in as near as they dared to the edge of the surf; I gave one parting embrace to Fayaway, who seemed speechless with sorrow, and the next instant I found myself safe in the boat, and Karakoee by my side, who told the rowers at once to give way. Marheyo and Kory-Kory, and a great many of the women, followed me into the water, and I was determined, as the only mark of gratitude I could show, to give them the articles which had been brought as my ransom. I handed the musket to Kory-Kory, with a rapid gesture which was equivalent to a "Deed of Gift"; threw the roll of cotton to old Marheyo, pointing as I did so to poor Fayaway, who had retired from the edge of the water and was sitting down disconsolate on the shingles; and tumbled the powder-bags out to the nearest young ladies, all of whom were vastly willing to take them. This distribution did not occupy ten seconds, and before it was over the boat was under full way; the Kannaka all the while exclaiming loudly against what he considered a useless throwing away of valuable property.

Although it was clear that my movements had been noticed by several of the natives, still they had not suspended the conflict in which they were engaged, and it was not until the boat was above fifty yards from the shore that Mow-Mow and some six or seven other warriors rushed into the sea and hurled their javelins at us. Some of the weapons passed quite as close to us as was desirable, but no one was wounded, and the men pulled away gallantly. But although soon out of the reach of the spears, our progress was extremely slow; it blew strong upon the shore, and the tide was against us; and I saw Karakoee, who was steering the boat, give many a look towards a jutting point of the bay round which we had to pass.

For a minute or two after our departure, the savages, who had formed into different groups, remained perfectly motionless and silent. All at once the enraged chief showed by his gestures that he had resolved what course he would take. Shouting loudly to his companions, and pointing with his tomahawk towards the headland, he set off at full speed in that direction, and was followed by about thirty of the natives, among whom were several of the priests, all yelling out "Roo-ne! Roo-ne!" at the very top of their voices. Their intention was evidently to swim off from the headland and intercept us in our course. The wind was freshening every minute, and was right in our teeth, and it was one of those chopping angry seas in which it is so difficult to row. Still the chances seemed in our favor, but when we came within a hundred yards of the point, the active savages were already dashing into the water, and we all feared that within five minutes' time we should have a score of the infuriated wretches around us. If so our doom was sealed, for these savages, unlike the feeble swimmers of civilized countries, are, if anything, more formidable antagonists in the water than when on the land. It was all a trial of strength; our natives pulled till their oars bent again, and the crowd of swimmers shot through the water despite its roughness, with fearful rapidity.

By the time we had reached the headland, the savages were spread right across our course. Our rowers got out their knives and held them ready between their teeth, and I seized the boat-hook. We were well aware that if they succeeded in intercepting us they would practise upon us the manœuvre which has proved so fatal to many a boat's crew in these seas.

They would grapple the oars, and seizing hold of the gunwale, capsize the boat, and then we should be entirely at their mercy.

After a few breathless moments I discerned Mow-Mow. The athletic islander, with his tomahawk between his teeth, was dashing the water before him till it foamed again. He was the nearest to us, and in another instant he would have seized one of the oars. Even at the moment I felt horror at the act I was about to commit; but it was no time for pity or compunction, and with a true aim, and exerting all my strength, I dashed the boat-hook at him. It struck him just below the throat, and forced him downwards. I had no time to repeat my blow, but I saw him rise to the surface in the wake of the boat, and never shall I forget the ferocious expression of his countenance.

Only one other of the savages reached the boat. He seized the gunwale, but the knives of our rowers so mauled his wrists, that he was forced to quit his hold, and the next minute we were past them all, and in safety. The strong excitement which had thus far kept me up, now left me, and I fell back fainting into the arms of Karakoee.

* * *

The circumstances connected with my most unexpected escape may be very briefly stated. The captain of an Australian vessel, being in distress for men in these remote seas, had put into Nukuheva in order to recruit his ship's company; but not a single man was to be obtained; and the barque was about to get under weigh, when she was boarded by Karakoee, who informed the disappointed Englishman that an American sailor was detained by the savages in the neighboring bay of Typee; and he offered, if supplied with suitable articles of traffic, to undertake his release. The Kannaka had gained his intelligence from Marnoo, to whom, after all, I was indebted for my escape. The proposition was acceded to; and Karakoee, taking with him five tabooed natives of Nukuheva, again repaired aboard the barque, which in a few hours sailed to that part of the island, and threw her main-top-sail aback right off the entrance to the Typee bay. The whale-boat, manned by the tabooed crew, pulled towards the head of the inlet, while the ship lay "off and on" awaiting its return.

The events which ensued have already been detailed, and little more remains to be related. On reaching the "Julia" I was lifted over the side, and my strange appearance and remarkable adventure occasioned the liveliest interest. Every attention was bestowed upon me that humanity could suggest. But to such a state was I reduced, that three months elapsed before I recovered my health.

The mystery which hung over the fate of my friend and companion Toby has never been cleared up. I still remain ignorant whether he succeeded in leaving the valley, or perished at the hands of the islanders.

From OMOO

CHAPTER II

Some Account of the Ship [1]

First and foremost, I must give some account of the Julia herself; or "Little Jule," as the sailors familiarly styled her.

She was a small barque of a beautiful model, something more than two hundred tons, Yankee-built and very old. Fitted for a privateer out of a New England port during the war of 1812, she had been captured at sea by a British cruiser, and, after seeing all sorts of service, was at last employed as a government packet in the Australian seas. Being condemned, however, about two years previous, she was purchased at auction by a house in Sydney, who, after some slight repairs, dispatched her on the present voyage.

Notwithstanding the repairs, she was still in a miserable plight. The lower masts were said to be unsound; the standing rigging was much worn; and, in some places, even the bulwarks were quite rotten. Still, she was tolerably tight, and but little more than the ordinary pumping of a morning served to keep her free.

But all this had nothing to do with her sailing; at that, brave Little Jule, plump Little Jule, was a witch. Blow high, or blow low, she was always ready for the breeze; and when she dashed the waves from her prow, and pranced, and pawed the sea, you never thought of her patched sails and blistered hull. How the fleet creature would fly before the wind! rolling, now and then, to be sure, but in very playfulness. Sailing to windward, no gale could blow her over: with spars erect, she looked right up into the wind's eye, and so she went.

But after all, Little Jule was not to be confided in. Lively enough, and playful she was, but on that very account the more to be distrusted. Who knew, but that like some vivacious old mortal all at once sinking into a decline, she might, some dark night, spring a leak and carry us all to the bottom. However, she played us no such ugly trick, and therefore, I wrong Little Jule in supposing it.

She had a free, roving commission. According to her papers she might go whither she pleased—whaling, sealing, or any thing else. Sperm whaling, however, was what she relied upon; though, as yet, only two fish had been brought alongside.

The day they sailed out of Sydney Heads, the ship's company, all told, numbered some thirty-two souls; now, they mustered about twenty; the rest had deserted. Even the three junior mates who had headed the whale boats were gone; and of the four harpooners, only one was left, a wild New Zealander, or "*Mowree,*" as his countrymen are more commonly called in the Pacific. But this was not all. More than half the seamen remaining were more or less unwell from a long sojourn in a dissipated port; some of them wholly unfit for duty, one or two dangerously ill, and the rest managing to stand their watch though they could do but little.

The captain was a young cockney, who, a few years before, had emigrated to Australia, and, by some favoritism or other, had procured the command of the vessel, though in no wise competent. He was essentially a landsman, and though a man of education, no more meant for the sea than a hair-dresser. Hence everybody made fun of him. They called him "The Cabin Boy," "Paper Jack," and half a dozen other undignified names. In truth, the men made no secret of the derision in which they held him; and as for the slender gentleman himself, he knew it all very well, and bore himself with becoming meekness. Holding as little intercourse with them as possible, he left every thing to the chief mate, who, as the story went, had been given his captain in charge. Yet, despite his apparent unobtrusiveness, the silent captain had more to do with the men than they thought. In short, although one of your sheepish-looking fellows, he had a sort of still, timid cunning, which no one would have suspected, and which, for that very reason, was all the more active. So the bluff mate, who always thought he did what he pleased, was occasionally made a tool of; and some obnoxious measures which he carried out, in spite of all growlings, were little thought to originate with the dapper little fellow in nankeen jacket and white canvas pumps. But, to all appearance, at least, the mate had every thing his own way; indeed, in most things this was actually the case; and it was quite plain that the captain stood in awe of him.

So far as courage, seamanship, and a natural aptitude for keeping riotous spirits in subjection were concerned, no man was better qualified for his vocation than John Jermin. He was the very beau-ideal of the efficient race of short, thick-set men. His hair curled in little rings of iron gray all over his round, bullet head. As for his countenance, it was strongly marked, deeply pitted with the small-pox. For the rest, there was a fierce little squint out of one eye; the nose had a rakish twist to one side; while his large mouth, and great white teeth, looked absolutely sharkish when he laughed. In a word, no one, after getting a fair look at him, would ever think of improving the shape of his nose, wanting in symmetry if it was. Notwithstanding his pugnacious looks, however, Jermin had a heart as big as a bullock's; that you saw at a glance.

Such was our mate; but he had one failing: he abhorred all weak infusions, and cleaved manfully to strong drink. At all times he was more or less under the influence of it. Taken in moderate quantities, I believe, in my soul, it did a man like him good; brightened his eyes, swept the cobwebs out of his brain, and regulated his pulse. But the worst of it was, that sometimes he drank too much, and a more obstreperous fellow than Jermin in his cups, you seldom came across. He was always for having a fight; but the very men he flogged loved him as a brother, for he had such an irresistibly good-natured way of knocking them down, that no one could find it in his heart to bear malice against him. So much for stout little Jermin.

All English whalemen are bound by law to carry a physician, who, of course, is rated a gentleman, and lives in the cabin, with nothing but his professional duties to attend to; but incidentally he drinks "flip" and plays cards with the captain.

There was such a worthy aboard of the Julia; but, curious to tell, he lived in the forecastle with the men. And this was the way it happened.

In the early part of the voyage the doctor and the captain lived together as pleasantly as could be. To say nothing of many a can they drank over the cabin transom, both of them had read books, and one of them had traveled; so their stories never flagged. But once on a time they got into a dispute about politics, and the doctor, moreover, getting into a rage, drove home an argument with his fist, and left the captain on the floor literally silenced. This was carrying it with a high hand; so he was shut up in his state-room for ten days, and left to meditate on bread and water, and the impropriety of flying into a passion. Smarting under his disgrace, he undertook, a short time after his liberation, to leave the vessel clandestinely at one of the islands, but was brought back ignominiously, and again shut up. Being set at large for the second time, he vowed he would not live any longer with the captain, and went forward with his chests among the sailors, where he was received with open arms, as a good fellow and an injured man.

I must give some further account of him, for he figures largely in the narrative. His early history, like that of many other heroes, was enveloped in the profoundest obscurity; though he threw out hints of a patrimonial estate, a nabob uncle, and an unfortunate affair which sent him a-roving. All that was known, however, was this. He had gone out to Sydney as assistant-surgeon of an emigrant ship. On his arrival there, he went back into the country, and after a few months' wanderings, returned to Sydney penniless, and entered as doctor aboard of the Julia.

His personal appearance was remarkable. He was over six feet high—a tower of bones, with a complexion absolutely colorless, fair hair, and a light, unscrupulous gray eye, twinkling occasionally with the very devil of mischief. Among the crew, he went by the name of the Long Doctor, or, more frequently still, Doctor Long Ghost. And from whatever high estate Doctor Long Ghost might have fallen, he had certainly at some time or other spent money, drunk Burgundy, and associated with gentlemen.

As for his learning, he quoted Virgil, and talked of Hobbes of Malmsbury, besides repeating poetry by the canto, especially Hudibras. He was, moreover, a man who had seen the world. In the easiest way imaginable, he could refer to an amour he had in Palermo, his lion hunting before breakfast among the Caffres, and the quality of the coffee to be drunk in Muscat; and about these places, and a hundred others, he had more anecdotes than I can tell of. Then such mellow old songs as he sang, in a voice so round and racy, the real juice of sound. How such notes came forth from his lank body was a constant marvel.

Upon the whole, Long Ghost was as entertaining a companion as one could wish; and to me in the Julia, an absolute godsend.

CHAPTER XXVII [2]

A Glance at Papeetee—We Are Sent Aboard the Frigate

The village of Papeetee struck us all very pleasantly. Lying in a semicircle round the bay, the tasteful mansions of the chiefs and foreign residents impart an air of tropical elegance, heightened by the palm-trees waving here and there, and the deep-green groves of the Bread-Fruit in the background. The squalid huts of the common people are out of sight, and there is nothing to mar the prospect.

All round the water, extends a wide, smooth beach of mixed pebbles and fragments of coral. This forms the thoroughfare of the village; the handsomest houses all facing it—the fluctuations of the tides[3] being so inconsiderable, that they cause no inconvenience.

The Pritchard[4] residence—a fine large building—occupies a site on one side of the bay: a green lawn slopes off to the sea; and in front waves the English flag. Across the water, the tricolor also, and the stars and stripes, distinguish the residences of the other consuls.

What greatly added to the picturesqueness of the bay at this time, was the condemned hull of a large ship, which at the farther end of the harbor lay bilged upon the beach, its stern settled low in the water, and the other end high and dry. From where we lay, the trees behind seemed to lock their leafy boughs over its bowsprit; which, from its position, looked nearly upright.

She was an American whaler, a very old craft. Having sprung a leak at sea, she had made all sail for the island, to heave down for repairs. Found utterly unseaworthy, however, her oil was taken out and sent home in another vessel; the hull was then stripped and sold for a trifle.

Before leaving Tahiti, I had the curiosity to go over this poor old ship, thus stranded on a strange shore. What were my emotions, when I saw upon her stern the name of a small town on the river Hudson! She was from the noble stream on whose banks I was born; in whose waters I had a hundred times bathed. In an instant, palm-trees and elms—canoes and skiffs—church spires and bamboos—all mingled in one vision of the present and the past.

But we must not leave Little Jule.

At last the wishes of many were gratified; and like an aeronaut's grapnel, her rusty little anchor was caught in the coral groves at the bottom of Papeetee Bay. This must have been more than forty days after leaving the Marquesas.

The sails were yet unfurled, when a boat came alongside with our esteemed friend Wilson, the consul.

"How's this, how's this, Mr. Jermin?" he began, looking very savage as he touched the deck. "What brings you in without orders?"

"You did not come off to us, as you promised, sir; and there was no hanging on longer with nobody to work the ship," was the blunt reply.

"So the infernal scoundrels held out—did they? Very good; I'll make them *sweat* for it," and he eyed the scowling men with unwonted intrepidity. The truth was, he felt safer *now*, than when outside the reef.

"Muster the mutineers on the quarter-deck," he continued. "Drive them aft, sir, sick and well: I have a word to say to them."

"Now, men," said he, "you think it's all well with you, I suppose. You wished the ship in, and here she is. Captain Guy's ashore, and you think you must go too: but we'll see about that—I'll miserably disappoint you." (These last were his very words.) "Mr. Jermin, call off the names of those who did not refuse duty, and let them go over to the starboard side."

This done, a list was made out of the "mutineers," as he was pleased to call the rest. Among these, the doctor and myself were included; though the former stepped forward, and boldly pleaded the office held by him when the vessel left Sydney. The mate also—who had always been friendly—stated the service rendered by myself two nights previous, as well as my conduct when he announced his intention to enter the harbor. For myself, I stoutly maintained, that according to the tenor of the agreement made with Captain Guy, my time aboard the ship had expired—the cruise being virtually at an end, however it had been brought about—and I claimed my discharge.

But Wilson would hear nothing. Marking something in my manner, nevertheless, he asked my name and country; and then observed with a sneer, "Ah, you are the lad, I see, that wrote the Round Robin[5]; I'll take good care of *you*, my fine fellow—step back, sir."

As for poor Long Ghost, he denounced him as a "Sydney Flash-Gorger"; though what under heaven he meant by that euphonious title, is more than I can tell. Upon this, the doctor gave him such a piece of his mind, that the consul furiously commanded him to hold his peace, or he would instantly have him seized into the rigging, and flogged. There was no help for either of us—we were judged by the company we kept.

All were now sent forward; not a word being said as to what he intended doing with us.

After a talk with the mate, the consul withdrew, going aboard the French frigate, which lay within a cable's length. We now suspected his object; and since matters had come to this pass, were rejoiced at it. In a day or two the Frenchman was to sail for Valparaiso, the usual place of rendezvous for the English squadron in the Pacific; and doubtless, Wilson meant to put us on board, and send us thither to be delivered up. Should our conjecture prove correct, all we had to expect, according to our most experienced shipmates, was the fag end of a cruise in one of her majesty's ships, and a discharge before long at Portsmouth.

We now proceeded to put on all the clothes we could—frock over frock, and trowsers over trowsers—so as to be in readiness for removal at a moment's warning. Armed ships allow nothing superfluous to litter up the deck; and therefore, should we go aboard the frigate, our chests and their contents would have to be left behind.

In an hour's time, the first-cutter of the Reine Blanche came alongside, manned by eighteen or twenty sailors, armed with cutlasses and boarding-pistols—the officers, of course, wearing their side-arms, and the consul in an official cocked hat, borrowed for the occasion. The boat was painted a "pirate black," its crew were a dark, grim-looking set, and the officers uncommonly fierce-looking little Frenchmen. On the whole they were calculated to intimidate—the consul's object, doubtless, in bringing them.

Summoned aft again, every one's name was called separately; and being solemnly reminded that it was his last chance to escape punishment, was asked if he still refused duty. The response was instantaneous: "Ay, sir, I do." In some cases followed up by divers explanatory observations, cut short by Wilson's ordering the delinquent into the cutter. As a general thing, the order was promptly obeyed—some taking a sequence of hops, skips, and jumps, by way of showing, not only their unimpaired activity of body, but their alacrity in complying with all reasonable requests.

Having avowed their resolution not to pull another rope of the Julia's—even if at once restored to perfect health—all the invalids, with the exception of the two to be set ashore, accompanied us into the cutter. They were in high spirits; so much so, that something was insinuated about their not having been quite as ill as pretended.

The cooper's name was the last called; we did not hear what he answered, but he stayed behind. Nothing was done about the Mowree.

Shoving clear from the ship, three loud cheers were raised; Flash Jack and others receiving a sharp reprimand for it from the consul.

"Good-bye, Little Jule," cried Navy Bob, as we swept under the bows. "Don't fall overboard, Ropey," said another to the poor land-lubber, who, with Wymontoo, the Dane, and others left behind, was looking over at us from the forecastle.

"Give her three more!" cried Salem, springing to his feet and whirling his hat round. "You sacre dam raskeel," shouted the lieutenant of the party, bringing the flat of his sabre across his shoulders, "you now keepy steel."

The doctor and myself, more discreet, sat quietly in the bow of the cutter; and for my own part, though I did not repent what I had done, my reflections were far from being enviable.

CHAPTER XXX

They Take Us Ashore—What Happened There

Five days and nights, if I remember right, we were aboard the frigate. On the afternoon of the fifth, we were told that the next morning she sailed for Valparaiso. Rejoiced at this, we prayed for a speedy passage. But, as it turned out, the consul had no idea of letting us off so easily. To our no small surprise, an officer came along toward night, and ordered us out of irons. Being then mustered in the gangway, we were escorted into a cutter alongside, and pulled ashore.

Accosted by Wilson as we struck the beach, he delivered us up to a numerous guard of natives, who at once conducted us to a house near by. Here we were made to sit down under a shade without; and the consul and two elderly European residents passed by us, and entered.

After some delay, during which we were much diverted by the hilarious good-nature of our guard—one of our number was called out for, followed by an order for him to enter the house alone.

On returning a moment after, he told us we had little to encounter. It had simply been asked, whether he still continued of the same mind; on replying yes, something was put down upon a piece of paper, and he was waved outside. All being summoned in rotation, my own turn came at last.

Within, Wilson and his two friends were seated magisterially at a table—an inkstand, a pen, and a sheet of paper, lending quite a business-like air to the apartment. These three gentlemen, being arrayed in coats and pantaloons, looked respectable, at least in a country where complete suits of garments are so seldom met with. One present essayed a solemn aspect; but having a short neck and a full face, only made out to look stupid.

It was this individual who condescended to take a paternal interest in myself. After declaring my resolution with respect to the ship unalterable, I was proceeding to withdraw, in compliance with a sign from the consul, when the stranger turned round to him, saying, "Wait a minute, if you please, Mr. Wilson; let me talk to that youth. Come here, my young friend: I'm extremely sorry to see you associated with these bad men; do you know what it will end in?"

"Oh, that's the lad that wrote the Round Robin," interposed the consul. "He and that rascally doctor are at the bottom of the whole affair—go outside, sir."

I retired as from the presence of royalty; backing out with many bows.

The evident prejudice of Wilson against both the doctor and myself, was by no means inexplicable. A man of any education before the mast is always looked upon with dislike by his captain; and, never mind how peaceable he may be, should any disturbance arise, from his intellectual superiority, he is deemed to exert an underhand influence against the officers.

Little as I had seen of Captain Guy, the few glances cast upon me after being on board a week or so, were sufficient to reveal his enmity—a feeling quickened by my undisguised companionship with Long Ghost, whom he both feared and cordially hated. Guy's relations with the consul, readily explains the latter's hostility.

The examination over, Wilson and his friends advanced to the doorway; when the former, assuming a severe expression, pronounced our perverseness, infatuation in the extreme. Nor was there any hope left: our last chance for pardon was gone. Even were we to become contrite, and crave permission to return to duty, it would not now be permitted.

"Oh! get along with your gammon, *counselor*," exclaimed Black Dan, absolutely indignant that his understanding should be thus insulted.

Quite enraged, Wilson bade him hold his peace; and then, summoning a fat old native to his side, addressed him in Tahitian, giving directions for leading us away to a place of safe keeping.

Hereupon, being marshaled in order, with the old man at our head, we were put in motion, with loud shouts, along a fine pathway, running far on, through wide groves of the cocoa-nut and bread-fruit.

The rest of our escort trotted on beside us in high good-humor; jabbering broken English, and in a hundred ways giving us to understand that Wilson was no favorite of theirs, and that we were prime, good fellows for holding out as we did. They seemed to know our whole history.

The scenery around was delightful. The tropical day was fast drawing to a close; and from where we were, the sun looked like a vast red fire burning in the woodlands—its rays falling aslant through the endless ranks of trees, and every leaf fringed with flame. Escaped from the confined decks of the frigate, the air breathed spices to us; streams were heard flowing; green boughs were rocking; and far inland, all sunset flushed, rose the still, steep peaks of the island.

As we proceeded, I was more and more struck by the picturesqueness of the wide, shaded road. In several places, durable bridges of wood were thrown over large water-courses; others were spanned by a single arch of stone. In any part of the road, three horsemen might have ridden abreast.

This beautiful avenue—by far the best thing which civilization has done for the island—is called by foreigners "the Broom Road," though for what reason I do not know. Originally planned for the convenience of the missionaries journeying from one station to another, it almost completely encompasses the larger peninsula; skirting for a distance of at least sixty miles along the low, fertile lands bordering the sea. But on the side next Taiarboo, or the lesser peninsula, it sweeps through a narrow, secluded valley, and thus crosses the island in that direction.

The uninhabited interior, being almost impenetrable from the densely wooded glens, frightful precipices, and sharp mountain ridges absolutely inaccessible, is but little known, even to the natives themselves; and so, instead of striking directly across from one village to another, they follow the Broom Road round and round.[6]

It is by no means, however, altogether traveled on foot; horses being now quite plentiful. They were introduced from Chili; and possessing all the gayety, fleetness, and docility of the Spanish breed, are admirably adapted to the tastes of the higher classes, who as equestrians have become very expert. The missionaries and chiefs never think of journeying except in the saddle; and at all hours of the day, you see the latter galloping along at full speed. Like the Sandwich Islanders, they ride like Pawnee-Loups.

For miles and miles I have traveled the Broom Road, and never wearied of the continual change of scenery. But wherever it leads you—whether through level woods, across grassy glens, or over hills waving with palms—the bright blue sea on one side, and the green mountain pinnacles on the other, are always in sight.

CHAPTER XXXI

The Calabooʒa Beretanee

About a mile from the village we came to a halt.

It was a beautiful spot. A mountain stream here flowed at the foot of a verdant slope; on one hand, it murmured along until the waters, spreading themselves upon a beach of small, sparkling shells, trickled into the sea; on the other, was a long defile, where the eye pursued a gleaming, sinuous thread, lost in shade and verdure.

The ground next the road was walled in by a low, rude parapet of stones; and, upon the summit of the slope beyond, was a large, native house, the thatch dazzling white, and, in shape, an oval.

"Calabooza! Calabooza Beretanee!" (the English Jail), cried our conductor, pointing to the building.

For a few months past, having been used by the consul as a house of confinement for his refractory sailors, it was thus styled to distinguish it from similar places in and about Papeetee.

Though extremely romantic in appearance, on a near approach it proved but ill adapted to domestic comfort. In short, it was a mere shell, recently built, and still unfinished. It was open all round, and tufts of grass were growing here and there under the very roof. The only piece of furniture was the "stocks," a clumsy machine for keeping people in one place, which, I believe, is pretty much out of date in most countries. It is still in use, however, among the Spaniards in South America; from whom, it seems, the Tahitians have borrowed the contrivance, as well as the name by which all places of confinement are known among them.

The stocks were nothing more than two stout timbers, about twenty feet in length, and precisely alike. One was placed edgeways on the ground, and the other resting on top, left, at regular intervals along the seam, several round holes, the object of which was evident at a glance.

By this time, our guide had informed us, that he went by the name of *"Capin Bob"* (Captain Bob); and a hearty old Bob he proved. It was just the name for him. From the first, so pleased were we with the old man, that we cheerfully acquiesced in his authority.

Entering the building, he set us about fetching heaps of dry leaves to spread behind the stocks for a couch. A trunk of a small cocoa-nut tree was then placed for a bolster—rather a hard one, but the natives are used to it. For a pillow, they use a little billet of wood, scooped out, and standing on four short legs—a sort of head-stool.

These arrangements completed, Captain Bob proceeded to "hannapar," or secure us, for the night. The upper timber of the machine being lifted at one end, and our ankles placed in the semicircular spaces of the lower one, the other beam was then dropped; both being finally secured together by an old iron hoop at either extremity. This initiation was performed to the boisterous mirth of the natives, and diverted ourselves not a little.

Captain Bob now bustled about, like an old woman seeing the children to bed. A basket of baked "taro," or Indian turnip, was brought in, and we were given a piece all round. Then a great counterpane, of coarse, brown "tappa," was stretched over the whole party; and, after sundry injunctions to "mooe-mooe," and be "maitai"—in other words, to go to sleep, and be good boys—we were left to ourselves, fairly put to bed and tucked in.

Much talk was now had concerning our prospects in life; but the doctor and I, who lay side by side, thinking the occasion better adapted to meditation, kept pretty silent; and, before long, the rest ceased conversing, and, wearied with loss of rest on board the frigate, were soon sound asleep.

After sliding from one revery into another, I started, and gave the doctor a pinch. He was dreaming, however; and resolved to follow his example, I troubled him no more.

How the rest managed, I know not; but, for my own part I found it very hard to get asleep. The consciousness of having one's foot *pinned;* and the impossibility of getting it anywhere else than just where it was, was most distressing.

But this was not all: there was no way of lying but straight on your back; unless, to be sure, one's limb went round and round in the ankle, like a swivel. Upon getting into a sort of doze, it was no wonder this uneasy posture gave me the nightmare. Under the delusion that I was about some gymnastics or other, I gave my unfortunate member such a twitch, that I started up with the idea that some one was dragging the stocks away.

Captain Bob and his friends lived in a little hamlet hard by; and when morning showed in the East, the old gentleman came forth from that direction likewise, emerging from a grove, and saluting us loudly as he approached.

Finding everybody awake, he set us at liberty; and, leading us down to the stream, ordered every man to strip and bathe. "All han's, my boy, hanna-hanna, wash!" he cried. Bob was a linguist, and had been to sea in his day, as he many a time afterward told us.

At this moment, we were all alone with him; and it would have been the easiest thing in the world to have given him the slip; but he seemed to have no idea of such a thing; treating us so frankly and cordially, indeed, that even had we thought of running, we would have been ashamed of attempting it. He very well knew, nevertheless (as we ourselves were not slow in finding out), that, for various reasons, any attempt of the kind, without some previously arranged plan for leaving the island, would be certain to fail.

As Bob was a rare one every way, I must give some account of him. There was a good deal of "personal appearance" about him; in short, he was a corpulent giant, over six feet in height, and literally as big round as a hogshead. The enormous bulk of some of the Tahitians has been frequently spoken of by voyagers.

Beside being the English consul's jailer, as it were, he carried on a little Tahitian farming; that is to say, he owned several groves of the bread-fruit and palm, and never hindered their growing. Close by was a "taro" patch of his, which he occasionally visited.

Bob seldom disposed of the produce of his lands; it was all needed for domestic consumption. Indeed, for gormandizing, I would have matched him against any three common-council men at a civic feast.

A friend of Bob's told me, that, owing to his voraciousness, his visits to other parts of the island were much dreaded; for, according to Tahitian customs, hospitality without charge is enjoined upon every one; and though it is reciprocal in most cases, in Bob's it was almost out of the question. The damage done to a native larder in one of his morning calls, was more than could be made good by his entertainer's spending the holydays with him.

The old man, as I have hinted, had, once upon a time, been a cruise or two in a whaling-vessel; and, therefore, he prided himself upon his English. Having acquired what he knew of it in the forecastle, he talked little else than sailor phrases, which sounded whimsically enough.

I asked him one day how old he was. "Olee?" he exclaimed, looking very profound in consequence of thoroughly understanding so subtile a question—"Oh! very olee—'tousand 'ear —more—big man when Capin Tootee (Captain Cook) heavey in sight." (In sea parlance, came into view.)

This was a thing impossible; but adapting my discourse to the man, I rejoined—"Ah! you see Capin Tootee—well, how you like him?"

"Oh! he maitai: (good) friend of me, and know my wife."

On my assuring him strongly, that he could not have been born at the time, he explained himself by saying, that he was speaking of his father, all the while. This, indeed, might very well have been.

It is a curious fact, that all these people, young and old, will tell you that they have enjoyed the honor of a personal acquaintance with the great navigator; and if you listen to them, they will go on and tell anecdotes without end. This spring from nothing but their great desire to please; well knowing tha a more agreeable topic for a white man could not be selected. As for the anachronism of the thing, they seem to have no idea of it: days and years are all the same to them.

After our sunrise bath, Bob once more placed us in the stocks, almost moved to tears at subjecting us to so great a hardship; but he could not treat us otherwise, he said, on pain of the consul's displeasure. How long we were to be confined, he did not know; nor what was to be done with us in the end.

As noon advanced, and no signs of a meal were visible, some one inquired whether we were to be boarded, as well as lodged, at the Hotel de Calabooza?

"Vast heavey" (avast heaving, or wait a bit)—said Bob—"kow-kow" (food) "come ship by by."

And, sure enough, along comes Rope Yarn with a wooden bucket of the Julia's villainous biscuit. With a grin, he said it was a present from Wilson; it was all we were to get that day. A great cry was now raised; and well was it for the land-lubber that he had a pair of legs, and the men could not use theirs. One and all, we resolved not to touch the bread, come what come might; and so we told the natives.

Being extravagantly fond of ship-biscuit—the harder the better—they were quite overjoyed; and offered to give us every day, a small quantity of baked bread-fruit and Indian turnip in exchange for the bread. This we agreed to; and every morning afterward, when the bucket came, its contents were at once handed over to Bob and his friends, who never ceased munching until nightfall.

Our exceedingly frugal meal of bread-fruit over, Captain Bob waddled up to us with a couple of long poles hooked at one end, and several large baskets of woven cocoa-nut branches.

Not far off was an extensive grove of orange-trees in full bearing; and myself and another were selected to go with him, and gather a supply for the party. When we went in among the trees, the sumptuousness of the orchard was unlike any thing I had ever seen; while the fragrance shaken from the gently waving boughs, regaled our senses most delightfully.

In many places the trees formed a dense shade, spreading overhead a dark, rustling vault, groined with boughs, and studded here and there with the ripened spheres, like gilded balls. In several places, the overladen branches were borne to the earth, hiding the trunk in a tent of foliage. Once fairly in the grove, we could see nothing else; it was oranges all round.

To preserve the fruit from bruising, Bob, hooking the twigs with his pole, let them fall into his basket. But this would not do for us. Seizing hold of a bough, we brought such a shower to the ground, that our old friend was fain to run from under. Heedless of remonstrance, we then reclined in the shade, and feasted to our heart's content. Heaping up the baskets afterward, we returned to our comrades, by whom our arrival was hailed with loud plaudits; and in a marvellously short time, nothing was left of the oranges we brought, but the rinds.

While inmates of the Calabooza, we had as much of the fruit as we wanted; and to this cause, and others that might be mentioned, may be ascribed the speedy restoration of our sick to comparative health.

The orange of Tahiti is delicious—small and sweet, with a thin, dry rind. Though now abounding, it was unknown before Cook's time, to whom the natives are indebted for so great a blessing. He likewise introduced several other kinds of fruit; among these were the fig, pine-apple, and lemon, now seldom met with. The lime still grows, and some of the poorer natives express the juice to sell to the shipping. It is highly valued as an anti-scorbutic. Nor was the variety of foreign fruits and vegetables which were introduced, the only benefit conferred by the first visitors to the Society group. Cattle and sheep were left at various places. More of them anon.

Thus, after all that of late years has been done for these islanders, Cook and Vancouver may, in one sense at least, be considered their greatest benefactors.

CHAPTER XXXIII

We Receive Calls at the Hotel de Calabooza

Our place of confinement being open all round, and so near the Broom Road, of course we were in plain sight of every body passing; and, therefore, we had no lack of visitors among such an idle, inquisitive set as the Tahitians. For a few days, they were coming and going continually; while thus ignobly fast by the foot, we were fain to give passive audience.

During this period, we were the lions of the neighborhood; and, no doubt, strangers from the distant villages were taken to see the "Karhowrees" (white men), in the same way that countrymen, in a city, are gallanted to the Zoological Gardens.

All this gave us a fine opportunity of making observations. I was painfully struck by the considerable number of sickly or deformed persons; undoubtedly made so by a virulent complaint, which, under native treatment, almost invariably affects, in the end, the muscles and bones of the body. In particular, there is a distortion of the back, most unsightly to behold, originating in a horrible form of the malady.

Although this, and other bodily afflictions, were unknown before the discovery of the islands by the whites, there are several cases found of the Fa-Fa, or Elephantiasis—a native disease, which seems to have prevailed among them from the earliest antiquity. Affecting the legs and feet alone, it swells them, in some instances, to the girth of a man's body, covering the skin with scales. It might be supposed, that one, thus afflicted, would be incapable of walking; but, to all appearance, they seem to be nearly as active as any body; apparently, suffering no pain, and bearing the calamity with a degree of cheerfulness truly marvellous.

The Fa-Fa is very gradual in its approaches, and years elapse before the limb is fully swollen. Its origin is ascribed by the natives to various causes; but the general impression seems to be, that it arises, in most cases, from the eating of unripe breadfruit and Indian turnip. So far as I could find out, it is not hereditary. In no stage do they attempt a cure; the complaint being held incurable.

Speaking of the Fa-Fa, reminds me of a poor fellow, a sailor, whom I afterward saw at Roorootoo, a lone island, some two days' sail from Tahiti.

The island is very small, and its inhabitants nearly extinct. We sent a boat off to see whether any yams were to be had, as formerly, the yams of Roorootoo were as famous among the islands round about, as Sicily oranges in the Mediterranean. Going ashore, to my surprise, I was accosted, near a little shanty of a church, by a white man, who limped forth from a wretched hut. His hair and beard were unshorn, his face deadly pale and haggard, and one limb swelled with the Fa-Fa to an incredible bigness. This was the first instance of a foreigner suffering from it, that I had ever seen, or heard of; and the spectacle shocked me accordingly.

He had been there for years. From the first symptoms, he could not believe his complaint to be what it really was, and trusted it would soon disappear. But when it became plain, that his only chance for recovery was a speedy change of climate, no ship would receive him as a sailor: to think of being taken as a passenger, was idle. This speaks little for the humanity of sea captains; but the truth is, that those in the Pacific have little enough of the virtue; and, nowadays, when so many charitable appeals are made to them, they have become callous.

I pitied the poor fellow from the bottom of my heart; but nothing could I do, as our captain was inexorable. "Why," said he, "here we are—started on a six months' cruise—I can't put back; and he is better off on the island than at sea. So on Roorootoo he must die." And probably he did.

I afterward heard of this melancholy object, from two seamen. His attempts to leave were still unavailing, and his hard fate was fast closing in.

Notwithstanding the physical degeneracy of the Tahitians as a people, among the chiefs, individuals of personable figures are still frequently met with; and, occasionally, majestic-looking men, and diminutive women as lovely as the nymphs who, nearly a century ago, swam round the ships of Wallis. In these instances, Tahitian beauty is quite as seducing as it proved to the crew of the Bounty; the young girls being just such creatures as a poet would picture in the tropics—soft, plump, and dreamy-eyed.

The natural complexion of both sexes is quite light; but the males appear much darker, from their exposure to the sun. A dark complexion, however, in a man, is highly esteemed, as indicating strength of both body and soul. Hence there is a saying, of great antiquity among them,

> "If dark the cheek of the mother,
> The son will sound the war-conch;
> If strong her frame, he will give laws."

With this idea of manliness, no wonder the Tahitians regard all pale and tepid-looking Europeans, as weak and feminine; whereas, a sailor, with a cheek like the breast of a roast turkey, is held a lad of brawn: to use their own phrase, a "taata tona," or man of bones.

Speaking of bones, recalls an ugly custom of theirs, now obsolete—that of making fish-hooks and gimblets out of those of their enemies. This beats the Scandinavians turning people's skulls into cups and saucers.

But to return to the Calabooza Beretanee. Immense was the interest we excited among the throngs that called there; they would stand talking about us by the hour, growing most unnecessarily excited too, and dancing up and down with all the vivacity of their race. They invariably sided with us; flying out against the consul, and denouncing him as "Ita maitai nuee," or very bad exceedingly. They must have borne him some grudge or other.

Nor were the women, sweet souls, at all backward in visiting. Indeed, they manifested even more interest than the men; gazing at us with eyes full of a thousand meanings, and conversing with marvellous rapidity. But, alas! inquisitive though they were, and, doubtless, taking some passing compassion on us, there was little real feeling in them after all, and still less sentimental sympathy. Many of them laughed outright at us, noting only what was ridiculous in our plight.

I think it was the second day of our confinement, that a wild, beautiful girl burst into the Calabooza, and, throwing herself into an arch attitude, stood afar off, and gazed at us. She was a heartless one:—tickled to death with Black Dan's nursing his chafed ankle, and indulging in certain moral reflections on the consul and Captain Guy. After laughing her fill at him, she condescended to notice the rest; glancing from one to another, in the most methodical and provoking manner imaginable. Whenever any thing struck her comically, you saw it like a flash —her finger levelled instantaneously, and, flinging herself back, she gave loose to strange, hollow little notes of laughter, that sounded like the bass of a music-box, playing a lively air with the lid down.

Now, I knew not, that there was any thing in my own appearance calculated to disarm ridicule; and, indeed, to have looked at all heroic, under the circumstances, would have been rather difficult. Still, I could not but feel exceedingly annoyed at the prospect of being screamed at in turn, by this mischievous young witch, even though she were but an islander. And, to tell a secret, her beauty had something to do with this sort of feeling; and, pinioned as I was, to a log, and clad most unbecomingly, I began to grow sentimental.

Ere her glance fell upon me, I had, unconsciously, thrown myself into the most graceful attitude I could assume, leaned my head upon my hand, and summoned up as abstracted an expression as possible. Though my face was averted, I soon felt it flush, and knew that the glance was on me: deeper and deeper grew the flush, and not a sound of laughter.

Delicious thought! she was moved at the sight of me. I could stand it no longer, but started up. Lo! there she was; her great hazel eyes rounding and rounding in her head, like two stars, her whole frame in a merry quiver, and an expression about the mouth that was sudden and violent death to any thing like sentiment.

The next moment she spun round, and, bursting from peal to peal of laughter, went racing out of the Calabooza; and, in mercy to me, never returned.

CHAPTER XXXIV

Life at the Calabooza

A few days passed; and, at last, our docility was rewarded by some indulgence on the part of Captain Bob.

He allowed the entire party to be at large during the day; only enjoining upon us always to keep within hail. This, to be sure, was in positive disobedience to Wilson's orders; and so, care had to be taken that he should not hear of it. There was little fear of the natives telling him; but strangers traveling the Broom Road might. By way of precaution, boys were stationed as scouts along the road. At sight of a white man, they sounded the alarm; when we all made for our respective holes (the stocks being purposely left open): the beam then descended, and we were prisoners. As soon as the traveler was out of sight, of course, we were liberated.

Notwithstanding the regular supply of food which we obtained from Captain Bob and his friends, it was so small, that we often felt most intolerably hungry. We could not blame them for not bringing us more, for we soon became aware that they had to pinch themselves, in order to give us what they did; beside, they received nothing for their kindness but the daily bucket of bread.

Among a people, like the Tahitians, what we call "hard times," can only be experienced in a scarcity of edibles; yet, so destitute are many of the common people, that this most distressing consequence of civilization may be said, with them, to be ever present. To be sure, the natives about the Calabooza, had abundance of limes and oranges; but what were *these* good for, except to impart a still keener edge to appetites which there was so little else to gratify? During the height of the bread-fruit season, they fare better; but, at other times, the demands of the shipping exhaust the uncultivated resources of the island; and the lands being mostly owned by the chiefs, the inferior orders have to suffer for their cupidity. Deprived of their nets, many of them would starve.

As Captain Bob insensibly remitted his watchfulness, and we began to stroll farther and farther from the Calabooza, we managed, by a systematic foraging upon the country round about, to make up for some of our deficiencies. And fortunate it was, that the houses of the wealthier natives were just as open to us as those of the most destitute; we were treated as kindly in one as the other.

Once in a while, we came in at the death of a chief's pig; the noise of whose slaughtering was generally to be heard at a great distance. An occasion like this gathers the neighbors together, and they have a bit of a feast, where a stranger is always welcome. A good loud squeal, therefore, was music in our ears. It showed something going on in that direction.

Breaking in upon the party tumultuously, as we did, we always created a sensation. Sometimes, we found the animal still alive and struggling; in which case, it was generally dropped at our approach. To provide for these emergencies, Flash Jack generally repaired to the scene of operations with a sheath knife between his teeth, and a club in his hand. Others were exceedingly officious in singeing off the bristles, and disembowelling. Doctor Long Ghost and myself, however, never meddled with these preliminaries, but came to the feast itself, with unimpaired energies.

Like all lank men, my long friend had an appetite of his own. Others occasionally went about seeking what they might devour, but *he* was always on the alert.

He had an ingenious way of obviating an inconvenience which we all experienced at times. The islanders seldom use salt with their food; so he begged Rope Yarn to bring him some from the ship; also a little pepper, if he could; which, accordingly, was done. This he placed in a small leather wallet—a "monkey bag" (so called by sailors)—usually worn as a purse about the neck.

"In my poor opinion," said Long Ghost, as he tucked the wallet out of sight, "it behooves a stranger, in Tahiti, to have his knife in readiness, and his caster slung."

CHAPTER XXXV

Visit from an Old Acquaintance

We had not been many days ashore, when Doctor Johnson was espied coming along the Broom Road.

We had heard that he meditated a visit, and suspected what he was after. Being upon the consul's hands, all our expenses were of course payable by him in his official capacity; and, therefore, as a friend of Wilson, and sure of good pay, the shore doctor had some idea of allowing us to run up a bill with him. True, it was rather awkward to ask us to take medicines, which, on board the ship, he told us were not needed. However, he resolved to put a bold face on the matter, and give us a call.

His approach was announced by one of the scouts, upon which some one suggested that we should let him enter, and then put him in the stocks. But Long Ghost proposed better sport. What it was, we shall presently see.

Very bland and amiable, Doctor Johnson advanced, and, resting his cane on the stocks, glanced to right and left, as we lay before him. "Well, my lads"—he began—"how do you find yourselves to-day?"

Looking very demure, the men made some rejoinder; and he went on.

"Those poor fellows I saw the other day—the sick, I mean—how are they?" and he scrutinized the company. At last, he singled out one who was assuming a most unearthly appearance, and remarked, that he looked as if he were extremely ill. "Yes," said the sailor dolefully, "I'm afeard, doctor, I'll soon be losing the number of my mess!" (a sea phrase, for departing this life) and he closed his eyes, and moaned.

"*What* does he say?" said Johnson, turning round eagerly.

"Why," exclaimed Flash Jack, who volunteered as interpreter, "he means he's going to *croak*" (die).

"*Croak!* and what does that mean, applied to a patient?"

"Oh! I understand," said he, when the word was explained; and he stepped over the stocks, and felt the man's pulse.

"What's his name?" he asked, turning this time to old Navy Bob.

"We calls him Jingling Joe," replied that worthy.

"Well then, men, you must take good care of poor Joseph; and I will send him a powder, which must be taken according to the directions. Some of you know how to read, I presume?"

"That ere young cove does," replied Bob, pointing toward the place where I lay, as if he were directing attention to a sail at sea.

After examining the rest—some of whom were really invalids, but convalescent, and others only pretending to be laboring under divers maladies, Johnson turned round, and addressed the party.

"Men," said he, "if any more of you are ailing, speak up, and let me know. By order of the consul, I'm to call every day; so if any of you are at all sick, it's my duty to prescribe for you. This sudden change from ship fare to shore living plays the deuce with you sailors, so be cautious about eating fruit. Goodday! I'll send you the medicines the first thing in the morning."

Now, I am inclined to suspect that with all his want of understanding, Johnson must have had some idea that we were quizzing him. Still, that was nothing, so long as it answered his purpose; and therefore, if he *did* see through us, he never showed it.

Sure enough, at the time appointed, along came a native lad with a small basket of cocoa-nut stalks, filled with powders, pillboxes, and vials, each with names and directions written in a large, round hand. The sailors, one and all, made a snatch at the collection, under the strange impression that some of the vials were seasoned with spirits. But, asserting his privilege as physician to the first reading of the labels, Doctor Long Ghost was at last permitted to take possession of the basket.

The first thing lighted upon, was a large vial, labelled— "For William—rub well in."

This vial certainly had a spirituous smell; and upon handing it to the patient, he made a summary internal application of its contents. The doctor looked aghast.

There was now a mighty commotion. Powders and pills were voted mere drugs in the market, and the holders of vials were pronounced lucky dogs. Johnson must have known enough of sailors to make some of his medicines palatable—this, at least, Long Ghost suspected. Certain it was, every one took to the vials; if at all spicy, directions were unheeded, their contents all going one road.

The largest one of all, quite a bottle indeed, and having a sort of burnt brandy odor, was labelled—"For Daniel, drink freely, and until relieved." This, Black Dan proceeded to do; and would have made an end of it at once, had not the bottle, after a hard struggle, been snatched from his hands, and passed round, like a jovial decanter. The old tar had complained of the effects of an immoderate eating of fruit.

Upon calling the following morning, our physician found his precious row of patients reclining behind the stocks, and doing "as well as could be expected."

But the pills and powders were found to have been perfectly inactive: probably because none had been taken. To make them efficacious, it was suggested that, for the future, a bottle of Pisco should be sent along with them. According to Flash Jack's notions, unmitigated medical compounds were but dry stuff at the best, and needed something good to wash them down.

Thus far, our own M.D., Doctor Long Ghost, after starting the frolic, had taken no further part in it; but on the physician's third visit, he took him to one side, and had a private confabulation. What it was, exactly, we could not tell; but from certain illustrative signs and gestures, I fancied that he was describing the symptoms of some mysterious disorganization of the vitals, which must have come on within the hour. Assisted by his familiarity with medical terms, he seemed to produce a marked impression. At last, Johnson went his way, promising aloud that he would send Long Ghost what he desired.

When the medicine boy came along the following morning,

the doctor was the first to accost him, walking off with a small purple vial. This time, there was little else in the basket but a case bottle of the burnt brandy cordial, which, after much debate, was finally disposed of by some one pouring the contents, little by little, into the half of a cocoa-nut shell, and so giving all who desired, a glass. No further medicinal cheer remaining, the men dispersed.

An hour or two passed, when Flash Jack directed attention to my long friend, who, since the medicine boy left, had not been noticed till now. With eyes closed, he was lying behind the stocks, and Jack was lifting his arm and letting it fall as if life were extinct. On running up with the rest, I at once connected the phenomenon with the mysterious vial. Searching his pocket, I found it, and holding it up, it proved to be laudanum. Flash Jack, snatching it from my hand in a rapture, quickly informed all present, what it was; and with much glee, proposed a nap for the company. Some of them not comprehending him exactly, the apparently defunct Long Ghost—who lay so still that I a little suspected the genuineness of his sleep—was rolled about as an illustration of the virtues of the vial's contents. The idea tickled everybody mightily; and throwing themselves down, the magic draught was passed from hand to hand. Thinking that, as a matter of course, they must at once become insensible, each man, upon taking his sip, fell back, and closed his eyes.

There was little fear of the result, since the narcotic was equally distributed. But, curious to see how it would operate, I raised myself gently after a while, and looked around. It was about noon, and perfectly still; and as we all daily took the siesta, I was not much surprised to find every one quiet. Still, in one or two instances, I thought I detected a little peeping.

Presently, I heard a footstep, and saw Doctor Johnson approaching.

And perplexed enough did he look at the sight of his prostrate file of patients, plunged apparently, in such unaccountable slumbers.

"Daniel," he cried, at last, punching in the side with his

cane, the individual thus designated—"Daniel, my good fellow, get up! do you hear?"

But Black Dan was immovable; and he poked the next sleeper.

"Joseph, Joseph! come, wake up! it's me, Doctor Johnson."

But Jingling Joe, with mouth open, and eyes shut, was not to be started.

"Bless my soul!" he exclaimed, with uplifted hands and cane, "what's got into 'em? I say, *men*"—he shouted, running up and down—"come to life, men! what under the sun's the matter with you?" and he struck the stocks, and bawled with increased vigor.

At last he paused, folded his hands over the head of his cane, and steadfastly gazed upon us. The notes of the nasal orchestra were rising and falling upon his ear, and a new idea suggested itself.

"Yes, yes; the rascals must have been getting boozy. Well, it's none of my business—I'll be off"; and off he went.

No sooner was he out of sight, than nearly all started to their feet, and a hearty laugh ensued.

Like myself, most of them had been watching the event from under a sly eyelid. By this time, too, Doctor Long Ghost was as wide awake as anybody. What were his reasons for taking laudanum,—if, indeed, he took any whatever,—is best known to himself; and, as it is neither mine nor the reader's business, we will say no more about it.[7]

CHAPTER XXXVI

We Are Carried before the Consul and Captain

We had been inmates of the Calabooza Beretanee about two weeks, when, one morning, Captain Bob, coming from the bath, in a state of utter nudity, brought into the building an armful of old tappa, and began to dress to go out.

The operation was quite simple. The tappa—of the coarsest kind—was in one long, heavy piece; and, fastening one end to

a column of Hibiscus wood, supporting the Calabooza, he
went off a few paces, and putting the other about his waist,
wound himself right up to the post. This unique costume, in
rotundity something like a farthingale, added immensely to his
large bulk; so much so, that he fairly waddled in his gait. But
he was only adhering to the fashion of his fathers; for, in the
olden time, the "Kihee," or big girdle, was quite the mode for
both sexes. Bob, despising recent innovations, still clung to it.
He was a gentleman of the old school—one of the last of the
Kihees.

He now told us, that he had orders to take us before the
consul. Nothing loath, we formed in procession; and, with
the old man at our head, sighing and laboring like an engine,
and flanked by a guard of some twenty natives, we started for
the village.

Arrived at the consular office, we found Wilson there, and
four or five Europeans, seated in a row facing us; probably
with the view of presenting as judicial an appearance as possible.

On one side was a couch, where Captain Guy reclined. He
looked convalescent; and, as we found out, intended soon to go
aboard his ship. He said nothing, but left everything to the
consul.

The latter now rose, and, drawing forth a paper from a large
roll, tied with red tape, commenced reading aloud.

It purported to be, "The affidavit of John Jermin, first officer
of the British Colonial Barque Julia; Guy, Master"; and proved
to be a long statement of matters, from the time of leaving
Sydney, down to our arrival in the harbor. Though artfully
drawn up, so as to bear hard against every one of us, it was
pretty correct in the details; excepting, that it was wholly silent
as to the manifold derelictions of the mate himself—a fact which
imparted unusual significance to the concluding sentence, "And
furthermore, this deponent sayeth not."

No comments were made, although we all looked round for
the mate, to see whether it was possible that he could have
authorized this use of his name. But he was not present.

The next document produced, was the deposition of the captain himself. As on all other occasions, however, he had very little to say for himself, and it was soon set aside.

The third affidavit, was that of the seamen remaining aboard the vessel, including the traitor Bungs, who, it seemed, had turned ship's evidence. It was an atrocious piece of exaggeration, from beginning to end; and those who signed it could not have known what they were about. Certainly Wymontoo did not, though his mark was there. In vain the consul commanded silence during the reading of this paper; comments were shouted out upon every paragraph.

The affidavits read, Wilson, who, all the while, looked as stiff as a poker, solemnly drew forth the ship's articles from their tin case. This document was a discolored, musty, bilious-looking affair, and hard to read. When finished, the consul held it up; and, pointing to the marks of the ship's company, at the bottom, asked us, one by one, whether we acknowledged the same for our own.

"What's the use of asking that?" said Black Dan; "Captain Guy there, knows as well as we they are."

"Silence, sir!" said Wilson, who, intending to produce a suitable impression by this ridiculous parade, was not a little mortified by the old sailor's bluntness.

A pause of a few moments now ensued; during which the bench of judges communed with Captain Guy, in a low tone, and the sailors canvassed the motives of the consul in having the affidavits taken.

The general idea seemed to be, that it was done with a view of "bouncing," or frightening us into submission. Such proved to be the case; for Wilson, rising to his feet again, addressed us as follows:—

"You see, men, that every preparation has been made to send you to Sydney for trial. The Rosa (a small Australian schooner, lying in the harbor) will sail for that place in the course of ten days, at farthest. The Julia sails on a cruise this day week. Do you still refuse duty?"

We did.

Hereupon the consul and captain exchanged glances; and the latter looked bitterly disappointed.

Presently I noticed Guy's eye upon me; and, for the first time, he spoke, and told me to come near. I stepped forward.

"Was it not you that was taken off the island?"

"It was."

"It is *you* then who owe your life to my humanity. Yet this is the gratitude of a sailor, Mr. Wilson!"

"Not so, sir." And I at once gave him to understand, that I was perfectly acquainted with his motives in sending a boat into the bay; his crew was reduced, and he merely wished to procure the sailor whom he expected to find there. The *ship* was the means of my deliverance, and no thanks to the benevolence of its captain.

Doctor Long Ghost also, had a word to say. In two masterly sentences he summed up Captain Guy's character, to the complete satisfaction of every seaman present.

Matters were now growing serious; especially as the sailors became riotous, and talked about taking the consul and the captain back to the Calabooza with them.

The other judges fidgeted, and loudly commanded silence. It was at length restored; when Wilson, for the last time addressing us, said something more about the Rosa and Sydney, and concluded by reminding us, that a week would elapse ere the Julia sailed.

Leaving these hints to operate for themselves, he dismissed the party, ordering Captain Bob and his friends to escort us back whence we came.

CHAPTER XXXVII

The French Priests Pay Their Respects

A day or two after the events just related, we were lounging in the Calabooza Beretanee, when we were honored by a visit from three of the French priests; and as about the only notice ever taken of us by the English missionaries, was their leaving their cards for us in the shape of a package of tracts, we could not help thinking, that the Frenchmen, in making a personal call, were at least much better bred.

By this time they had settled themselves down quite near our habitation. A pleasant little stroll down the Broom Road, and a rustic cross peeped through the trees; and soon you came to as charming a place as one would wish to see: a soft knoll, planted with old bread-fruit trees; in front, a savannah, sloping to a grove of palms, and, between these, glimpses of blue, sunny waves.

On the summit of the knoll, was a rude chapel, of bamboos; quite small, and surmounted by the cross. Between the canes, at nightfall, the natives stole peeps at a small portable altar; a crucifix to correspond, and gilded candlesticks and censers. Their curiosity carried them no further; nothing could induce them to worship there. Such queer ideas as they entertained, of the hated strangers! Masses and chants were nothing more than evil spells. As for the priests themselves, they were no better than diabolical sorcerers; like those who, in old times, terrified their fathers.

Close by the chapel, was a range of native houses; rented from a chief, and handsomely furnished. Here lived the priests; and, very comfortably, too. They looked sanctimonious enough abroad; but that went for nothing: since, at home, in their retreat, they were a club of Friar Tucks; holding priestly wassail over many a good cup of red brandy, and rising late in the morning.

Pity it was, they couldn't marry—pity for the ladies of the island, I mean, and the cause of morality; for what business had the ecclesiastical old bachelors, with such a set of trim little native handmaidens? These damsels were their first converts; and devoted ones they were.

The priests, as I said before, were accounted necromancers: the appearance of two of our three visitors might have justified the conceit.

They were little, dried-up Frenchmen, in long, straight gowns of black cloth, and unsightly three-cornered hats—so preposterously big, that, in putting them on, the reverend fathers seemed extinguishing themselves.

Their companion was dressed differently. He wore a sort of yellow, flannel morning-gown, and a broad-brimmed Manila hat. Large and portly, he was also hale and fifty; with a complexion like an autumnal leaf—handsome blue eyes—fine teeth, and a racy Milesian brogue. In short, he was an Irishman; Father Murphy, by name; and, as such, pretty well known, and very thoroughly disliked, throughout all the Protestant missionary settlements in Polynesia. In early youth, he had been sent to a religious seminary in France; and, taking orders there, had, but once or twice afterward, revisited his native land.

Father Murphy marched up to us briskly; and the first words he uttered were, to ask whether there were any of his countrymen among us. There were two of them; one, a lad of sixteen—a bright, curly-headed rascal—and, being a young Irishman, of course, his name was Pat. The other, was an ugly, and rather melancholy-looking scamp; one M'Gee, whose prospects in life had been blasted by a premature transportation to Sydney. This was the report, at least, though it might have been scandal.

In most of my shipmates, were some redeeming qualities; but about M'Gee, there was nothing of the kind; and forced to consort with him, I could not help regretting, a thousand times, that the gallows had been so tardy. As if impelled, against her will, to send him into the world, Nature had done all she could to insure his being taken for what he was. About the eyes, there was no mistaking him; with a villainous cast in one, they seemed suspicious of each other.

Glancing away from him at once, the bluff priest rested his gaze on the good-humored face of Pat, who, with a pleasant roguishness, was "twigging" the enormous hats (or "Hytee Belteezers," as land beavers are called by sailors), from under which, like a couple of snails, peeped the two little Frenchmen.

Pat and the priest were both from the same town in Meath; and, when this was found out, there was no end to the questions of the latter. To him, Pat seemed a letter from home, and said a hundred times as much.

After a long talk between these two, and a little broken English from the Frenchmen, our visitors took leave; but

Father Murphy had hardly gone a dozen rods, when back he came, inquiring whether we were in want of anything.

"Yes," cried one, "something to eat." Upon this, he promised to send us some fresh wheat bread, of his own baking; a great luxury in Tahiti.

We all felicitated Pat upon picking up such a friend, and told him his fortune was made.

The next morning, a French servant of the priest's made his appearance, with a small bundle of clothing for our young Hibernian; and the promised bread for the party. Pat, being out at the knees and elbows, and, like the rest of us, not full inside, the present was acceptable all round.

In the afternoon, Father Murphy himself came along; and, in addition to his previous gifts, gave Pat a good deal of advice: said he was sorry to see him in limbo, and that he would have a talk with the consul about having him set free.

We saw nothing more of him for two or three days; at the end of which time he paid us another call, telling Pat, that Wilson was inexorable, having refused to set him at liberty, unless to go aboard the ship. This, the priest now besought him to do forthwith; and so escape the punishment which, it seems, Wilson had been hinting at to his intercessor. Pat, however, was staunch against entreaties; and, with all the ardor of a sophomorean sailor, protested his intention to hold out to the last. With none of the meekness of a good little boy about him, the blunt youngster stormed away at such a rate, that it was hard to pacify him; and the priest said no more.

How it came to pass—whether from Murphy's speaking to the consul, or otherwise, we could not tell—but the next day, Pat was sent for by Wilson, and being escorted to the village by our good old keeper, three days elapsed before he returned.

Bent upon reclaiming him, they had taken him on board the ship; feasted him in the cabin; and, finding that of no avail, down they thrust him into the hold, in double irons, and on bread and water. All would not do; and so he was sent back to the Calabooza. Boy that he was, they must have counted upon his being more susceptible to discipline than the rest.

The interest felt in Pat's welfare, by his benevolent country-man, was very serviceable to the rest of us; especially as we all turned Catholics, and went to mass every morning, much to Captain Bob's consternation. Upon finding it out, he threatened to keep us in the stocks, if we did not desist. He went no farther than this, though; and so, every few days, we strolled down to the priest's residence, and had a mouthful to eat, and something generous to drink. In particular, Doctor Long Ghost and myself became huge favorites with Pat's friend; and many a time he regaled us from a quaint-looking traveling-case for spirits, stowed away in one corner of his dwelling. It held four square flasks, which, somehow or other, always contained just enough to need emptying. In truth, the fine old Irishman was a rosy fellow in canonicals. His countenance and his soul were always in a glow. It may be ungenerous to reveal his failings, but he often talked thick, and sometimes was perceptibly eccentric in his gait.

I never drink French brandy, but I pledge Father Murphy. His health again! And many jolly proselytes may he make in Polynesia!

CHAPTER XXXVIII

Little Jule Sails without Us

To make good the hint thrown out by the consul upon the conclusion of the Farce of the Affidavits, we were again brought before him within the time specified.

It was the same thing over again: he got nothing out of us, and we were remanded; our resolute behavior annoying him prodigiously.

What we observed, led us to form the idea, that on first learning the state of affairs on board the Julia, Wilson must have addressed his invalid friend, the captain, something in the following style:

"Guy, my poor fellow, don't worry yourself now about those rascally sailors of yours. I'll dress them out for you— just leave it all to me, and set your mind at rest."

But handcuffs and stocks, big looks, threats, dark hints, and depositions, had all gone for naught.

Conscious that, as matters now stood, nothing serious could grow out of what had happened; and never dreaming that our being sent home for trial, had ever been really thought of, we thoroughly understood Wilson, and laughed at him accordingly.

Since leaving the Julia, we had caught no glimpse of the mate; but we often heard of him.

It seemed that he remained on board, keeping house in the cabin for himself and Viner[8]; who, going to see him according to promise, was induced to remain a guest. These two cronies now had fine times; tapping the captain's quarter-casks, playing cards on the transom, and giving balls of an evening to the ladies ashore. In short, they cut up so many queer capers, that the missionaries complained of them to the consul; and Jermin received a sharp reprimand.

This so affected him, that he drank still more freely than before; and one afternoon, when mellow as a grape, he took umbrage at a canoe full of natives, who, on being hailed from the deck to come aboard and show their papers, got frightened, and paddled for the shore. Lowering a boat instantly, he equipped Wymontoo and the Dane with a cutlass apiece, and seizing another himself, off they started in pursuit, the ship's ensign flying in the boat's stern. The alarmed islanders, beaching their canoe, with loud cries fled through the village, the mate after them, slashing his naked weapon to right and left. A crowd soon collected; and the "Karhowree toonee," or crazy stranger, was quickly taken before Wilson.

Now, it so chanced, that in a native house hard by, the consul and Captain Guy were having a quiet game at cribbage by themselves, a decanter on the table standing sentry. The obstreperous Jermin was brought in; and finding the two thus pleasantly occupied, it had a soothing effect upon him; and he insisted upon taking a hand at the cards, and a drink of the brandy. As the consul was nearly as tipsy as himself, and the captain dared not object for fear of giving offense, at it they went,—all three of them—and made a night of it; the mate's delinquencies being summarily passed over, and his captors sent away.

An incident worth relating grew out of this freak.

There wandered about Papeetee, at this time, a shrivelled little fright of an Englishwoman, known among sailors as "Old Mother Tot." From New Zealand to the Sandwich Islands, she had been all over the South Seas; keeping a rude hut of entertainment for mariners, and supplying them with rum and dice. Upon the missionary islands, of course, such conduct was severely punishable; and at various places, Mother Tot's establishment had been shut up, and its proprietor made to quit in the first vessel that could be hired to land her elsewhere. But, with a perseverance invincible, wherever she went, she always started afresh; and so became notorious everywhere.

By some wicked spell of hers, a patient, one-eyed little cobbler followed her about, mending shoes for white men, doing the old woman's cooking, and bearing all her abuse without grumbling. Strange to relate, a battered Bible was seldom out of his sight; and whenever he had leisure, and his mistress' back was turned, he was for ever poring over it. This pious propensity used to enrage the old crone past belief; and oftentimes she boxed his ears with the book, and tried to burn it. Mother Tot and her man Josy were, indeed, a curious pair.

But to my story.

A week or so after our arrival in the harbor, the old lady had once again been hunted down, and forced for the time to abandon her nefarious calling. This was brought about chiefly by Wilson, who, for some reason unknown, had contracted the most violent hatred for her; which, on her part, was more than reciprocated.

Well: passing, in the evening, where the consul and his party were making merry, she peeped through the bamboos of the house; and straightway resolved to gratify her spite.

The night was very dark; and providing herself with a huge ship's lantern, which usually swung in her hut, she waited till they came forth. This happened about midnight; Wilson making his appearance, supported by two natives, holding him up by the arms. These three went first; and just as they got under a deep shade, a bright light was thrust within an inch of Wilson's nose. The old hag was kneeling before him, holding the lantern with uplifted hands.

"Ha, ha! my fine *counselor*," she shrieked; "ye persecute a lone old body like me for selling rum—do ye? And here ye are, carried home drunk—Hoot! ye villain, I scorn ye!" And she spat upon him.

Terrified at the apparition, the poor natives—arrant believers in ghosts—dropped the trembling consul, and fled in all directions. After giving full vent to her rage, Mother Tot hobbled away, and left the three revelers to stagger home the best way they could.

The day following our last interview with Wilson, we learned that Captain Guy had gone on board his vessel, for the purpose of shipping a new crew. There was a round bounty offered; and a heavy bag of Spanish dollars, with the Julia's articles ready for signing, were laid on the capstan-head.

Now, there was no lack of idle sailors ashore, mostly "Beach-combers," who had formed themselves into an organized gang, headed by one Mack, a Scotchman, whom they styled the Commodore. By the laws of the fraternity, no member was allowed to ship on board a vessel, unless granted permission by the rest. In this way the gang controlled the port, all discharged seamen being forced to join them.

To Mack and his men our story was well known; indeed, they had several times called to see us; and of course, as sailors and congenial spirits, they were hard against Captain Guy.

Deeming the matter important, they came in a body to the Calabooza, and wished to know, whether, all things considered, we thought it best for any of them to join the Julia.

Anxious to pack the ship off as soon as possible, we answered, by all means. Some went so far as to laud the Julia to the skies, as the best and fastest of ships. Jermin too, as a good fellow, and a sailor every inch, came in for *his* share of praise; and as for the captain—quiet man, he would never trouble any one. In short, every inducement we could think of was presented; and Flash Jack ended by assuring the beach-combers solemnly, that now we were all well and hearty, nothing but a regard to principle, prevented us from returning on board ourselves.

The result was, that a new crew was finally obtained, together with a steady New Englander for second mate, and three good whalemen for harpooneers. In part, what was wanting for the ship's larder was also supplied; and as far as could be done in a place like Tahiti, the damages the vessel had sustained were re-paired. As for the Mowree, the authorities refusing to let him be put ashore, he was carried to sea in irons, down in the hold. What eventually became of him, we never heard.

Ropey, poor, poor Ropey, who a few days previous had fallen sick, was left ashore at the sailor hospital at Townor, a small place upon the beach between Papeetee and Matavai. Here, some time after, he breathed his last. No one knew his complaint; he must have died of hard times. Several of us saw him interred in the sand, and I planted a rude post to mark his resting-place.

The cooper, and the rest who had remained aboard from the first, of course, composed part of the Julia's new crew.

To account for the conduct, all along, of the consul and captain, in trying so hard to alter our purpose with respect to the ship, the following statement is all that is requisite. Beside an advance of from fifteen to twenty-five dollars demanded by every sailor shipping at Tahiti, an additional sum for each man so shipped, has to be paid into the hands of the government, as a charge of the port. Beside this, the men—with here and there an exception—will only ship for one cruise, thus becoming entitled to a discharge before the vessel reaches home; which, in time, creates the necessity of obtaining other men, at a similar cost. Now, the Julia's exchequer was at low-water mark, or rather, it was quite empty; and to meet these expenses, a good part of what little oil there was aboard, had to be sold for a song to a merchant of Papeetee.

It was Sunday in Tahiti, and a glorious morning, when

Captain Bob, waddling into the Calabooza, startled us by announcing, "Ah—my boy—shippy you, harree—maky sail!" In other words, the Julia was off.

The beach was quite near, and in this quarter altogether uninhabited; so down we ran, and, at a cable's length, saw little Jule gliding past—top-gallant-sails hoisting, and a boy aloft with one leg thrown over the yard, loosing the fore-royal. The decks were all life and commotion; the sailors on the forecastle singing "Ho, cheerly men!" as they catted the anchor; and the gallant Jermin, bareheaded as his wont, standing up on the bowsprit, and issuing his orders. By the man at the helm, stood Captain Guy, very quiet and gentlemanly, and smoking a cigar. Soon the ship drew near the reef, and altering her course, glided out through the break, and went on her way.

Thus disappeared little Jule, about three weeks after entering the harbor; and nothing more have I ever heard of her.[9]

CHAPTER XLVIII

Tahiti as It Is

As in the last few chapters, several matters connected with the general condition of the natives have been incidentally touched upon, it may be well not to leave so important a subject in a state calculated to convey erroneous impressions. Let us bestow upon it, therefore, something more than a mere cursory glance.

But in the first place, let it be distinctly understood, that in all I have to say upon this subject, both here and elsewhere, I mean no harm to the missionaries nor their cause; I merely desire to set forth things as they actually exist.

Of the results which have flowed from the intercourse of foreigners with the Polynesians, including the attempts to civilize and christianize them by the missionaries, Tahiti, on many accounts, is obviously the fairest practical example. Indeed, it may now be asserted, that the experiment of christianizing the Tahitians, and improving their social condition by the introduction of foreign customs, has been fully tried. The present generation have grown up under the auspices of their religious instructors. And although it may be urged, that the labors of the latter have at times been more or less obstructed by unprincipled foreigners, still, this in no wise renders Tahiti any the less a fair illustration; for, with obstacles like these, the missionaries in Polynesia must always, and everywhere struggle.

Nearly sixty years have elapsed since the Tahitian mission was started; and during this period, it has received the unceasing prayers and contributions of its friends abroad. Nor has any enterprise of the kind called forth more devotion on the part of those directly employed in it.

It matters not, that the earlier laborers in the work, although strictly conscientious, were, as a class, ignorant, and, in many cases, deplorably bigoted: such traits have, in some degree, characterized the pioneers of all faiths. And although in zeal and disinterestedness, the missionaries now on the island are, perhaps, inferior to their predecessors, they have, nevertheless, in their own way at least, labored hard to make a Christian people of their charge.

Let us now glance at the most obvious changes wrought in their condition.

The entire system of idolatry has been done away; together with several barbarous practices engrafted thereon. But this result is not so much to be ascribed to the missionaries, as to the civilizing effects of a long and constant intercourse with whites of all nations; to whom, for many years, Tahiti has been one of the principal places of resort in the South Seas. At the Sandwich Islands, the potent institution of the Taboo, together with the entire paganism of the land, was utterly abolished by a voluntary act of the natives, some time previous to the arrival of the first missionaries among them.

The next most striking change in the Tahitians is this. From the permanent residence among them of influential and respectable foreigners, as well as from the frequent visits of ships-of-war, recognizing the nationality of the island, its inhabitants are no longer deemed fit subjects for the atrocities practiced upon mere savages; and hence, secure from retaliation, vessels of all kinds now enter their harbors with perfect safety.

But let us consider what results are directly ascribable to the missionaries alone.

In all cases, they have striven hard to mitigate the evils resulting from the commerce with the whites in general. Such attempts, however, have been rather injudicious, and often ineffectual: in truth, a barrier almost insurmountable is presented in the dispositions of the people themselves. Still, in this respect, the morality of the islanders is, upon the whole, improved by the presence of the missionaries.

But the greatest achievement of the latter, and one which in itself is most hopeful and gratifying is, that they have translated the entire Bible into the language of the island; and I have myself known several who were able to read it with facility. They have also established churches, and schools for both children and adults; the latter, I regret to say, are now much neglected; which must be ascribed, in a great measure, to the disorders growing out of the proceedings of the French.

It were unnecessary here, to enter diffusely into matters connected with the internal government of the Tahitian churches and schools. Nor, upon this head, is my information copious enough to warrant me in presenting details. But we do not need them. We are merely considering general *results*, as made apparent in the moral and religious condition of the island at large.

Upon a subject like this, however, it would be altogether too assuming for a single individual to decide; and, so, in place of my own random observations, which may be found elsewhere, I will here present those of several known authors, made under various circumstances, at different periods, and down to a comparative late date. A few very brief extracts will enable the reader to mark for himself what progressive improvement, if any, has taken place.

Nor must it be overlooked, that of these authorities, the two first in order are largely quoted by the Right Reverend M.

Russell, in a work composed for the express purpose of imparting information on the subject of Christian missions in
Polynesia. And he frankly acknowledges, moreover, that they
are such as "can not fail to have great weight with the public." [10]

After alluding to the manifold evils entailed upon the natives
by foreigners, and their singularly inert condition; and after
somewhat too severely denouncing the undeniable errors of
the mission, Kotzebue, the Russian navigator, says, "A religion
like this, which forbids every innocent pleasure, and cramps or
annihilates every mental power, is a libel on the divine founder
of Christianity. It is true, that the religion of the missionaries
has, with a great deal of evil, effected some good. It has restrained the vices of theft and incontinence; but it has given
birth to ignorance, hypocrisy, and a hatred of all other modes
of faith, which was once foreign to the open and benevolent
character of the Tahitian." [11]

Captain Beechey says, that while at Tahiti, he saw scenes
"which must have convinced the greatest skeptic of the thoroughly immoral condition of the people, and which would force
him to conclude, as Turnbull [12] did, many years previous, that
their intercourse with the Europeans had tended to debase
rather than exalt, their condition." [13]

About the year 1834, Daniel Wheeler, an honest-hearted
Quaker, prompted by motives of the purest philanthropy,
visited, in a vessel of his own, most of the missionary settlements
in the South Seas. He remained some time at Tahiti; receiving
the hospitalities of the missionaries there, and, from time to
time, exhorting the natives.

After bewailing their social condition, he frankly says of
their religious state, "Certainly, appearances are unpromising;
and however unwilling to adopt such a conclusion, there is
reason to apprehend, that Christian principle is a great rarity." [14]

Such, then, is the testimony of good and unbiased men,
who have been upon the spot; but, how comes it to differ so
widely from impressions of others at home? Simply thus:
instead of estimating the result of missionary labors by the
number of heathens who have actually been made to under-

stand and practice (in some measure, at least) the precepts of Christianity, this result has been unwarrantably inferred from the number of those, who, without any understanding of these things, have in any way been induced to abandon idolatry and conform to certain outward observances.

By authority of some kind or other, exerted upon the natives through their chiefs, and prompted by the hope of some worldly benefit to the latter, and not by appeals to the reason, have conversions in Polynesia been in most cases brought about.

Even in one or two instances—so often held up as wonderful examples of divine power—where the natives have impulsively burned their idols, and rushed to the waters of baptism, the very suddenness of the change has but indicated its unsoundness. Williams, the martyr of Erromanga, relates an instance where the inhabitants of an island professing Christianity, voluntarily assembled, and solemnly revived all their heathen customs.

All the world over, facts are more eloquent than words; and the following will show in what estimation the missionaries themselves hold the present state of Christianity and morals among the converted Polynesians.

On the island of Imeeo (attached to the Tahitian mission), is a seminary under the charge of the Rev. Mr. Simpson and wife, for the education of the children of the missionaries, exclusively. Sent home—in many cases, at a very early age—to finish their education, the pupils here are taught nothing but the rudiments of knowledge; nothing more than may be learned in the native schools. Notwithstanding this, the two races are kept as far as possible from associating; the avowed reason being, to preserve the young whites from moral contamination. The better to insure this end, every effort is made to prevent them from acquiring the native language.

They went even further at the Sandwich Islands; where, a few years ago, a play-ground for the children of the missionaries was enclosed with a fence many feet high, the more effectually to exclude the wicked little Hawaiians.

And yet, strange as it may seem, the depravity among the Polynesians, which renders precautions like these necessary, was in a measure unknown before their intercourse with the whites. The excellent Captain Wilson, who took the first missionaries out to Tahiti, affirms, that the people of that island had, in many things, "more refined ideas of decency than ourselves."[15] Vancouver, also, has some noteworthy ideas on this subject, respecting the Sandwich Islanders.[16]

That the immorality alluded to is continually increasing, is plainly shown in the numerous, severe, and perpetually violated laws against licentiousness of all kinds, in both groups of islands.

It is hardly to be expected, that the missionaries would send home accounts of this state of things. Hence, Captain Beechey, in alluding to the "Polynesian Researches" of Ellis, says, that the author has impressed his readers with a far more elevated idea of the moral condition of the Tahitians, and the degree of civilization to which they have attained, than they deserve; or, at least, than the facts which came under his observation, authorized. He then goes on to say, that in his intercourse with the islanders, "they had no fear of him, and consequently acted from the impulse of their natural feelings; so that he was the better enabled to obtain a correct knowledge of their real disposition and habits."[17]

From my own familiar intercourse with the natives, this last reflection still more forcibly applies to myself.

CHAPTER LXII

Tamai

Long before sunrise, the next morning, my sandals were laced on, and the doctor had vaulted into Zeke's boots.[18]

Expecting to see us again before we went to Taloo, the planters wished us a pleasant journey; and, on parting, very generously presented us with a pound or two of what sailors call "plug" tobacco; telling us to cut it up into small change; the Virginian weed being the principal circulating medium on the island.

Tamai, we were told, was not more than three or four leagues distant; so making allowances for a wild road, a few hours to rest at noon, and our determination to take the journey leisurely, we counted upon reaching the shores of the lake some time in the flush of the evening.

For several hours we went on slowly through wood and ravine, and over hill and precipice, seeing nothing but occasional herds of wild cattle, and often resting; until we found ourselves, about noon, in the very heart of the island.

It was a green, cool hollow among the mountains, into which we at last descended with a bound. The place was gushing with a hundred springs, and shaded over with great solemn trees, on whose mossy boles the moisture stood in beads. Strange to say, no traces of the bullocks ever having been here were revealed. Nor was there a sound to be heard, nor a bird to be seen, nor any breath of wind stirring the leaves. The utter solitude and silence were oppressive; and after peering about under the shades, and seeing nothing but ranks of dark, motionless trunks, we hurried across the hollow, and ascended a steep mountain opposite.

Midway up, we rested where the earth had gathered about the roots of three palms, and thus formed a pleasant lounge, from which we looked down upon the hollow, now one dark-green tuft of woodland at our feet. Here we brought forth a small calabash of "*poee*," a parting present from Tonoi.[19] After eating heartily, we obtained fire by two sticks, and throwing ourselves back, puffed forth our fatigue in wreaths of smoke. At last we fell asleep; nor did we waken till the sun had sunk so low, that its rays darted in upon us under the foliage.

Starting up, we then continued our journey; and as we gained the mountain top—there, to our surprise, lay the lake and village of Tamai. We had thought it a good league off. Where we stood, the yellow sunset was still lingering; but over the valley below, long shadows were stealing—the rippling green lake reflecting the houses and trees, just as they stood along its banks. Several small canoes, moored here and there to posts in the water, were dancing upon the waves; and one solitary fisherman was paddling over to a grassy point. In front of the houses, groups of natives were seen; some thrown at full length upon the ground, and others indolently leaning against the bamboos.

With whoop and halloo, we ran down the hills, the villagers soon hurrying forth to see who were coming. As we drew near, they gathered round, all curiosity to know what brought the "karhowries" [20] into their quiet country. The doctor contriving to make them understand the purely social object of our visit, they gave us a true Tahitian welcome; pointing into their dwellings, and saying they were ours as long as we chose to remain.

We were struck by the appearance of these people, both men and women; so much more healthful than the inhabitants of the bays. As for the young girls, they were more retiring and modest, more tidy in their dress, and far fresher and more beautiful than the damsels of the coast. A thousand pities, thought I, that they should bury their charms in this nook of a valley.

That night we abode in the house of Rartoo, a hospitable old chief. It was right on the shore of the lake; and at supper, we looked out through a rustling screen of foliage upon the surface of the starlit water.

The next day we rambled about, and found a happy little community, comparatively free from many deplorable evils to which the rest of their countrymen are subject. Their time, too, was more occupied. To my surprise, the manufacture of tappa was going on in several buildings. European calicoes were seldom seen, and not many articles of foreign origin of any description.

The people of Tamai were nominally Christians; but being so remote from ecclesiastical jurisdiction, their religion sat lightly upon them. We had been told, even, that many heathenish games and dances still secretly lingered in their valley.

Now the prospect of seeing an old-fashioned "hevar," or Tahitian reel, was one of the inducements which brought us here; and so, finding Rartoo rather liberal in his religious ideas, we disclosed our desire. At first, he demurred; and shrugging his shoulders like a Frenchman, declared it could not be brought about—was a dangerous matter to attempt, and might bring all concerned into trouble. But we overcame all this, convinced him that the thing could be done, and a "hevar," a genuine pagan fandango, was arranged for that very night.

CHAPTER LXIII

A Dance in the Valley

There were some ill-natured people—tell-tales—it seemed, in Tamai; and hence there was a deal of mystery about getting up the dance.

An hour or two before midnight, Rartoo entered the house, and, throwing robes of tappa over us, bade us follow at a distance behind him; and, until out of the village, hood our faces. Keenly alive to the adventure, we obeyed. At last, after taking a wide circuit, we came out upon the farthest shore of the lake. It was a wide, dewy space; lighted up by a full moon, and carpeted with a minute species of fern, growing closely together. It swept right down to the water, showing the village opposite, glistening among the groves.

Near the trees, on one side of the clear space, was a ruinous pile of stones, many rods in extent; upon which had formerly stood a temple of Oro. At present, there was nothing but a rude hut, planted on the lowermost terrace. It seemed to have been used as a "*tappa herree*"; or house for making the native cloth.

Here, we saw lights gleaming from between the bamboos, and casting long, rod-like shadows upon the ground without. Voices also were heard. We went up, and had a peep at the dancers; who were getting ready for the ballet. They were some twenty in number; waited upon by hideous old crones, who might have been duennas. Long Ghost proposed to send the latter packing; but Rartoo said it would never do, and so they were permitted to remain.

We tried to effect an entrance at the door, which was fastened; but, after a noisy discussion with one of the old witches within, our guide became fidgety, and, at last, told us to desist, or we would spoil all. He then led us off to a distance, to await the performance; as the girls, he said, did not wish to be recognized. He, furthermore, made us promise to remain where we were, until all was over, and the dancers had retired.

We waited impatiently; and, at last, they came forth. They were arrayed in short tunics of white tappa; with garlands of flowers on their heads. Following them, were the duennas, who remained clustering about the house, while the girls advanced a few paces; and, in an instant, two of them, taller than their companions, were standing, side by side, in the middle of a ring, formed by the clasped hands of the rest. This movement was made in perfect silence.

Presently, the two girls join hands overhead; and, crying out, "Ahloo! ahloo!" wave them to and fro. Upon which, the ring begins to circle slowly; the dancers moving sideways, with their arms a little drooping. Soon they quicken their pace; and, at last, fly round and round: bosoms heaving, hair streaming, flowers dropping, and every sparkling eye circling in what seemed a line of light.

Meanwhile, the pair within are passing and repassing each other incessantly. Inclining sideways, so that their long hair falls far over, they glide this way and that; one foot continually in the air, and their fingers thrown forth, and twirling in the moonbeams.

"Ahloo! ahloo!" again cry the dance queens; and, coming together in the middle of the ring, they once more lift up the arch, and stand motionless.

"Ahloo! ahloo!" Every link of the circle is broken; and the girls, deeply breathing, stand perfectly still. They pant hard and fast, a moment or two; and then, just as the deep flush is dying away from their faces, slowly recede, all round; thus enlarging the ring.

Again the two leaders wave their hands, when the rest pause; and now, far apart, stand in the still moonlight, like a circle of fairies. Presently, raising a strange chant, they softly sway themselves, gradually quickening the movement, until, at length, for a few passionate moments, with throbbing bosoms and glowing cheeks, they abandon themselves to all the spirit of the dance, apparently lost to everything around. But soon subsiding again into the same languid measure, as before, they become motionless; and then, reeling forward on all sides, their eyes swimming in their heads, join in one wild chorus, and sink into each other's arms.

Such is the Lory-Lory, I think they call it; the dance of the backsliding girls of Tamai.

While it was going on, we had as much as we could do, to keep the doctor from rushing forward and seizing a partner.

They would give us no more "hevars" that night; and Rartoo fairly dragged us away to a canoe, hauled up on the lake shore; when we reluctantly embarked, and, paddling over to the village, arrived there in time for a good nap before sunrise.

The next day, the doctor went about, trying to hunt up the overnight dancers. He thought to detect them by their late rising; but never was man more mistaken; for, on first sallying out, the whole village was asleep, waking up in concert about an hour after. But, in the course of the day, he came across several, whom he at once charged with taking part in the "hevar." There were some prim-looking fellows standing by (visiting elders from Afrehitoo,[21] perhaps), and the girls looked embarrassed; but parried the charge most skilfully.

Though soft as doves, in general, the ladies of Tamai are, nevertheless, flavored with a slight tincture of what we queerly enough call the "*devil*"; and they showed it on the present occasion. For when the doctor pressed one rather hard, she all at once turned round upon him, and, giving him a box on the ear, told him to "hanree perrar!" (be off with himself).

CHAPTER LXXII

A Dealer in the Contraband

It must have been at least the tenth day, reckoning from the Hegira, that we found ourselves the guests of Varvy, an old hermit of an islander, who kept house by himself, perhaps a couple of leagues from Taloo.

A stone's cast from the beach there was a fantastic rock, moss-grown, and deep in a dell. It was insulated by a shallow brook, which, dividing its waters, flowed on both sides, until united below. Twisting its roots round the rock, a gnarled "Aoa" spread itself overhead in a wilderness of foliage; the elastic branch-roots depending from the larger boughs, insinuating themselves into every cleft, thus forming supports to the parent stem. In some places, these pendulous branches, half-grown, had not yet reached the rock; swinging their loose fibrous ends in the air like whiplashes.

Varvy's hut, a mere coop of bamboos, was perched upon a level part of the rock, the ridge-pole resting at one end in a crotch of the "Aoa," and the other, propped by a forked bough planted in a fissure.

Notwithstanding our cries as we drew near, the first hint the old hermit received of our approach, was the doctor's stepping up and touching his shoulder, as he was kneeling over on a stone, cleaning fish in the brook. He leaped up, and stared at us. But with a variety of uncouth gestures, he soon made us welcome; informing us, by the same means, that he was both deaf and dumb; he then motioned us into his dwelling.

Going in, we threw ourselves upon an old mat, and peered round. The soiled bamboos and calabashes looked so uninviting, that the doctor was for pushing on to Taloo that night, notwithstanding it was near sunset. But at length we concluded to stay where we were.

After a good deal of bustling outside under a decrepit shed, the old man made his appearance with our supper. In one hand he held a flickering taper, and in the other, a huge, flat calabash, scantily filled with viands. His eyes were dancing in his head, and he looked from the calabash to us, and from us to the calabash, as much as to say, "Ah, my lads, what do ye think of this, eh? Pretty good cheer, eh?" But the fish and Indian turnip being none of the best, we made but a sorry meal. While discussing it, the old man tried hard to make himself understood by signs; most of which were so excessively ludicrous, that we made no doubt he was perpetrating a series of pantomimic jokes.

The remnants of the feast removed, our host left us for a moment, returning with a calabash of portly dimensions, and furnished with a long, hooked neck, the mouth of which was stopped with a wooden plug. It was covered with particles of earth, and looked as if just taken from some place under ground.

With sundry winks and horrible giggles peculiar to the dumb, the vegetable demijohn was now tapped; the old fellow looking round cautiously, and pointing at it; as much as to intimate, that it contained some thing which was "taboo," or forbidden.

Aware that intoxicating liquors were strictly prohibited to the natives, we now watched our entertainer with much interest. Charging a cocoa-nut shell, he tossed it off, and then filling up again, presented the goblet to me. Disliking the smell, I made faces at it; upon which he became highly excited; so much so, that a miracle was wrought upon the spot. Snatching the cup from my hands, he shouted out, "Ah, karhowree sabbee lee-lee, ena arva tee maitai!" in other words, what a blockhead of a white man! this is the real stuff!

We could not have been more startled, had a frog leaped from his mouth. For an instant, he looked confused enough himself; and then placing a finger mysteriously upon his mouth, he contrived to make us understand, that at times he was subject to a suspension of the powers of speech.

Deeming the phenomenon a remarkable one, every way, the doctor desired him to open his mouth, so that he might have a look down. But he refused.

This occurrence made us rather suspicious of our host; nor could we afterward account for his conduct, except by supposing that his feigning dumbness might in some way or other assist him in the nefarious pursuits, in which it afterward turned out that he was engaged. This conclusion, however, was not altogether satisfactory.

To oblige him, we at last took a sip of his "arva tee," and found it very crude, and strong as Lucifer. Curious to know whence it was obtained, we questioned him; when, lighting up with pleasure, he seized the taper, and led us outside the hut, bidding us follow.

After going some distance through the woods, we came to a dismantled old shed of boughs, apparently abandoned to decay. Underneath, nothing was to be seen but heaps of decaying leaves and an immense, clumsy jar, wide-mouthed, and, by some means, rudely hollowed out from a ponderous stone.

Here, for a while, we were left to ourselves; the old man placing the light in the jar, and then disappearing. He returned, carrying a long, large bamboo, and a crotched stick. Throwing these down, he poked under a pile of rubbish, and brought out a rough block of wood, pierced through and through with a hole, which was immediately clapped on top of the jar. Then planting the crotched stick upright about two yards distant, and making it sustain one end of the bamboo, he inserted the other end of the latter into the hole in the block; concluding these arrangements, by placing an old calabash under the farther end of the bamboo.

Coming up to us now with a sly, significant look, and pointing admiringly at his apparatus, he exclaimed, "Ah, karhowree, ena hannahanna arva tee!" as much as to say, "*This*, you see, is the way it's done."

His contrivance was nothing less than a native still, where he manufactured his island "poteen." The disarray in which we found it, was probably intentional, as a security against detection. Before we left the shed, the old fellow toppled the whole concern over, and dragged it away piecemeal.

His disclosing his secret to us thus, was characteristic of the "Tootai Owrees," or contemners of the missionaries among the natives; who, presuming that all foreigners are opposed to the ascendancy of the missionaries, take pleasure in making them confidants, whenever the enactments of their rulers are secretly set at naught.

The substance from which the liquor is produced is called "Tee," which is a large, fibrous root, something like a yam, but smaller. In its green state, it is exceedingly acrid; but boiled or baked, has the sweetness of the sugar-cane. After being subjected to the fire, macerated, and reduced to a certain stage of fermentation, the "Tee" is stirred up with water, and is then ready for distillation.

On returning to the hut, pipes were introduced; and, after a while, Long Ghost, who, at first, had relished the "Arva Tee" as little as myself, to my surprise, began to wax sociable over it, with Varvy; and, before long, absolutely got mellow, the old toper keeping him company.

It was a curious sight. Every one knows, that, so long as the occasion lasts, there is no stronger bond of sympathy and good-feeling among men, than getting tipsy together. And how earnestly, nay, movingly, a brace of worthies, thus employed, will endeavor to shed light upon, and elucidate their mystical ideas!

Fancy Varvy and the doctor, then; lovingly tippling, and brimming over with a desire to become better acquainted; the doctor politely bent upon carrying on the conversation in the language of his host, and the old hermit persisting in trying to talk English. The result was, that between the two, they made such a fricassee of vowels and consonants, that it was enough to turn one's brain.

The next morning, on waking, I heard a voice from the tombs. It was the doctor, solemnly pronouncing himself a dead man. He was sitting up, with both hands clasped over his forehead, and his pale face a thousand times paler than ever.

"That infernal stuff has murdered me!" he cried. "Heavens! my head's all wheels and springs, like the automaton chess-player! What's to be done, Paul? [22] I'm poisoned."

But, after drinking an herbal draught, concocted by our host, and eating a light meal, at noon, he felt much better; so much so, that he declared himself ready to continue our journey.

When we came to start, the Yankee's boots were missing; and, after a diligent search, were not to be found. Enraged beyond measure, their proprietor said that Varvy must have stolen them; but, considering his hospitality, I thought this extremely improbable; though, to whom else to impute the theft, I knew not. The doctor maintained, however, that one who was capable of drugging an innocent traveller with "Arva Tee," was capable of anything.

But it was in vain that he stormed, and Varvy and I searched; the boots were gone.

Were it not for this mysterious occurrence, and Varvy's detestable liquors, I would here recommend all travellers going round by the beach to Partoowye, to stop at the Rock, and patronize the old gentleman—the more especially as he entertains gratis.

CHAPTER LXXX

Queen Pomaree

It is well to learn something about people before being introduced to them; and so, we will here give some account of Pomaree and her family.

Every reader of Cook's Voyages must remember "Otoo," who, in that navigator's time, was king of the larger peninsula of Tahiti. Subsequently, assisted by the muskets of the Bounty's men, he extended his rule over the entire island. This Otoo, before his death, had his name changed into Pomaree, which has ever since been the royal patronymic.

He was succeeded by his son, Pomaree II., the most famous prince in the annals of Tahiti. Though a sad debauchee and drunkard, and even charged with unnatural crimes, he was a great friend of the missionaries, and one of their very first proselytes. During the religious wars into which he was hurried, by his zeal for the new faith, he was defeated, and expelled from the island. After a short exile, he returned from Imeeo, with an army of eight hundred warriors; and, in the battle of Narii, routed the rebellious pagans with great slaughter, and reëstablished himself upon the throne. Thus, by force of arms, was Christianity finally triumphant in Tahiti.

Pomaree II. dying, in 1821, was succeeded by his infant son, under the title of Pomaree III. This young prince survived his father but six years; and the government then descended to his elder sister, Aimata, the present queen, who is commonly called

Pomaree Vahinee I., or the first female Pomaree. Her majesty must be now upward of thirty years of age. She has been twice married. Her first husband was a son of the old King of Tahar, an island about one hundred miles from Tahiti. This proving an unhappy alliance, the pair were soon after divorced. The present husband of the queen is a chief of Imeeo.

The reputation of Pomaree is not what it ought to be. She, and also her mother, were, for a long time, excommunicated members of the Church; and the former, I believe, still is. Among other things, her conjugal fidelity is far from being unquestioned. Indeed, it was upon this ground, chiefly, that she was excluded from the communion of the Church.

Previous to her misfortunes, she spent the greater portion of her time sailing about from one island to another, attended by a licentious court; and wherever she went, all manner of games and festivities celebrated her arrival.

She was always given to display. For several years, the maintenance of a regiment of household troops drew largely upon the royal exchequer. They were trowserless fellows, in a uniform of calico shirts and pasteboard hats; armed with muskets of all shapes and calibres, and commanded by a great noisy chief, strutting it in a coat of fiery red. These heroes escorted their mistress whenever she went abroad.

Some time ago, the queen received from her English sister, Victoria, a very showy, though uneasy, headdress—a crown; probably made to order, at some tinman's in London. Having no idea of reserving so pretty a bauble for coronation days, which come so seldom, her majesty sported it whenever she appeared in public; and, to show her familiarity with European customs, politely touched it to all foreigners of distinction— whaling captains, and the like—whom she happened to meet in her evening walk on the Broom Road.

The arrival and departure of royalty were always announced at the palace by the court artilleryman—a fat old gentleman, who, in a prodigious hurry and perspiration, discharged minute fowling-pieces, as fast as he could load and fire the same.

The Tahitian princess leads her husband a hard life. Poor

fellow! he not only caught a queen, but a Tartar, when he married her. The style by which he is addressed is rather significant—"Pomaree-Tanee" (Pomaree's man). All things considered, as appropriate a title for a king-consort as could be hit upon.

If ever there were a henpecked husband, that man is the prince. One day, his cara-sposa, giving audience to a deputation from the captains of the vessels lying in Papeetee, he ventured to make a suggestion which was very displeasing to her. She turned round, and, boxing his ears, told him to go over to his beggarly island of Imeeo, if he wanted to give himself airs.

Cuffed and contemned, poor Tanee flies to the bottle, or rather, to the calabash, for solace. Like his wife and mistress, he drinks more than he ought.

Six or seven years ago, when an American man-of-war was lying at Papeetee, the town was thrown into the greatest commotion by a conjugal assault and battery, made upon the sacred person of Pomaree by her intoxicated Tanee.

Captain Bob once told me the story. And by way of throwing more spirit into the description, as well as to make up for his oral deficiencies, the old man went through the accompanying action: myself being proxy for the Queen of Tahiti.

It seems, that on a Sunday morning, being dismissed contemptuously from the royal presence, Tanee was accosted by certain good fellows, friends and boon companions, who condoled with him on his misfortunes—railed against the queen, and finally dragged him away to an illicit vender of spirits, in whose house the party got gloriously mellow. In this state, Pomaree Vahinee I., was the topic upon which all dilated—"A vixen of a queen," probably suggested one. "It's infamous," said another; "and I'd have satisfaction," cried a third. "And so I will!"—Tanee must have hiccoughed; for off he went; and ascertaining that his royal half was out riding, he mounted his horse, and galloped after her.

Near the outskirts of the town, a cavalcade of women came cantering toward him, in the centre of which was the object of his fury. Smiting his beast right and left, he dashed in among them; completely overturning one of the party, leaving her on the field, and dispersing everybody else except Pomaree. Backing her horse dexterously, the incensed queen heaped upon him every scandalous epithet she could think of; until at last, the enraged Tanee leaped out of his saddle, caught Pomaree by her dress, and dragging her to the earth, struck her repeatedly in the face, holding on meanwhile by the hair of her head. He was proceeding to strangle her on the spot, when the cries of the frightened attendants brought a crowd of natives to the rescue, who bore the nearly insensible queen away.

But his frantic rage was not yet sated. He ran to the palace; and before it could be prevented, demolished a valuable supply of crockery, a recent present from abroad. In the act of perpetrating some other atrocity, he was seized from behind, and carried off with rolling eyes and foaming at the mouth.

This is a fair example of a Tahitian in a passion. Though the mildest of mortals in general, and hard to be roused, when once fairly up, he is possessed with a thousand devils.

The day following, Tanee was privately paddled over to Imeeo, in a canoe; where, after remaining in banishment for a couple of weeks, he was allowed to return, and once more give in his domestic adhesion.

Though Pomaree Vahinee I. be something of a Jezebel in private life, in her public rule, she is said to have been quite lenient and forbearing. This was her true policy; for an hereditary hostility to her family had always lurked in the hearts of many powerful chiefs, the descendants of the old Kings of Taiarboo, dethroned by her grandfather Otoo. Chief among these, and in fact the leader of his party, was Poofai; a bold, able man, who made no secret of his enmity to the missionaries, and the government which they controlled. But while events were occurring calculated to favor the hopes of the disaffected and turbulent, the arrival of the French gave a most unexpected turn to affairs.

During my sojourn in Tahiti, a report was rife—which I knew to originate with what is generally called the "missionary party"—that Poofai and some other chiefs of note, had actually agreed, for a stipulated bribe, to acquiesce in the appropriation of their country. But subsequent events have rebutted the calumny. Several of these very men have recently died in battle against the French.

Under the sovereignty of the Pomarees, the great chiefs of Tahiti were something like the barons of King John. Holding feudal sway over their patrimonial valleys, and on account of their descent, warmly beloved by the people, they frequently cut off the royal revenues by refusing to pay the customary tribute due from them as vassals.

The truth is, that with the ascendancy of the missionaries, the regal office in Tahiti lost much of its dignity and influence. In the days of Paganism, it was supported by all the power of a numerous priesthood, and was solemnly connected with the entire superstitious idolatry of the land. The monarch claimed to be a sort of bye-blow of Tararroa, the Saturn of the Polynesian mythology, and cousin-german to inferior deities. His person was thrice holy; if he entered an ordinary dwelling, never mind for how short a time, it was demolished when he left; no common mortal being thought worthy to inhabit it afterward.

"I'm a greater man than King George," said the incorrigible young Otoo, to the first missionaries; "he rides on a horse, and I on a man." Such was the case. He travelled post through his dominions on the shoulders of his subjects; and relays of immortal beings were provided in all the valleys.

But alas! how times have changed; how transient human greatness. Some years since, Pomaree Vahinee I., the grand-daughter of the proud Otoo, went into the laundry business; publicly soliciting, by her agents, the washing of the linen belonging to the officers of ships touching in her harbors.

It is a significant fact, and one worthy of record, that while the influence of the English missionaries at Tahiti has tended to so great a diminution of the regal dignity there, that of the American missionaries at the Sandwich Islands, has been purposely exerted to bring about a contrary result.

CHAPTER LXXXI

We Visit the Court

It was about the middle of the second month of the Hegira, and therefore some five weeks after our arrival in Partoowye, that we at last obtained admittance to the residence of the queen.

It happened thus. There was a Marquesan in the train of Pomaree, who officiated as nurse to her children. According to the Tahitian custom, the royal youngsters are carried about until it requires no small degree of strength to stand up under them. But Marbonna was just the man for this—large and muscular, well made as a statue, and with an arm like a degenerate Tahitian's thigh.

Embarking at his native island, as a sailor, on board of a French whaler, he afterward ran away from the ship at Tahiti; where, being seen and admired by Pomaree, he had been prevailed upon to enlist in her service.

Often, when visiting the grounds, we saw him walking about in the shade, carrying two handsome boys, who encircled his neck with their arms. Marbonna's face, tattooed as it was in the ornate style of his tribe, was as good as a picture-book to these young Pomarees. They delighted to trace with their fingers, the outlines of the strange shapes there delineated.

The first time my eyes lighted upon the Marquesan, I knew his country in a moment; and hailing him in his own language, he turned round, surprised that a person so speaking should be a stranger. He proved to be a native of Tior, a glen of Nuku-heva. I had visited the place more than once; and so, on the island of Imeeo, we met like old friends.

In my frequent conversations with him over the bamboo picket, I found this islander a philosopher of nature—a wild heathen, moralizing upon the vices and follies of the Christian court of Tahiti—a savage, scorning the degeneracy of the people among whom fortune had thrown him.

I was amazed at the national feelings of the man. No Euro-

pean, when abroad, could speak of his country with more pride
than Marbonna. He assured me, again and again, that so soon
as he had obtained sufficient money to purchase twenty muskets,
and as many bags of powder, he was going to return to a place,
with which Imeeo was not worthy to be compared.

It was Marbonna, who, after one or two unsuccessful attempts,
at last brought about our admission into the queen's grounds.
Through a considerable crowd, he conducted us along the pier
to where an old man was sitting; to whom he introduced us as
a couple of "karhowrees" of his acquaintance, anxious to see the
sights of the palace. The venerable chamberlain stared at us,
and shook his head: the doctor, thinking he wanted a fee,
placed a plug of tobacco in his hand. This was ingratiating, and
we were permitted to pass on. Upon the point of entering one
of the houses, Marbonna's name was shouted in half-a-dozen
different directions, and he was obliged to withdraw.

Thus left at the very threshold to shift for ourselves, my companion's assurance stood us in good stead. He stalked right in,
and I followed. The place was full of women, who, instead
of exhibiting the surprise we expected, accosted us as cordially
as if we had called to take our Souchong with them, by express
invitation. In the first place, nothing would do but we must
each devour a calabash of "poee," and several roasted bananas.
Pipes were then lighted, and a brisk conversation ensued.

These ladies of the court, if not very polished, were surprisingly free and easy in their manners; quite as much so as King
Charles's Beauties. There was one of them—an arch little miss,
who could converse with us pretty fluently—to whom we
strove to make ourselves particularly agreeable, with the view
of engaging her services as cicerone.

As such, she turned out to be everything we could desire.
No one disputing her will, every place was entered without
ceremony, curtains brushed aside, mats lifted, and each nook
and corner explored. Whether the little damsel carried her
mistress' signet, that every thing opened to her thus, I know not;
but Marbonna himself, the bearer of infants, could not have
been half so serviceable.

Among other houses which we visited, was one of large size and fine exterior; the special residence of a European—formerly the mate of a merchant vessel,—who had done himself the honor of marrying into the Pomaree family. The lady he wedded being a near kinswoman of the queen, he became a permanent member of her majesty's household. This adventurer rose late, dressed theatrically in calico and trinkets, assumed a dictatorial tone in conversation, and was evidently upon excellent terms with himself.

We found him reclining on a mat, smoking a reed-pipe of tobacco, in the midst of an admiring circle of chiefs and ladies. He must have noticed our approach; but instead of rising and offering civilities, he went on talking and smoking, without even condescending to look at us.

"His Highness feels his 'poee,'" carelessly observed the doctor. The rest of the company gave us the ordinary salutation, our guide announcing us beforehand.

In answer to our earnest requests to see the queen, we were now conducted to an edifice, by far the most spacious, in the enclosure. It was at least one hundred and fifty feet in length, very wide, with low eaves, and an exceedingly steep roof of pandannas leaves. There were neither doors nor windows—nothing along the sides but the slight posts supporting the rafters. Between these posts, curtains of fine matting and tappa were rustling, all round; some of them were festooned, or partly withdrawn, so as to admit light and air, and afford a glimpse now and then of what was going on within.

Pushing aside one of the screens, we entered. The apartment was one immense hall; the long and lofty ridge-pole fluttering with fringed matting and tassels, full forty feet from the ground. Lounges of mats, piled one upon another, extended on either side; while here and there were slight screens, forming as many recesses, where groups of natives—all females—were reclining at their evening meal.

As we advanced, these various parties ceased their buzzing, and in explanation of our appearance among them, listened to a few cabalistic words from our guide.

The whole scene was a strange one; but what most excited our surprise, was the incongruous assemblage of the most costly objects from all quarters of the globe. Cheek by jowl, they lay beside the rudest native articles, without the slightest attempt at order. Superb writing-desks of rose-wood, inlaid with silver and mother-of-pearl; decanters and goblets of cut glass; embossed volumes of plates; gilded candelabras; sets of globes and mathematical instruments; the finest porcelain; richly mounted sabres and fowling pieces; laced hats and sumptuous garments of all sorts, with numerous other matters of European manufacture, were strewn about among greasy calabashes half-filled with "*poee*," rolls of old tappa and matting, paddles and fish-spears, and the ordinary furniture of a Tahitian dwelling.

All the articles first mentioned, were, doubtless, presents from foreign powers. They were more or less injured: the fowling-pieces and swords were rusted; the finest woods were scratched; and a folio volume of Hogarth lay open, with a cocoa-nut shell of some musty preparation capsized among the miscellaneous furniture of the Rake's apartment, where that inconsiderate young gentleman is being measured for a coat.

While we were amusing ourselves in this museum of curiosities, our conductor plucked us by the sleeve, and whispered, "Pomaree! Pomaree! aramai kow kow."

"She is coming to sup, then," said the doctor, staring in the direction indicated. "What say you, Paul, suppose we step up?" Just then a curtain near by, lifted; and from a private building a few yards distant, the queen entered, unattended.

She wore a loose gown of blue silk, with two rich shawls, one red and the other yellow, tied about her neck. Her royal majesty was barefooted.

She was about the ordinary size, rather matronly; her features not very handsome; her mouth, voluptuous; but there was a care-worn expression in her face, probably attributable to her late misfortunes. From her appearance, one would judge her about forty; but she is not so old.

As the queen approached one of the recesses, her attendants hurried up, escorted her in, and smoothed the mats on which she at last reclined. Two girls soon appeared, carrying their mistress' repast; and then, surrounded by cut-glass and porcelain, and jars of sweetmeats and confections, Pomaree Vahinee I., the titular Queen of Tahiti, ate fish and poee out of her native calabashes, disdaining either knife or spoon.

"Come on," whispered Long Ghost, "let's have an audience at once"; and he was on the point of introducing himself, when our guide, quite alarmed, held him back, and implored silence. The other natives also interfered; and as he was pressing forward, raised such an outcry, that Pomaree lifted her eyes, and saw us for the first time.

She seemed surprised, and offended; and issuing an order in a commanding tone to several of her women waved us out of the house. Summary as the dismissal was, court etiquet, no doubt, required our compliance. We withdrew; making a profound inclination as we disappeared behind the tappa arras.

We departed the grounds without seeing Marbonna; and previous to vaulting over the picket, feed our pretty guide, after a fashion of our own. Looking round a few moments after, we saw the damsel escorted back by two·men, who seemed to have been sent after her. I trust she received nothing more than a reprimand.

The next day Po-Po[23] informed us that strict orders had been issued, to admit no strangers within the palace precincts.

CHAPTER LXXXII

Which Ends the Book

Disappointed in going to court, we determined upon going to sea. It would never do, longer to trespass on Po-Po's hospitality; and then, weary somewhat of life in Imeeo, like all sailors ashore, I at last pined for the billows.

Now, if her crew were to be credited, the Leviathan was not the craft to our mind. But I had seen the captain, and liked him. He was an uncommonly tall, robust, fine-looking man, in the prime of life. There was a deep crimson spot in the middle of each sun-burnt cheek, doubtless the effect of his sea-potations. He was a Vineyarder, or native of the island of Martha's Vineyard (adjoining Nantucket), and—I would have sworn it—a sailor, and no tyrant.

Previous to this, we had rather avoided the Leviathan's men, when they came ashore; but now, we purposely threw ourselves in their way, in order to learn more of the vessel.

We became acquainted with the third mate, a Prussian, and an old merchant seaman—a right jolly fellow, with a face like a ruby. We took him to Po-Po's, and gave him a dinner of baked pig and bread-fruit; with pipes and tobacco for dessert. The account he gave us of the ship, agreed with my own surmises. A cosier old craft never floated; and the captain was the finest man in the world. There was plenty to eat, too; and, at sea, nothing to do but sit on the windlass and sail. The only bad trait about the vessel was this: she had been launched under some baleful star; and so, was a luckless ship in the fishery. She dropped her boats into the brine often enough, and they frequently got fast to the whales; but lance and harpoon almost invariably "drew" when darted by the men of the Leviathan. But what of that? We would have all the sport of chasing the monsters, with none of the detestable work which follows their capture. So, hurrah for the coast of Japan! Thither the ship was bound.

A word now, about the hard stories we heard, the first time we visited the ship. They were nothing but idle fictions, got up by the sailors for the purpose of frightening us away, so as to oblige the captain, who was in want of more hands, to lie the longer in a pleasant harbor.

The next time the Vineyarder came ashore, we flung ourselves in his path. When informed of our desire to sail with him, he wanted to know our history; and, above all, what countrymen we were. We said, that we had left a whaler in Tahiti, some time previous; and, since then, had been—in the most praiseworthy manner—employed upon a plantation. As for our country, sailors belong to no nation in particular; we were, on this occasion, both Yankees. Upon this he looked decidedly incredulous; and freely told us, that he verily believed we were both from Sydney.

Be it known here, that American sea captains, in the Pacific, are mortally afraid of these Sydney gentry; who, to tell the truth, wherever known, are in excessively bad odor. Is there a mutiny on board a ship in the South Seas, ten to one a Sydney man is the ringleader. Ashore, these fellows are equally riotous.

It was on this account, that we were anxious to conceal the fact of our having belonged to the Julia; though it annoyed me much, thus to deny the dashing little craft. For the same reason, also, the doctor fibbed about his birth-place.

Unfortunately, one part of our raiment—Arfretee's blue frocks—was deemed a sort of collateral evidence against us. For, curiously enough, an American sailor is generally distinguished by his red frock; and an English tar, by his blue one: thus reversing the national colors. The circumstance was pointed out by the captain; and we quickly explained the anomaly. But, in vain: he seemed inveterately prejudiced against us; and, in particular, eyed the doctor most distrustfully.

By way of propping the latter's pretensions, I was throwing out a hint concerning Kentucky, as a land of tall men, when our Vineyarder turned away abruptly, and desired to hear nothing more. It was evident that he took Long Ghost for an exceedingly problematical character.

Perceiving this, I resolved to see what a private interview would do. So, one afternoon, I found the captain smoking a pipe in the dwelling of a portly old native—one Mai-Mai—who, for a reasonable compensation, did the honors of Partoowye, to illustrious strangers.

His guest had just risen from a sumptuous meal of baked pig and taro pudding; and the remnants of the repast were still visible. Two reeking bottles, also, with their necks wrenched off, lay upon the mat. All this was encouraging; for, after a good dinner, one feels affluent and amiable, and peculiarly open to conviction. So, at all events, I found the noble Vineyarder.

I began by saying, that I called for the purpose of setting him right, touching certain opinions of his concerning the place of my nativity:—I was an American—thank Heaven!—and wanted to convince him of the fact.

After looking me in the eye for some time, and, by so doing, revealing an obvious unsteadiness in his own visual organs, he begged me to reach forth my arm. I did so; wondering what upon earth that useful member had to do with the matter in hand.

He placed his fingers upon my wrist; and holding them there for a moment, sprang to his feet; and, with much enthusiasm, pronounced me a Yankee, every beat of my pulse!

"Here, Mai-Mai!" he cried, "another bottle!" And, when it came, with one stroke of a knife, he summarily beheaded it, and commanded me to drain it to the bottom. He then told me, that if I would come on board his vessel the following morning, I would find the ship's articles on the cabin transom.

This was getting along famously. But what was to become of the doctor?

I forthwith made an adroit allusion to my long friend. But it was worse than useless. The Vineyarder swore he would have nothing to do with him—he (my long friend) was a "bird" from Sydney, and nothing would make him (the man of little faith) believe otherwise.

I could not help loving the free-hearted captain; but indignant at this most unaccountable prejudice against my comrade, I abruptly took leave.

Upon informing the doctor of the result of the interview, he was greatly amused; and laughingly declared, that the Vineyarder must be a penetrating fellow. He then insisted upon my going to sea in the ship, since he well knew how anxious I was to leave. As for himself, on second thoughts, he was no sailor; and although "landsmen" very often compose part of a whaler's crew, he did not quite relish the idea of occupying a position so humble. In short, he had made up his mind to tarry awhile in Imeeo.

I turned the matter over; and at last decided upon quitting the island. The impulse urging me to sea once more, and the prospect of eventually reaching home, were too much to be resisted; especially, as the Leviathan was so comfortable a craft, was now bound on her last whaling cruise, and, in little more than a year's time, would be going round Cape Horn.

I did not, however, covenant to remain in the vessel for the residue of the voyage; which would have been needlessly binding myself. I merely stipulated for the coming cruise, leaving my subsequent movements unrestrained; for, there was no knowing that I might not change my mind, and prefer journeying home by short and easy stages.[24]

The next day I paddled off to the ship, signed and sealed, and stepped ashore with my "advance"—fifteen Spanish dollars, tasselling the ends of my neck-handkerchief.

I forced half of the silver on Long Ghost; and having little use for the remainder, would have given it to Po-Po as some small return for his kindness; but, although he well knew the value of the coin, not a dollar would he accept.

In three days' time, the Prussian came to Po-Po's, and told us, that the captain, having made good the number of his crew, by shipping several islanders, had determined upon sailing with the land breeze, at dawn the following morning. These tidings were received in the afternoon. The doctor immediately disappeared, returning soon after with a couple of flasks of wine concealed in the folds of his frock. Through the agency of the Marquesan, he had purchased them from an understrapper of the court.

I prevailed upon Po-Po to drink a parting shell; and even little Loo, actually looking conscious that one of her hopeless admirers was about leaving Partoowye for ever, sipped a few drops from a folded leaf. As for the warm-hearted Arfretee, her grief was unbounded. She even besought me to spend my last night under her own palm-thatch; and then, in the morning, she would herself paddle me off to the ship.

But this I would not consent to; and so, as something to remember her by, she presented me with a roll of fine matting, and another of tappa. These gifts placed in my hammock, I afterward found very agreeable in the warm latitudes to which we were bound; nor did they fail to awaken most grateful remembrances.

About nightfall, we broke away from this generous-hearted household, and hurried down to the water.

It was a mad, merry night among the sailors: they had on tap a small cask of wine, procured in the same way as the doctor's flasks.

An hour or two after midnight, everything was noiseless; but when the first streak of the dawn showed itself over the mountains, a sharp voice hailed the forecastle, and ordered the ship unmoored. The anchors came up cheerily; the sails were soon set; and with the early breath of the tropical morning, fresh and fragrant from the hillsides, we slowly glided down the bay, and were swept through the opening in the reef. Presently, we "hove to," and the canoes came alongside to take off the islanders who had accompanied us thus far. As he stepped over the side, I shook the doctor long and heartily, by the hand. I have never seen or heard of him since.

Crowding all sail, we braced the yards square; and, the breeze freshening, bowled straight away from the land. Once more the sailor's cradle rocked under me, and I found myself rolling in my gait.

By noon, the island had gone down in the horizon; and all before us was the wide Pacific.

CHAPTER CXLV

Chiefly of King Bello

"Now Taji," said Media, "with old Bello of the Hump whose island of Dominora is before us, I am at variance."[1]

"Ah! How so?"

"A dull recital, but you shall have it."

And forthwith his Highness began.

This princely quarrel originated, it seems, in a slight jostling concerning the proprietorship of a barren islet in a very remote quarter of the lagoon. At the outset the matter might have been easily adjusted, had the parties but exchanged a few amicable words. But each disdaining to visit the other, to discuss so trivial an affair, the business of negotiating an understanding was committed to certain plenipos, men with lengthy tongues, who scorned to utter a word short of a polysyllable.

Now, the more these worthies penetrated into the difficulty, the wider became the breach; till what was at first a mere gap, became a yawning gulf.

But that which had perhaps tended more than any thing else to deepen the variance of the kings, was hump-backed Bello's dispatching to Odo, as his thirtieth plenipo, a diminutive little negotiator, who all by himself, in a solitary canoe, sailed over to have audience of Media; into whose presence he was immediately ushered.

Darting one glance at him, the king turned to his chieftains, and said:—"By much straining of your eyes, my lords, can you perceive this insignificant mannikin? What! are there no tall men in Dominora, that King Bello must needs send this dwarf hither?"

And charging his attendants to feed the embassador extraordinary with the soft pap of the cocoanut, and provide nurses during his stay, the monarch retired from the arbor of audience.

"As I am a man," shouted the despised plenipo, raising himself on his toes, "my royal master will resent this affront!— A dwarf, forsooth!—Thank Oro,[2] I am no long-drawn giant! There is as much stuff in me, as in others; what is spread out in their clumsy carcasses, in me is condensed. I am much in little! And that much, thou shalt know full soon, disdainful King of Odo!"

"Speak not against our lord the king," cried the attendants.

"And speak not ye to me, ye headless spear poles!"

And so saying, under sufferance of being small, the plenipo was permitted to depart unmolested; for all his bravadoes, fobbing his credentials and affronts.

Apprized of his servant's ignoble reception, the choleric Bello burst forth in a storm of passion; issuing orders for one thousand conch shells to be blown, and his warriors to assemble by land and by sea.

But bethinking him of the hostilities that might ensue, the sagacious Media hit upon an honorable expedient to ward off an event for which he was then unprepared. With all haste he dispatched to the hump-backed king a little dwarf of his own; who voyaging over to Dominora in a canoe, sorry and solitary as that of Bello's plenipo, in like manner, received the same insults. The effect whereof, was, to strike a balance of affronts; upon the principle, that a blow given, heals one received.

Nevertheless, these proceedings but amounted to a postponement of hostilities; for soon after, nothing prevented the two kings from plunging into war, but the following judicious considerations. First: Media was almost afraid of being beaten. Second: Bello was almost afraid to conquer. Media, because he was inferior in men and arms; Bello, because his aggrandizement was already a subject of warlike comment among the neighboring kings.

Indeed, did the old chronicler Braid-Beard speak truth, there were some tribes in Mardi, that accounted this king of Dominora a testy, quarrelsome, rapacious old monarch; the indefatigable breeder of contentions and wars; the elder brother of this household of nations, perpetually essaying to lord it over the juveniles; and though his patrimonial dominions were situated to the north of the lagoon, not the slightest misunderstanding took place between the rulers of the most distant islands, than this doughty old cavalier on a throne, forthwith thrust his insolent spear into the matter, though it in no wise concerned him, and fell to irritating all parties by his gratuitous interference.

Especially was he officious in the concerns of Porpheero,[3] a neighboring island, very large and famous, whose numerous broad valleys were divided among many rival kings: —the king of Franko, a small-framed, poodle-haired, fine, fiery gallant; finical in his tattooing; much given to the dance and glory;—the king of Ibeereea, a tall and stately cavalier, proud, generous, punctilious, temperate in wine; one hand forever on his javelin, the other, in superstitious homage, lifted to his gods; his limbs all over marks of stakes and crosses;—the king of Luzianna; a slender, dark-browed chief; at times wrapped in a moody robe, beneath which he fumbled something, as if it were a dagger; but otherwise a sprightly troubadour, given to serenades and moonlight;—the many chiefs of sunny Latianna; minstrel monarchs, full of song and sentiment; fiercer in love than war; glorious bards of freedom; but rendering tribute while they sang;—the priest-king of Vatikanna; his chest marked over with antique tattooings; his crown, a cowl; his rusted scepter swaying over falling towers, and crumbling mounds; full of the superstitious past; askance, eyeing the suspicious time to come;—the king of Hapzaboro; portly, pleasant; a lover of wild boar's meat; a frequent quaffer from the can; in his better moods, much fancying solid comfort;—the eight-and-thirty banded kings, chieftains, seigniors, and oligarchies of the broad hill and dale of Tutoni; clubbing together their domains, that none might wrest his neighbor's; an earnest race; deep thinkers, deep drinkers; long pipes, long heads; their wise ones given to mystic cogitations, and consultations with the devil;—the twin kings of Zandinavia; hardy, frugal mountaineers; upright of spine and heart; clad in skins of bears;—the king of Jutlanda; much

like their Highnesses of Zandinavia; a seal-skin cap his crown;
a fearless sailor of his frigid seas;—the king of Muzkovi; a
shaggy, icicled White-bear of a despot in the north; said to
reign over millions of acres of glaciers; had vast provinces of
snow-drifts, and many flourishing colonies among the floating
ice-bergs. Absolute in his rule as Predestination in metaphysics,
did he command all his people to give up the ghost, it would
be held treason to die last. Very precise and foppish in his
imperial tastes was this monarch. Disgusted with the want of
uniformity in the stature of his subjects, he was said to nourish
thoughts of killing off all those below his prescribed standard—
six feet, long measure. Immortal souls were of no account in
his fatal wars; since, in some of his self-breeding estates, they
were daily manufactured to order.

Now, to all the above-mentioned monarchs, old Bello would
frequently dispatch heralds; announcing, for example, his unalterable resolution, to espouse the cause of this king, against
that; at the very time, perhaps, that their Serene Superfluities,
instead of crossing spears, were touching flagons. And upon
these occasions, the kings would often send back word to old
Bello, that instead of troubling himself with their concerns, he
might far better attend to his own; which, they hinted, were in
a sad way, and much needed reform.

The royal old warrior's pretext for these and all similar proceedings, was the proper adjustment in Porpheero, of what he
facetiously styled the "Equipoise of Calabashes"[4]; which he
stoutly swore was essential to the security of the various tribes
in that country.

"But who put the balance in thy hands, King Bello?" cried
the indignant nations.

"Oro!" shouted the hump-backed king, shaking his javelin.

Superadded to the paternal interest which Bello betrayed in
the concerns of the kings of Porpheero, according to our chronicler, he also manifested no less interest in those of the remotest
islands. Indeed, where he found a rich country, inhabited by a
people, deemed by him barbarous and incapable of wise legislation, he sometimes relieved them from their political anxieties,

by assuming the dictatorship over them. And if incensed at his conduct, they flew to their spears, they were accounted rebels, and treated accordingly. But as old Mohi very truly observed, —herein, Bello was not alone; for throughout Mardi, all strong nations, as well as all strong men, loved to govern the weak. And those who most taunted King Bello for his political rapacity, were open to the very same charge. So with Vivenza,[5] a distant island, at times very loud in denunciations of Bello, as a great national brigand. Not yet wholly extinct in Vivenza, were its aboriginal people, a race of wild Nimrods and hunters, who year by year were driven further and further into remoteness, till one of their sad warriors said, after continual removes along the log, his race was on the point of being remorselessly pushed off the end.

Now, Bello was a great geographer, and land surveyor, and gauger of the seas. Terraqueous Mardi, he was continually exploring in quest of strange empires. Much he loved to take the altitude of lofty mountains, the depth of deep rivers, the breadth of broad isles. Upon the highest pinnacles of commanding capes and promontories, he loved to hoist his flag. He circled Mardi with his watch-towers: and the distant voyager passing wild rocks in the remotest waters, was startled by hearing the tattoo, or the reveille, beating from hump-backed Bello's omnipresent drum. Among Antarctic glaciers, his shrill bugle calls mingled with the scream of the gulls; and so impressed seemed universal nature with the sense of his dominion, that the very clouds in heaven never sailed over Dominora without rendering the tribute of a shower; whence the air of Dominora was more moist than that of any other clime.

In all his grand undertakings, King Bello was marvelously assisted by his numerous fleets of war-canoes; his navy being the largest in Mardi. Hence his logicians swore that the entire Lagoon was his; and that all prowling whales, prowling keels, and prowling sharks were invaders. And with this fine conceit to inspire them, his poets-laureate composed some glorious old salt-water odes, enough to make your very soul sing to hear them.

But though the rest of Mardi much delighted to list to such noble minstrelsy, they agreed not with Bello's poets in deeming the lagoon their old monarch's hereditary domain.

Once upon a time, the paddlers of the hump-backed king, meeting upon the broad lagoon certain canoes belonging to the before-mentioned island of Vivenza; these paddlers seized upon several of their occupants[6]; and feeling their pulses, declared them born men of Dominora; and therefore, not free to go whithersoever they would; for, unless they could somehow get themselves born over again, they must forever remain subject to Bello. Shed your hair; nay, your skin, if you will, but shed your allegiance you can not; while you have bones, they are Bello's. So, spite of all expostulations and attempts to prove alibis, these luckless paddlers were dragged into the canoes of Dominora, and commanded to paddle home their captors.

Whereof hearing, the men of Vivenza were thrown into a great ferment; and after a mighty pow-wow over their council fire, fitting out several double-keeled canoes, they sailed out to sea, in quest of those, whom they styled the wholesale corsairs of Dominora.

But lucky perhaps it was, that at this juncture, in all parts of Mardi, the fleets of the hump-backed king, were fighting, gunwale to gunwale, alongside of numerous foes[7]; else there had borne down upon the canoes of the men of Vivenza so tremendous an armada, that the very swell under its thousand prows might have flooded their scattered proas forever out of sight.

As it was, Bello dispatched a few of his smaller craft to seek out, and incidentally run down the enemy; and without returning home, straightway proceed upon more important enterprises.

But it so chanced, that Bello's crafts, one by one meeting the foe, in most cases found the canoes of Vivenza much larger than their own; and manned by more men, with hearts bold as theirs; whence, in the ship-duels that ensued, they were worsted; and the canoes of Vivenza, locking their yard-arms into those of the vanquished, very courteously gallanted them into their coral harbors.

Solely imputing these victories to their superior intrepidity and skill, the people of Vivenza were exceedingly boisterous in their triumph; raising such obstreperous peans, that they gave themselves hoarse throats; insomuch, that according to Mohi, some of the present generation are fain to speak through their noses.

CHAPTER CXLVI

Dominora and Vivenza

The three canoes still gliding on, some further particulars were narrated concerning Dominora; and incidentally, of other isles.

It seems that his love of wide dominion sometimes led the otherwise sagacious Bello into the most extravagant actions. If the chance accumulation of soil and drift-wood about any detached shelf of coral in the lagoon held forth the remotest possibility of the eventual existence of an islet there, with all haste he dispatched canoes to the spot, to take prospective possession of the as yet nearly sub-marine territory; and if possible, eject the zoophytes.

During an unusually low tide, here and there baring the outer reef of the Archipelago, Bello caused his royal spear to be planted upon every place thus exposed, in token of his supreme claim thereto.

Another anecdote was this: that to Dominora there came a rumor, that in a distant island dwelt a man with an uncommonly large nose; of most portentous dimensions, indeed; by the sooth-sayers supposed to foreshadow some dreadful calamity. But disregarding these superstitious conceits, Bello forthwith dispatched an agent, to discover whether this huge promontory of a nose was geographically available; if so, to secure the same, by bringing the proprietor back.

Now, by sapient old Mohi, it was esteemed a very happy thing for Mardi at large, that the subjects whom Bello sent to populate his foreign acquisitions, were but too apt to throw off their vassalage, so soon as they deemed themselves able to cope with him.

Indeed, a fine country in the western part of Mardi, in this very manner, became a sovereign—nay, a republican state. It was the nation to which Mohi had previously alluded—Vivenza. But in the flush and pride of having recently attained their national majority, the men of Vivenza were perhaps too much inclined to carry a vauntful crest. And because intrenched in their fastnesses, after much protracted fighting, they had eventually succeeded in repelling the warriors dispatched by Bello to crush their insurrection, they were unanimous in the opinion, that the hump-backed king had never before been so signally chastised. Whereas, they had not so much vanquished Bello, as defended their shores; even as a young lion will protect its den against legions of unicorns, though, away from home, he might be torn to pieces. In truth, Braid-Beard declared, that at the time of this war, Dominora couched ten long spears for every short javelin Vivenza could dart; though the javelins were stoutly hurled as the spears.

But, superior in men and arms, why, at last, gave over King Bello the hope of reducing those truculent men of Vivenza? One reason was, as Mohi said, that many of his fighting men were abundantly occupied in other quarters of Mardi; nor was he long in discovering, that fight he never so valiantly, Vivenza —not yet its inhabitants—was wholly unconquerable. Thought Bello, Mountains are sturdy foes; fate hard to dam.

Yet, the men of Vivenza were no dastards; not to lie, coming from lion-like loins, they were a lion-loined race. Did not their bards pronounce them a fresh start in the Mardian species; requiring a new world for their full development? For be it known, that the great land of Kolumbo, no inconsiderable part of which was embraced by Vivenza, was the last island discovered in the Archipelago.

In good round truth, and as if an impartialist from Arcturus spoke it, Vivenza was a noble land. Like a young tropic tree she stood, laden down with greenness, myriad blossoms, and the ripened fruit thick-hanging from one bough. She was promising as the morning.

Or Vivenza might be likened to St. John, feeding on locusts

and wild honey, and with prophetic voice, crying to the nations from the wilderness. Or, child-like, standing among the old robed kings and emperors of the Archipelago, Vivenza seemed a young Messiah, to whose discourse the bearded Rabbis bowed.

So seemed Vivenza in its better aspect. Nevertheless, Vivenza was a braggadocio in Mardi; the only brave one ever known. As an army of spurred and crested roosters, her people chanticleered at the resplendent rising of their sun. For shame, Vivenza! Whence thy undoubted valor? Did ye not bring it with ye from the bold old shores of Dominora, where there is a fullness of it left? What isle but Dominora could have supplied thee with that stiff spine of thine?—That heart of boldest beat? Oh, Vivenza! know that true grandeur is too big for a boast; and nations, as well as men, may be too clever to be great.

But what more of King Bello? Notwithstanding his territorial acquisitiveness, and aversion to relinquishing stolen nations, he was yet a glorious old king; rather choleric—a word and a blow—but of a right royal heart. Rail at him as they might, at bottom, all the isles were proud of him. And almost in spite of his rapacity, upon the whole, perhaps, they were the better for his deeds. For if sometimes he did evil with no very virtuous intentions, he had fifty ways of accomplishing good with the best; and a thousand ways of doing good without meaning it. According to an ancient oracle, the hump-backed monarch was but one of the most conspicuous pieces on a board, where the gods played for their own entertainment.

But here it must not be omitted, that of late, King Bello had somewhat abated his efforts to extend his dominions. Various causes were assigned. Some thought it arose from the fact that already he found his territories too extensive for one scepter to rule; that his more remote colonies largely contributed to his tribulations, without correspondingly contributing to his revenues. Others affirmed that his hump was getting too mighty for him to carry; others still, that the nations were waxing too strong for him. With prophetic solemnity, head-shaking sages averred that he was growing older and older; had passed his grand climacteric; and though it was a hale old age with him, yet it was not his lusty youth; that though he was daily getting rounder, and rounder in girth, and more florid of face, that these, howbeit, were rather the symptoms of a morbid obesity, than of a healthful robustness. These wise ones predicted that very soon poor Bello would go off in an apoplexy.

But in Vivenza there were certain blusterers, who often thus prated: "The Hump-back's hour is come; at last the old teamster will be gored by the nations he's yoked; his game is done,—let him show his hand and throw up his scepter; he cumbers Mardi,—let him be cut down and burned; he stands in the way of his betters,—let him sheer to one side; he has shut up many eyes, and now himself grows blind; he hath committed horrible atrocities during his long career, the old sinner!—now, let him quickly say his prayers and be beheaded."

Howbeit, Bello lived on; enjoying his dinners, and taking his jorums as of yore. Ah, I have yet a jolly long lease of life, thought he over his wine; and like unto some obstinate old uncle, he persisted in flourishing, in spite of the prognostications of the nephew nations, which at his demise, perhaps hoped to fall heir to odd parts of his possessions: Three streaks of fat valleys to one of lean mountains!

CHAPTER CXLVII

They Land at Dominora

As erewhile recounted, not being on the best terms in Mardi with the King of Dominora, Media saw fit to draw nigh unto his dominions in haughty state; he (Media) being upon excellent terms with himself. Our sails were set, our paddles paddling, streamers streaming, and Vee-Vee[8] in the shark's mouth, clamorous with his conch. The din was soon heard; and sweeping into a fine broad bay we beheld its margin seemingly pebbled in the distance with heads; so populous the land.

Winding through a noble valley, we presently came to Bello's palace, couchant and bristling in a grove. The upright canes composing its front projected above the eaves in a long row of spear-heads fluttering with scarlet pennons; while below, from the intervals of the canes, were slantingly thrust three tiers of decorated lances. A warlike aspect! The entire structure looking like the broadside of the Macedonian phalanx, advancing to the charge, helmeted with a roof.

"Ah, Bello," said Media, "thou dwellest among thy quills like the porcupine."

"I feel a prickly heat coming over me," cried Mohi, "my lord Media, let us enter."

"Ay," said Babbalanja, "safer the center of peril, than the circumference."

Passing under an arch, formed by two pikes crossed, we found ourselves targets in prospective, for certain flingers of javelins, with poised weapons, occupying the angles of the palace.

Fronting us, stood a portly old warrior, spear in hand, hump on back, and fire in eye.

"Is it war?" he cried, pointing his pike, "or peace?" reversing it.

"Peace," said Media.

Whereupon advancing, King Bello courteously welcomed us.

He was an arsenal to behold: Upon his head the hereditary crown of Dominora,—a helmet of the sea-porcupine's hide, bristling all over with spikes, in front displaying a river horse's horn, leveled to the charge; thrust through his ears were barbed arrows; and from his dyed shark-skin girdle, depended a kilt of strung javelins.

The broad chest of Bello was the chart of Mardi. Tattooed in sea-blue were all the groups and clusters of the Archipelago; and every time he breathed, rose and fell the isles, as by a tide: Dominora full upon his heart.

His sturdy thighs were his triumphal arch; whereon in numerous medallions, crests, and shields, were blazoned all his victories by sea and land.

His strong right arm was Dominora's scroll of Fame, where all her heroes saw their names recorded.—An endless roll!

Our chronicler avouched, that on the sole of Bello's dexter foot was stamped the crest of Franko's king, his hereditary foe. "Thus, thus," cried Bello, stamping, "thus I hourly crush him."

In stature, Bello was a mountaineer; but, as over some tall tower impends the hill-side cliff, so Bello's Athos hump hung over him. Could it be, as many of his nobles held, that the old monarch's hump was his sensorium and source of strength; full of nerves, muscles, ganglions and tendons? Yet, year by year it grew, ringed like the bole of his palms. The toils of war increased it. But another skirmish with the isles, said the wiseacres of Porpheero, and Bello's mount will crush him.

Against which calamity to guard, his medicos and Sangredos[9] sought the hump's reduction. But down it would not come. Then by divers mystic rites, his magi tried. Making a deep pit, many teeth[10] they dropped therein. But they could not fill it. Hence, they called it the Sinking Pit, for bottom it had none. Nevertheless, the magi said, when this pit is filled, Bello's hump you'll see no more. "Then, hurrah for the hump!" cried the nobles, "for he will never hurl it off. Long life to the hump! By the hump we will rally and die! Cheer up, King Bello! Stand up, old King!"

But these were they, who when their sovereign went abroad, with the Athos on his back, followed idly in its shade; while Bello leaned heavily upon his people, staggering as they went.

Ay, sorely did Bello's goodly stature lean; but though many swore he soon must fall; nevertheless, like Pisa's Leaning Tower, he may long lean over, yet never nod.

Visiting Dominora in a friendly way, in good time, we found King Bello very affable; in hospitality, almost exceeding portly Borabolla[11]: October-plenty reigned throughout his palace borders.

Our first reception over, a sumptuous repast was served, at which much lively talk was had.

Of Taji, Bello sought to know, whether his solar Majesty had yet made a province of the moon; whether the Astral hosts were of much account as territories, or mere Motoos, as the little tufts of verdure are denominated, here and there clinging to Mardi's circle reef; whether the people in the sun vilified him (Bello) as they did in Mardi; and what they thought of an event, so ominous to the liberties of the universe, as the addition to his navy of three large canoes.

Ere long, so fused in social love we grew, that Bello, filling high his can, and clasping Media's palm, drank everlasting amity with Odo.

So over their red cups, the two kings forgot their differences, and concerning the disputed islet nothing more was ever heard; especially, as it so turned out, that while they were most hot about it, it had suddenly gone out of sight, being of volcanic origin.

CHAPTER CXLVIII

Through Dominora, They Wander after Yillah

At last, withdrawing from the presence of King Bello, we went forth, still intent on our search.

Many brave sights we saw. Fair fields; the whole island a garden; green hedges all round; neat lodges, thick as white mice in the landscape; old oak woods, hale and hearty as ever; old temples buried in ivy; old shrines of old heroes, deep buried in broad groves of bay trees; old rivers laden with heavy-freighted canoes; humped hills, like droves of camels, piled up with harvests; every sign and token of a glorious abundance, every sign and token of generations of renown. Rare sight! fine sight! none rarer, none finer in Mardi.

But roving on through this ravishing region, we passed through a corn-field in full beard, where a haggard old reaper laid down his hook, beseeching charity for the sake of the gods. —"Bread, bread! or I die mid these sheaves!"

"Thrash out your grain, and want not."

"Alas, masters, this grain is not mine; I plough, I sow, I reap, I bind, I stack,—Lord Primo garners." [12]

Rambling on, we came to a hamlet, hidden in a hollow; and beneath weeping willows saw many mournful maidens seated on a bank; beside each, a wheel that was broken. "Lo, we starve," they cried, "our distaffs are snapped; no more may we weave and spin!"

Then forth issued from vaults clamorous crowds of men, hands tied to their backs.—"Bread, bread!" they cried. "The magician hath turned us out from our glen, where we labored of yore in the days of the merry Green Queen. He has pinioned us hip and arm that we starve. Like sheep we die off with the rot.—Curse on the magician. A curse on his spell."

Bending our steps toward the glen, roaring down the rocks we descried a stream from the mountains. But ere those waters gained the sea, vassal tribute they rendered. Conducted through culverts and moats, they turned great wheels, giving life to ten thousand fangs and fingers, whose gripe no power could withstand, yet whose touch was soft as the velvet paw of a kitten. With brute force, they heaved down great weights, then daintily wove and spun; like the trunk of the elephant, which lays lifeless a river-horse, and counts the pulses of a moth. On all sides, the place seemed alive with its spindles. Round and round, round and round; throwing off wondrous births at every revolving; ceaseless as the cycles that circle in heaven. Loud hummed the loom, flew the shuttle like lightning, red roared the grim forge, rung anvil and sledge; yet no mortal was seen.

"What ho, magician! Come forth from thy cave!"

But all deaf were the spindles, as the mutes, that mutely wait on the Sultan.

"Since we are born, we will live!" so we read on a crimson banner, flouting the crimson clouds, in the van of a riotous red-bonnetted mob, racing by us as we came from the glen.[13] Many more followed: black, or blood-stained:—

"Mardi is man's!"

"Down with landholders!"

"Our turn now!"

"Up rights! Down wrongs!"

"Bread! Bread!"

"Take the tide, ere it turns!"

Waving their banners, and flourishing aloft clubs, hammers,

and sickles, with fierce yells the crowd ran on toward the palace of Bello. Foremost, and inciting the rest by mad outcries and gestures, were six masks; "This way! This way!" they cried,— "by the wood; by the dark wood!" Whereupon all darted into the groves; when of a sudden, the masks leaped forward, clearing a long covered trench, into which fell many of those they led. But on raced the masks; and gaining Bello's palace, and raising the alarm, there sallied from thence a woodland of spears, which charged upon the disordered ranks in the grove. A crash as of icicles against icebergs round Zembla, and down went the hammers and sickles. The host fled, hotly pursued. Meanwhile brave heralds from Bello advanced, and with chaplets crowned the six masks.—"Welcome, heroes! worthy and valiant!" they cried. "Thus our lord Bello rewards all those, who do him a service, for hire betray their kith and their kin."

Still pursuing our quest, wide we wandered through all the sun and shade of Dominora; but nowhere was Yillah found.

CHAPTER CLVIII

They Visit the Great Central Temple of Vivenza[14]

The throng that greeted us upon landing were exceedingly boisterous.

"Whence came ye?" they cried. "Whither bound? Saw ye ever such a land as this? Is it not a great and extensive republic? Pray, observe how tall we are; just feel of our thighs; Are we not a glorious people? Here, feel of our beards. Look round; look round; be not afraid; Behold those palms; swear now, that this land surpasses all others. Old Bello's mountains are mole-hills to ours; his rivers, rills; his empires, villages; his palm-trees, shrubs."

"True," said Babbalanja. "But great Oro must have had some hand in making your mountains and streams.—Would ye have been as great in a desert?"

"Where is your king?" asked Media, drawing himself up in his robe, and cocking his crown.

"Ha, ha, my fine fellow! We are all kings here; royalty breathes in the common air. But come on, come on. Let us show you our great Temple of Freedom."

And so saying, irreverently grasping his sacred arm, they conducted us toward a lofty structure, planted upon a bold hill, and supported by thirty pillars of palm; four quite green[15]; as if recently added; and beyond these, an almost interminable vacancy, as if all the palms in Mardi, were at some future time, to aid in upholding that fabric.

Upon the summit of the temple was a staff; and as we drew nigh, a man with a collar round his neck, and the red marks of stripes upon his back,[16] was just in the act of hoisting a tappa standard—correspondingly striped. Other collared menials were going in and out of the temple.

Near the porch, stood an image like that on the top of the arch we had seen. Upon its pedestal, were pasted certain hieroglyphical notices; according to Mohi, offering rewards for missing men, so many hands high.

Entering the temple, we beheld an amphitheatrical space,[17] in the middle of which, a great fire was burning. Around it, were many chiefs, robed in long togas, and presenting strange contrasts in their style of tattooing.

Some were sociably laughing and chatting; others diligently making excavations between their teeth with slivers of bamboo; or turning their heads into mills, were grinding up leaves and ejecting their juices. Some were busily inserting the down of a thistle into their ears. Several stood erect, intent upon maintaining striking attitudes; their javelins tragically crossed upon their chests. They would have looked very imposing, were it not, that in rear their vesture was sadly disordered. Others, with swelling fronts, seemed chiefly indebted to their dinners for their dignity. Many were nodding and napping. And, here and there, were sundry indefatigable worthies, making a great show of imperious and indispensable business; sedulously folding banana leaves into scrolls, and recklessly placing them into the hands of little boys, in gay turbans and trim little girdles, who thereupon fled as if with salvation for the dying.

It was a crowded scene; the dusky chiefs, here and there, grouped together, and their fantastic tattooings showing like the carved work on quaint old chimney-stacks, seen from afar. But one of their number overtopped all the rest. As when, drawing nigh unto old Rome, amid the crowd of sculptured columns and gables, St. Peter's grand dome soars far aloft, serene in the upper air; so, showed one calm grand forehead among those of this mob of chieftains. That head was Saturnina's.[18] Gall and Spurzheim![19] saw you ever such a brow?— poised like an avalanche, under the shadow of a forest! woe betide the devoted valleys below! Lavatar![19] behold those lips, —like mystic scrolls! Those eyes,—like panthers' caves at the base of Popocatepetl!

"By my right hand, Saturnina," cried Babbalanja, "but thou wert made in the image of thy Maker! Yet, have I beheld men, to the eye as commanding as thou; and surmounted by heads globe-like as thine, who never had thy caliber. We must measure brains, not heads, my lord; else, the sperm-whale, with his tun of an occiput, would transcend us all."

Near by, were arched ways, leading to subterranean places, whence issued a savory stream, and an extraordinary clattering of calabashes, and smacking of lips, as if something were being eaten down there by the fattest of fat fellows, with the heartiest of appetites, and the most irresistible of relishes. It was a quaffing, guzzling, gobbling noise. Peeping down, we beheld a company, breasted up against a board, groaning under numerous viands. In the middle of all, was a mighty great gourd, yellow as gold, and jolly round like a pumpkin in October, and so big it must have grown in the sun. Thence flowed a tide of red wine. And before it, stood plenty of paunches being filled therewith like portly stone jars at a fountain. Melancholy to tell, before that fine flood of old wine, and among those portly old topers, was a lean man; who occasionally ducked in his bill. He looked like an ibis standing in the Nile at flood tide, among a tongue-lapping herd of hippopotami.

They were jolly as the jolliest; and laughed so uproariously, that their hemispheres all quivered and shook, like vast provinces in an earthquake. Ha! ha! ha! how they laughed, and they roared. A deaf man might have heard them; and no milk could have soured within a forty-two-pounder ball shot of that place.

Now, the smell of good things is no very bad thing in itself. It is the savor of good things beyond; proof positive of a glorious good meal. So snuffing up those zephyrs from Araby the blest, those boisterous gales, blowing from out the mouths of baked boars, stuffed with bread-fruit, bananas, and sage, we would fain have gone down and partaken.

But this could not be; for we were told that those worthies below, were a club in secret conclave; very busy in settling certain weighty state affairs upon a solid basis. They were all chiefs of immense capacity:—how many gallons, there was no finding out.

Be sure, now, a most riotous noise came up from those catacombs, which seemed full of the ghosts of fat Lamberts[20]; and this uproar it was, that heightened the din above ground.

But heedless of all, in the midst of the amphitheater, stood a tall, gaunt warrior,[21] ferociously tattooed, with a beak like a buzzard; long dusty locks; and his hands full of headless arrows. He was laboring under violent paroxysms; three benevolent individuals essaying to hold him. But repeatedly breaking loose, he burst anew into his delirium; while with an absence of sympathy, distressing to behold, the rest of the assembly seemed wholly engrossed with themselves; nor did they appear to care how soon the unfortunate lunatic might demolish himself by his frantic proceedings.

Toward one side of the amphitheatrical space, perched high upon an elevated dais, sat a white-headed old man with a tomahawk in his hand: earnestly engaged in over-seeing the tumult; though not a word did he say. Occasionally, however, he was regarded by those present with a mysterious sort of deference; and when they chanced to pass between him and the crazy man, they invariably did so in a stooping position; probably to elude the atmospheric grape and cannister, continually flying from the mouth of the lunatic.

"What mob is this?" cried Media.

"'Tis the grand council of Vivenza," cried a bystander. "Hear ye not Alanno?" and he pointed to the lunatic.

Now coming close to Alanno, we found, that with incredible volubility, he was addressing the assembly upon some all-absorbing subject connected with King Bello, and his presumed encroachments toward the northwest of Vivenza.

One hand smiting his hip, and the other his head, the lunatic thus proceeded; roaring like a wild beast, and beating the air like a windmill:—

"I have said it! the thunder is flashing, the lightning is crashing! already there's an earthquake in Dominora! Full soon will old Bello discover that his diabolical machinations against this ineffable land must soon come to naught. Who dare not declare, that we are not invincible? I repeat it, we are. Ha! ha! Audacious Bello must bite the dust! Hair by hair, we will trail his gory gray beard at the end of our spears! Ha! ha! I grow hoarse; but would mine were a voice like the wild bulls of Bullorom, that I might be heard from one end of this great and gorgeous land to its farthest zenith; ay, to the uttermost diameter of its circumference. Awake! oh Vivenza. The signs of the times are portentous; nay, extraordinary; I hesitate not to add, peculiar! Up! up! Let us not descend to the bathos, when we should soar to the climax! Does not all Mardi wink and look on? Is the great sun itself a frigid spectator? Then let us double up our mandibles to the deadly encounter. Me-thinks I see it now. Old Bello is crafty, and his oath is recorded to obliterate us! Across this wide lagoon he casts his serpent eyes; whets his insatiate bill; mumbles his barbarous tusks; licks his forked tongues; and who knows when we shall have the shark in our midst? Yet be not deceived; for though as yet, Bello has forborn molesting us openly, his emissaries are at work; his infernal sappers, and miners, and wet-nurses, and midwives, and grave-diggers are busy! His canoe-yards are all in commotion! In navies his forests are being launched upon the wave; and ere long typhoons, zephyrs, white-squalls, balmy breezes, hurricanes, and besoms will be raging round us!"

His philippic concluded, Alanno was conducted from the

place; and being now quite exhausted, cold cobble-stones were applied to his temples, and he was treated to a bath in a stream.

This chieftain, it seems, was from a distant western valley, called Hio-Hio, one of the largest and most fertile in Vivenza, though but recently settled. Its inhabitants, and those of the vales adjoining,—a right sturdy set of fellows,—were accounted the most dogmatically democratic and ultra of all the tribes in Vivenza; ever seeking to push on their brethren to the uttermost; and especially were they bitter against Bello. But they were a fine young tribe, nevertheless. Like strong new wine they worked violently in becoming clear. Time, perhaps, would make them all right.

An interval of greater uproar than ever now ensued; during which, with his tomahawk, the white-headed old man repeatedly thumped and pounded the seat where he sat, apparently to augment the din, though he looked anxious to suppress it.

At last, tiring of his posture, he whispered in the ear of a chief, his friend; who, approaching a portly warrior present, prevailed upon him to rise and address the assembly. And no sooner did this one do so, than the whole convocation dispersed, as if to their yams; and with a grin, the little old man leaped from his seat, and stretched his legs on a mat.

The fire was now extinguished, and the temple deserted.

CHAPTER CLXI

They Hearken unto a Voice from the Gods

Next day we retraced our voyage northward, to visit that section of Vivenza.

In due time we landed.

To look round was refreshing. Of all the lands we had seen, none looked more promising. The groves stood tall and green; the fields spread flush and broad; the dew of the first morning seemed hardly vanished from the grass. On all sides was heard the fall of waters, the swarming of bees, and the rejoicing hum of a thriving population.

"Ha, ha!" laughed Yoomy, "Labor laughs in this land; and claps his hands in the jubilee groves! methinks that Yillah will yet be found."

Generously entertained, we tarried in this land; till at length, from over the Lagoon, came full tidings of the eruption we had witnessed in Franko, with many details. The conflagration[22] had spread through Porpheero; and the kings were to and fro hunted, like malefactors by blood-hounds; all that part of Mardi was heaving with throes.

With the utmost delight, these tidings were welcomed by many; yet others heard them with boding concern.

Those, too, there were, who rejoiced that the kings were cast down; but mourned that the people themselves stood not firmer. A victory, turned to no wise and enduring account, said they, is no victory at all. Some victories revert to the vanquished.

But day by day great crowds ran down to the beach, in wait for canoes periodically bringing further intelligence. Every hour new cries startled the air. "Hurrah! another kingdom is burnt down to the earth's edge; another demi-god is unhelmed; another republic is dawning. Shake hands, freemen, shake hands! Soon will we hear of Dominora down in the dust; of hapless Verdanna free as ourselves; all Porpheero's volcanoes are bursting! Who may withstand the people? The times tell terrible tales to tyrants! Ere we die, freemen, all Mardi will be free."

Overhearing these shouts, Babbalanja thus addressed Media: —"My lord, I can not but believe, that these men, are far more excited than those with whom they so ardently sympathize. But no wonder. The single discharges which are heard in Porpheero; here come condensed in one tremendous report. Every arrival is a firing off of events by platoons."

Now, during this tumultuous interval, King Media very prudently kept himself exceedingly quiet. He doffed his regalia; and in all things carried himself with a dignified discretion. And many hours he absented himself; none knowing whither he went, or what his employment.

So also with Babbalanja. But still pursuing our search, at

last we all journeyed into a great valley, whose inhabitants were more than commonly inflated with the ardor of the times.

Rambling on, we espied a clamorous crowd gathered about a conspicuous palm, against which, a scroll was fixed.

The people were violently agitated; storming out maledictions against the insolent knave, who, over night must have fixed there, that scandalous document. But whoever he may have been, certain it was, he had contrived to hood himself effectually.

After much vehement discussion, during which sundry inflammatory harangues were made from the stumps of trees near by, it was proposed, that the scroll should be read aloud, so that all might give ear.

Seizing it, a fiery youth mounted upon the bowed shoulders of an old man, his sire; and with a shrill voice, ever and anon interrupted by outcries, read as follows:—

"Sovereign-kings of Vivenza! it is fit you should hearken to wisdom. But well aware, that you give ear to little wisdom except of your own; and that as freemen, you are free to hunt down him who dissents from your majesties; I deem it proper to address you anonymously.

"And if it please you, you may ascribe this voice to the gods: for never will you trace it to man.

"It is not unknown, sovereign-kings! that in these boisterous days, the lessons of history are almost discarded, as superseded by present experiences. And that while all Mardi's Present has grown out of its Past, it is becoming obsolete to refer to what has been. Yet, peradventure, the Past is an apostle.

"The grand error of this age, sovereign-kings! is the general supposition, that the very special Diabolus is abroad; whereas, the very special Diabolus has been abroad ever since Mardi began.

"And the grand error of your nation, sovereign-kings! seems this:—The conceit that Mardi is now in the last scene of the last act of her drama; and that all preceding events were ordained, to bring about the catastrophe you believe to be at hand,—a universal and permanent Republic.

"May it please you, those who hold to these things are fools, and not wise.

"Time is made up of various ages; and each thinks its own a novelty. But imbedded in the walls of the pyramids, which outrun all chronologies, sculptured stones are found, belonging to yet older fabrics. And as in the mound-building period of yore, so every age thinks its erections will forever endure. But as your forests grow apace, sovereign-kings! overrunning the tumuli in your western vales; so, while deriving their substance from the past, succeeding generations overgrow it; but in time, themselves decay.

"Oro decrees these vicissitudes.

"In chronicles of old, you read, sovereign-kings! that an eagle from the clouds presaged royalty to the fugitive Taquinoo[23]; and a king, Taquinoo reigned; No end to my dynasty, thought he.

"But another omen descended, foreshadowing the fall of Zooperbi, his son; and Zooperbi returning from his camp, found his country a fortress against him. No more kings would she have. And for five hundred twelve-moons the Regifugium or King's-flight, was annually celebrated like your own jubilee day. And rampant young orators stormed out detestation of kings; and augurs swore that their birds presaged immortality to freedom.

"Then, Romara's free eagles flew over all Mardi, and perched on the topmost diadems of the east.

"Ever thus must it be.

"For, mostly, monarchs are gemmed bridles upon the world, checking the plungings of a steed from the Pampas. And republics are as vast reservoirs, draining down all streams to one level; and so, breeding a fullness which can not remain full, without overflowing. And thus, Romara flooded all Mardi, till scarce an Ararat was left of the lofty kingdoms which had been.

"Thus, also, did Franko, fifty twelve-moons ago. Thus may she do again. And though not yet, have you, sovereign-kings! in any large degree done likewise, it is because you overflow your redundancies within your own mighty borders; having a wild western waste, which many shepherds with their flocks could not overrun in a day. Yet overrun at last it will be; and then, the recoil must come.

"And, may it please you, that thus far your chronicles had narrated a very different story, had your population been pressed and packed, like that of your old sire-land Dominora. Then, your great experiment might have proved an explosion; like the chemist's who, stirring his mixture, was blown by it into the air.

"For though crossed, and recrossed by many brave quarterings, and boasting the great Bull in your pedigree; yet, sovereign-kings! you are not meditative philosophers like the people of a small republic of old; nor enduring stoics, like their neighbors. Pent up, like them, may it please you, your thirteen original tribes had proved more turbulent, than so many mutinous legions. Free horses need wide prairies; and fortunate for you, sovereign-kings! that you have room enough, wherein to be free.

"And, may it please you, you are free, partly, because you are young. Your nation is like a fine, florid youth, full of fiery impulses, and hard to restrain; his strong hand nobly championing his heart. On all sides, freely he gives, and still seeks to acquire. The breath of his nostrils is like smoke in spring air; every tendon is electric with generous resolves. The oppressor he defies to his beard; the high walls of old opinions he scales with a bound. In the future he sees all the domes of the East.

"But years elapse, and this bold boy is transformed. His eyes open not as of yore; his heart is shut up as a vice. He yields not a groat; and seeking no more acquisitions, is only bent on preserving his hoard. The maxims once trampled under foot, are now printed on his front; and he who hated oppressors is become an oppressor himself.

"Thus, often, with men; thus, often, with nations. Then marvel not, sovereign-kings! that old states are different from yours; and think not, your own must forever remain liberal as now.

"Each age thinks its own is eternal. But though for five hundred twelve-moons, all Romara, by courtesy of history, was republican; yet, at last, her terrible king-tigers came, and spotted themselves with gore.

"And time was, when Dominora was republican, down to her

sturdy back-bone. The son of an absolute monarch became the man Karolus[24]; and his crown and head, both rolled in the dust. And Dominora had her patriots by thousands; and lusty Defenses, and glorious Areopagiticas were written, not since surpassed; and no turban was doffed save in homage of Oro.

"Yet, may it please you, to the sound of pipe and tabor, the second King Karolus returned in good time; and was hailed gracious majesty by high and low.

"Throughout all eternity, the parts of the past are but parts of the future reversed. In the old foot-prints, up and down, you mortals go, eternally traveling your Sierras. And not more infallible the ponderings of the Calculating Machine than the deductions from the decimals of history.

"In nations, sovereign-kings! there is a transmigration of souls; in you, is a marvelous destiny. The eagle of Romara revives in your own mountain bird, and once more is plumed for her flight. Her screams are answered by the vauntful cries of a hawk; his red comb yet reeking with slaughter. And one East, one West, those bold birds may fly, till they lock pinions in the midmost beyond.

"But, soaring in the sky over the nations that shall gather their broods under their wings, that bloody hawk may hereafter be taken for the eagle.

"And though crimson republics may rise in constellations, like fiery Aldebarans, speeding to their culminations; yet, down must they sink at last, and leave the old sultan-sun in the sky; in time, again to be deposed.

"For little longer, may it please you, can republics subsist now, than in days gone by. For, assuming that Mardi is wiser than of old; nevertheless, though all men approached sages in intelligence, some would yet be more wise than others; and so, the old degrees be preserved. And no exemption would an equality of knowledge furnish, from the inbred servility of mortal to mortal; from all the organic causes, which inevitably divide mankind into brigades and battalions, with captains at their head.

"Civilization has not ever been the brother of equality.

Freedom was born among the wild eyries in the mountains;
and barbarous tribes have sheltered under her wings, when the
enlightened people of the plain have nestled under different
pinions.

"Though, thus far, for you, sovereign-kings! your republic
has been fruitful of blessings; yet, in themselves, monarchies are
not utterly evil. For many nations, they are better than republics; for many, they will ever so remain. And better, on all
hands, that peace should rule with a scepter, than that the
tribunes of the people should brandish their broadswords.
Better be the subject of a king, upright and just; than a freeman
in Franko, with the executioner's ax at every corner.

"It is not the prime end, and chief blessing, to be politically
free. And freedom is only good as a means; is no end in itself.
Nor, did man fight it out against his masters to the haft, not then,
would he uncollar his neck from the yoke. A born thrall to the
last, yelping out his liberty, he still remains a slave unto Oro;
and well is it for the universe, that Oro's scepter is absolute.

"World-old the saying, that it is easier to govern others, than
oneself. And that all men should govern themselves as nations,
needs that all men be better, and wiser, than the wisest of one-
man rulers. But in no stable democracy do all men govern
themselves. Though an army be all volunteers, martial law
must prevail. Delegate your power, you leagued mortals must.
The hazard you must stand. And though unlike King Bello
of Dominora, your great chieftain, sovereign-kings! may not
declare war of himself; nevertheless, has he done a still more
imperial thing:—gone to war without declaring intentions.
You yourselves were precipitated upon a neighboring nation,[25]
ere you knew your spears were in your hands.

"But, as in stars you have written it on the welkin, sovereign-
kings! you are a great and glorious people. And verily, yours
is the best and happiest land under the sun. But not wholly,
because you, in your wisdom, decreed it: your origin and
geography necessitated it. Nor, in their germ, are all your
blessings to be ascribed to the noble sires, who of yore fought
in your behalf, sovereign-kings! Your nation enjoyed no little

independence before your Declaration declared it. Your ancient pilgrims fathered your liberty; and your wild woods harbored the nursling. For the state that to-day is made up of slaves, can not to-morrow transmute her bond into free; though lawlessness may transform them into brutes. Freedom is the name for a thing that is *not* freedom; this, a lesson never learned in an hour or an age. By some tribes it will never be learned.

"Yet, if it please you, there may be such a thing as being free under Caesar. Ages ago, there were as many vital freemen, as breathe vital air to-day.

"Names make not distinctions; some despots rule without swaying scepters. Though King Bello's palace was not put together by yoked men; your fedèral temple of freedom, sovereign-kings! was the handiwork of slaves.

"It is not gildings, and gold maces, and crown-jewels alone, that make a people servile. There is much bowing and cringing among you yourselves, sovereign-kings! Poverty is abased before riches, all Mardi over; any where, it is hard to be a debtor; any where, the wise will lord it over fools; every where, suffering is found.

"Thus, freedom is more social than political. And its real felicity is not to be shared. *That* is of a man's own individual getting and holding. It is not, who rules the state, but who rules me. Better be secure under one king, than exposed to violence from twenty millions of monarchs, though oneself be of the number.

"But superstitious notions you harbor, sovereign-kings! Did you visit Dominora, you would not be marched straight into a dungeon. And though you would behold sundry sights displeasing, you would start to inhale such liberal breezes; and hear crowds boasting of their privileges; as you, of yours. Nor has the wine of Dominora, a monarchical flavor.

"Now, though far and wide, to keep equal pace with the times, great reforms, of a verity, be needed; nowhere are bloody revolutions required. Though it be the most certain of remedies, no prudent invalid opens his veins, to let out his disease with his life. And though all evils may be assuaged; all evils can not be done away. For evil is the chronic malady of the universe; and checked in one place, breaks forth in another.

"Of late, on this head, some wild dreams have departed.

"There are many, who erewhile believed that the age of pikes and javelins was passed; that after a heady and blustering youth, old Mardi was at last settling down into a serene old age; and that the Indian summer, first discovered in your land, sovereign-kings! was the hazy vapor emitted from its tranquil pipe. But it has not so proved. Mardi's peaces are but truces. Long absent, at last the red comets have returned. And return they must, though their periods be ages. And should Mardi endure until mountain melt into mountain, and all the isles form one table-land; yet, would it but expand the old battle-plain.

"Students of history are horror-struck at the massacres of old; but in the shambles, men are being murdered to-day. Could time be reversed, and the future change places with the past, the past would cry out against us, and our future, full as loudly, as we against the ages foregone. All the Ages are his children, calling each other names.

"Hark ye, sovereign-kings! cheer not on the yelping pack too furiously. Hunters have been torn by their hounds. Be advised; wash your hands. Hold aloof. Oro has poured out an ocean for an everlasting barrier between you and the worst folly which other republics have perpetrated. That barrier hold sacred. And swear never to cross over to Porpheero, by manifesto or army, unless you traverse dry land.

"And be not too grasping, nearer home. It is not freedom to filch. Expand not your area too widely, now. Seek you proselytes? Neighboring nations may be free without coming under your banner. And if you can not lay your ambition, know this: that it is best served, by waiting events.

"Time, but Time only, may enable you to cross the equator; and give you the Arctic Circles for your boundaries."

So read the anonymous scroll; which straightway, was torn into shreds.

"Old tory, and monarchist!" they shouted, "Preaching over

his benighted sermons in these enlightened times! Fool! does he not know that all the Past and its graves are being dug over?"

They were furious; so wildly rolling their eyes after victims, that well was it for King Media, he wore not his crown; and in silence, we moved unnoted from out the crowd.

"My lord, I am amazed at the indiscretion of a demi-god," said Babbalanja, as we passed on our way; "I recognized your sultanic style the very first sentence. This, then, is the result of your hours of seclusion."

"Philosopher! I am astounded at your effrontery. I detected your philosophy the very first maxim. Who posted that parchment for you?"

So, each charged the other with its authorship: and there was no finding out, whether, indeed, either knew aught of its origin.

Now, could it have been Babbalanja? Hardly. For, philosophic as the document was, it seemed too dogmatic and conservative for him. King Media? But though imperially absolute in his political sentiments, Media delivered not himself so boldly, when actually beholding the eruption in Franko.

Indeed, the settlement of this question must be left to the commentators on Mardi,[26] some four or five hundred centuries hence.

CHAPTER CLXII

They Visit the Extreme South of Vivenza

We penetrated further and further into the valleys around; but, though, as elsewhere, at times we heard whisperings that promised an end to our wanderings;—we still wandered on; and once again, even Yoomy abated his sanguine hopes.

And now, we prepared to embark for the extreme south of the land.

But we were warned by the people, that in that portion of Vivenza, whither we were going, much would be seen repulsive to strangers. Such things, however, indulgent visitors overlooked. For themselves, they were well aware of those evils. Northern Vivenza had done all it could to assuage them; but in vain; the inhabitants of those southern valleys were a fiery, and intractable race; heeding neither expostulations, nor entreaties. They were wedded to their ways. Nay, they swore, that if the northern tribes persisted in intermeddlings, they would dissolve the common alliance, and establish a distinct confederacy among themselves.

Our coasting voyage at an end, our keels grated the beach among many prostrate palms, decaying, and washed by the billows. Though part and parcel of the shore we had left, this region seemed another land. Fewer thriving things were seen; fewer cheerful sounds were heard.

"Here labor has lost his laugh!" cried Yoomy.

It was a great plain where we landed; and there, under a burning sun, hundreds of collared men were toiling in trenches, filled with the taro plant: a root most flourishing in that soil. Standing grimly over these, were men unlike them; armed with long thongs, which descended upon the toilers, and made wounds. Blood and sweat mixed; and in great drops, fell.

"Who eat these plants thus nourished?" cried Yoomy.

"Are these men?" asked Babbalanja.

"Which mean you?" said Mohi.

Heeding him not, Babbalanja advanced toward the foremost of those with the thongs,—one Nulli[27]: a cadaverous, ghost-like man; with a low ridge of forehead; hair, steel-gray; and wondrous eyes;—bright, nimble, as the twin Corposant balls, playing about the ends of ships' royal-yards in gales.

The sun passed under a cloud; and Nulli, darting at Babbalanja those wondrous eyes, there fell upon him a baleful glare.

"Have they souls?" he asked, pointing to the serfs.

"No," said Nulli, "their ancestors may have had; but their souls have been bred out of their descendants; as the instinct of scent is killed in pointers."

Approaching one of the serfs, Media took him by the hand, and felt of it long; and looked into his eyes; and placed his ear to his side; and exclaimed, "Surely this being has flesh that is warm; he has Oro in his eye; and a heart in him that beats. I swear he is a man."

"Is this our lord the king?" cried Mohi, starting.

"What art thou," said Babbalanja to the serf. "Dost ever feel in thee a sense of right and wrong? Art ever glad or sad?— They tell us thou art not a man:—speak, then, for thyself; say, whether thou beliest thy Maker."

"Speak not of my Maker to me. Under the lash, I believe my masters, and account myself a brute; but in my dreams, bethink myself an angel. But I am bond; and my little ones;—their mother's milk is gall."

"Just Oro!" cried Yoomy, "do no thunders roll,—no lightnings flash in this accursed land!"

"Asylum for all Mardi's thralls!" cried Media.

"Incendiaries!" cried he with the wondrous eyes, "come ye, firebrands, to light the flame of revolt? Know ye not, that here are many serfs, who, incited to obtain their liberty, might wreak some dreadful vengeance? Avaunt, thou king! *thou* horrified at this? Go back to Odo, and right her wrongs! These serfs are happier than thine; though thine, no collars wear; more happy as they are, than if free. Are they not fed, clothed, and cared for? Thy serfs pine for food: never yet did these; who have no thoughts, no cares."

"Thoughts and cares are life, and liberty, and immortality!" cried Babbalanja; "and are their souls, then, blown out as candles?"

"Ranter! they are content," cried Nulli. "They shed no tears."

"Frost never weeps," said Babbalanja; "and tears are frozen in those frigid eyes."

"Oh fettered sons of fettered mothers, conceived and born in manacles," cried Yoomy; "dragging them through life; and falling with them, clanking in the grave:—oh, beings as ourselves, how my stiff arm shivers to avenge you! 'Twere absolution for the matricide, to strike one rivet from your chains. My heart outswells its home!"

"Oro! Art thou?" cried Babbalanja; "and doth this thing exist? It shakes my little faith." Then, turning upon Nulli, "How can ye abide to sway this curs'd dominion?"

"Peace, fanatic! Who else may till unwholesome fields, but these? And as these beings are, so shall they remain; 'tis right and righteous! Maramma[28] champions it!—*I* swear it! The first blow struck for them, dissolves the union of Vivenza's vales. The northern tribes well know it; and know me."

Said Media, "Yet if—"

"No more! another word, and, king as thou art, thou shalt be dungeoned:—here, there is such a law; thou art not among the northern tribes."

"And this is freedom!" murmured Media; "when heaven's own voice is throttled. And were these serfs to rise, and fight for it; like dogs, they would be hunted down by her pretended sons!"

"Pray, heaven!" cried Yoomy, "they may yet find a way to loose their bonds without one drop of blood. But hear me, Oro! were there no other way, and should their masters not relent, all honest hearts must cheer this tribe of Hamo on; though they cut their chains with blades thrice edged, and gory to the haft! 'Tis right to fight for freedom, whoever be the thrall."

"These South savannahs may yet prove battle-fields," said Mohi, gloomily, as we retraced our steps.

"Be it," said Yoomy. "Oro will van the right."

"Not always has it proved so," said Babbalanja. "Oft-times, the right fights single-handed against the world; and Oro champions none. In all things, man's own battles, man himself must fight. Yoomy: so far as feeling goes, your sympathies are not more hot than mine; but for these serfs you would cross spears; yet, I would not. Better present woes for some, than future woes for all."

"No need to fight," cried Yoomy, "to liberate that tribe of Hamo instantly; a way may be found, and no irretrievable evil ensue."

"Point it out, and be blessed, Yoomy."

"That is for Vivenza; but the head is dull, where the heart is cold."

"My lord," said Babbalanja, "you have startled us by your

kingly sympathy for suffering; say thou, then, in what wise manner it shall be relieved."

"That is for Vivenza," said Media.

"Mohi, you are old: speak thou."

"Let Vivenza speak," said Mohi.

"Thus, then, we all agree; and weeping, all but echo hard-hearted Nulli. Tears are not swords; and wrongs seem almost natural as rights. For the righteous to suppress an evil, is sometimes harder than for others to uphold it. Humanity cries out against this vast enormity:—not one man knows a prudent remedy. Blame not, then, the North; and wisely judge the South. Ere, as a nation, they became responsible, this thing was planted in their midst. Such roots strike deep. Place to-day those serfs in Dominora; and with them, all Vivenza's Past;—and serfs, for many years, in Dominora, they would be. Easy is it to stand afar and rail. All men are censors who have lungs. We can say, the stars are wrongly marshaled. Blind men say the sun is blind. A thousand muscles wag our tongues; though our tongues were housed, that they might have a home. Whoso is free from crime, let him cross himself—but hold his cross upon his lips. That he is not bad, is not of him. Potters' clay and wax are all, molded by hands invisible. The soil decides the man. And, ere birth, man wills not to be born here or there. These southern tribes have grown up with this thing; bond-women were their nurses, and bondmen serve them still. Nor are all their serfs such wretches as those we saw. Some seem happy: yet not as men. Unmanned, they know not what they are. And though, of all the south, Nulli must stand almost alone in his insensate creed; yet, to all wrong-doers, custom backs the sense of wrong. And if to every Mardian, conscience be the awarder of its own doom; then, of these tribes, many shall be found exempted from the least penalty of this sin. But sin it is, no less;—a blot, foul as the crater-pool of hell; it puts out the sun at noon; it parches all fertility; and, conscience or no conscience—ere he die—let every master who wrenches bond-babe from mother, that the nipple tear; unwreathes the arms of sisters; or cuts the holy unity in twain; till apart fall man and wife, like one bleeding body cleft:—let that master thrice shrive his soul; take every sacrament; on his bended knees give up the ghost;—yet shall he die despairing; and live again, to die forever damned. The future is all hieroglyphics. Who may read? But, methinks the great laggard Time must now march up apace, and somehow befriend these thralls. It can not be, that misery is perpetually entailed; though, in a land proscribing primogeniture, the first-born and last of Hamo's tribe must still succeed to all their sires' wrongs. Yes: Time—all-healing Time—Time, great Philanthropist!—Time must befriend these thralls!"

"Oro grant it!" cried Yoomy "and let Mardi say, amen!"

"Amen! amen! amen!" cried echoes echoing echoes.

We traversed many of these southern vales; but as in Dominora,—so, throughout Vivenza, North and South,—Yillah harbored not.

From WHITE–JACKET

CHAPTER IV

Jack Chase[1]

The first night out of port was a clear, moonlight one; the frigate gliding through the water, with all her batteries.

It was my Quarter Watch in the top; and there I reclined on the best possible terms with my top-mates. Whatever the other seamen might have been, these were a noble set of tars, and well worthy an introduction to the reader.

First and foremost was Jack Chase, our noble First Captain of the Top. He was a Briton, and a true-blue; tall and well-knit, with a clear open eye, a fine broad brow, and an abounding nut-brown beard. No man ever had a better heart or a bolder. He was loved by the seamen and admired by the officers; and even when the Captain spoke to him, it was with a slight air of respect. Jack was a frank and charming man.

No one could be better company in forecastle or saloon; no man told such stories, sang such songs, or with greater alacrity sprang to his duty. Indeed, there was only one thing wanting about him; and that was, a finger of his left hand, which finger he had lost at the great battle of Navarino.

He had a high conceit of his profession as a seaman; and being deeply versed in all things pertaining to a man-of-war, was universally regarded as an oracle. The main-top, over which he presided, was a sort of oracle of Delphi; to which, many pilgrims ascended, to have their perplexities or differences settled.

There was such an abounding air of good sense and good feeling about the man, that he who could not love him, would thereby pronounce himself a knave. I thanked my sweet stars, that kind fortune had placed me near him, though under him, in the frigate; and from the outset Jack and I were fast friends.

Wherever you may be now rolling over the blue billows, dear Jack! take my best love along with you; and God bless you, wherever you go!

Jack was a gentleman. What though his hand was hard, so was not his heart, too often the case with soft palms. His manners were easy and free; none of the boisterousness, so common to tars; and he had a polite, courteous way of saluting you, if it were only to borrow your knife. Jack had read all the verses of Byron, and all the romances of Scott. He talked of Rob Roy, Don Juan, and Pelham[2]; Macbeth and Ulysses; but, above all things, was an ardent admirer of Camoens. Parts of the Lusiad,[3] he could recite in the original. Where he had obtained his wonderful accomplishments, it is not for me, his humble subordinate, to say. Enough, that those accomplishments were so various; the languages he could converse in, so numerous; that he more than furnished an example of that saying of Charles the Fifth—*he who speaks five languages is as good as five men.* But Jack, he was better than a hundred common mortals; Jack was a whole phalanx, an entire army; Jack was a thousand strong; Jack would have done honor to the Queen of England's drawing-room; Jack must have been a by-blow of some British Admiral of the Blue. A finer specimen of the island race of Englishmen could not have been picked out of Westminster Abbey of a coronation day.[4]

His whole demeanor was in strong contrast to that of one of the Captains of the fore-top. This man, though a good seaman, furnished an example of those insufferable Britons, who, while preferring other countries to their own as places of residence; still, overflow with all the pompousness of national and individual vanity combined. "When I was on board the Audacious"—for a long time, was almost the invariable exordium to the fore-top Captain's most cursory remarks. It is often the custom of men-of-war's-men, when they deem anything to be going on wrong aboard ship, to refer to *last cruise*, when of course everything was done *ship-shape and Bristol fashion.* And by referring to the *Audacious*—an expressive name by the way—the fore-top Captain meant a ship in the

English navy, in which he had had the honor of serving. So continual were his allusions to this craft with the amiable name, that at last, the *Audacious* was voted a bore by his shipmates. And one hot afternoon, during a calm, when the fore-top Captain, like many others, was standing still and yawning on the spar-deck; Jack Chase, his own countryman, came up to him, and pointing at his open mouth, politely inquired, whether that was the way they caught *flies* in Her Britannic Majesty's ship, the *Audacious?* After that, we heard no more of the craft.

Now, the tops of a frigate are quite spacious and cosy. They are railed in behind so as to form a kind of balcony, very pleasant of a tropical night. From twenty to thirty loungers may agreeably recline there, cushioning themselves on old sails and jackets. We had rare times in that top. We accounted ourselves the best seamen in the ship; and from our airy perch, literally looked down upon the landlopers below, sneaking about the deck, among the guns. In a large degree, we nourished that feeling of "*esprit de corps*," always pervading, more or less, the various sections of a man-of-war's crew. We main-top-men were brothers, one and all; and we loaned ourselves to each other with all the freedom in the world.

Nevertheless, I had not long been a member of this fraternity of fine fellows, ere I discovered that Jack Chase, our Captain, was—like all prime favorites and oracles among men—a little bit of a dictator; not peremptorily, or annoyingly so, but amusingly intent on egotistically mending our manners and improving our taste, so that we might reflect credit upon our tutor.

He made us all wear our hats at a particular angle—instructed us in the tie of our neck handkerchiefs; and protested against our wearing vulgar *dungeree* trowsers; besides giving us lessons in seamanship; and solemnly conjuring us, forever to eschew the company of any sailor we suspected of having served in a whaler. Against all whalers, indeed, he cherished the unmitigated detestation of a true man-of-war's-man. Poor Tubbs can testify to that.

Tubbs was in the After-Guard; a long, lank Vineyarder, eternally talking of line-tubs, Nantucket, sperm oil, stove boats, and Japan. Nothing could silence him; and his comparisons were ever invidious.

Now, with all his soul, Jack abominated this Tubbs. He said he was vulgar, an upstart—Devil take him, he's been in a whaler. But like many men, who have been where *you* haven't been; or seen what *you* haven't seen; Tubbs, on account of his whaling experiences, absolutely affected to look down upon Jack, even as Jack did upon him; and this it was that so enraged our noble captain.

One night, with a peculiar meaning in his eye, he sent me down on deck to invite Tubbs up aloft for a chat. Flattered by so marked an honor—for we were somewhat fastidious, and did not extend such invitations to everybody—Tubbs quickly mounted the rigging, looking rather abashed at finding himself in the august presence of the assembled Quarter-Watch of main-top-men. Jack's courteous manner, however, very soon relieved his embarrassment; but it is no use to be courteous to *some* men in this world. Tubbs belonged to that category. No sooner did the bumpkin feel himself at ease, than he launched out, as usual, into tremendous laudations of whalemen; declaring that whalemen alone deserved the name of sailors. Jack stood it some time; but when Tubbs came down upon men-of-war, and particularly upon main-top-men, his sense of propriety was so outraged, that he launched into Tubbs like a forty-two pounder.

"Why, you limb of Nantucket! you train-oil man! you sea-tallow strainer! you bobber after carrion! do *you* pretend to vilify a man-of-war? Why, you lean rogue, you, a man-of-war is to whalemen, as a metropolis to shire-towns, and sequestered hamlets. *Here's* the place for life and commotion; *here's* the place to be gentlemanly and jolly. And what did you know, you bumpkin! before you came on board this *Andrew Miller?* [5] What knew you of gun-deck, or orlop,[6] mustering round the capstan, beating to quarters, and piping to dinner? Did you ever roll to *grog* on board your greasy ballyhoo of blazes? Did you ever winter at Mahon?[7] Did you ever '*lash and carry*'? Why, what are even a merchant-seaman's sorry yarns of voyages to China after tea-caddies, and voyages to the West Indies after sugar puncheons, and voyages to the Shetlands after seal-skins —what are even these yarns, you Tubbs you! to high life in a man-of-war? Why, you dead-eye! I have sailed with lords and marquises for captains; and the King of the Two Sicilies has passed me, as I here stood up at my gun. Bah! you are full of the fore-peak [8] and the forecastle; you are only familiar with Burtons [9] and Billy-tackles; your ambition never mounted above pig-killing! which, in my poor opinion, is the proper phrase for whaling! Top-mates! has not this Tubbs here been but a misuser of good oak planks, and a vile desecrator of the thrice holy sea? turning his ship, my hearties! into a fat-kettle, and the ocean into a whale-pen? Begone! you graceless, god-less knave! pitch him over the top there, White-Jacket!" [10]

But there was no necessity for my exertions. Poor Tubbs, astounded at these fulminations, was already rapidly descending by the rigging.

This outburst on the part of my noble friend Jack made me shake all over, spite of my padded surtout; and caused me to offer up devout thanksgivings, that in no evil hour had I divulged the fact of having myself served in a whaler; for having previously marked the prevailing prejudice of men-of-war's-men to that much-maligned class of mariners, I had wisely held my peace concerning stove boats on the coast of Japan.

CHAPTER V

Jack Chase on a Spanish Quarter-Deck [11]

Here, I must frankly tell a story about Jack, which, as touching his honor and integrity, I am sure, will not work against him, in any charitable man's estimation. On this present cruise of the frigate Neversink, Jack had deserted; and after a certain interval, had been captured.

But with what purpose had he deserted? To avoid naval discipline? to riot in some abandoned sea-port? for love of some worthless signorita? Not at all. He abandoned the frigate from far higher and nobler, nay, glorious motives. Though bowing to naval discipline afloat; yet ashore, he was a stickler for the Rights of Man, and the liberties of the world. He went to draw a partisan blade in the civil commotions of Peru; and befriend, heart and soul, what he deemed the cause of the Right.

At the time, his disappearance excited the utmost astonishment among the officers, who had little suspected him of any such conduct as deserting.

"What? Jack, my great man of the main-top, gone!" cried the Captain: "I'll not believe it."

"Jack Chase cut and run!" cried a sentimental middy. "It must have been all for love, then; the signoritas have turned his head."

"Jack Chase not to be found?" cried a growling old sheet-anchor-man, one of your malicious prophets of past events: "I thought so; I know'd it; I could have sworn it—just the chap to make sail on the sly. I always s'pected him."

Months passed away, and nothing was heard of Jack; till at last, the frigate came to anchor on the coast, alongside of a Peruvian sloop of war.

Bravely clad in the Peruvian uniform, and with a fine, mixed martial and naval step, a tall, striking figure of a long-bearded officer was descried, promenading the Quarter-deck of the stranger; and superintending the salutes, which are exchanged between national vessels on these occasions.

This fine officer touched his laced hat most courteously to our Captain, who, after returning the compliment, stared at him, rather impolitely, through his spy-glass.

"By Heaven!" he cried at last—"it is he—he can't disguise his walk—that's his beard; I'd know him in Cochin China. —Man the first cutter there! Lieutenant Blink, go on board that sloop of war, and fetch me yon officer."

All hands were aghast—What? when a piping-hot peace was between the United States and Peru, to send an armed body on board a Peruvian sloop of war, and seize one of its officers, in broad daylight?—Monstrous infraction of the Law of Nations! What would Vattel[12] say?

But Captain Claret must be obeyed. So off went the cutter, every man armed to the teeth, the lieutenant-commanding having secret instructions, and the midshipmen attending looking ominously wise, though, in truth, they could not tell what was coming.

Gaining the sloop of war, the lieutenant was received with the customary honors; but by this time the tall, bearded officer had disappeared from the Quarter-deck. The Lieutenant now inquired for the Peruvian Captain; and being shown into the cabin, made known to him, that on board his vessel was a person belonging to the United States Ship Neversink; and his orders were, to have that person delivered up instanter.

The foreign captain curled his moustache in astonishment and indignation; he hinted something about beating to quarters, and chastising this piece of Yankee insolence.

But resting one gloved hand upon the table, and playing with his sword-knot, the Lieutenant, with a bland firmness, repeated his demand. At last, the whole case being so plainly made out, and the person in question being so accurately described, even to a mole on his cheek, there remained nothing but immediate compliance.

So the fine-looking, bearded officer, who had so courteously doffed his chapeau to our Captain, but disappeared upon the arrival of the Lieutenant, was summoned into the cabin, before his superior, who addressed him thus:—

"Don John, this gentleman declares, that of right you belong to the frigate Neversink. Is it so?"

"It is even so, Don Sereno," said Jack Chase, proudly folding his gold-laced coat-sleeves across his chest—"and as there is no resisting the frigate, I comply.—Lieutenant Blink, I am ready. Adieu! Don Sereno, and Madre de Dios protect you! You have been a most gentlemanly friend and captain to me. I hope you will yet thrash your beggarly foes."

With that he turned; and entering the cutter, was pulled back to the frigate, and stepped up to Captain Claret,[13] where that gentleman stood on the quarter-deck.

"Your servant, my fine Don," said the Captain, ironically

lifting his chapeau, but regarding Jack at the same time with a look of intense displeasure.

"Your most devoted and penitent Captain of the Main-top, sir; and one who, in his very humility of contrition is yet proud to call Captain Claret his commander," said Jack, making a glorious bow, and then tragically flinging overboard his Peruvian sword.

"Reinstate him at once," shouted Captain Claret—"and now, sir, to your duty; and discharge that well to the end of the cruise, and you will hear no more of your having run away."

So Jack went forward among crowds of admiring tars, who swore by his nut-brown beard, which had amazingly length-ened and spread during his absence. They divided his laced hat and coat among them; and on their shoulders, carried him in triumph along the gun-deck.

CHAPTER XXXIII

A Flogging

If you begin the day with a laugh, you may, nevertheless, end it with a sob and a sigh.[14]

Among the many who were exceedingly diverted with the scene between the Down Easter and the Lieutenant, none laughed more heartily than John, Peter, Mark, and Antone—four sailors of the starboard-watch. The same evening these four found themselves prisoners in the "brig," with a sentry standing over them. They were charged with violating a well-known law of the ship—having been engaged in one of those tangled, general fights sometimes occurring among sailors. They had nothing to anticipate but a flogging, at the Captain's pleasure.

Toward evening of the next day, they were startled by the dread summons of the boatswain and his mates at the principal hatchway—a summons that ever sends a shudder through every manly heart in a frigate:

"*All hands witness punishment, ahoy!*"

The hoarseness of the cry, its unrelenting prolongation, its being caught up at different points, and sent through the lower-most depths of the ship; all this produces a most dismal effect upon every heart not calloused by long habituation to it.

However much you may desire to absent yourself from the scene that ensues, yet behold it you must; or, at least, stand near it you must; for the regulations enjoin the attendance of the entire ship's company, from the corpulent Captain himself to the smallest boy who strikes the bell.

"*All hands witness punishment, ahoy!*"

To the sensitive seaman that summons sounds like a doom. He knows that the same law which impels it—the same law by which the culprits of the day must suffer; that by that very law he also is liable at any time to be judged and condemned. And the inevitableness of his own presence at the scene; the strong arm that drags him in view of the scourge, and holds him there till all is over; forcing upon his loathing eye and soul the sufferings and groans of men who have familiarly consorted with him, eaten with him, battled out watches with him—men of his own type and badge—all this conveys a terrible hint of the omnipotent authority under which he lives. Indeed, to such a man the naval summons to witness punishment carries a thrill, somewhat akin to what we may impute to the quick and the dead, when they shall hear the Last Trump, that is to bid them all arise in their ranks, and behold the final penalties inflicted upon the sinners of our race.

But it must not be imagined that to all men-of-war's-men this summons conveys such poignant emotions; but it is hard to decide whether one should be glad or sad that this is not the case; whether it is grateful to know that so much pain is avoided, or whether it is far sadder to think that, either from constitu-tional hard-heartedness or the multiplied searings of habit, hundreds of men-of-war's-men have been made proof against the sense of degradation, pity, and shame.

As if in sympathy with the scene to be enacted, the sun, which the day previous had merrily flashed upon the tin pan of the disconsolate Down Easter, was now setting over the dreary waters, veiling itself in vapors. The wind blew hoarsely in the cordage; the seas broke heavily against the bows; and the frigate, staggering under whole top-sails, strained as in agony on her way.

"All hands witness punishment, ahoy!"

At the summons the crew crowded round the main-mast; multitudes eager to obtain a good place on the booms, to overlook the scene; many laughing and chatting, others canvassing the case of the culprits; some maintaining sad, anxious countenances, or carrying a suppressed indignation in their eyes; a few purposely keeping behind to avoid looking on; in short, among five hundred men, there was every possible shade of character.

All the officers—midshipmen included—stood together in a group on the starboard side of the main-mast: the First Lieutenant in advance, and the surgeon, whose special duty it is to be present at such times, standing close by his side.

Presently the Captain came forward from his cabin, and stood in the centre of this solemn group, with a small paper in his hand. That paper was the daily report of offences, regularly laid upon his table every morning or evening, like the day's journal placed by a bachelor's napkin at breakfast.

"Master-at-arms, bring up the prisoners," he said.

A few moments elapsed, during which the Captain, now clothed in his most dreadful attributes, fixed his eyes severely upon the crew, when suddenly a lane formed through the crowd of seamen, and the prisoners advanced—the master-at-arms, rattan in hand, on one side, and an armed marine on the other—and took up their stations at the mast.

"You John, you Peter, you Mark, you Antone," said the Captain, "were yesterday found fighting on the gun-deck. Have you anything to say?"

Mark and Antone, two steady, middle-aged men, whom I had often admired for their sobriety, replied that they did not strike the first blow; that they had submitted to much before they had yielded to their passions; but as they acknowledged that they had at last defended themselves, their excuse was overruled.

John—a brutal bully, who, it seems, was the real author of the disturbance—was about entering into a long extenuation, when he was cut short by being made to confess, irrespective of circumstances, that he had been in the fray.

Peter, a handsome lad about nineteen years old, belonging to the mizzen-top, looked pale and tremulous. He was a great favorite in his part of the ship, and especially in his own mess, principally composed of lads of his own age. That morning two of his young mess-mates had gone to his bag, taken out his best clothes, and, obtaining the permission of the marine sentry at the "brig," had handed them to him, to be put on against being summoned to the mast. This was done to propitiate the Captain, as most captains love to see a tidy sailor. But it would not do. To all his supplications the Captain turned a deaf ear. Peter declared that he had been struck twice before he had returned a blow. "No matter," said the Captain, "you struck at last, instead of reporting the case to an officer. I allow no man to fight on board here but myself. *I* do the fighting."

"Now, men," he added, "you all admit the charge; you know the penalty. Strip! Quarter-masters, are the gratings rigged?"

The gratings are square frames of barred wood-work, sometimes placed over the hatch-ways. One of these squares was now laid on the deck, close to the ship's bulwarks, and while the remaining preparations were being made, the master-at-arms assisted the prisoners in removing their jackets and shirts. This done, their shirts were loosely thrown over their shoulders.

At a sign from the Captain, John, with a shameless leer, advanced, and stood passively upon the grating, while the bare-headed old Quarter-master, with gray hair streaming in the wind, bound his feet to the cross-bars, and, stretching out his arms over his head, secured them to the hammock-nettings above. He then retreated a little space, standing silent.

Meanwhile, the boatswain stood solemnly on the other side, with a green bag in his hand, from which taking four instruments of punishment, he gave one to each of his mates; for a fresh "cat," applied by a fresh hand, is the ceremonious privilege accorded to every man-of-war culprit.

At another sign from the Captain, the master-at-arms, stepping up, removed the shirt from the prisoner. At this juncture a wave broke against the ship's side, and dashed the spray over his exposed back. But though the air was piercing cold, and the water drenched him, John stood still, without a shudder.

The Captain's finger was now lifted, and the first boatswain's-mate advanced, combing out the nine tails of his *cat* with his hand, and then, sweeping them round his neck, brought them with the whole force of his body upon the mark. Again, and again, and again; and at every blow, higher and higher rose the long, purple bars on the prisoner's back. But he only bowed over his head, and stood still. Meantime, some of the crew whispered among themselves in applause of their ship-mate's nerve; but the greater part were breathlessly silent as the keen scourge hissed through the wintry air, and fell with a cutting, wiry sound upon the mark. One dozen lashes being applied, the man was taken down, and went among the crew with a smile, saying, "D—n me! it's nothing when you're used to it! Who wants to fight?"

The next was Antone, the Portuguese. At every blow he surged from side to side, pouring out a torrent of involuntary blasphemies. Never before had he been heard to curse. When cut down, he went among the men, swearing to have the life of the Captain. Of course, this was unheard by the officers.

Mark, the third prisoner, only cringed and coughed under his punishment. He had some pulmonary complaint. He was off duty for several days after the flogging; but this was partly to be imputed to his extreme mental misery. It was his first scourging, and he felt the insult more than the injury. He became silent and sullen for the rest of the cruise.

The fourth and last was Peter, the mizzen-top lad. He had often boasted that he had never been degraded at the gangway. The day before his cheek had worn its usual red, but now no ghost was whiter. As he was being secured to the gratings, and the shudderings and creepings of his dazzlingly white back were revealed, he turned round his head imploringly; but his weeping entreaties and vows of contrition were of no avail.

"I would not forgive God Almighty!" cried the Captain. The fourth boatswain's-mate advanced, and at the first blow, the boy, shouting *"My God! Oh! my God!"* writhed and leaped so as to displace the gratings, and scatter the nine tails of the scourge all over his person. At the next blow he howled, leaped, and raged in unendurable torture.

"What are you stopping for, boatswain's-mate?" cried the Captain. "Lay on!" and the whole dozen was applied.

"I don't care what happens to me now!" wept Peter, going among the crew, with blood-shot eyes, as he put on his shirt. "I have been flogged once, and they may do it again, if they will. Let them look out for me now!"

"Pipe down!" cried the Captain, and the crew slowly dispersed.

Let us have the charity to believe them—as we do—when some Captains in the Navy say, that the thing of all others most repulsive to them, in the routine of what they consider their duty, is the administration of corporal punishment upon the crew; for, surely, not to feel scarified to the quick at these scenes would argue a man but a beast.

You see a human being, stripped like a slave; scourged worse than a hound. And for what? For things not essentially criminal, but only made so by arbitrary laws.

CHAPTER XXXIV

Some of the Evil Effects of Flogging

There are incidental considerations touching this matter of flogging, which exaggerate the evil into a great enormity. Many illustrations might be given, but let us be content with a few.

One of the arguments advanced by officers of the Navy in favor of corporal punishment is this: it can be inflicted in a moment; it consumes no valuable time; and when the prisoner's shirt is put on, *that* is the last of it. Whereas, if another punishment were substituted, it would probably occasion a great waste of time and trouble, besides thereby begetting in the sailor an undue idea of his importance.

Absurd, or worse than absurd, as it may appear, all this is true; and if you start from the same premises with these officers, you must admit that they advance an irresistible argument. But in accordance with this principle, captains in the Navy, to a certain extent, inflict the scourge—which is ever at hand—for nearly all degrees of transgression. In offences not cognizable by a court martial, little, if any, discrimination is shown. It is of a piece with the penal laws that prevailed in England some sixty years ago, when one hundred and sixty different offences were declared by the statute-book to be capital, and the servant-maid who but pilfered a watch was hung beside the murderer of a family.

It is one of the most common punishments for very trivial offences in the Navy, to "stop" a seaman's *grog* for a day or a week. And as most seamen so cling to their *grog*, the loss of it is generally deemed by them a very serious penalty. You will sometimes hear them say, "I would rather have my wind *stopped* than my *grog!*"

But there are some sober seamen that would much rather draw the money for it, instead of the grog itself, as provided by law; but they are too often deterred from this by the thought of receiving a scourging for some inconsiderable offence, as a substitute for the stopping of their spirits. This is a most serious obstacle to the cause of temperance in the Navy. But, in many cases, even the reluctant drawing of his grog can not exempt a prudent seaman from ignominy; for besides the formal ad-ministering of the "*cat*" at the gangway for petty offences, he is liable to the "colt," or rope's-end, a bit of *ratlin-stuff*, indis-criminately applied—without stripping the victim—at any time, and in any part of the ship, at the merest wink from the Captain. By an express order of that officer, most boatswain's mates carry the "colt" coiled in their hats, in readiness to be administered at a minute's warning upon any offender. This was the custom in the Neversink. And until so recent a period as the administra-tion of President Polk, when the historian Bancroft,[15] Secretary of the Navy, officially interposed, it was an almost universal thing for the officers of the watch, at their own discretion, to inflict chastisement upon a sailor, and this, too, in the face of the ordinance restricting the power of flogging solely to Captains and Courts Martial. Nor was it a thing unknown for a Lieutenant, in a sudden outburst of passion, perhaps inflamed by brandy, or smarting under the sense of being disliked or hated by the seamen, to order a whole watch of two hundred and fifty men, at dead of night, to undergo the indignity of the "colt."

It is believed that, even at the present day, there are instances of Commanders still violating the law, by delegating the power of the colt to subordinates. At all events, it is certain that, almost to a man, the Lieutenants in the Navy bitterly rail against the officiousness of Bancroft, in so materially abridging their usurped functions by snatching the colt from their hands. At the time, they predicted that this rash and most ill-judged interference of the Secretary would end in the breaking up of all discipline in the Navy. But it has not so proved. These officers *now* predict that, if the "cat" be abolished, the same unfulfilled prediction would be verified.

Concerning the license with which many captains violate the express laws laid down by Congress for the government of the Navy, a glaring instance may be quoted. For upward of forty years there has been on the American Statute-book a law prohibiting a Captain from inflicting, on his own authority, more than twelve lashes at one time. If more are to be given, the sentence must be passed by a Court Martial. Yet, for nearly half a century, this law has been frequently, and with almost perfect impunity, set at naught: though of late, through the exertions of Bancroft and others, it has been much better observed than formerly; indeed, at the present day, it is generally respected. Still, while the Neversink was lying in a South American port, on the cruise now written of, the seamen belonging to another American frigate informed us that their captain sometimes inflicted, upon his own authority, eighteen and twenty lashes. It is worth while to state that this frigate was vastly admired by the shore ladies for her wonderfully neat appearance. One of her forecastle-men told me that he had used up three jack-knives (charged to him on the books of the purser) in scraping the belaying-pins and the combings of the hatchways.

It is singular that while the Lieutenants of the Watch in American men-of-war so long usurped the power of inflicting corporal punishment with the *colt*, few or no similar abuses were known in the English Navy. And though the captain of an English armed ship is authorized to inflict, at his own discretion, *more* than a dozen lashes (I think three dozen), yet it is to be doubted whether, upon the whole, there is as much flogging at present in the English Navy as in the American. The chivalric Virginian, John Randolph of Roanoke, declared, in his place in Congress, that on board of the American man-of-war that carried him out Embassador to Russia he had witnessed more flogging than had taken place on his own plantation of five hundred African slaves in ten years. Certain it is, from what I have personally seen, that the English officers, as a general thing, seem to be less disliked by their crews than the American officers by theirs. The reason probably is, that many of them, from their station in life, have been more accustomed to social command; hence, quarter-deck authority sits more naturally on them. A coarse, vulgar man, who happens to rise to high naval rank by the exhibition of talents not incompatible with vulgarity, invariably proves a tyrant to his crew. It is a thing that American man-of-war's-men have often observed, that the Lieutenants from the Southern States, the descendants of the old Virginians, are much less severe, and much more gentle and gentlemanly in command, than the Northern officers, as a class.

According to the present laws and usages of the Navy, a seaman, for the most trivial alleged offences, of which he may be entirely innocent, must, without a trial, undergo a penalty the traces whereof he carries to the grave; for to a man-of-war's-man's experienced eye the marks of a naval scourging with the "*cat*" are through life discernible. And with these marks on his back, this image of his Creator must rise at the Last Day.

Yet so untouchable is true dignity, that there are cases wherein to be flogged at the gangway is no dishonor; though, to abase and hurl down the last pride of some sailor who has piqued him, be sometimes the secret motive, with some malicious officer, in procuring him to be condemned to the lash. But this feeling of the innate dignity remaining untouched, though outwardly the body be scarred for the whole term of the natural life, is one of the hushed things, buried among the holiest privacies of the soul; a thing between a man's God and himself; and for ever undiscernible by our fellow-men, who account *that* a degradation which seems so to the corporal eye. But what torments must that seaman undergo who, while his back bleeds at the gangway, bleeds agonized drops of shame from his soul! Are we not justified in immeasurably denouncing this thing? Join hands with me, then; and, in the name of that Being in whose image the flogged sailor is made, let us demand of Legislators, by what right they dare profane what God himself accounts sacred.

Is it lawful for you to scourge a man that is a Roman? asks the intrepid Apostle, well knowing, as a Roman citizen, that it was not.[16] And now, eighteen hundred years after, is it lawful for you, my countrymen, to scourge a man that is an American? to scourge him round the world in your frigates?

It is to no purpose that you apologetically appeal to the general depravity of the man-of-war's-man. Depravity in the oppressed is no apology for the oppressor; but rather an additional stigma to him, as being, in a large degree, the effect, and not the cause and justification of oppression.

CHAPTER LXI

The Surgeon of the Fleet[17]

Cadwallader Cuticle, M.D., and Honorary Member of the most distinguished Colleges of Surgeons both in Europe and America, was our Surgeon of the Fleet. Nor was he at all blind to the dignity of his position; to which, indeed, he was rendered peculiarly competent, if the reputation he enjoyed was deserved. He had the name of being the foremost Surgeon in the Navy, a gentleman of remarkable science, and a veteran practitioner.

He was a small, withered man, nearly, perhaps quite, sixty years of age. His chest was shallow, his shoulders bent, his pantaloons hung round skeleton legs, and his face was singularly attenuated. In truth, the corporeal vitality of this man seemed, in a good degree, to have died out of him. He walked abroad, a curious patch-work of life and death, with a wig, one glass eye, and a set of false teeth, while his voice was husky and thick; but his mind seemed undebilitated as in youth; it shone out of his remaining eye with basilisk brilliancy.

Like most old physicians and surgeons who have seen much service, and have been promoted to high professional place for their scientific attainments, this Cuticle was an enthusiast in his calling. In private, he had once been heard to say, confidentially, that he would rather cut off a man's arm than dismember the wing of the most delicate pheasant. In particular, the department of Morbid Anatomy was his peculiar love; and in his state-room below he had a most unsightly collection of Parisian casts, in plaster and wax, representing all imaginable malformations of the human members, both organic and induced by disease. Chief among these was a cast, often to be met with in the Anatomical Museums of Europe, and no doubt an unexaggerated copy of a genuine original; it was the head of an elderly woman, with an aspect singularly gentle and meek, but at the same time wonderfully expressive of a gnawing sorrow, never to be relieved. You would almost have thought it the face of some abbess, for some unspeakable crime voluntarily sequestered from human society, and leading a life of agonized penitence without hope; so marvellously sad and tearfully pitiable was this head. But when you first beheld it, no such emotions ever crossed your mind. All your eyes and all your horrified soul were fast fascinated and frozen by the sight of a hideous, crumpled horn, like that of a ram, downward, growing out from the forehead, and partly shadowing the face; but as you gazed, the freezing fascination of its horribleness gradually waned, and then your whole heart burst with sorrow, as you contemplated those aged features, ashy pale and wan. The horn seemed the mark of a curse for some mysterious sin, conceived and committed before the spirit had entered the flesh. Yet that sin seemed something imposed, and not voluntarily sought; some sin growing out of the heartless necessities of the predestination of things; some sin under which the sinner sank in sinless woe.

But no pang of pain, not the slightest touch of concern, ever crossed the bosom of Cuticle when he looked on this cast. It was immovably fixed to a bracket, against the partition of his state-room, so that it was the first object that greeted his eyes when he opened them from his nightly sleep. Nor was it to hide the face, that upon retiring, he always hung his Navy cap upon the upward curling extremity of the horn, for that obscured it but little.

The Surgeon's cot-boy, the lad who made up his swinging bed and took care of his room, often told us of the horror he sometimes felt when he would find himself alone in his master's retreat. At times he was seized with the idea that Cuticle was a preternatural being; and once entering his room in the middle watch of the night, he started at finding it enveloped in a thick, bluish vapor, and stifling with the odors of brimstone. Upon hearing a low groan from the smoke, with a wild cry he darted from the place, and, rousing the occupants of the neighboring state-rooms, it was found that the vapor proceeded from smoldering bunches of Lucifer matches, which had become ignited through the carelessness of the Surgeon. Cuticle, almost dead, was dragged from the suffocating atmosphere, and it was several days ere he completely recovered from its effects. This accident took place immediately over the powder magazine; but as Cuticle, during his sickness, paid dearly enough for transgressing the laws prohibiting combustibles in the gun-room, the Captain contented himself with privately remonstrating with him.

Well knowing the enthusiasm of the Surgeon for all specimens of morbid anatomy, some of the ward-room officers used to play upon his credulity, though, in every case, Cuticle was not long in discovering their deceptions. Once, when they had some sago pudding for dinner, and Cuticle chanced to be ashore, they made up a neat parcel of this bluish-white, firm, jelly-like preparation, and placing it in a tin box, carefully sealed with wax, they deposited it on the gun-room table, with a note, purporting to come from an eminent physician in Rio, connected with the Grand National Museum on the Praca d'Acclamacao, begging leave to present the scientific Senhor Cuticle—with the donor's compliments—an uncommonly fine specimen of a cancer.

Descending to the ward-room, Cuticle spied the note, and no sooner read it, than, clutching the case, he opened it, and exclaimed, "Beautiful! splendid! I have never seen a finer specimen of this most interesting disease."

"What have you there, Surgeon Cuticle?" said a Lieutenant, advancing.

"Why, sir, look at it; did you ever see any-thing more exquisite?"

"Very exquisite indeed; let me have a bit of it, will you, Cuticle?"

"Let you have a bit of it!" shrieked the Surgeon, starting back. "Let you have one of my limbs! I wouldn't mar so large a specimen for a hundred dollars; but what can you want of it? You are not making collections!"

"I'm fond of the article," said the Lieutenant; "it's a fine cold relish to bacon or ham. You know, I was in New Zealand last cruise, Cuticle, and got into sad dissipation there among the cannibals; come, let's have a bit, if it's only a mouthful."

"Why, you infernal Feejee!" shouted Cuticle, eyeing the other with a confounded expression; "you don't really mean to eat a piece of this cancer?"

"Hand it to me, and see whether I will not," was the reply.

"In God's name, take it!" cried the Surgeon, putting the case into his hands, and then standing with his own uplifted.

"Steward!" cried the Lieutenant, "the castor—quick! I always use plenty of pepper with this dish, Surgeon; it's oystery. Ah!

this is really delicious," he added, smacking his lips over a mouthful. "Try it now, Surgeon, and you'll never keep such a fine dish as this, lying uneaten on your hands, as a mere scientific curiosity."

Cuticle's whole countenance changed; and, slowly walking up to the table, he put his nose close to the tin case, then touched its contents with his finger and tasted it. Enough. Buttoning up his coat, in all the tremblings of an old man's rage he burst from the ward-room, and, calling for a boat, was not seen again for twenty-four hours.

But though, like all other mortals, Cuticle was subject at times to these fits of passion—at least under outrageous provocation—nothing could exceed his coolness when actually employed in his imminent vocation. Surrounded by moans and shrieks, by features distorted with anguish inflicted by himself, he yet maintained a countenance almost supernaturally calm; and unless the intense interest of the operation flushed his wan face with a momentary tinge of professional enthusiasm, he toiled away, untouched by the keenest misery coming under a fleet-surgeon's eye. Indeed, long habituation to the dissecting-room and the amputation-table had made him seemingly impervious to the ordinary emotions of humanity. Yet you could not say that Cuticle was essentially a cruel-hearted man. His apparent heartlessness must have been of a purely scientific origin. It is not to be imagined even that Cuticle would have harmed a fly, unless he could procure a microscope powerful enough to assist him in experimenting on the minute vitals of the creature.

But notwithstanding his marvellous indifference to the sufferings of his patients, and spite even of his enthusiasm in his vocation—not cooled by frosting old age itself—Cuticle, on some occasions, would affect a certain disrelish of his profession, and declaim against the necessity that forced a man of his humanity to perform a surgical operation. Especially was it apt to be thus with him, when the case was one of more than ordinary interest. In discussing it, previous to setting about it, he would veil his eagerness under an aspect of great circumspection, curiously marred, however, by continual sallies of unsuppressible impatience. But the knife once in his hand, the compassionless surgeon himself, undisguised, stood before you. Such was Cadwallader Cuticle, our Surgeon of the Fleet.

CHAPTER LXII

A Consultation of Man-of-War Surgeons

It seems customary for the Surgeon of the Fleet, when any important operation in his department is on the anvil, and there is nothing to absorb professional attention from it, to invite his brother surgeons, if at hand at the time, to a ceremonious consultation upon it. And this, in courtesy, his brother surgeons expect.

In pursuance of this custom, then, the surgeons of the neighboring American ships of war were requested to visit the Neversink in a body, to advise concerning the case of the top-man,[18] whose situation had now become critical. They assembled on the half-deck, and were soon joined by their respected senior, Cuticle. In a body they bowed as he approached, and accosted him with deferential regard.

"Gentlemen," said Cuticle, unostentatiously seating himself on a camp-stool, handed him by his cot-boy, "we have here an extremely interesting case. You have all seen the patient, I believe. At first I had hopes that I should have been able to cut down to the ball, and remove it; but the state of the patient forbade. Since then, the inflammation and sloughing of the part has been attended with a copious suppuration, great loss of substance, extreme debility and emaciation. From this, I am convinced that the ball has shattered and deadened the bone, and now lies impacted in the medullary canal. In fact, there can be no doubt that the wound is incurable, and that amputation is the only resource. But, gentlemen, I find myself placed in a very delicate predicament. I assure you I feel no professional anxiety to perform the operation. I desire your advice, and if you will now again visit the patient with me, we can then return here, and decide what is best to be done. Once more, let me say, that I feel no personal anxiety whatever to use the knife."

The assembled surgeons listened to this address with the most serious attention, and, in accordance with their superior's desire, now descended to the sick-bay, where the patient was languishing. The examination concluded, they returned to the half-deck, and the consultation was renewed.

"Gentlemen," began Cuticle, again seating himself, "you have now just inspected the limb; you have seen that there is no resource but amputation; and now, gentlemen, what do you say? Surgeon Bandage, of the Mohawk, will you express your opinion?"

"The wound is a very serious one," said Bandage—a corpulent man, with a high German forehead—shaking his head solemnly.

"Can any thing save him but amputation?" demanded Cuticle.

"His constitutional debility is extreme," observed Bandage, "but I have seen more dangerous cases."

"Surgeon Wedge, of the Malay," said Cuticle, in a pet, "be pleased to give *your* opinion; and let it be definitive, I entreat": this was said with a severe glance toward Bandage.

"If I thought," began Wedge, a very spare, tall man, elevating himself still higher on his toes, "that the ball had shattered and divided the whole *femur*, including the *Greater* and *Lesser Trochanter*, the *Linear aspera*, the *Digital fossa*, and the *Intertrochanteric*, I should certainly be in favor of amputation; but that, sir, permit me to observe, is not my opinion."

"Surgeon Sawyer, of the Buccaneer," said Cuticle, drawing in his thin lower lip with vexation, and turning to a round-faced, florid, frank, sensible-looking man, whose uniform coat very handsomely fitted him, and was adorned with an unusual quantity of gold lace; "Surgeon Sawyer, of the Buccaneer, let us now hear *your* opinion, if you please. Is not amputation the only resource, sir?"

"Excuse me," said Sawyer, "I am decidedly opposed to it;

for if hitherto the patient has not been strong enough to undergo the extraction of the ball, I do not see how he can be expected to endure a far more severe operation. As there is no immediate danger of mortification, and you say the ball cannot be reached without making large incisions, I should support him, I think, for the present, with tonics, and gentle antiphlogistics, locally applied. On no account would I proceed to amputation until further symptoms are exhibited."

"Surgeon Patella, of the Algerine," said Cuticle, in an ill-suppressed passion, abruptly turning round on the person addressed, "will *you* have the kindness to say whether *you* do not think that amputation is the only resource?"

Now Patella was the youngest of the company, a modest man, filled with a profound reverence for the science of Cuticle, and desirous of gaining his good opinion, yet not wishing to commit himself altogether by a decided reply, though, like Surgeon Sawyer, in his own mind he might have been clearly against the operation.

"What you have remarked, Mr. Surgeon of the Fleet," said Patella, respectfully hemming, "concerning the dangerous condition of the limb, seems obvious enough; amputation would certainly be a cure to the wound; but then, as, notwithstanding his present debility, the patient seems to have a strong constitution, he might rally as it is, and by your scientific treatment, Mr. Surgeon of the Fleet"—bowing—"be entirely made whole, without risking an amputation. Still, it is a very critical case, and amputation may be indispensable; and if it *is* to be performed, there ought to be no delay whatever. That is my view of the case, Mr. Surgeon of the Fleet."

"Surgeon Patella, then, gentlemen," said Cuticle, turning round triumphantly, "is clearly of opinion that amputation should be immediately performed. For my own part—individually, I mean, and without respect to the patient—I am sorry to have it so decided. But this settles the question, gentlemen—in my own mind, however, it was settled before. At ten o'clock to-morrow morning the operation will be performed. I shall be happy to see you all on the occasion, and also your juniors" (alluding to the absent *Assistant Surgeons*). "Good-morning, gentlemen; at ten o'clock, remember."

And Cuticle retreated to the Ward-room.

CHAPTER LXIII

The Operation

Next morning, at the appointed hour, the surgeons arrived in a body. They were accompanied by their juniors, young men ranging in age from nineteen years to thirty. Like the senior surgeons, these young gentlemen were arrayed in their blue navy uniforms, displaying a profusion of bright buttons, and several broad bars of gold lace about the wristbands. As in honor of the occasion, they had put on their best coats; they looked exceedingly brilliant.

The whole party immediately descended to the half-deck, where preparations had been made for the operation. A large garrison-ensign was stretched across the ship by the main-mast, so as completely to screen the space behind. This space included the whole extent aft to the bulk-head of the Commodore's cabin, at the door of which the marine-orderly paced, in plain sight, cutlass in hand.

Upon two gun-carriages, dragged amidships, the Death-board (used for burials at sea) was horizontally placed, covered with an old royal-stun'-sail. Upon this occasion, to do duty as an amputation-table, it was widened by an additional plank. Two match-tubs, near by, placed one upon another, at either end supported another plank, distinct from the table, whereon was exhibited an array of saws and knives of various and peculiar shapes and sizes; also, a sort of steel, something like the dinner-table implement, together with long needles, crooked at the end for taking up the arteries, and large darning-needles, thread and bee's-wax, for sewing up a wound.

At the end nearest the larger table was a tin basin of water, surrounded by small sponges, placed at mathematical intervals. From the long horizontal pole of a great-gun rammer—fixed in its usual place overhead—hung a number of towels, with "U.S." marked in the corners.

All these arrangements had been made by the "Surgeon's steward," a person whose important functions in a man-of-war will, in a future chapter, be entered upon at large. Upon the present occasion, he was bustling about, adjusting and readjusting the knives, needles, and carver, like an over-conscientious butler fidgeting over a dinner-table just before the convivialists enter.

But by far the most striking object to be seen behind the ensign was a human skeleton, whose every joint articulated with wires. By a rivet at the apex of the skull, it hung dangling from a hammock-hook fixed in a beam above. Why this object was here, will presently be seen; but why it was placed immediately at the foot of the amputation-table, only Surgeon Cuticle can tell.

While the final preparations were being made, Cuticle stood conversing with the assembled Surgeons and Assistant Surgeons, his invited guests.

"Gentlemen," said he, taking up one of the glittering knives and artistically drawing the steel across it; "Gentlemen, though these scenes are very unpleasant, and in some moods, I may say, repulsive to me—yet how much better for our patient to have the contusions and lacerations of his present wound—with all its dangerous symptoms—converted into a clean incision, free from these objections, and occasioning so much less subsequent anxiety to himself and the Surgeon. Yes," he added, tenderly feeling the edge of his knife, "amputation is our only resource. Is it not so, Surgeon Patella?" turning toward that gentleman, as if relying upon some sort of an assent, however clogged with conditions.

"Certainly," said Patella, "amputation is your only resource, Mr. Surgeon of the Fleet; that is, I mean, if you are fully persuaded of its necessity."

The other surgeons said nothing, maintaining a somewhat reserved air, as if conscious that they had no positive authority in the case, whatever might be their own private opinions;

but they seemed willing to behold, and, if called upon, to assist at the operation, since it could not now be averted.

The young men, their Assistants, looked very eager, and cast frequent glances of awe upon so distinguished a practitioner as the venerable Cuticle.

"They say he can drop a leg in one minute and ten seconds from the moment the knife touches it," whispered one of them to another.

"We shall see," was the reply, and the speaker clapped his hand to his fob, to see if his watch would be forthcoming when wanted.

"Are you all ready here?" demanded Cuticle, now advancing to his steward; "have not those fellows got through yet?" pointing to three men of the carpenter's gang, who were placing bits of wood under the gun-carriages supporting the central table.

"They are just through, sir," respectfully answered the Steward, touching his hand to his forehead, as if there were a cap-front there.

"Bring up the patient, then," said Cuticle.

"Young gentlemen," he added, turning to the row of Assistant Surgeons, "seeing you here reminds me of the classes of students once under my instruction at the Philadelphia College of Physicians and Surgeons. Ah, those were happy days!" he sighed, applying the extreme corner of his handkerchief to his glass eye. "Excuse an old man's emotions, young gentlemen; but when I think of the numerous rare cases that then came under my treatment, I can not but give way to my feelings. The town, the city, the metropolis, young gentlemen, is the place for you students; at least in these dull times of peace, when the army and navy furnish no inducements for a youth ambitious of rising in our honorable profession. Take an old man's advice, and if the war now threatening between the States and Mexico should break out, exchange your Navy commissions for commissions in the army. From having no military marine herself, Mexico has always been backward in furnishing subjects for the amputation-tables of foreign navies. The cause of science has languished in her hands. The army, young gentlemen, is your best school; depend upon it. You will hardly believe it, Surgeon Bandage," turning to that gentleman, "but this is my first important case of surgery in a nearly three years' cruise. I have been almost wholly confined in this ship to doctor's practice—prescribing for fevers and fluxes. True, the other day a man fell from the mizzen-top-sail yard; but that was merely an aggravated case of dislocations and bones splintered and broken. No one, sir, could have made an amputation of it, without severely contusing his conscience. And mine—I may say it, gentlemen, without ostentation—is peculiarly susceptible."

And so saying, the knife and carver touchingly dropped to his sides, and he stood for a moment fixed in a tender reverie. But a commotion being heard beyond the curtain, he started, and, briskly crossing and recrossing the knife and carver, exclaimed, "Ah, here comes our patient; surgeons, this side of the table, if you please; young gentlemen, a little further off, I beg. Steward, take off my coat—so; my neckerchief now; I must be perfectly unencumbered, Surgeon Patella, or I can do nothing whatever."

These articles being removed, he snatched off his wig, placing it on the gun-deck capstan; then took out his set of false teeth, and placed it by the side of the wig; and, lastly, putting his forefinger to the inner angle of his blind eye, spirted out the glass optic with professional dexterity, and deposited that, also, next to the wig and false teeth.

Thus divested of nearly all inorganic appurtenances, what was left of the Surgeon slightly shook itself, to see whether anything more could be spared to advantage.

"Carpenter's mates," he now cried, "will you never get through with that job?"

"Almost through, sir—just through," they replied, staring round in search of the strange, unearthly voice that addressed them; for the absence of his teeth had not at all improved the conversational tones of the Surgeon of the Fleet.

With natural curiosity, these men had purposely been lingering, to see all they could; but now, having no further excuse, they snatched up their hammers and chisels, and—like the stage-builders decamping from a public meeting at the eleventh hour, after just completing the rostrum in time for the first speaker—the Carpenter's gang withdrew.

The broad ensign now lifted, revealing a glimpse of the crowd of man-of-war's-men outside, and the patient, borne in the arms of two of his mess-mates, entered the place. He was much emaciated, weak as an infant, and every limb visibly trembled, or rather jarred, like the head of a man with the palsy. As if an organic and involuntary apprehension of death had seized the wounded leg, its nervous motions were so violent that one of the mess-mates was obliged to keep his hand upon it.

The top-man was immediately stretched upon the table, the attendants steadying his limbs, when, slowly opening his eyes, he glanced about at the glittering knives and saws, the towels and sponges, the armed sentry at the Commodore's cabin-door, the row of eager-eyed students, the meagre death's-head of a Cuticle, now with his shirt sleeves rolled up upon his withered arms and knife in hand, and, finally, his eye settled in horror upon the skeleton, slowly vibrating and jingling before him, with the slow, slight roll of the frigate in the water.

"I would advise perfect repose of your every limb, my man," said Cuticle, addressing him; "the precision of an operation is often impaired by the inconsiderate restlessness of the patient. But if you consider, my good fellow," he added, in a patronizing and almost sympathetic tone, and slightly pressing his hand on the limb, "if you consider how much better it is to live with three limbs than to die with four, and especially if you but knew to what torments both sailors and soldiers were subjected before the time of Celsus,[19] owing to the lamentable ignorance of surgery then prevailing, you would certainly thank God from the bottom of your heart that *your* operation has been postponed to the period of this enlightened age, blessed with a Bell, a Brodie, and a Lally.[20] My man, before Celsus's time, such was the general ignorance of our noble science, that, in order to prevent the excessive effusion of blood, it was deemed indispensable to operate with a red-hot knife"—making a professional movement toward the thigh—"and pour scalding oil upon the parts"—elevating his elbow, as if with a tea-pot in his hand—"still further to sear them, after amputation had been performed."

"He is fainting!" said one of his mess-mates; "quick! some water!" The steward immediately hurried to the top-man with the basin.

Cuticle took the top-man by the wrist, and feeling it a while, observed, "Don't be alarmed, men," addressing the two mess-mates; "he'll recover presently; this fainting very generally takes place." And he stood for a moment, tranquilly eyeing the patient.

Now the Surgeon of the Fleet and the top-man presented a spectacle which, to a reflecting mind, was better than a church-yard sermon on the mortality of man.

Here was a sailor, who, four days previous, had stood erect—a pillar of life—with an arm like a royal-mast and a thigh like a windlass. But the slightest conceivable finger-touch of a bit of crooked trigger had eventuated in stretching him out, more helpless than an hour-old babe, with a blasted thigh, utterly drained of its brawn. And who was it that now stood over him like a superior being, and, as if clothed himself with the at-tributes of immortality, indifferently discoursed of carving up his broken flesh, and thus piecing out his abbreviated days? Who was it, that in capacity of Surgeon, seemed enacting the part of a Regenerator of life? The withered, shrunken, one-eyed, toothless, hairless Cuticle; with a trunk half dead—a *memento mori* to behold!

And while, in those soul-sinking and panic-striking pre-monitions of speedy death which almost invariably accompany a severe gun-shot wound, even with the most intrepid spirits; while thus drooping and dying, this once robust top-man's eye was now waning in his head like a Lapland moon being eclipsed in clouds—Cuticle, who for years had still lived in his withered tabernacle of a body—Cuticle, no doubt sharing in the common self-delusion of old age—Cuticle must have felt his hold of life as secure as the grim hug of a grizzly bear. Verily, Life is more awful than Death; and let no man, though his live heart beat in him like a cannon—let him not hug his life to himself; for, in the predestinated necessities of things, that bounding life of his is not a whit more secure than the life of a man on his death-bed. To-day we inhale the air with expanding lungs, and life runs through us like a thousand Niles; but to-morrow we may collapse in death, and all our veins be dry as the Brook Kedron in a drought.

"And now, young gentlemen," said Cuticle, turning to the Assistant Surgeons, "while the patient is coming to, permit me to describe to you the highly-interesting operation I am about to perform."

"Mr. Surgeon of the Fleet," said Surgeon Bandage, "if you are about to lecture, permit me to present you with your teeth; they will make your discourse more readily understood." And so saying, Bandage, with a bow, placed the two semicircles of ivory into Cuticle's hands.

"Thank you, Surgeon Bandage," said Cuticle, and slipped the ivory into its place.

"In the first place, now, young gentlemen, let me direct your attention to the excellent preparation before you. I have had it unpacked from its case, and set up here from my state-room, where it occupies the spare berth; and all this for your express benefit, young gentlemen. This skeleton I procured in person from the Hunterian department of the Royal College of Surgeons in London. It is a master-piece of art. But we have no time to examine it now. Delicacy forbids that I should amplify at a juncture like this"—casting an almost benignant glance toward the patient, now beginning to open his eyes; "but let me point out to you upon this thigh-bone"—disengaging it from the skeleton, with a gentle twist—"the precise place where I propose to perform the operation. *Here*, young gentlemen, *here* is the place. You perceive it is very near the point of articulation with the trunk."

"Yes," interposed Surgeon Wedge, rising on his toes, "yes, young gentlemen, the point of articulation with the *acetabulum* of the *os innominatum*."

"Where's your 'Bell on Bones,' Dick?" whispered one of the assistants to the student next him. "Wedge has been spending the whole morning over it, getting out the hard names."

"Surgeon Wedge," said Cuticle, looking round severely, "we will dispense with your commentaries, if you please, at present. Now, young gentlemen, you cannot but perceive, that the point of operation being so near the trunk and the vitals, it becomes an unusually beautiful one, demanding a steady hand and a true eye; and, after all, the patient may die under my hands."

"Quick, Steward! water, water; he's fainting again!" cried the two mess-mates.

"Don't be alarmed for your comrade, men," said Cuticle, turning round. "I tell you it is not an uncommon thing for the patient to betray some emotion upon these occasions—most usually manifested by swooning; it is quite natural it should be so. But we must not delay the operation. Steward, that knife—no, the next one—there, that's it. He is coming to, I think"—feeling the top-man's wrist. "Are you all ready, sir?"

This last observation was addressed to one of the Neversink's assistant surgeons, a tall, lank, cadaverous young man, arrayed in a sort of shroud of white canvas, pinned about his throat, and completely enveloping his person. He was seated on a match-tub—the skeleton swinging near his head—at the foot of the table, in readiness to grasp the limb, as when a plank is being severed by a carpenter and his apprentice.

"The sponges, Steward," said Cuticle, for the last time taking out his teeth, and drawing up his shirt sleeve still further. Then, taking the patient by the wrist, "Stand by, now, you messmates; keep hold of his arms; pin him down. Steward, put your hand on the artery; I shall commence as soon as his pulse begins to—*now, now!*" Letting fall the wrist, feeling the thigh carefully, and bowing over it an instant, he drew the fatal knife unerringly across the flesh. As it first touched the part, the row of surgeons simultaneously dropped their eyes to the watches in their hands, while the patient lay, with eyes horribly distended, in a kind of waking trance. Not a breath was heard;

but as the quivering flesh parted in a long, lingering gash, a spring of blood welled up between the living walls of the wound, and two thick streams, in opposite directions, coursed down the thigh. The sponges were instantly dipped in the purple pool; every face present was pinched to a point with suspense; the limb writhed; the man shrieked; his mess-mates pinioned him; while round and round the leg went the unpitying cut.

"The saw!" said Cuticle.

Instantly it was in his hand.

Full of the operation, he was about to apply it, when, looking up, and turning to the assistant surgeons, he said, "Would any of you young gentlemen like to apply the saw? A splendid subject!"

Several volunteered; when, selecting one, Cuticle surrendered the instrument to him, saying, "Don't be hurried, now; be steady."

While the rest of the assistants looked upon their comrade with glances of envy, he went rather timidly to work; and Cuticle, who was earnestly regarding him, suddenly snatched the saw from his hand. "Away, butcher! you disgrace the profession. Look at *me!*"

For a few moments the thrilling, rasping sound was heard; and then the top-man seemed parted in twain at the hip, as the leg slowly slid into the arms of the pale, gaunt man in the shroud, who at once made away with it, and tucked it out of sight under one of the guns.

"Surgeon Sawyer," now said Cuticle, courteously turning to the surgeon of the Mohawk, "would you like to take up the arteries? They are quite at your service, sir."

"Do, Sawyer; be prevailed upon," said Surgeon Bandage.

Sawyer complied; and while, with some modesty, he was conducting the operation, Cuticle, turning to the row of assistants, said, "Young gentlemen, we will now proceed with our illustration. Hand me that bone, Steward." And taking the thigh-bone in his still bloody hands, and holding it conspicuously before his auditors, the Surgeon of the Fleet began:

"Young gentlemen, you will perceive that precisely at this

spot—*here*—to which I previously directed your attention—
at the corresponding spot precisely—the operation has been
performed. About here, young gentlemen, *here*"—lifting his
hand some inches from the bone—"about *here* the great artery
was. But you noticed that I did not use the tourniquet; I never
do. The forefinger of my steward is far better than a tourniquet, being so much more manageable, and leaving the smaller
veins uncompressed. But I have been told, young gentlemen,
that a certain Seignior Seignioroni, a surgeon of Seville, has
recently invented an admirable substitute for the clumsy, old-
fashioned tourniquet. As I understand it, it is something like
a pair of *calipers*, working with a small Archimedes screw—a
very clever invention, according to all accounts. For the
padded points at the end of the arches"—arching his forefinger
and thumb—"can be so worked as to approximate in such a
way, as to—but you don't attend to me, young gentlemen,"
he added, all at once starting.

Being more interested in the active proceedings of Surgeon
Sawyer, who was now threading a needle to sew up the over-
lapping of the stump, the young gentlemen had not scrupled
to turn away their attention altogether from the lecturer.

A few moments more, and the top-man, in a swoon, was removed below into the sick-bay. As the curtain settled again
after the patient had disappeared, Cuticle, still holding the
thigh-bone of the skeleton in his ensanguined hands, proceeded
with his remarks upon it; and having concluded them, added,
"Now, young gentlemen, not the least interesting consequence
of this operation will be the finding of the ball, which, in case
of non-amputation, might have long eluded the most careful
search. That ball, young gentlemen, must have taken a most
circuitous route. Nor, in cases where the direction is oblique,
is this at all unusual. Indeed, the learned Henner[21] gives us a
most remarkable—I had almost said an incredible—case of a
soldier's neck, where the bullet, entering at the part called
Adam's Apple——"

"Yes," said Surgeon Wedge, elevating himself, "the *pomum
Adami.*"

"Entering the point called *Adam's Apple*," continued Cuticle, severely emphasizing the last two words, "ran completely round the neck, and, emerging at the same hole it had entered, shot the next man in the ranks. It was afterward extracted, says Henner, from the second man, and pieces of the other's skin were found adhering to it. But examples of foreign substances being received into the body with a ball, young gentlemen, are frequently observed. Being attached to a United States ship at the time, I happened to be near the spot of the battle of Ayacucho, in Peru. The day after the action, I saw in the barracks of the wounded a trooper, who, having been severely injured in the brain, went crazy, and, with his own holster-pistol, committed suicide in the hospital. The ball drove inward a portion of his woollen nightcap——"

"In the form of a *cul-de-sac*, doubtless," said the undaunted Wedge.

"For once, Surgeon Wedge, you use the only term that can be employed; and let me avail myself of this opportunity to say to you, young gentlemen, that a man of true science"— expanding his shallow chest a little—"uses but few hard words, and those only when none other will answer his purpose; whereas the smatterer in science"—slightly glancing toward Wedge—"thinks, that by mouthing hard words, he proves that he understands hard things. Let this sink deep in your minds, young gentlemen; and, Surgeon Wedge"—with a stiff bow—"permit me to submit the reflection to yourself. Well, young gentlemen, the bullet was afterward extracted by pulling upon the external parts of the *cul-de-sac*—a simple, but exceedingly beautiful operation. There is a fine example, somewhat similar, related in Guthrie[22]; but, of course, you must have met with it, in so well-known a work as his Treatise upon Gun-shot Wounds. When, upward of twenty years ago, I was with Lord Cochrane, then Admiral of the fleets of this very country"— pointing shoreward, out of a port-hole—"a sailor of the vessel to which I was attached, during the blockade of Bahia, had his leg——" But by this time the fidgets had completely taken possession of his auditors, especially of the senior surgeons;

and turning upon them abruptly, he added, "But I will not detain you longer, gentlemen"—turning round upon all the surgeons—"your dinners must be waiting you on board your respective ships. But, Surgeon Sawyer, perhaps you may desire to wash your hands before you go. There is the basin, sir; you will find a clean towel on the rammer. For myself, I seldom use them"—taking out his handkerchief. "I must leave you now, gentlemen"—bowing. "To-morrow, at ten, the limb will be upon the table, and I shall be happy to see you all upon the occasion. Who's there?" turning to the curtain, which then rustled.

"Please, sir," said the Steward, entering, "the patient is dead."

"The body also, gentlemen, at ten precisely," said Cuticle, once more turning round upon his guests. "I predicted that the operation might prove fatal; he was very much run down. Good-morning"; and Cuticle departed.

"He does not, surely, mean to touch the body?" exclaimed Surgeon Sawyer, with much excitement.

"Oh, no!" said Patella, "that's only his way; he means, doubt-less, that it may be inspected previous to being taken ashore for burial."

The assemblage of gold-laced surgeons now ascended to the quarter-deck; the second cutter was called away by the bugler, and, one by one, they were dropped aboard of their respective ships.

The following evening the mess-mates of the top-man rowed his remains ashore, and buried them in the ever-vernal Protestant cemetery, hard by the Beach of the Flamingoes, in plain sight from the bay.

CHAPTER LXVII

White-Jacket Arraigned at the Mast

When with five hundred others I made one of the compelled spectators at the scourging of poor Rose-Water,[23] I little thought what Fate had ordained for myself the next day.

Poor mulatto! thought I, one of an oppressed race, they degrade you like a hound. Thank God! I am a white. Yet I had seen whites also scourged; for, black or white, all my shipmates were liable to that. Still, there is something in us, somehow, that, in the most degraded condition, we snatch at a chance to deceive ourselves into a fancied superiority to others, whom we suppose lower in the scale than ourselves.

Poor Rose-Water! thought I; poor mulatto! Heaven send you a release from your humiliation!

To make plain the thing about to be related, it needs to repeat what has somewhere been previously mentioned, that in *tacking ship* every seaman in a man-of-war has a particular station assigned him. What that station is, should be made known to him by the First Lieutenant; and when the word is passed to *tack* or *wear*, it is every seaman's duty to be found at his post. But among the various *numbers* and *stations* given to me by the senior Lieutenant, when I first came on board the frigate, he had altogether omitted informing me of my particular place at those times, and, up to the precise period now written of, I had hardly known that I should have had any special place then at all. For the rest of the men, they seemed to me to catch hold of the first rope that offered, as in a merchantman upon similar occasions. Indeed, I subsequently discovered, that such was the state of discipline—in this one particular, at least—that very few of the seamen could tell where their proper stations were, at *tacking* or *wearing*.

"All hands tack ship, ahoy!" such was the announcement made by the boatswain's mates at the hatchways the morning after the hard fate of Rose-Water. It was just eight bells—noon, and springing from my white jacket, which I had spread between the guns for a bed on the main-deck, I ran up the ladders, and, as usual, seized hold of the main-brace, which fifty hands were streaming along forward. When *main-top-sail haul!* was given through the trumpet, I pulled at this brace with such heartiness and good-will, that I almost flattered myself that my instrumentality in getting the frigate round on the other tack, deserved a public vote of thanks, and a silver tankard from Congress.

But something happened to be in the way aloft when the yards swung round; a little confusion ensued; and, with anger on his brow, Captain Claret came forward to see what occasioned it. No one to let go the weather-lift of the main-yard! The rope was cast off, however, by a hand, and the yards, unobstructed, came round.

When the last rope was coiled away, the Captain desired to know of the First Lieutenant who it might be that was stationed at the weather (then the starboard) main-lift. With a vexed expression of countenance the First Lieutenant sent a midshipman for the Station Bill, when, upon glancing it over, my own name was found put down at the post in question.

At the time I was on the gun-deck below, and did not know of these proceedings; but a moment after, I heard the boatswain's mates bawling my name at all the hatchways, and along all three decks. It was the first time I had ever heard it so sent through the furthest recesses of the ship, and well knowing what this generally betokened to other seamen, my heart jumped to my throat, and I hurriedly asked Flute, the boatswain's-mate at the fore-hatchway, what was wanted of me.

"Captain wants ye at the mast," he replied. "Going to flog ye, I guess."

"What for?"

"My eyes! you've been chalking your face, hain't ye?"

"What am I wanted for?" I repeated.

But at that instant my name was again thundered forth by the other boatswain's mate, and Flute hurried me away, hinting that I would soon find out what the captain desired of me.

I swallowed down my heart in me as I touched the spar-deck, for a single instant balanced myself on my best centre, and then, wholly ignorant of what was going to be alleged against me, advanced to the dread tribunal of the frigate.

As I passed through the gangway, I saw the quarter-master rigging the gratings; the boatswain with his green bag of scourges; the master-at-arms ready to help off some one's shirt.

Again I made a desperate swallow of my whole soul in me and found myself standing before Captain Claret. His flushed face obviously showed him in ill humor. Among the group of officers by his side was the First Lieutenant, who, as I came aft, eyed me in such a manner, that I plainly perceived him to be extremely vexed at me for having been the innocent means of reflecting upon the manner in which he kept up the discipline of the ship.

"Why were you not at your station, sir?" asked the Captain.

"What station do you mean, sir?" said I.

It is generally the custom with man-of-war's-men to stand obsequiously touching their hat at every sentence they address to the Captain. But as this was not obligatory upon me by the Articles of War, I did not do so upon the present occasion, and previously, I had never had the dangerous honor of a personal interview with Captain Claret.

He quickly noticed my omission of the homage usually rendered him, and instinct told me, that to a certain extent, it set his heart against me.

"What station, sir, do you mean?" said I.

"You pretend ignorance," he replied; "it will not help you, sir."

Glancing at the Captain, the First Lieutenant now produced the Station Bill, and read my name in connexion with that of the starboard main-lift.

"Captain Claret," said I, "it is the first time I ever heard of my being assigned to that post."

"How is this, Mr. Bridewell?" he said, turning to the First Lieutenant, with a fault-finding expression.

"It is impossible, sir," said that officer, striving to hide his vexation, "but this man must have known his station."

"I have never known it before this moment, Captain Claret," said I.

"Do you contradict my officer?" he returned. "I shall flog you."

I had now been on board the frigate upward of a year, and remained unscourged; the ship was homeward-bound, and in a few weeks, at most, I would be a freeman. And now, after making a hermit of myself in some things, in order to avoid the possibility of the scourge, here it was hanging over me for a thing utterly unforeseen, for a crime of which I was as utterly innocent. But all that was as naught. I saw that my case was hopeless; my solemn disclaimer was thrown in my teeth, and the boatswain's mate stood curling his fingers through the *cat*.

There are times when wild thoughts enter a man's heart, when he seems almost irresponsible for his act and his deed. The Captain stood on the weather-side of the deck. Sideways, on an unobstructed line with him, was the opening of the lee-gangway, where the side-ladders are suspended in port. Nothing but a slight bit of sinnate-stuff served to rail in this opening, which was cut right down to the level of the Captain's feet, showing the far sea beyond. I stood a little to windward of him, and, though he was a large, powerful man, it was certain that a sudden rush against him, along the slanting deck, would infallibly pitch him head foremost into the ocean, though he who so rushed must needs go over with him. My blood seemed clotting in my veins; I felt icy cold at the tips of my fingers, and a dimness was before my eyes. But through that dimness the boatswain's mate, scourge in hand, loomed like a giant, and Captain Claret, and the blue sea seen through the opening at the gangway, showed with an awful vividness. I can not analyze my heart, though it then stood still within me. But the thing that swayed me to my purpose was not altogether the thought that Captain Claret was about to degrade me, and that I had taken an oath with my soul that he should not. No, I felt my man's manhood so bottomless within me, that no word, no blow, no scourge of Captain Claret could cut me deep enough for that. I but swung to an instinct in me—the instinct diffused through all animated nature, the same that prompts even a worm to turn under the heel. Locking souls with him, I meant to drag Captain Claret from this earthly tribunal of his to that of Jehovah, and let Him decide between us. No other way could I escape the scourge.

Nature has not implanted any power in man that was not meant to be exercised at times, though too often our power have been abused. The privilege, inborn and inalienable, that every man has, of dying himself, and inflicting death upon another, was not given to us without a purpose. These are the last resources of an insulted and unendurable existence.

"To the gratings, sir!" said Captain Claret; "do you hear?"

My eye was measuring the distance between him and the sea.

"Captain Claret," said a voice advancing from the crowd. I turned to see who this might be, that audaciously interposed at a juncture like this. It was the same remarkably handsome and gentlemanly corporal of marines, Colbrook, who has been previously alluded to, in the chapter describing killing time in a man-of-war.

"I know that man," said Colbrook, touching his cap, and speaking in a mild, firm, but extremely deferential manner; "and I know that he would not be found absent from his station, if he knew where it was."

This speech was almost unprecedented. Seldom or never before had a marine dared to speak to the Captain of a frigate in behalf of a seaman at the mast. But there was something so unostentatiously commanding in the calm manner of the man, that the Captain, though astounded, did not in any way reprimand him. The very unusualness of his interference seemed Colbrook's protection.

Taking heart, perhaps, from Colbrook's example, Jack Chase interposed, and in a manly but carefully respectful manner, in substance repeated the corporal's remark, adding that he had never found me wanting in the top.

Captain Claret looked from Chase to Colbrook, and from Colbrook to Chase—one the foremost man among the seamen, the other the foremost man among the soldiers—then all round upon the packed and silent crew, and, as if a slave to Fate, though supreme Captain of a frigate, he turned to the First Lieutenant, made some indifferent remark, and saying to me *you may go*, sauntered aft into his cabin; while I, who, in the desperation of my soul, had but just escaped being a murderer and a suicide, almost burst into tears of thanksgiving where I stood.[24]

CHAPTER XCII

The Last of the Jacket [25]

Already has White-Jacket chronicled the mishaps and incon-
veniences, troubles and tribulations of all sorts brought upon
him by that unfortunate but indispensable garment of his. But
now it befalls him to record how this jacket, for the second and
last time, came near proving his shroud.

Of a pleasant midnight, our good frigate, now somewhere off
the Capes of Virginia, was running on bravely, when the breeze,
gradually dying, left us slowly gliding toward our still invisible
port.

Headed by Jack Chase, the quarter-watch were reclining in
the top, talking about the shore delights into which they intended to plunge, while our captain often broke in with allusions
to similar conversations when he was on board the English
line-of-battle ship, the Asia, drawing nigh to Portsmouth, in
England, after the battle of Navarino.

Suddenly an order was given to set the main-top-gallant-
stun'-sail, and the halyards not being rove, Jack Chase assigned
to me that duty. Now this reeving of the halyards of a main-
top-gallant-stun'-sail is a business that eminently demands sharp-
sightedness, skill, and celerity.

Consider that the end of a line, some two hundred feet long,
is to be carried aloft, in your teeth, if you please, and dragged
far out on the giddiest of yards, and after being wormed and
twisted about through all sorts of intricacies—turning abrupt
corners at the abruptest of angles—is to be dropped, clear of
all obstructions, in a straight plum-line right down to the
deck. In the course of this business, there is a multitude of
sheeve-holes and blocks, through which you must pass it; often
the rope is a very tight fit, so as to make it like threading a fine
cambric needle with rather coarse thread. Indeed, it is a thing
only deftly to be done, even by day. Judge, then, what it
must be to be threading cambric needles by night, and at sea,
upward of a hundred feet aloft in the air.

With the end of the line in one hand, I was mounting the top-mast shrouds, when our Captain of the Top told me that I had better off jacket; but though it was not a very cold night, I had been reclining so long in the top, that I had become somewhat chilly, so I thought best not to comply with the hint.

Having reeved the line through all the inferior blocks, I went out with it to the end of the weather-top-gallant-yard-arm, and was in the act of leaning over and passing it through the suspended jewel-block there, when the ship gave a plunge in the sudden swells of the calm sea, and pitching me still further over the yard, threw the heavy skirts of my jacket right over my head, completely muffling me. Somehow I thought it was the sail that had flapped, and, under that impression, threw up my hands to drag it from my head, relying upon the sail itself to support me meanwhile. Just then the ship gave another sudden jerk, and, head foremost, I pitched from the yard. I knew where I was, from the rush of the air by my ears, but all else was a nightmare. A bloody film was before my eyes, through which, ghost-like, passed and repassed my father, mother, and sisters. An unutterable nausea oppressed me; I was conscious of gasping; there seemed no breath in my body. It was over one hundred feet that I fell—down, down, with lungs collapsed as in death. Ten thousand pounds of shot seemed tied to my head, as the irresistible law of gravitation dragged me, head foremost and straight as a die, toward the infallible centre of this terraqueous globe. All I had seen, and read, and heard, and all I had thought and felt in my life, seemed intensified in one fixed idea in my soul. But dense as this idea was, it was made up of atoms. Having fallen from the projecting yard-arm end, I was conscious of a collected satisfaction in feeling, that I should not be dashed on the deck, but would sink into the speechless profound of the sea.

With the bloody, blind film before my eyes, there was a still stranger hum in my head, as if a hornet were there; and I thought to myself, Great God! this is Death! Yet these thoughts were unmixed with alarm. Like frost-work that flashes and shifts its scared hues in the sun, all my braided, blended emotions were in themselves icy cold and calm.

So protracted did my fall seem, that I can even now recall the feeling of wondering how much longer it would be, ere all was over and I struck. Time seemed to stand still, and all the worlds seemed poised on their poles, as I fell, soul-becalmed, through the eddying whirl and swirl of the Mael-strom air.

At first, as I have said, I must have been precipitated head foremost; but I was conscious, at length, of a swift, flinging motion of my limbs, which involuntarily threw themselves out, so that at last I must have fallen in a heap. This is more likely, from the circumstance, that when I struck the sea, I felt as if some one had smote me slantingly across the shoulder and along part of my right side.

As I gushed into the sea, a thunder-boom sounded in my ear; my soul seemed flying from my mouth. The feeling of death flooded over me with the billows. The blow from the sea must have turned me, so that I sank almost feet foremost through a soft, seething, foamy lull. Some current seemed hurrying me away; in a trance I yielded, and sank deeper down with a glide. Purple and pathless was the deep calm now around me, flecked by summer lightnings in an azure afar. The horrible nausea was gone; the bloody, blind film turned a pale green; I wondered whether I was yet dead, or still dying. But of a sudden some fashionless form brushed my side—some inert, coiled fish of the sea; the thrill of being alive again tingled in my nerves, and the strong shunning of death shocked me through.

For one instant an agonizing revulsion came over me as I found myself utterly sinking. Next moment the force of my fall was expended; and there I hung, vibrating in the mid-deep. What wild sounds then rang in my ear! One was a soft moan-ing, as of low waves on the beach; the other wild and heartlessly jubilant, as of the sea in the height of a tempest. Oh soul! thou then heardest life and death: as he who stands upon the Corinthian shore hears both the Ionian and the Ægean waves. The life-and-death poise soon passed; and then I found myself slowly ascending, and caught a dim glimmering of light.

Quicker and quicker I mounted; till at last I bounded up like a buoy, and my whole head was bathed in the blessed air.

I had fallen in a line with the main-mast; I now found myself nearly abreast of the mizzen-mast, the frigate slowly gliding by like a black world in the water. Her vast hull loomed out of the night, showing hundreds of seamen in the hammock-nettings, some tossing over ropes, others madly flinging overboard the hammocks; but I was too far out from them immediately to reach what they threw. I essayed to swim toward the ship; but instantly I was conscious of a feeling like being pinioned in a feather-bed, and, moving my hands, felt my jacket puffed out above my tight girdle with water. I strove to tear it off; but it was looped together here and there, and the strings were not then to be sundered by hand. I whipped out my knife, that was tucked at my belt, and ripped my jacket straight up and down, as if I were ripping open myself. With a violent struggle I then burst out of it, and was free. Heavily soaked, it slowly sank before my eyes.

Sink! sink! oh shroud! thought I; sink forever! accursed jacket that thou art!

"See that white shark!" cried a horrified voice from the taff-rail; "he'll have that man down his hatchway! Quick! the *grains!* the *grains!*" [26]

The next instant that barbed bunch of harpoons pierced through and through the unfortunate jacket, and swiftly sped down with it out of sight.

Being now astern of the frigate, I struck out boldly toward the elevated pole of one of the life-buoys which had been cut away. Soon after, one of the cutters picked me up. As they dragged me out of the water into the air, the sudden transition of elements made my every limb feel like lead, and I helplessly sunk into the bottom of the boat.

Ten minutes after, I was safe on board, and, springing aloft, was ordered to reeve anew the stun'-sail-halyards, which, slipping through the blocks when I had let go the end, had unrove and fallen to the deck.

The sail was soon set; and, as if purposely to salute it, a gentle breeze soon came, and the Neversink once more glided over the water, a soft ripple at her bows, and leaving a tranquil wake behind.

CHAPTER XXVI

Knights and Squires

The chief mate of the Pequod was Starbuck, a native of Nantucket, and a Quaker by descent. He was a long, earnest man, and though born on an icy coast, seemed well adapted to endure hot latitudes, his flesh being hard as twice-baked biscuit. Transported to the Indies, his live blood would not spoil like bottled ale. He must have been born in some time of general drought and famine, or upon one of those fast days for which his state is famous. Only some thirty arid summers had he seen; those summers had dried up all his physical superfluousness. But this, his thinness, so to speak, seemed no more the token of wasting anxieties and cares, than it seemed the indication of any bodily blight. It was merely the condensation of the man. He was by no means ill-looking; quite the contrary. His pure tight skin was an excellent fit; and closely wrapped up in it, and embalmed with inner health and strength, like a revivified Egyptian, this Starbuck seemed prepared to endure for long ages to come, and to endure always, as now; for be it Polar snow or torrid sun, like a patent chronometer, his interior vitality was warranted to do well in all climates. Looking into his eyes, you seemed to see there the yet lingering images of those thousand-fold perils he had calmly confronted through life. A staid, steadfast man, whose life for the most part was a telling pantomime of action, and not a tame chapter of sounds. Yet, for all his hardy sobriety and fortitude, there were certain qualities in him which at times affected, and in some cases seemed well nigh to overbalance all the rest. Uncommonly conscientious for a seaman, and endued with a deep natural reverence, the wild watery loneliness of his life did therefore strongly incline him to superstition; but to that sort of superstition, which in some organizations seems rather to spring, somehow, from intelligence than from ignorance. Outward portents and inward presentiments were his. And if at times these things bent the welded iron of his soul, much more did his far-away domestic memories of his young Cape wife and child, tend to bend him still more from the original ruggedness of his nature, and open him still further to those latent influences which, in some honest-hearted men, restrain the gush of dare-devil daring, so often evinced by others in the more perilous vicissitudes of the fishery. "I will have no man in my boat," said Starbuck, "who is not afraid of a whale." By this, he seemed to mean, not only that the most reliable and useful courage was that which arises from the fair estimation of the encountered peril, but that an utterly fearless man is a far more dangerous comrade than a coward.

"Aye, aye," said Stubb, the second mate, "Starbuck, there, is as careful a man as you'll find anywhere in this fishery." But we shall ere long see what that word "careful" precisely means when used by a man like Stubb, or almost any other whale hunter.

Starbuck was no crusader after perils; in him courage was not a sentiment; but a thing simply useful to him, and always at hand upon all mortally practical occasions. Besides, he thought, perhaps, that in this business of whaling, courage was one of the great staple outfits of the ship, like her beef and her bread, and not to be foolishly wasted. Wherefore he had no fancy for lowering for whales after sun-down; nor for persisting in fighting a fish that too much persisted in fighting him. For, thought Starbuck, I am here in this critical ocean to kill whales for my living, and not to be killed by them for theirs; and that hundreds of men had been so killed Starbuck well knew. What doom was his own father's? Where, in the bottomless deeps, could he find the torn limbs of his brother?

With memories like these in him, and, moreover, given to a certain superstitiousness, as has been said; the courage of this Starbuck, which could, nevertheless, still flourish, must indeed have been extreme. But it was not in reasonable nature that a man so organized, and with such terrible experiences and remembrances as he had; it was not in nature that these things should fail in latently engendering an element in him, which, under suitable circumstances, would break out from its confinement, and burn all his courage up. And brave as he might be, it was that sort of bravery chiefly, visible in some intrepid men, which, while generally abiding firm in the conflict with seas, or winds, or whales, or any of the ordinary irrational horrors of the world, yet cannot withstand those more terrific, because more spiritual terrors, which sometimes menace you from the concentrating brow of an enraged and mighty man.

But were the coming narrative to reveal, in any instance, the complete abasement of poor Starbuck's fortitude, scarce might I have the heart to write it; for it is a thing most sorrowful, nay shocking, to expose the fall of valor in the soul. Men may seem detestable as joint stock-companies and nations; knaves, fools, and murderers there may be; men may have mean and meagre faces; but man, in the ideal, is so noble and so sparkling, such a grand and glowing creature, that over any ignominious blemish in him all his fellows should run to throw their costliest robes. That immaculate manliness we feel within ourselves, so far within us, that it remains intact though all the outer character seem gone; bleeds with keenest anguish at the undraped spectacle of a valor-ruined man. Nor can piety itself, at such a shameful sight, completely stifle her upbraidings against the permitting stars. But this august dignity I treat of, is not the dignity of kings and robes, but that abounding dignity which has no robed investiture. Thou shalt see it shining in the arm that wields a pick or drives a spike; that democratic dignity which, on all hands, radiates without end from God; Himself! The great God absolute! The centre and circumference of all democracy! His omnipresence, our divine equality!

If, then, to meanest mariners, and renegades and castaways, I shall hereafter ascribe high qualities, though dark; weave round them tragic graces; if even the most mournful, perchance the most abased, among them all, shall at times lift himself to the

exalted mounts; if I shall touch that workman's arm with some
ethereal light; if I shall spread a rainbow over his disastrous set
of sun; then against all mortal critics bear me out in it, thou
just Spirit of Equality, which hast spread one royal mantle of
humanity over all my kind! Bear me out in it, thou great democratic God! who didst not refuse to the swart convict, Bunyan,
the pale, poetic pearl; Thou who didst clothe with doubly hammered leaves of finest gold, the stumped and paupered arm of
old Cervantes; Thou who didst pick up Andrew Jackson from
the pebbles; who didst hurl him upon a war-horse; who didst
thunder him higher than a throne! Thou who, in all Thy
mighty, earthly marchings, ever cullest Thy selectest champions
from the kingly commons; bear me out in it, O God!

CHAPTER XXVII

Knights and Squires

Stubb was the second mate. He was a native of Cape Cod;
and hence, according to local usage, was called a Cape-Cod-
man. A happy-go-lucky; neither craven nor valiant; taking
perils as they came with an indifferent air; and while engaged
in the most imminent crisis of the chase, toiling away, calm and
collected as a journeyman joiner engaged for the year. Good-
humored, easy, and careless, he presided over his whale-boat
as if the most deadly encounter were but a dinner, and his
crew all invited guests. He was as particular about the comfortable arrangement of his part of the boat, as an old stage-
driver is about the snugness of his box. When close to the
whale, in the very death-lock of the fight, he handled his unpitying lance coolly and off-handedly, as a whistling tinker
his hammer. He would hum over his old rigadig tunes while
flank and flank with the most exasperated monster. Long usage
had, for this Stubb, converted the jaws of death into an easy
chair. What he thought of death itself, there is no telling.
Whether he ever thought of it at all, might be a question;
but, if he ever did chance to cast his mind that way after a

comfortable dinner, no doubt, like a good sailor, he took it to be a sort of call of the watch to tumble aloft, and bestir themselves there, about something which he would find out when he obeyed the order, and not sooner.

What, perhaps, with other things, made Stubb such an easy-going, unfearing man, so cheerily trudging off with the burden of life in a world full of grave peddlers, all bowed to the ground with their packs; what helped to bring about that almost impious good-humor of his; that thing must have been his pipe. For, like his nose, his short, black little pipe was one of the regular features of his face. You would almost as soon have expected him to turn out of his bunk without his nose as without his pipe. He kept a whole row of pipes there ready loaded, stuck in a rack, within easy reach of his hand; and, whenever he turned in, he smoked them all out in succession, lighting one from the other to the end of the chapter; then loading them again to be in readiness anew. For, when Stubb dressed, instead of first putting his legs into his trowsers, he put his pipe into his mouth.

I say this continual smoking must have been one cause, at least, of his peculiar disposition; for every one knows that this earthly air, whether ashore or afloat, is terribly infected with the nameless miseries of the numberless mortals who have died exhaling it; and as in time of the cholera, some people go about with a camphorated handkerchief to their mouths; so, likewise, against all mortal tribulations, Stubb's tobacco smoke might have operated as a sort of disinfecting agent.

The third mate was Flask, a native of Tisbury, in Martha's Vineyard. A short, stout, ruddy young fellow, very pugnacious concerning whales, who somehow seemed to think that the great Leviathans had personally and hereditarily affronted him; and therefore it was a sort of point of honor with him, to destroy them whenever encountered. So utterly lost was he to all sense of reverence for the many marvels of their majestic bulk and mystic ways; and so dead to anything like an apprehension of any possible danger from encountering them; that in his poor opinion, the wondrous whale was but a species of magnified mouse, or at least water-rat, requiring only a little circumvention and some small application of time and trouble in order to kill and boil. This ignorant, unconscious fearlessness of his made him a little waggish in the matter of whales; he followed these fish for the fun of it; and a three years' voyage round Cape Horn was only a jolly joke that lasted that length of time. As a carpenter's nails are divided into wrought nails and cut nails; so mankind may be similarly divided. Little Flask was one of the wrought ones; made to clinch tight and last long. They called him King-Post on board of the Pequod; because, in form, he could be well likened to the short, square timber known by that name in Arctic whalers; and which by the means of many radiating side timbers inserted into it, serves to brace the ship against the icy concussions of those battering seas.

Now these three mates—Starbuck, Stubb, and Flask, were momentous men. They it was who by universal prescription commanded three of the Pequod's boats as headsmen. In that grand order of battle in which Captain Ahab would probably marshal his forces to descend on the whales, these three headsmen were as captains of companies. Or, being armed with their long keen whaling spears, they were as a picked trio of lancers; even as the harpooneers were flingers of javelins.

And since in this famous fishery, each mate or headsman, like a Gothic Knight of old, is always accompanied by his boat-steerer or harpooneer, who in certain conjunctures provides him with a fresh lance, when the former one has been badly twisted, or elbowed in the assault; and moreover, as there generally subsists between the two, a close intimacy and friend-liness; it is therefore but meet, that in this place we set down who the Pequod's harpooneers were, and to what headsman each of them belonged.

First of all was Queequeg, whom Starbuck, the chief mate, had selected for his squire. But Queequeg is already known.[1]

Next was Tashtego, an unmixed Indian from Gay Head, the most westerly promontory of Martha's Vineyard, where there still exists the last remnant of a village of red men, which has long supplied the neighboring island of Nantucket with many of her most daring harpooneers. In the fishery, they usually go by the generic name of Gay-Headers. Tashtego's long, lean, sable hair, his high cheek bones, and black rounding eyes—for an Indian, Oriental in their largeness, but Antarctic in their glittering expression—all this sufficiently proclaimed him an inheritor of the unvitiated blood of those proud warrior hunters, who, in quest of the great New England moose, had scoured, bow in hand, the aboriginal forests of the main. But no longer snuffing in the trail of the wild beasts of the woodland, Tashtego now hunted in the wake of the great whales of the sea; the unerring harpoon of the son fitly replacing the infallible arrow of the sires. To look at the tawny brawn of his lithe snaky limbs, you would almost have credited the superstitions of some of the earlier Puritans, and half believed this wild Indian to be a son of the Prince of the Powers of the Air. Tashtego was Stubb the second mate's squire.

Third among the harpooneers was Daggoo, a gigantic, coal-black negro-savage, with a lion-like tread—an Ahasuerus[2] to behold. Suspended from his ears were two golden hoops, so large that the sailors called them ring-bolts, and would talk of securing the top-sail halyards to them. In his youth Daggoo had voluntarily shipped on board of a whaler, lying in a lonely bay on his native coast. And never having been anywhere in the world but in Africa, Nantucket, and the pagan harbors most frequented by whalemen; and having now led for many years the bold life of the fishery in the ships of owners uncommonly heedful of what manner of men they shipped; Daggoo retained all his barbaric virtues, and erect as a giraffe, moved about the decks in all the pomp of six feet five in his socks. There was a corporeal humility in looking up at him; and a white man standing before him seemed a white flag come to beg truce of a fortress. Curious to tell, this imperial negro, Ahasuerus Daggoo, was the Squire of little Flask, who looked like a chess-man beside him. As for the residue of the Pequod's company, be it said, that at the present day not one in two of the many thousand men before the mast employed in the American whale fishery, are Americans born, though pretty nearly all the officers are. Herein it is the same with the American whale fishery as with the American army and military and merchant navies, and the engineering forces employed in the construction of the American Canals and Railroads. The same, I say, because in all these cases the native American liberally provides the brains, the rest of the world as generously supplying the muscles. No small number of these whaling seamen belong to the Azores, where the outward bound Nantucket whalers frequently touch to augment their crews from the hardy peasants of those rocky shores. In like manner, the Greenland whalers sailing out of Hull or London, put in at the Shetland Islands, to receive the full complement of their crew. Upon the passage homewards, they drop them there again. How it is, there is no telling, but Islanders seem to make the best whalemen. They were nearly all Islanders in the Pequod, *Isolatoes* too, I call such, not acknowledging the common continent of men, but each *Isolato* living on a separate continent of his own. Yet now, federated along one keel, what a set these Isolatoes were! An Anacharsis Clootz[3] deputation from all the isles of the sea, and all the ends of the earth, accompanying Old Ahab in the Pequod to lay the world's grievances before that bar from which not very many of them ever come back. Black Little Pip—he never did—oh, no! he went before. Poor Alabama boy! On the grim Pequod's forecastle, ye shall ere long see him, beating his tambourine; prelusive of the eternal time, when sent for, to the great quarter-deck on high, he was bid strike in with angels, and beat his tambourine in glory; called a coward here, hailed a hero there!

CHAPTER XXVIII

Ahab

For several days after leaving Nantucket, nothing above hatches was seen of Captain Ahab. The mates regularly relieved each other at the watches, and for aught that could be seen to the contrary, they seemed to be the only commanders of the ship; only they sometimes issued from the cabin with orders so sudden and peremptory, that after all it was plain they but commanded vicariously. Yes, their supreme lord and dictator was there, though hitherto unseen by any eyes not permitted to penetrate into the now sacred retreat of the cabin.

Every time I ascended to the deck from my watches below, I instantly gazed aft to mark if any strange face were visible; for my first vague disquietude touching the unknown captain, now in the seclusion of the sea, became almost a perturbation. This was strangely heightened at times by the ragged Elijah's[4] diabolical incoherences uninvitedly recurring to me, with a subtle energy I could not have before conceived of. But poorly could I withstand them, much as in other moods I was almost ready to smile at the solemn whimsicalities of that outlandish prophet of the wharves. But whatever it was of apprehensiveness or uneasiness—to call it so—which I felt, yet whenever I came to look about me in the ship, it seemed against all warrantry to cherish such emotions. For though the harpooneers, with the great body of the crew, were a far more barbaric, heathenish, and motley set than any of the tame merchant-ship companies which my previous experiences had made me acquainted with, still I ascribed this—and rightly ascribed it— to the fierce uniqueness of the very nature of that wild Scandinavian vocation in which I had so abandonedly embarked. But it was especially the aspect of the three chief officers of the ship, the mates, which was most forcibly calculated to allay these colorless misgivings, and induce confidence and cheerfulness in every presentment of the voyage. Three better, more likely sea-officers and men, each in his own different way, could not readily be found, and they were every one of them Americans; a Nantucketer, a Vineyarder, a Cape man. Now, it being Christmas when the ship shot from out her harbor, for a space we had biting Polar weather, though all the time running away from it to the southward; and by every degree and minute of latitude which we sailed, gradually leaving that merciless winter, and all its intolerable weather behind us. It was one of those less lowering, but still grey and gloomy enough mornings of the transition, when with a fair wind the ship was rushing through the water with a vindictive sort of leaping and melancholy rapidity, that as I mounted to the deck at the call of the forenoon watch, so soon as I levelled my glance towards the taffrail, foreboding shivers ran over me. Reality outran apprehension; Captain Ahab stood upon his quarter-deck.

There seemed no sign of common bodily illness about him, nor of the recovery from any. He looked like a man cut away from the stake, when the fire has overrunningly wasted all the limbs without consuming them, or taking away one particle from their compacted aged robustness. His whole high, broad form, seemed made of solid bronze, and shaped in an unalterable mould, like Cellini's cast Perseus. Threading its way out from among his grey hairs, and continuing right down one side of his tawny scorched face and neck, till it disappeared in his clothing, you saw a slender rod-like mark, lividly whitish. It resembled that perpendicular seam sometimes made in the straight, lofty trunk of a great tree, when the upper lightning tearingly darts down it, and without wrenching a single twig, peels and grooves out the bark from top to bottom, ere running off into the soil, leaving the tree still greenly alive, but branded. Whether that mark was born with him, or whether it was the scar left by some desperate wound, no one could certainly say. By some tacit consent, throughout the voyage little or no allusion was made to it, especially by the mates. But once Tashtego's senior, an old Gay-Head Indian among the crew, superstitiously asserted that not till he was full forty years old did Ahab become that way branded, and then it came upon him, not in the fury of any mortal fray, but in an elemental strife at sea. Yet, this wild hint seemed inferentially negatived, by what a grey Manxman insinuated, an old sepulchral man, who, having never before sailed out of Nantucket, had never ere this laid eye upon wild Ahab. Nevertheless, the old sea-traditions, the immemorial credulities, popularly invested this old Manxman with preternatural powers of discernment. So that no white sailor seriously contradicted him when he said that if ever Captain Ahab should be tranquilly laid out—which might hardly come to pass, so he muttered—then, whoever should do that last office for the dead, would find a birth-mark on him from crown to sole.

So powerfully did the whole grim aspect of Ahab affect me, and the livid brand which streaked it, that for the first few moments I hardly noted that not a little of this overbearing grimness was owing to the barbaric white leg upon which he partly stood. It had previously come to me that this ivory leg had at sea been fashioned from the polished bone of the sperm whale's jaw. "Aye, he was dismasted off Japan," said the old Gay-Head Indian once; "but like his dismasted craft, he shipped another mast without coming home for it. He has a quiver of 'em."

I was struck with the singular posture he maintained. Upon each side of the Pequod's quarter deck, and pretty close to the mizen shrouds, there was an auger hole, bored about half an inch or so, into the plank. His bone leg steadied in that hole; one arm elevated, and holding by a shroud; Captain Ahab stood erect, looking straight out beyond the ship's ever-pitching prow. There was an infinity of firmest fortitude, a determinate, unsurrenderable wilfulness, in the fixed and fearless, forward dedication of that glance. Not a word he spoke; nor did his officers say aught to him; though by all their minutest gestures and expressions, they plainly showed the uneasy, if not painful, consciousness of being under a troubled master-eye. And not only that, but moody stricken Ahab stood before them with a crucifixion in his face; in all the nameless regal overbearing dignity of some mighty woe.

Ere long, from his first visit in the air, he withdrew into his cabin. But after that morning, he was every day visible to the crew; either standing in his pivot-hole, or seated upon an ivory stool he had; or heavily walking the deck. As the sky grew less gloomy; indeed, began to grow a little genial, he became still less and less a recluse; as if, when the ship had sailed from home, nothing but the dead wintry bleakness of the sea had then kept him so secluded. And, by and by, it came to pass, that he was almost continually in the air; but, as yet, for all that he said, or perceptibly did, on the at last sunny deck, he seemed as unnecessary there as another mast. But the Pequod was only making a passage now; not regularly cruising; nearly all whaling preparatives needing supervision the mates were fully competent to, so that there was little or nothing, out of himself, to employ or excite Ahab, now; and thus chase away, for that one interval, the clouds that layer upon layer were piled upon his brow, as ever all clouds choose the loftiest peaks to pile themselves upon.

Nevertheless, ere long, the warm, warbling persuasiveness of the pleasant, holiday weather we came to, seemed gradually to charm him from his mood. For, as when the red-cheeked, dancing girls, April and May, trip home to the wintry, misanthropic woods; even the barest, ruggedest, most thunder-cloven old oak will at least send forth some few green sprouts, to welcome such glad-hearted visitants; so Ahab did, in the end, a little respond to the playful allurings of that girlish air. More than once did he put forth the faint blossom of a look, which, in any other man, would have soon flowered out in a smile.

CHAPTER XXXVI

The Quarter-Deck

(*Enter Ahab: Then, all.*)

It was not a great while after the affair of the pipe,[5] that one morning shortly after breakfast, Ahab, as was his wont, ascended the cabin-gangway to the deck. There most sea-captains usually walk at that hour, as country gentlemen, after the same meal, take a few turns in the garden.

Soon his steady, ivory stride was heard, as to and fro he paced his old rounds, upon planks so familiar to his tread, that they were all over dented, like geological stones, with the peculiar mark of his walk. Did you fixedly gaze, too, upon that ribbed and dented brow; there also, you would see still stranger foot-prints—the foot-prints of his one unsleeping, ever-pacing thought.

But on the occasion in question, those dents looked deeper, even as his nervous step that morning left a deeper mark. And, so full of his thought was Ahab, that at every uniform turn that he made, now at the main-mast and now at the binnacle, you could almost see that thought turn in him as he turned, and pace in him as he paced; so completely possessing him, indeed, that it all but seemed the inward mould of every outer movement.

"D'ye mark him, Flask?" whispered Stubb; "the chick that's in him pecks the shell. 'Twill soon be out."

The hours wore on;—Ahab now shut up within his cabin; anon, pacing the deck, with the same intense bigotry of purpose in his aspect.

It drew near the close of day. Suddenly he came to a halt by the bulwarks, and inserting his bone leg into the auger-hole there, and with one hand grasping a shroud, he ordered Starbuck to send everybody aft.

"Sir!" said the mate, astonished at an order seldom or never given on ship-board except in some extraordinary case.

"Send everybody aft," repeated Ahab. "Mast-heads, there! come down!"

When the entire ship's company were assembled, and with curious and not wholly unapprehensive faces, were eyeing him, for he looked not unlike the weather horizon when a storm is coming up, Ahab, after rapidly glancing over the bulwarks, and then darting his eyes among the crew, started from his standpoint; and as though not a soul were nigh him resumed his heavy turns upon the deck. With bent head and half-slouched hat he continued to pace, unmindful of the wondering whispering among the men; till Stubb cautiously whispered to Flask, that Ahab must have summoned them there for the purpose of witnessing a pedestrian feat. But this did not last long. Vehemently pausing, he cried:—

"What do ye do when ye see a whale, men?"

"Sing out for him!" was the impulsive rejoinder from a score of clubbed voices.

"Good!" cried Ahab, with a wild approval in his tones; ob-

serving the hearty animation into which his unexpected question
had so magnetically thrown them.

"And what do ye next, men?"

"Lower away, and after him!"

"And what tune is it ye pull to, men?"

"A dead whale or a stove boat!"

More and more strangely and fiercely glad and approving,
grew the countenance of the old man at every shout; while the
mariners began to gaze curiously at each other, as if marvelling
how it was that they themselves became so excited at such
seemingly purposeless questions.

But, they were all eagerness again, as Ahab, now half-revolv-
ing in his pivot-hole, with one hand reaching high up a shroud,
and tightly, almost convulsively grasping it, addressed them
thus:—

"All ye mast-headers have before now heard me give orders
about a white whale. Look ye! d'ye see this Spanish ounce
of gold?"—holding up a broad bright coin to the sun—"it is
a sixteen dollar piece, men. D'ye see it? Mr. Starbuck, hand
me yon top-maul."

While the mate was getting the hammer, Ahab, without speaking, was slowly rubbing the gold piece against the skirts of his
jacket, as if to heighten its lustre, and without using any words
was meanwhile lowly humming to himself, producing a sound
so strangely muffled and inarticulate that it seemed the mechanical humming of the wheels of his vitality in him.

Receiving the top-maul from Starbuck, he advanced towards
the main-mast with the hammer uplifted in one hand, exhibiting
the gold with the other, and with a high raised voice exclaiming:
"Whosoever of ye raises me a white-headed whale with a
wrinkled brow and a crooked jaw; whosoever of ye raises me
that white-headed whale, with three holes punctured in his
starboard fluke—look ye, whosoever of ye raises me that same
white whale, he shall have this gold ounce, my boys!"

"Huzza! huzza!" cried the seamen, as with swinging tar-
paulins they hailed the act of nailing the gold to the mast.

"It's a white whale, I say," resumed Ahab, as he threw down

the top-maul; "a white whale. Skin your eyes for him, men; look sharp for white water; if ye see but a bubble, sing out."

All this while Tashtego, Daggoo, and Queequeg had looked on with even more intense interest and surprise than the rest, and at the mention of the wrinkled brow and crooked jaw they had started as if each was separately touched by some specific recollection.

"Captain Ahab," said Tashtego, "that white whale must be the same that some call Moby Dick."

"Moby Dick?" shouted Ahab. "Do ye know the white whale then, Tash?"

"Does he fan-tail a little curious, sir, before he goes down?" said the Gay-Header deliberately.

"And has he a curious spout, too," said Daggoo, "very bushy, even for a parmacetty, and mighty quick, Captain Ahab?"

"And he have one, two, tree—oh! good many iron in him hide, too, Captain," cried Queequeg disjointedly, "all twiske-tee be-twisk, like him—him—" faltering hard for a word, and screwing his hand round and round as though uncorking a bottle—"like him—him—"

"Corkscrew!" cried Ahab, "aye, Queequeg, the harpoons lie all twisted and wrenched in him; aye, Daggoo, his spout is a big one, like a whole shock of wheat, and white as a pile of our Nantucket wool after the great annual sheep-shearing; aye, Tashtego, and he fan-tails like a split jib in a squall. Death and devils! men, it is Moby Dick ye have seen—Moby Dick—Moby Dick!"

"Captain Ahab," said Starbuck, who, with Stubb and Flask, had thus far been eyeing his superior with increasing surprise, but at last seemed struck with a thought which somewhat ex-plained all the wonder. "Captain Ahab, I have heard of Moby Dick—but it was not Moby Dick that took off thy leg?"

"Who told thee that?" cried Ahab; then pausing, "Aye, Starbuck; aye, my hearties all round; it was Moby Dick that dismasted me; Moby Dick that brought me to this dead stump I stand on now. Aye, aye," he shouted with a terrific, loud, animal sob, like that of a heart-stricken moose; "Aye, aye! it was that accursed white whale that razeed me; made a poor pegging lubber of me for ever and a day!" Then tossing both arms, with measureless imprecations he shouted out: "Aye, aye! and I'll chase him round Good Hope, and round the Horn, and round the Norway Maelstrom, and round perdition's flames before I give him up. And this is what ye have shipped for, men! to chase that white whale on both sides of land, and over all sides of earth, till he spouts black blood and rolls fin out. What say ye, men, will ye splice hands on it, now? I think ye do look brave."

"Aye, aye!" shouted the harpooneers and seamen, running closer to the excited old man: "A sharp eye for the White Whale; a sharp lance for Moby Dick!"

"God bless ye," he seemed to half sob and half shout. "God bless ye, men. Steward! go draw the great measure of grog. But what's this long face about, Mr. Starbuck; wilt thou not chase the white whale? art not game for Moby Dick?"

"I am game for his crooked jaw, and for the jaws of Death too, Captain Ahab, if it fairly comes in the way of the business we follow; but I came here to hunt whales, not my commander's vengeance. How many barrels will thy vengeance yield thee even if thou gettest it, Captain Ahab? it will not fetch thee much in our Nantucket market."

"Nantucket market! Hoot! But come closer, Starbuck; thou requirest a little lower layer. If money's to be the measurer, man, and the accountants have computed their great counting-house the globe, by girdling it with guineas, one to every three parts of an inch; then, let me tell thee, that my vengeance will fetch a great premium *here!*"

"He smites his chest," whispered Stubb, "what's that for? methinks it rings most vast, but hollow."

"Vengeance on a dumb brute!" cried Starbuck, "that simply smote thee from blindest instinct! Madness! To be enraged with a dumb thing, Captain Ahab, seems blasphemous."

"Hark ye yet again,—the little lower layer. All visible objects, man, are but as pasteboard masks. But in each event— in the living act, the undoubted deed—there, some unknown but still reasoning thing puts forth the mouldings of its features from behind the unreasoning mask. If man will strike, strike through the mask! How can the prisoner reach outside except by thrusting through the wall? To me, the white whale is that wall, shoved near to me. Sometimes I think there's naught beyond. But 'tis enough. He tasks me; he heaps me; I see in him outrageous strength, with an inscrutable malice sinewing it. That inscrutable thing is chiefly what I hate; and be the white whale agent, or be the white whale principal, I will wreak that hate upon him. Talk not to me of blasphemy, man; I'd strike the sun if it insulted me. For could the sun do that, then could I do the other; since there is ever a sort of fair play herein, jealousy presiding over all creations. But not my master, man, is even that fair play. Who's over me? Truth hath no confines. Take off thine eye! more intolerable than fiends' glarings is a doltish stare! So, so; thou reddenest and palest; my heat has melted thee to anger-glow. But look ye, Starbuck, what is said in heat, that thing unsays itself. There are men from whom warm words are small indignity. I meant not to incense thee. Let it go. Look! see yonder Turkish cheeks of spotted tawn—living, breathing pictures painted by the sun. The Pagan leopards—the unrecking and unworshipping things, that live; and seek, and give no reasons for the torrid life they feel! The crew, man, the crew! Are they not one and all with Ahab, in this matter of the whale? See Stubb! he laughs! See yonder Chilian! he snorts to think of it. Stand up amid the general hurricane, thy one tost sapling cannot, Starbuck! And what is it? Reckon it. 'Tis but to help strike a fin; no wondrous feat for Starbuck. What is it more? From this one poor hunt, then, the best lance out of all Nantucket, surely he will not hang back, when every foremast-hand has clutched a whetstone? Ah! constrainings seize thee; I see! the billow lifts thee! Speak, but speak!—Aye, aye! thy silence, then, *that* voices thee. (*Aside*) Something shot from my dilated nostrils, he has inhaled it in his lungs. Starbuck now is mine; cannot oppose me now, without rebellion."

"God keep me!—keep us all!" murmured Starbuck, lowly.

But in his joy at the enchanted, tacit acquiescence of the mate, Ahab did not hear his foreboding invocation; nor yet the low laugh from the hold; nor yet the presaging vibrations of the winds in the cordage; nor yet the hollow flap of the sails against the masts, as for a moment their hearts sank in. For again Starbuck's downcast eyes lighted up with the stubbornness of life; the subterranean laugh died away; the winds blew on; the sails filled out; the ship heaved and rolled as before. Ah, ye admonitions and warnings! why stay ye not when ye come? But rather are ye predictions than warnings, ye shadows! Yet not so much predictions from without, as verifications of the foregoing things within. For with little external to constrain us, the innermost necessities in our being, these still drive us on.

"The measure! the measure!" cried Ahab.

Receiving the brimming pewter, and turning to the harpooneers, he ordered them to produce their weapons. Then ranging them before him near the capstan, with their harpoons in their hands, while his three mates stood at his side with their lances, and the rest of the ship's company formed a circle round the group; he stood for an instant searchingly eyeing every man of his crew. But those wild eyes met his, as the bloodshot eyes of the prairie wolves meet the eye of their leader, ere he rushes on at their head in the trail of the bison; but, alas! only to fall into the hidden snare of the Indian.

"Drink and pass!" he cried, handing the heavy charged flagon to the nearest seamen. "The crew alone now drink. Round with it, round! Short draughts—long swallows, men; 'tis hot as Satan's hoof. So, so; it goes round excellently. It spiralizes in ye; forks out at the serpent-snapping eye. Well done; almost drained. That way it went, this way it comes. Hand it me—here's a hollow! Men, ye seem the years; so brimming life is gulped and gone. Steward, refill!

"Attend now, my braves. I have mustered ye all round this capstan; and ye mates, flank me with your lances; and ye harpooneers, stand there with your irons; and ye, stout mariners, ring me in, that I may in some sort revive a noble custom of my fishermen fathers before me. O men, you will yet see that—— Ha! boy, come back? bad pennies come not sooner. Hand it me. Why, now, this pewter had run brimming again, wer't not thou St. Vitus' imp—away, thou ague!

"Advance, ye mates! Cross your lances full before me. Well done! Let me touch the axis." So saying, with extended arm, he grasped the three level, radiating lances at their crossed centre; while so doing, suddenly and nervously twitched them; meanwhile, glancing intently from Starbuck to Stubb; from Stubb to Flask. It seemed as though, by some nameless, interior volition, he would fain have shocked into them the same fiery emotion accumulated within the Leyden jar of his own magnetic life. The three mates quailed before his strong, sustained, and mystic aspect. Stubb and Flask looked sideways from him; the honest eye of Starbuck fell downright.

"In vain!" cried Ahab; "but, maybe, 'tis well. For did ye three but once take the full-forced shock, then mine own electric thing, *that* had perhaps expired from out me. Perchance, too, it would have dropped ye dead. Perchance ye need it not. Down lances! And now, ye mates, I do appoint ye three cup-bearers to my three pagan kinsmen there—yon three most honorable gentlemen and noblemen, my valiant harpooneers. Disdain the task? What, when the great Pope washes the feet of beggars, using his tiara for ewer? Oh, my sweet cardinals! your own condescension, *that* shall bend ye to it. I do not order ye; ye will it. Cut your seizings and draw the poles, ye harpooneers!"

Silently obeying the order, the three harpooneers now stood with the detached iron part of their harpoons, some three feet long, held, barbs up, before him.

"Stab me not with that keen steel! Cant them; cant them over! know ye not the goblet end? Turn up the socket! So, so; now, ye cup-bearers, advance. The irons! take them; hold them while I fill!" Forthwith, slowly going from one officer to the other, he brimmed the harpoon sockets with the fiery waters from the pewter.

"Now, three to three, ye stand. Commend the murderous chalices! Bestow them, ye who are now made parties to this indissoluble league. Ha! Starbuck! but the deed is done! Yon ratifying sun now waits to sit upon it. Drink, ye harpooneers! drink and swear, ye men that man the deathful whaleboat's bow—Death to Moby Dick! God hunt us all, if we do not hunt Moby Dick to his death!" The long, barbed steel goblets were lifted; and to cries and maledictions against the white whale, the spirits were simultaneously quaffed down with a hiss. Starbuck paled, and turned, and shivered. Once more, and finally, the replenished pewter went the rounds among the frantic crew; when, waving his free hand to them, they all dispersed; and Ahab retired within his cabin.

CHAPTER XLI

Moby Dick [6]

I, Ishmael, was one of that crew; my shouts had gone up with the rest; my oath had been welded with theirs; and stronger I shouted, and more did I hammer and clinch my oath, because of the dread in my soul. A wild, mystical, sympathetical feeling was in me; Ahab's quenchless feud seemed mine. With greedy ears I learned the history of that murderous monster against whom I and all the others had taken our oaths of violence and revenge.

For some time past, though at intervals only, the unaccompanied, secluded White Whale had haunted those uncivilized seas mostly frequented by the Sperm Whale fishermen. But not all of them knew of his existence; only a few of them, comparatively, had knowingly seen him; while the number who as yet had actually and knowingly given battle to him, was small indeed. For, owing to the large number of whale-cruisers; the disorderly way they were sprinkled over the entire watery circumference, many of them adventurously pushing their quest along solitary latitudes, so as seldom or never for a whole twelvemonth or more on a stretch, to encounter a single news-telling sail of any sort; the inordinate length of each separate voyage; the irregularity of the times of sailing from home; all these, with other circumstances, direct and indirect, long obstructed the spread through the whole world-wide whaling-fleet of the special individualizing tidings concerning Moby Dick. It was hardly to be doubted, that several vessels reported to have encountered, at such or such a time, or on such or such a meridian, a Sperm Whale of uncommon magnitude and malignity, which whale, after doing great mischief to his assailants, had completely escaped them; to some minds it was not an unfair presumption, I say, that the whale in question must have been no other than Moby Dick. Yet as of late the Sperm Whale fishery had been marked by various and not unfrequent instances of great ferocity, cunning, and malice in the monster attacked; therefore it was, that those who by accident ignorantly gave battle to Moby Dick; such hunters, perhaps, for the most part, were content to ascribe the peculiar terror he bred, more, as it were, to the perils of the Sperm Whale fishery at large, than to the individual cause. In that way, mostly, the disastrous encounter between Ahab and the whale had hitherto been popularly regarded.

And as for those who, previously hearing of the White Whale, by chance caught sight of him; in the beginning of the thing they had every one of them, almost, as boldly and fearlessly lowered for him, as for any other whale of that species. But at length, such calamities did ensue in these assaults—not restricted to sprained wrists and ankles, broken limbs, or devouring amputations—but fatal to the last degree of fatality; those repeated disastrous repulses, all accumulating and piling their terrors upon Moby Dick; those things had gone far to shake the fortitude of many brave hunters, to whom the story of the White Whale had eventually come.

Nor did wild rumors of all sorts fail to exaggerate, and still the more horrify the true histories of these deadly encounters. For not only do fabulous rumors naturally grow out of the very body of all surprising terrible events,—as the smitten tree gives birth to its fungi; but, in maritime life, far more than in that of terra firma, wild rumors abound, wherever there is any adequate reality for them to cling to. And as the sea surpasses the land in this matter, so the whale fishery surpasses every other sort of maritime life, in the wonderfulness and fearfulness of the rumors which sometimes circulate there. For not only are whalemen as a body unexempt from that ignorance and superstitiousness hereditary to all sailors; but of all sailors, they are by all odds the most directly brought into contact with whatever is appallingly astonishing in the sea; face to face they not only eye its greatest marvels, but, hand to jaw, give battle to them. Alone, in such remotest waters, that though you sailed a thousand miles, and passed a thousand shores, you would not come to any chiselled hearthstone, or aught hospitable beneath that part of the sun; in such latitudes and longitudes, pursuing too such a calling as he does, the whaleman is wrapped by influences all tending to make his fancy pregnant with many a mighty birth.

No wonder, then, that ever gathering volume from the mere transit over the wildest watery spaces, the outblown rumors of the White Whale did in the end incorporate with themselves all manner of morbid hints, and half-formed fœtal suggestions of supernatural agencies, which eventually invested Moby Dick with new terrors unborrowed from anything that visibly appears. So that in many cases such a panic did he finally strike, that few who by those rumors, at least, had heard of the White Whale, few of those hunters were willing to encounter the perils of his jaw.

But there were still other and more vital practical influences at work. Not even at the present day has the original prestige of the Sperm Whale, as fearfully distinguished from all other species of the leviathan, died out of the minds of the whalemen as a body. There are those this day among them, who, though intelligent and courageous enough in offering battle to the Greenland or Right whale, would perhaps—either from professional inexperience, or incompetency, or timidity, decline a contest with the Sperm Whale; at any rate, there are plenty of whalemen, especially among those whaling nations not sailing under the American flag, who have never hostilely encountered the Sperm Whale, but whose sole knowledge of the leviathan is restricted to the ignoble monster primitively pursued in the North; seated on their hatches, these men will hearken with a childish fire-side interest and awe, to the wild, strange tales of Southern whaling. Nor is the pre-eminent tremendousness of the great Sperm Whale anywhere more feelingly comprehended, than on board of those prows which stem him.

And as if the now tested reality of his might had in former legendary times thrown its shadow before it; we find some book naturalists—Olassen and Povelson—declaring the Sperm Whale not only to be a consternation to every other creature in the sea, but also to be so incredibly ferocious as continually to be athirst for human blood. Nor even down to so late a time as Cuvier's, were these or almost similar impressions effaced. For in his Natural History, the Baron himself affirms that at sight of the Sperm Whale, all fish (sharks included) are "struck with the most lively terrors," and "often in the precipitancy of their flight dash themselves against the rocks with such violence as to cause instantaneous death." And however the general experiences in the fishery may amend such reports as these; yet in their full terribleness, even to the bloodthirsty item of Povelson, the superstitious belief in them is, in some vicissitudes of their vocation, revived in the minds of the hunters.

So that overawed by the rumors and portents concerning him, not a few of the fishermen recalled, in reference to Moby Dick, the earlier days of the Sperm Whale fishery, when it was oftentimes hard to induce long practised Right whalemen to embark in the perils of this new and daring warfare; such men protesting that although other leviathans might be hopefully pursued, yet to chase and point lances at such an apparition as the Sperm Whale was not for mortal man. That to attempt it, would be inevitably to be torn into a quick eternity. On this head, there are some remarkable documents that may be consulted.

Nevertheless, some there were, who even in the face of these things were ready to give chase to Moby Dick; and a still greater number who, chancing only to hear of him distantly and vaguely, without the specific details of any certain calamity, and without superstitious accompaniments, were sufficiently hardy not to flee from the battle if offered.

One of the wild suggestings referred to, as at last coming to be linked with the White Whale in the minds of the superstitiously inclined, was the unearthly conceit that Moby Dick was ubiquitous; that he had actually been encountered in opposite latitudes at one and the same instant of time.

Nor, credulous as such minds must have been, was this conceit altogether without some faint show of superstitious probability. For as the secrets of the currents in the seas have never yet been divulged, even to the most erudite research; so the hidden ways of the Sperm Whale when beneath the surface remain, in great part, unaccountable to his pursuers; and from time to time have originated the most curious and contradictory speculations regarding them, especially concerning the mystic modes whereby, after sounding to a great depth, he transports himself with such vast swiftness to the most widely distant points.

It is a thing well known to both American and English whaleships, and as well a thing placed upon authoritative record years ago by Scoresby, that some whales have been captured far north in the Pacific, in whose bodies have been found the barbs of harpoons darted in the Greenland seas. Nor is it to be gainsaid, that in some of these instances it has been declared that the interval of time between the two assaults could not have exceeded very many days. Hence, by inference, it has been believed by some whalemen, that the Nor' West Passage, so long a problem to man, was never a problem to the whale. So that here, in the real living experience of living men, the prodigies related in old times of the inland Strello mountain in Portugal (near whose top there was said to be a lake in which the wrecks of ships floated up to the surface); and that still more wonderful story of the Arethusa fountain near Syracuse (whose waters were believed to have come from the Holy Land by an underground passage); these fabulous narrations are almost fully equalled by the realities of the whaleman.

Forced into familiarity, then, with such prodigies as these;

and knowing that after repeated, intrepid assaults, the White Whale had escaped alive; it cannot be much matter of surprise that some whalemen should go still further in their superstitions; declaring Moby Dick not only ubiquitous, but immortal (for immortality is but ubiquity in time); that though groves of spears should be planted in his flanks, he would still swim away unharmed; or if indeed he should ever be made to spout thick blood, such a sight would be but a ghastly deception; for again in unensanguined billows hundreds of leagues away, his unsullied jet would once more be seen.

But even stripped of these supernatural surmisings, there was enough in the earthly make and incontestable character of the monster to strike the imagination with unwonted power. For, it was not so much his uncommon bulk that so much distinguished him from other sperm whales, but, as was elsewhere thrown out—a peculiar snow-white wrinkled forehead, and a high, pyramidical white hump. These were his prominent features; the tokens whereby, even in the limitless, uncharted seas, he revealed his identity, at a long distance, to those who knew him.

The rest of his body was so streaked, and spotted, and marbled with the same shrouded hue, that, in the end, he had gained his distinctive appellation of the White Whale; a name, indeed, literally justified by his vivid aspect, when seen gliding at high noon through a dark blue sea, leaving a milky-way wake of creamy foam, all spangled with golden gleamings.

Nor was it his unwonted magnitude, nor his remarkable hue, nor yet his deformed lower jaw, that so much invested the whale with natural terror, as that unexampled, intelligent malignity which, according to specific accounts, he had over and over again evinced in his assaults. More than all, his treacherous retreats struck more of dismay than perhaps aught else. For, when swimming before his exulting pursuers, with every apparent symptom of alarm, he had several times been known to turn round suddenly, and, bearing down upon them, either stave their boats to splinters, or drive them back in consternation to their ship.

Already several fatalities had attended his chase. But though similar disasters, however little bruited ashore, were by no means unusual in the fishery; yet, in most instances, such seemed the White Whale's infernal aforethought of ferocity, that every dismembering or death that he caused, was not wholly regarded as having been inflicted by an unintelligent agent.

Judge, then, to what pitches of inflamed, distracted fury the minds of his more desperate hunters were impelled, when amid the chips of chewed boats, and the sinking limbs of torn comrades, they swam out of the white curds of the whale's direful wrath into the serene, exasperating sunlight, that smiled on, as if at a birth or a bridal.

His three boats stove around him, and oars and men both whirling in the eddies; one captain, seizing the line-knife from his broken prow, had dashed at the whale, as an Arkansas duellist at his foe, blindly seeking with a six inch blade to reach the fathom-deep life of the whale. That captain was Ahab. And then it was, that suddenly sweeping his sickle-shaped lower jaw beneath him, Moby Dick had reaped away Ahab's leg, as a mower a blade of grass in the field. No turbaned Turk, no hired Venetian or Malay, could have smote him with more seeming malice. Small reason was there to doubt, then, that ever since that almost fatal encounter, Ahab had cherished a wild vindictiveness against the whale, all the more fell for that in his frantic morbidness he at last came to identify with him, not only all his bodily woes, but all his intellectual and spiritual exasperations. The White Whale swam before him as the monomaniac incarnation of all those malicious agencies which some deep men feel eating in them, till they are left living on with half a heart and half a lung. That intangible malignity which has been from the beginning; to whose dominion even the modern Christians ascribe one-half of the worlds; which the ancient Ophites[7] of the east reverenced in their statue devil;—Ahab did not fall down and worship it like them; but deliriously transferring its idea to the abhorred white whale, he pitted himself, all mutilated, against it. All that most maddens and torments; all that stirs up the lees of things; all truth with malice in it; all that cracks the sinews and cakes the brain; all the subtle demonisms of life and thought; all evil, to crazy Ahab, were visibly personified, and made practically assailable in Moby Dick. He piled upon the whale's white hump the sum of all the general rage and hate felt by his whole race from Adam down; and then, as if his chest had been a mortar, he burst his hot heart's shell upon it.

It is not probable that this monomania in him took its instant rise at the precise time of his bodily dismemberment. Then, in darting at the monster, knife in hand, he had but given loose to a sudden, passionate, corporal animosity; and when he received the stroke that tore him, he probably but felt the agonizing bodily laceration, but nothing more. Yet, when by this collision forced to turn towards home, and for long months of days and weeks, Ahab and anguish lay stretched together in one hammock, rounding in mid winter that dreary, howling Patagonian Cape; then it was, that his torn body and gashed soul bled into one another; and so interfusing, made him mad. That it was only then, on the homeward voyage, after the encounter, that the final monomania seized him, seems all but certain from the fact that, at intervals during the passage, he was a raving lunatic; and, though unlimbed of a leg, yet such vital strength yet lurked in his Egyptian chest, and was moreover intensified by his delirium, that his mates were forced to lace him fast, even there, as he sailed, raving in his hammock. In a strait-jacket, he swung to the mad rockings of the gales. And, when running into more sufferable latitudes, the ship, with mild stun'sails spread, floated across the tranquil tropics, and, to all appearances, the old man's delirium seemed left behind him with the Cape Horn swells, and he came forth from his dark den into the blessed light and air; even then, when he bore that firm, collected front, however pale, and issued his calm orders once again; and his mates thanked God the direful madness was now gone; even then, Ahab, in his hidden self, raved on. Human madness is oftentimes a cunning and most feline thing. When you think it fled, it may have but become transfigured into some still subtler form. Ahab's full lunacy subsided not, but deepeningly contracted; like the unabated Hudson, when that noble Northman flows narrowly, but unfathomably through the Highland gorge. But, as in his narrow-flowing monomania, not one jot of Ahab's broad madness had been left behind; so in that broad madness, not one jot of his great natural intellect had perished. That before living agent, now became the living instrument. If such a furious trope may stand, his special lunacy stormed his general sanity, and carried it, and turned all its concentred cannon upon its own mad mark; so that far from having lost his strength, Ahab, to that one end, did now possess a thousand fold more potency than ever he had sanely brought to bear upon any one reasonable object.

This is much; yet Ahab's larger, darker, deeper part remains unhinted. But vain to popularize profundities, and all truth is profound. Winding far down from within the very heart of this spiked Hotel de Cluny[8] where we here stand—however grand and wonderful, now quit it;—and take your way, ye nobler, sadder souls, to those vast Roman halls of Thermes; where far beneath the fantastic towers of man's upper earth, his root of grandeur, his whole awful essence sits in bearded state; an antique buried beneath antiquities, and throned on torsoes! So with a broken throne, the great gods mock that captive king; so like a Caryatid, he patient sits, upholding on his frozen brow the piled entablatures of ages. Wind ye down there, ye prouder, sadder souls! question that proud, sad king! A family likeness! aye, he did beget ye, ye young exiled royalties; and from your grim sire only will the old State-secret come.

Now, in his heart, Ahab had some glimpse of this, namely: all my means are sane, my motive and my object mad. Yet without power to kill, or change, or shun the fact; he likewise knew that to mankind he did long dissemble; in some sort, did still. But that thing of his dissembling was only subject to his perceptibility, not to his will determinate. Nevertheless, so well did he succeed in that dissembling, that when with ivory leg he stepped ashore at last, no Nantucketer thought him otherwise than but naturally grieved, and that to the quick, with the terrible casualty which had overtaken him.

The report of his undeniable delirium at sea was likewise popularly ascribed to a kindred cause. And so too, all the added moodiness which always afterwards, to the very day of sailing in the Pequod on the present voyage, sat brooding on his brow. Nor is it so very unlikely, that far from distrusting his fitness for another whaling voyage, on account of such dark symptoms, the calculating people of that prudent isle were inclined to harbor the conceit, that for those very reasons he was all the better qualified and set on edge, for a pursuit so full of rage and wildness as the bloody hunt of whales. Gnawed within and scorched without, with the infixed, unrelenting fangs of some incurable idea; such an one, could he be found, would seem the very man to dart his iron and lift his lance against the most appalling of all brutes. Or, if for any reason thought to be corporeally incapacitated for that, yet such an one would seem superlatively competent to cheer and howl on his underlings to the attack. But be all this as it may, certain it is, that with the mad secret of his unabated rage bolted up and keyed in him, Ahab had purposely sailed upon the present voyage with the one only and all-engrossing object of hunting the White Whale. Had any one of his old acquaintances on shore but half dreamed of what was lurking in him then, how soon would their aghast and righteous souls have wrenched the ship from such a fiendish man! They were bent on profitable cruises, the profit to be counted down in dollars from the mint. He was intent on an audacious, immitigable, and supernatural revenge.

Here, then, was this grey-headed, ungodly old man, chasing with curses a Job's whale[9] round the world, at the head of a crew, too, chiefly made up of mongrel renegades, and castaways, and cannibals—morally enfeebled also, by the incompetence of mere unaided virtue or right-mindedness in Starbuck, the invulnerable jollity of indifference and recklessness in Stubb, and the pervading mediocrity in Flask. Such a crew, so officered, seemed specially picked and packed by some infernal fatality to help him to his monomaniac revenge. How it was that they so aboundingly responded to the old man's ire—by what evil magic their souls were possessed, that at times his hate seemed almost theirs; the White Whale as much their insufferable foe as his; how all this came to be—what the White Whale was to them, or how to their unconscious understandings, also, in some dim, unsuspected way, he might have seemed the gliding great demon of the seas of life,—all this to explain, would be to dive deeper than Ishmael can go. The subterranean miner that works in us all, how can one tell whither leads his shaft by the ever shifting, muffled sound of his pick? Who does not feel the irresistible arm drag? What skiff in tow of a seventy-four can stand still? For one, I gave myself up to the abandonment of the time and the place; but while yet all a-rush to encounter the whale, could see naught in that brute but the deadliest ill.

CHAPTER XLII

The Whiteness of the Whale

What the white whale was to Ahab, has been hinted; what, at times, he was to me, as yet remains unsaid.

Aside from those more obvious considerations touching Moby Dick, which could not but occasionally awaken in any man's soul some alarm, there was another thought, or rather vague, nameless horror concerning him, which at times by its intensity completely overpowered all the rest; and yet so mystical and well nigh ineffable was it, that I almost despair of putting it in a comprehensible form. It was the whiteness of the whale that above all things appalled me. But how can I hope to explain myself here; and yet, in some dim, random way, explain myself I must, else all these chapters might be naught.

Though in many natural objects, whiteness refiningly enhances beauty, as if imparting some special virtue of its own, as in marbles, japonicas, and pearls; and though various nations have in some way recognised a certain royal pre-eminence in this hue; even the barbaric, grand old kings of Pegu[10] placing the title "Lord of the White Elephants" above all their other magniloquent ascriptions of dominion; and the modern kings of Siam unfurling the same snow-white quadruped in the royal standard; and the Hanoverian flag bearing the one figure of a snow-white charger; and the great Austrian Empire, Cæsarian, heir to overlording Rome, having for the imperial color the same imperial hue; and though this pre-eminence in it applies to the human race itself, giving the white man ideal mastership over every dusky tribe; and though, besides all this, whiteness has been even made significant of gladness, for among the Romans a white stone marked a joyful day; and though in other mortal sympathies and symbolizings, this same hue is made the emblem of many touching, noble things—the innocence of brides, the benignity of age; though among the Red Men of America the giving of the white belt of wampum was the deepest pledge of honor; though in many climes, whiteness typifies the majesty of Justice in the ermine of the Judge, and contributes to the daily state of kings and queens drawn by milk-white steeds; though even in the higher mysteries of the most august religions it has been made the symbol of the divine spotlessness and power; by the Persian fire worshippers, the white forked flame being held the holiest on the altar; and in the Greek mythologies, Great Jove himself being made incarnate in a snow-white bull; and though to the noble Iroquois, the midwinter sacrifice of the sacred White Dog was by far the holiest festival of their theology, that spotless, faithful creature being held the purest envoy they could send to the Great Spirit with the annual tidings of their own fidelity; and though directly from the Latin word for white, all Christian priests derive the name of one part of their sacred vesture, the alb or tunic, worn beneath the cassock; and though among the holy pomps of the Romish faith, white is specially employed in the celebration of the Passion of our Lord; though in the Vision of St. John,[11] white robes are given to the redeemed, and the four-and-twenty elders stand clothed in white before the great white throne, and the Holy One that sitteth there white like wool; yet for all these accumulated associations, with whatever is sweet, and honorable, and sublime, there yet lurks an elusive something in the innermost idea of this hue, which strikes more of panic to the soul than that redness which affrights in blood.

This elusive quality it is, which causes the thought of white-ness, when divorced from more kindly associations, and coupled with any object terrible in itself, to heighten that terror to the furthest bounds. Witness the white bear of the poles, and the white shark of the tropics; what but their smooth, flaky whiteness makes them the transcendent horrors they are? That ghastly whiteness it is which imparts such an abhorrent mild-ness, even more loathsome than terrific, to the dumb gloating of their aspect. So that not the fierce-fanged tiger in his heraldic coat can so stagger courage as the white-shrouded bear or shark.[12]

Bethink thee of the albatross, whence come those clouds of spiritual wonderment and pale dread, in which that white phantom sails in all imaginations? Not Coleridge first threw that spell; but God's great, unflattering laureate, Nature.[13]

Most famous in our Western annals and Indian traditions is that of the White Steed of the Prairies; a magnificent milk-white charger, large-eyed, small-headed, bluff-chested, and with the dignity of a thousand monarchs in his lofty, overscorning car-riage. He was the elected Xerxes of vast herds of wild horses, whose pastures in those days were only fenced by the Rocky Mountains and the Alleghanies. At their flaming head he westward trooped it like that chosen star which every evening leads on the hosts of light. The flashing cascade of his mane, the curving comet of his tail, invested him with housings more resplendent than gold and silver-beaters could have furnished him. A most imperial and archangelical apparition of that unfallen, western world, which to the eyes of the old trappers and hunters revived the glories of those primeval times when Adam walked majestic as a god, bluff-browed and fearless as this mighty steed. Whether marching amid his aides and marshals in the van of countless cohorts that endlessly streamed it over the plains, like an Ohio; or whether with his circum-ambient subjects browsing all around at the horizon, the White Steed gallopingly reviewed them with warm nostrils reddening through his cool milkiness; in whatever aspect he presented himself, always to the bravest Indians he was the object of trembling reverence and awe. Nor can it be questioned from what stands on legendary record of this noble horse, that it was his spiritual whiteness chiefly, which so clothed him with divineness; and that this divineness had that in it which, though commanding worship, at the same time enforced a certain nameless terror.

But there are other instances where this whiteness loses all that accessory and strange glory which invests it in the White Steed and Albatross.

What is it that in the Albino man so peculiarly repels and often shocks the eye, as that sometimes he is loathed by his own kith and kin! It is that whiteness which invests him, a thing expressed by the name he bears. The Albino is as well made as other men—has no substantive deformity—and yet this mere aspect of all-pervading whiteness makes him more strangely hideous than the ugliest abortion. Why should this be so?

Nor, in quite other aspects, does Nature in her least palpable but not the less malicious agencies, fail to enlist among her forces this crowning attribute of the terrible. From its snowy aspect, the gauntleted ghost of the Southern Seas has been denominated the White Squall. Nor, in some historic instances, has the art of human malice omitted so potent an auxiliary. How wildly it heightens the effect of that passage in Froissart, when, masked in the snowy symbol of their faction, the desperate White Hoods of Ghent murder their bailiff in the market-place![14]

Nor, in some things, does the common, hereditary experience of all mankind fail to bear witness to the supernaturalism of this hue. It cannot well be doubted, that the one visible quality in the aspect of the dead which most appals the gazer, is the marble pallor lingering there; as if indeed that pallor were as much like the badge of consternation in the other world, as of mortal trepidation here. And from that pallor of the dead, we borrow the expressive hue of the shroud in which we wrap them. Nor even in our superstitions do we fail to throw the same snowy mantle round our phantoms; all ghosts rising in a milk-white fog—Yea, while these terrors seize us, let us add, that even the king of terrors, when personified by the evangelist, rides on his pallid horse.[15]

Therefore, in his other moods, symbolize whatever grand or gracious thing he will by whiteness, no man can deny that in its profoundest idealized significance it calls up a peculiar apparition to the soul.

But though without dissent this point be fixed, how is mortal man to account for it? To analyse it, would seem impossible. Can we, then, by the citation of some of those instances wherein this thing of whiteness—though for the time either wholly or in great part stripped of all direct associations calculated to impart to it aught fearful, but, nevertheless, is found to exert over us the same sorcery, however modified;— can we thus hope to light upon some chance clue to conduct us to the hidden cause we seek?

Let us try. But in a matter like this, subtlety appeals to subtlety, and without imagination no man can follow another into these halls. And though, doubtless, some at least of the imaginative impressions about to be presented may have been shared by most men, yet few perhaps were entirely conscious of them at the time, and therefore may not be able to recall them now.

Why to the man of untutored ideality, who happens to be but loosely acquainted with the peculiar character of the day, does the bare mention of Whitsuntide marshal in the fancy such long, dreary, speechless processions of slow-pacing pilgrims, down-cast and hooded with new-fallen snow? Or, to the un-read, unsophisticated Protestant of the Middle American States, why does the passing mention of a White Friar or a White Nun, evoke such an eyeless statue in the soul?

Or what is there apart from the traditions of dungeoned warriors and kings (which will not wholly account for it) that makes the White Tower of London tell so much more strongly on the imagination of an untravelled American, than those other storied structures, its neighbors—the Byward Tower, or even the Bloody? And those sublimer towers, the White Mountains of New Hampshire, whence, in peculiar moods, comes that gigantic ghostliness over the soul at the bare mention of that name, while the thought of Virginia's Blue Ridge is full of a soft, dewy, distant dreaminess? Or why, irrespective of all latitudes and longitudes, does the name of the White Sea exert such a spectralness over the fancy, while that of the Yellow Sea lulls us with mortal thoughts of long lacquered mild afternoons on the waves, followed by the gaudiest and yet sleepiest of sunsets? Or, to choose a wholly unsubstantial instance, purely addressed to the fancy, why, in reading the old fairy tales of Central Europe, does "the tall pale man" of the Hartz forests, whose changeless pallor unrustlingly glides through the green of the groves—why is this phantom more terrible than all the whooping imps of the Blocksburg?[16]

Nor is it, altogether, the remembrance of her cathedral-toppling earthquakes; nor the stampedoes of her frantic seas: nor the tearlessness of arid skies that never rain; nor the sight of her wide field of leaning spires, wrenched cope-stones, and crosses all adroop (like canted yards of anchored fleets); and her suburban avenues of house-walls lying over upon each other, as a tossed pack of cards;—it is not these things alone which make tearless Lima, the strangest, saddest city thou can'st see. For Lima has taken the white veil; and there is a higher horror in this whiteness of her woe. Old as Pizarro, this whiteness keeps her ruins for ever new; admits not the cheerful greenness of complete decay; spreads over her broken ramparts the rigid pallor of an apoplexy that fixes its own distortions.

I know that, to the common apprehension, this phenomenon of whiteness is not confessed to be the prime agent in exaggerating the terror of objects otherwise terrible; nor to the unimaginative mind is there aught of terror in those appearances whose awfulness to another mind almost solely consists in this one phenomenon, especially when exhibited under any form at all approaching to muteness or universality. What I mean by these two statements may perhaps be respectively elucidated by the following examples.

First: The mariner, when drawing nigh the coasts of foreign lands, if by night he hear the roar of breakers, starts to vigilance,

and feels just enough of trepidation to sharpen all his faculties;
but under precisely similar circumstances, let him be called
from his hammock to view his ship sailing through a midnight
sea of milky whiteness—as if from encircling headlands shoals
of combed white bears were swimming round him, then he
feels a silent, superstitious dread; the shrouded phantom of the
whitened waters is horrible to him as a real ghost; in vain the
lead assures him he is still off soundings; heart and helm they
both go down; he never rests till blue water is under him again.
Yet where is the mariner who will tell thee, "Sir, it was not so
much the fear of striking hidden rocks, as the fear of that
hideous whiteness that so stirred me?"

Second: To the native Indian of Peru, the continual sight of
the snow-howdahed Andes conveys naught of dread, except,
perhaps, in the mere fancying of the eternal frosted desolateness
reigning at such vast altitudes, and the natural conceit of what a
fearfulness it would be to lose oneself in such inhuman solitudes.
Much the same is it with the backwoodsman of the West, who
with comparative indifference views an unbounded prairie
sheeted with driven snow, no shadow of tree or twig to break
the fixed trance of whiteness.   Not so the sailor, beholding the
scenery of the Antarctic seas; where at times, by some infernal
trick of legerdemain in the powers of frost and air, he, shivering
and half shipwrecked, instead of rainbows speaking hope and
solace to his misery, views what seems a boundless church-yard
grinning upon him with its lean ice monuments and splintered
crosses.

But thou sayest, methinks this white-lead chapter about
whiteness is but a white flag hung out from a craven soul;
thou surrenderest to a hypo, Ishmael.

Tell me, why this strong young colt, foaled in some peaceful
valley of Vermont, far removed from all beasts of prey—
why is it that upon the sunniest day, if you but shake a fresh
buffalo robe behind him, so that he cannot even see it, but only
smells its wild animal muskiness—why will he start, snort,
and with bursting eyes paw the ground in phrensies of affright?
There is no remembrance in him of any gorings of wild crea-

tures in his green northern home, so that the strange muskiness he smells cannot recall to him anything associated with the experience of former perils; for what knows he, this New England colt, of the black bisons of distant Oregon?

No: but here thou beholdest even in a dumb brute, the instinct of the knowledge of the demonism in the world. Though thousands of miles from Oregon, still when he smells that savage musk, the rending, goring bison herds are as present as to the deserted wild foal of the prairies, which this instant they may be trampling into dust.

Thus, then, the muffled rollings of a milky sea; the bleak rustlings of the festooned frosts of mountains; the desolate shiftings of the windrowed snows of prairies; all these, to Ishmael, are as the shaking of that buffalo robe to the frightened colt!

Though neither knows where lie the nameless things of which the mystic sign gives forth such hints; yet with me, as with the colt, somewhere those things must exist. Though in many of its aspects this visible world seems formed in love, the invisible spheres were formed in fright.

But not yet have we solved the incantation of this whiteness, and learned why it appeals with such power to the soul; and more strange and far more portentous—why, as we have seen, it is at once the most meaning symbol of spiritual things, nay, the very veil of the Christian's Deity; and yet should be as it is, the intensifying agent in things the most appalling to mankind.

Is it that by its indefiniteness it shadows forth the heartless voids and immensities of the universe, and thus stabs us from behind with the thought of annihilation, when beholding the white depths of the milky way? Or is it, that as in essence whiteness is not so much a color as the visible absence of color, and at the same time the concrete of all colors; is it for these reasons that there is such a dumb blankness, full of meaning, in a wide landscape of snows—a colorless, all-color of atheism from which we shrink? And when we consider that other theory of the natural philosophers, that all other earthly hues—every stately or lovely emblazoning—the sweet tinges of sunset skies and woods; yea, and the gilded velvets of butterflies, and the butterfly cheeks of young girls; all these are but subtile deceits, not actually inherent in substances, but only laid on from without; so that all deified Nature absolutely paints like the harlot, whose allurements cover nothing but the charnel-house within; and when we proceed further, and consider that the mystical cosmetic which produces every one of her hues, the great principle of light, for ever remains white or colorless in itself, and if operating without medium upon matter, would touch all objects, even tulips and roses, with its own blank tinge—pondering all this, the palsied universe lies before us a leper; and like wilful travellers in Lapland, who refuse to wear colored and coloring glasses upon their eyes, so the wretched infidel gazes himself blind at the monumental white shroud that wraps all the prospect around him. And of all these things the Albino whale was the symbol. Wonder ye then at the fiery hunt?

CHAPTER LXVII

Cutting In[17]

It was a Saturday night, and such a Sabbath as followed! Ex officio professors of Sabbath breaking are all whalemen. The ivory Pequod was turned into what seemed a shamble; every sailor a butcher. You would have thought we were offering up ten thousand red oxen to the sea gods.

In the first place, the enormous cutting tackles, among other ponderous things comprising a cluster of blocks generally painted green, and which no single man can possibly lift—this vast bunch of grapes was swayed up to the main-top and firmly lashed to the lower mast-head, the strongest point anywhere above a ship's deck. The end of the hawser-like rope winding through these intricacies, was then conducted to the windlass, and the huge lower block of the tackles was swung over the whale; to this block the great blubber hook, weighing some one hundred pounds, was attached. And now suspended in stages over the side, Starbuck and Stubb, the mates, armed with their long spades, began cutting a hole in the body for the in-

sertion of the hook just above the nearest of the two side-fins.
This done, a broad, semicircular line is cut round the hole,
the hook is inserted, and the main body of the crew striking up
a wild chorus, now commence heaving in one dense crowd
at the windlass. When instantly, the entire ship careens over
on her side; every bolt in her starts like the nail-heads of an old
house in frosty weather; she trembles, quivers, and nods her
frighted mast-heads to the sky. More and more she leans over
to the whale, while every gasping heave of the windlass is
answered by a helping heave from the billows; till at last, a
swift, startling snap is heard; with a great swash the ship rolls
upwards and backwards from the whale, and the triumphant
tackle rises into sight dragging after it the disengaged semicircular end of the first strip of blubber. Now as the blubber
envelopes the whale precisely as the rind does an orange, so
is it stripped off from the body precisely as an orange is sometimes stripped by spiralizing it. For the strain constantly kept
up by the windlass continually keeps the whale rolling over
and over in the water, and as the blubber in one strip uniformly
peels off along the line called the "scarf," simultaneously cut
by the spades of Starbuck and Stubb, the mates; and just as fast
as it is thus peeled off, and indeed by that very act itself, it is all
the time being hoisted higher and higher aloft till its upper end
grazes the main-top; the men at the windlass then cease heaving,
and for a moment or two the prodigious blood-dripping mass
sways to and fro as if let down from the sky, and every one
present must take good heed to dodge it when it swings, else
it may box his ears and pitch him headlong overboard.

One of the attending harpooneers now advances with a long,
keen weapon called a boarding-sword, and watching his chance
he dexterously slices out a considerable hole in the lower part of
the swaying mass. Into this hole, the end of the second
alternating great tackle is then hooked so as to retain a hold
upon the blubber, in order to prepare for what follows. Whereupon, this accomplished swordsman, warning all hands to
stand off, once more makes a scientific dash at the mass, and with
a few sidelong, desperate, lunging slicings, severs it completely

in twain; so that while the short lower part is still fast, the long upper strip, called a blanket-piece, swings clear, and is all ready for lowering. The heavers forward now resume their song, and while the one tackle is peeling and hoisting a second strip from the whale, the other is slowly slackened away, and down goes the first strip through the main hatchway right beneath, into an unfurnished parlor called the blubber-room. Into this twilight apartment sundry nimble hands keep coiling away the long blanket-piece as if it were a great live mass of plaited serpents. And thus the work proceeds; the two tackles hoisting and lowering simultaneously; both whale and windlass heaving, the heavers singing, the blubber-room gentlemen coiling, the mates scarfing, the ship straining, and all hands swearing occasionally, by way of assuaging the general friction.

CHAPTER LXVIII

The Blanket

I have given no small attention to that not unvexed subject, the skin of the whale. I have had controversies about it with experienced whalemen afloat, and learned naturalists ashore. My original opinion remains unchanged; but it is only an opinion.

The question is, what and where is the skin of the whale? Already you know what his blubber is. That blubber is something of the consistence of firm, close-grained beef, but tougher, more elastic and compact, and ranges from eight or ten to twelve and fifteen inches in thickness.

Now, however preposterous it may at first seem to talk of any creature's skin as being of that sort of consistence and thickness, yet in point of fact these are no arguments against such a presumption; because you cannot raise any other dense enveloping layer from the whale's body but that same blubber; and the outermost enveloping layer of any animal, if reasonably dense, what can that be but the skin? True, from the unmarred dead body of the whale, you may scrape off with your hand an infinitely thin, transparent substance, somewhat resembling the thinnest shreds of isinglass, only it is almost as flexible and soft as satin; that is, previous to being dried, when it not only contracts and thickens, but becomes rather hard and brittle. I have several such dried bits, which I use for marks in my whale-books. It is transparent, as I said before; and being laid upon the printed page, I have sometimes pleased myself with fancying it exerted a magnifying influence. At any rate, it is pleasant to read about whales through their own spectacles, as you may say. But what I am driving at here is this. That same infinitely thin, isinglass substance, which, I admit, invests the entire body of the whale, is not so much to be regarded as the skin of the creature, as the skin of the skin, so to speak; for it were simply ridiculous to say, that the proper skin of the tremendous whale is thinner and more tender than the skin of a new-born child. But no more of this.

Assuming the blubber to be the skin of the whale; then, when this skin, as in the case of a very large Sperm Whale, will yield the bulk of one hundred barrels of oil; and, when it is considered that, in quantity, or rather weight, that oil, in its expressed state, is only three fourths, and not the entire substance of the coat; some idea may hence be had of the enormousness of that animated mass, a mere part of whose mere integument yields such a lake of liquid as that. Reckoning ten barrels to the ton, you have ten tons for the net weight of only three quarters of the stuff of the whale's skin.

In life, the visible surface of the Sperm Whale is not the least among the many marvels he presents. Almost invariably it is all over obliquely crossed and re-crossed with numberless straight marks in thick array, something like those in the finest Italian line engravings. But these marks do not seem to be impressed upon the isinglass substance above mentioned, but seem to be seen through it, as if they were engraved upon the body itself. Nor is this all. In some instances, to the quick, observant eye, those linear marks, as in a veritable engraving, but afford the ground for far other delineations. These are hieroglyphical; that is, if you call those mysterious cyphers on the walls of pyramids hieroglyphics, then that is the proper word to use in the present connexion. By my retentive memory of the hieroglyphics upon one Sperm Whale in particular, I was much struck with a plate representing the old Indian characters chiselled on the famous hieroglyphic palisades on the banks of the Upper Mississippi. Like those mystic rocks, too, the mystic-marked whale remains undecipherable. This allusion to the Indian rocks reminds me of another thing. Besides all the other phenomena which the exterior of the Sperm Whale presents, he not seldom displays the back, and more especially his flanks, effaced in great part of the regular linear appearance, by reason of numerous rude scratches, altogether of an irregular, random aspect. I should say that those New England rocks on the sea-coast, which Agassiz imagines to bear the marks of violent scraping contact with vast floating icebergs—I should say, that those rocks must not a little resemble the Sperm Whale in this particular. It also seems to me that such scratches in the whale are probably made by hostile contact with other whales; for I have most remarked them in the large, full-grown bulls of the species.

A word or two more concerning this matter of the skin or blubber of the whale. It has already been said, that it is stript from him in long pieces, called blanket-pieces. Like most sea-terms, this one is very happy and significant. For the whale is indeed wrapt up in his blubber as in a real blanket or counterpane; or, still better, an Indian poncho slipt over his head, and skirting his extremity. It is by reason of this cosy blanketing of his body, that the whale is enabled to keep himself comfortable in all weathers, in all seas, times, and tides. What would become of a Greenland whale, say, in those shuddering, icy seas of the North, if unsupplied with his cosy surtout? True, other fish are found exceedingly brisk in those Hyperborean waters; but these, be it observed, are your cold-blooded, lungless fish, whose very bellies are refrigerators; creatures, that warm themselves under the lee of an iceberg, as a traveller in winter would bask before an inn fire; whereas, like man, the whale has lungs and warm blood. Freeze his blood, and he dies. How wonderful is it then—except after explanation— that this great monster, to whom corporeal warmth is as indispensable as it is to man; how wonderful that he should be found at home, immersed to his lips for life in those Arctic waters! where, when seamen fall overboard, they are sometimes found, months afterwards, perpendicularly frozen into the hearts of fields of ice, as a fly is found glued in amber. But more surprising is it to know, as has been proved by experiment, that the blood of a Polar whale is warmer than that of a Borneo negro in summer.

It does seem to me, that herein we see the rare virtue of a strong individual vitality, and the rare virtue of thick walls, and the rare virtue of interior spaciousness. Oh, man! admire and model thyself after the whale! Do thou, too, remain warm among ice. Do thou, too, live in this world without being of it. Be cool at the equator; keep thy blood fluid at the Pole. Like the great dome of St. Peter's, and like the great whale, retain, O man! in all seasons a temperature of thine own.

But how easy and how hopeless to teach these fine things! Of erections, how few are domed like St. Peter's! of creatures, how few vast as the whale!

CHAPTER LXIX

The Funeral

"Haul in the chains! Let the carcase go astern!"

The vast tackles have now done their duty. The peeled white body of the beheaded whale flashes like a marble sepulchre; though changed in hue, it has not perceptibly lost anything in bulk. It is still colossal. Slowly it floats more and more away, the water round it torn and splashed by the insatiate sharks, and the air above vexed with rapacious flights of screaming fowls, whose beaks are like so many insulting poniards in the whale. The vast white headless phantom floats further and further from the ship, and every rod that it so floats, what seem square roods of sharks and cubic roods of fowls, augment the murderous din. For hours and hours from the almost stationary ship that hideous sight is seen. Beneath the unclouded and mild azure sky, upon the fair face of the pleasant sea, wafted by the joyous breezes, that great mass of death floats on and on, till lost in infinite perspectives.

There's a most doleful and most mocking funeral! The sea-vultures all in pious mourning, the air-sharks all punctiliously in black or speckled. In life but few of them would have helped the whale, I ween, if peradventure he had needed it; but upon the banquet of his funeral they most piously do pounce. Oh, horrible vultureism of earth! from which not the mightiest whale is free.

Nor is this the end. Desecrated as the body is, a vengeful ghost survives and hovers over it to scare. Espied by some timid man-of-war or blundering discovery-vessel from afar, when the distance obscuring the swarming fowls, nevertheless still shows the white mass floating in the sun, and the white spray heaving high against it; straightway the whale's un-harming corpse, with trembling fingers is set down in the log— *shoals, rocks, and breakers hereabouts: beware!* And for years afterwards, perhaps, ships shun the place; leaping over it as silly sheep leap over a vacuum, because their leader originally leaped there when a stick was held. There's your law of precedents; there's your utility of traditions; there's the story of your obstinate survival of old beliefs never bottomed on the earth, and now not even hovering in the air! There's orthodoxy!

Thus, while in life the great whale's body may have been a real terror to his foes, in his death his ghost becomes a powerless panic to a world.

Are you a believer in ghosts, my friend? There are other ghosts than the Cock-Lane one,[18] and far deeper men than Doctor Johnson who believe in them.

CHAPTER LXXXVII

The Grand Armada

The long and narrow peninsula of Malacca, extending south-eastward from the territories of Birmah, forms the most southerly point of all Asia. In a continuous line from that peninsula stretch the long islands of Sumatra, Java, Bally, and

Timor; which, with many others, form a vast mole, or rampart, lengthwise connecting Asia with Australia, and dividing the long unbroken Indian ocean from the thickly studded oriental archipelagoes. This rampart is pierced by several sally-ports for the convenience of ships and whales; conspicuous among which are the straits of Sunda and Malacca. By the straits of Sunda, chiefly, vessels bound to China from the west, emerge into the China seas.

Those narrow straits of Sunda divide Sumatra from Java; and standing midway in that vast rampart of islands, buttressed by that bold green promontory, known to seamen as Java Head; they not a little correspond to the central gateway opening into some vast walled empire: and considering the inexhaustible wealth of spices, and silks, and jewels, and gold, and ivory, with which the thousand islands of that oriental sea are enriched, it seems a significant provision of nature, that such treasures, by the very formation of the land, should at least bear the appearance, however ineffectual, of being guarded from the all-grasping western world. The shores of the Straits of Sunda are unsupplied with those domineering fortresses which guard the entrances to the Mediterranean, the Baltic, and the Propontis. Unlike the Danes, these Orientals do not demand the obsequious homage of lowered top-sails from the endless procession of ships before the wind, which for centuries past, by night and by day, have passed between the islands of Sumatra and Java, freighted with the costliest cargoes of the east. But while they freely waive a ceremonial like this, they do by no means renounce their claim to more solid tribute.

Time out of mind the piratical proas of the Malays, lurking among the low shaded coves and islets of Sumatra, have sallied out upon the vessels sailing through the straits, fiercely demanding tribute at the point of their spears. Though by the repeated bloody chastisements they have received at the hands of European cruisers, the audacity of these corsairs has of late been somewhat repressed; yet, even at the present day, we occasionally hear of English and American vessels, which, in those waters, have been remorselessly boarded and pillaged.

With a fair, fresh wind, the Pequod was now drawing nigh to these straits; Ahab purposing to pass through them into the Javan sea, and thence, cruising northwards, over waters known to be frequented here and there by the Sperm Whale, sweep inshore by the Philippine Islands, and gain the far coast of Japan, in time for the great whaling season there. By these means, the circumnavigating Pequod would sweep almost all the known Sperm Whale cruising grounds of the world, previous to descending upon the Line in the Pacific; where Ahab, though everywhere else foiled in his pursuit, firmly counted upon giving battle to Moby Dick, in the sea he was most known to frequent; and at a season when he might most reasonably be presumed to be haunting it.

But how now? in this zoned quest, does Ahab touch no land? does his crew drink air? Surely, he will stop for water. Nay. For a long time, now, the circus-running sun has raced within his fiery ring, and needs no sustenance but what's in himself. So Ahab. Mark this, too, in the whaler. While other hulls are loaded down with alien stuff, to be transferred to foreign wharves; the world-wandering whale-ship carries no cargo but herself and crew, their weapons and their wants. She has a whole lake's contents bottled in her ample hold. She is ballasted with utilities; not altogether with unusable pig-lead and kentledge.[19] She carries years' water in her. Clear old prime Nantucket water; which, when three years afloat, the Nantucketer, in the Pacific, prefers to drink before the brackish fluid, but yesterday rafted off in casks, from the Peruvian or Indian streams. Hence it is, that, while other ships may have gone to China from New York, and back again, touching at a score of ports, the whale-ship, in all that interval, may not have sighted one grain of soil; her crew having seen no man but floating seamen like themselves. So that did you carry them the news that another flood had come; they would only answer—"Well, boys, here's the ark!"

Now, as many Sperm Whales had been captured off the western coast of Java, in the near vicinity of the Straits of Sunda; indeed, as most of the ground, roundabout, was generally recognised by the fishermen as an excellent spot for cruising; therefore, as the Pequod gained more and more upon Java Head, the look-outs were repeatedly hailed, and admonished to keep wide awake. But though the green palmy cliffs of the land soon loomed on the starboard bow, and with delighted nostrils the fresh cinnamon was snuffed in the air, yet not a single jet was descried. Almost renouncing all thought of falling in with any game hereabouts, the ship had well nigh entered the straits, when the customary cheering cry was heard from aloft, and ere long a spectacle of singular magnificence saluted us.

But here be it premised, that owing to the unwearied activity with which of late they have been hunted over all four oceans, the Sperm Whales, instead of almost invariably sailing in small detached companies, as in former times, are now frequently met with in extensive herds, sometimes embracing so great a multitude, that it would almost seem as if numerous nations of them had sworn solemn league and covenant for mutual assistance and protection. To this aggregation of the Sperm Whale into such immense caravans, may be imputed the circumstance that even in the best cruising grounds, you may now sometimes sail for weeks and months together, without being greeted by a single spout; and then be suddenly saluted by what sometimes seems thousands on thousands.

Broad on both bows, at the distance of some two or three miles, and forming a great semicircle, embracing one half of the level horizon, a continuous chain of whale-jets were up-playing and sparkling in the noon-day air. Unlike the straight perpendicular twin-jets of the Right Whale, which, dividing at top, fall over in two branches, like the cleft drooping boughs of a willow, the single forward-slanting spout of the Sperm Whale presents a thick curled bush of white mist, continually rising and falling away to leeward.

Seen from the Pequod's deck, then, as she would rise on a high hill of the sea, this host of vapory spouts, individually curling up into the air, and beheld through a blending atmosphere of bluish haze, showed like the thousand cheerful chimneys of some dense metropolis, descried of a balmy autumnal morning, by some horseman on a height.

As marching armies approaching an unfriendly defile in the mountains, accelerate their march, all eagerness to place that perilous passage in their rear, and once more expand in comparative security upon the plain; even so did this vast fleet of whales now seem hurrying forward through the straits; gradually contracting the wings of their semicircle, and swimming on, in one solid, but still crescentic centre.

Crowding all sail the Pequod pressed after them; the harpooneers handling their weapons, and loudly cheering from the heads of their yet suspended boats. If the wind only held, little doubt had they, that chased through these Straits of Sunda, the vast host would only deploy into the Oriental seas to witness the capture of not a few of their number. And who could tell whether, in that congregated caravan, Moby Dick himself might not temporarily be swimming, like the worshipped white-elephant in the coronation procession of the Siamese! So with stun-sail piled on stun-sail, we sailed along, driving these leviathans before us; when, of a sudden, the voice of Tashtego was heard, loudly directing attention to something in our wake.

Corresponding to the crescent in our van, we beheld another in our rear. It seemed formed of detached white vapors, rising and falling something like the spouts of the whales; only they did not so completely come and go; for they constantly hovered, without finally disappearing. Levelling his glass at this sight, Ahab quickly revolved in his pivot-hole, crying, "Aloft there, and rig whips and buckets to wet the sails[20];—Malays, sir, and after us!"

As if too long lurking behind the headlands, till the Pequod should fairly have entered the straits, these rascally Asiatics were now in hot pursuit, to make up for their over-cautious delay. But when the swift Pequod, with a fresh leading wind, was herself in hot chase; how very kind of these tawny philanthropists to assist in speeding her on to her own chosen pursuit, —mere riding-whips and rowels to her, that they were. As with glass under arm, Ahab to-and-fro paced the deck; in his forward turn beholding the monsters he chased, and in the after one the bloodthirsty pirates chasing *him;* some such fancy as the above seemed his. And when he glanced upon the green walls of the watery defile in which the ship was then sailing, and bethought him that through that gate lay the route to his vengeance, and beheld, how that through that same gate he was now both chasing and being chased to his deadly end; and not only that, but a herd of remorseless wild pirates and inhuman atheistical devils were infernally cheering him on with their curses;—when all these conceits had passed through his brain, Ahab's brow was left gaunt and ribbed, like the black sand beach after some stormy tide has been gnawing it, without being able to drag the firm thing from its place.

But thoughts like these troubled very few of the reckless crew; and when, after steadily dropping and dropping the pirates astern, the Pequod at last shot by the vivid green Cockatoo Point on the Sumatra side, emerging at last upon the broad waters beyond; then, the harpooneers seemed more to grieve that the swift whales had been gaining upon the ship, than to rejoice that the ship had so victoriously gained upon the Malays. But still driving on in the wake of the whales, at length they seemed abating their speed; gradually the ship neared them; and the wind now dying away, word was passed to spring to the boats. But no sooner did the herd, by some presumed wonderful instinct of the Sperm Whale, become notified of the three keels that were after them,—though as yet a mile in their rear,—than they rallied again, and forming in close ranks and battalions, so that their spouts all looked like flashing lines of stacked bayonets, moved on with redoubled velocity.

Stripped to our shirts and drawers, we sprang to the white-ash, and after several hours' pulling were almost disposed to renounce the chase, when a general pausing commotion among the whales gave animating token that they were now at last under the influence of that strange perplexity of inert irresolution, which, when the fishermen perceive it in the whale, they say he is gallied. The compact martial columns in which they had been hitherto rapidly and steadily swimming, were now

broken up in one measureless rout; and like King Porus' elephants in the Indian battle with Alexander, they seemed going
mad with consternation.[21]   In all directions expanding in vast
irregular circles, and aimlessly swimming hither and thither, by
their short thick spoutings, they plainly betrayed their distrac-
tion of panic.   This was still more strangely evinced by those
of their number, who, completely paralysed as it were, helplessly floated like water-logged dismantled ships on the sea.
Had these leviathans been but a flock of simple sheep, pursued
over the pasture by three fierce wolves, they could not possibly
have evinced such excessive dismay.   But this occasional timidity is characteristic of almost all herding creatures.   Though
banding together in tens of thousands, the lion-maned buffaloes
of the West have fled before a solitary horseman.   Witness, too,
all human beings, how when herded together in the sheepfold
of a theatre's pit, they will, at the slightest alarm of fire, rush
helter-skelter for the outlets, crowding, trampling, jamming,
and remorselessly dashing each other to death.   Best, therefore,
withhold any amazement at the strangely gallied whales before
us, for there is no folly of the beasts of the earth which is not
infinitely outdone by the madness of men.

Though many of the whales, as has been said, were in violent
motion, yet it is to be observed that as a whole the herd neither
advanced nor retreated, but collectively remained in one place.
As is customary in those cases, the boats at once separated,
each making for some one lone whale on the outskirts of the
shoal.   In about three minutes' time, Queequeg's harpoon was
flung; the stricken fish darted blinding spray in our faces,
and then running away with us like light, steered straight for
the heart of the herd.   Though such a movement on the part
of the whale struck under such circumstances, is in no wise unprecedented; and indeed is almost always more or less anticipated; yet does it present one of the more perilous vicissitudes
of the fishery.   For as the swift monster drags you deeper and
deeper into the frantic shoal, you bid adieu to circumspect life
and only exist in a delirious throb.

As, blind and deaf, the whale plunged forward, as if by sheer power of speed to rid himself of the iron leech that had fastened to him; as we thus tore a white gash in the sea, on all sides menaced as we flew, by the crazed creatures to and fro rushing about us; our beset boat was like a ship mobbed by ice-isles in a tempest, and striving to steer through their complicated channels and straits, knowing not at what moment it may be locked in and crushed.

But not a bit daunted, Queequeg steered us manfully; now sheering off from this monster directly across our route in advance; now edging away from that, whose colossal flukes were suspended overhead, while all the time, Starbuck stood up in the bows, lance in hand, pricking out of our way whatever whales he could reach by short darts, for there was no time to make long ones. Nor were the oarsmen quite idle, though their wonted duty was now altogether dispensed with. They chiefly attended to the shouting part of the business. "Out of the way, Commodore!" cried one, to a great dromedary that of a sudden rose bodily to the surface, and for an instant threatened to swamp us. "Hard down with your tail, there!" cried a second to another, which, close to our gunwale, seemed calmly cooling himself with his own fan-like extremity.

All whaleboats carry certain curious contrivances, originally invented by the Nantucket Indians, called druggs. Two thick squares of wood of equal size are stoutly clenched together, so that they cross each other's grain at right angles; a line of considerable length is then attached to the middle of this block, and the other end of the line being looped, it can in a moment be fastened to a harpoon. It is chiefly among gallied whales that this drugg is used. For then, more whales are close round you than you can possibly chase at one time. But sperm whales are not every day encountered; while you may, then, you must kill all you can. And if you cannot kill them all at once, you must wing them, so that they can be afterwards killed at your leisure. Hence it is, that at times like these the drugg comes into requisition. Our boat was furnished with three of them. The first and second were successfully darted, and we saw the whales staggeringly running off, fettered by the enormous sidelong resistance of the towing drugg. They were cramped like malefactors with the chain and ball. But upon flinging the third, in the act of tossing overboard the clumsy wooden block, it caught under one of the seats of the boat, and in an instant tore it out and carried it away, dropping the oarsman in the boat's bottom as the seat slid from under him. On both sides the sea came in at the wounded planks, but we stuffed two or three drawers and shirts in, and so stopped the leaks for the time.

It had been next to impossible to dart these drugged-harpoons, were it not that as we advanced into the herd, our whale's way greatly diminished; moreover, that as we went still further and further from the circumference of commotion, the direful disorders seemed waning. So that when at last the jerking harpoon drew out, and the towing whale sideways vanished; then, with the tapering force of his parting momentum, we glided between two whales into the innermost heart of the shoal, as if from some mountain torrent we had slid into a serene valley lake. Here the storms in the roaring glens between the outermost whales, were heard but not felt. In this central expanse the sea presented that smooth satin-like surface, called a sleek, produced by the subtle moisture thrown off by the whale in his more quiet moods. Yes, we were now in that enchanted calm which they say lurks at the heart of every commotion. And still in the distracted distance we beheld the tumults of the outer concentric circles, and saw successive pods of whales, eight or ten in each, swiftly going round and round, like multiplied spans of horses in a ring; and so closely shoulder to shoulder, that a Titanic circus-rider might easily have over-arched the middle ones, and so have gone round on their backs. Owing to the density of the crowd of reposing whales, more immediately surrounding the embayed axis of the herd, no possible chance of escape was at present afforded us. We must watch for a breach in the living wall that hemmed us in; the wall that had only admitted us in order to shut us up. Keeping at the centre of the lake, we were occasionally visited by small tame cows and calves; the women and children of this routed host.

Now, inclusive of the occasional wide intervals between the revolving outer circles, and inclusive of the spaces between the various pods in any one of those circles, the entire area at this juncture, embraced by the whole multitude, must have contained at least two or three square miles. At any rate—though indeed such a test at such a time might be deceptive—spoutings might be discovered from our low boat that seemed playing up almost from the rim of the horizon. I mention this circumstance, because, as if the cows and calves had been purposely locked up in this innermost fold; and as if the wide extent of the herd had hitherto prevented them from learning the precise cause of its stopping; or, possibly, being so young, unsophisticated, and every way innocent and inexperienced; however it may have been, these smaller whales—now and then visiting our becalmed boat from the margin of the lake—evinced a wondrous fearlessness and confidence, or else a still becharmed panic which it was impossible not to marvel at. Like household dogs they came snuffling round us, right up to our gunwales, and touching them; till it almost seemed that some spell had suddenly domesticated them. Queequeg patted their foreheads; Starbuck scratched their backs with his lance; but fearful of the consequences, for the time refrained from darting it.

But far beneath this wondrous world upon the surface, another and still stranger world met our eyes as we gazed over the side. For, suspended in those watery vaults, floated the forms of the nursing mothers of the whales, and those that by their enormous girth seemed shortly to become mothers. The lake, as I have hinted, was to a considerable depth exceedingly transparent; and as human infants while suckling will calmly and fixedly gaze away from the breast, as if leading two different lives at the time; and while yet drawing mortal nourishment, be still spiritually feasting upon some unearthly reminiscence;—even so did the young of these whales seem looking up towards us, but not at us, as if we were but a bit of Gulf-weed in their new-born sight. Floating on their sides, the mothers also seemed quietly eyeing us. One of these little infants, that from certain queer tokens seemed hardly a day old, might have measured some fourteen feet in length, and some six feet in girth. He was a little frisky; though as yet his body seemed scarce yet recovered from that irksome position it had so lately occupied in the maternal reticule; where, tail to head, and all ready for the final spring, the unborn whale lies bent like a Tartar's bow. The delicate side-fins, and the palms of his flukes, still freshly retained the plaited crumpled appearance of a baby's ears newly arrived from foreign parts.

"Line! line!" cried Queequeg, looking over the gunwale; "him fast! him fast!—Who line him! Who struck?—Two whale; one big, one little!"

"What ails ye, man?" cried Starbuck.

"Look-e here," said Queequeg pointing down.

As when the stricken whale, that from the tub has reeled out hundreds of fathoms of rope; as, after deep sounding, he floats up again, and shows the slackened curling line buoyantly rising and spiralling towards the air; so now, Starbuck saw long coils of the umbilical cord of Madame Leviathan, by which the young cub seemed still tethered to its dam. Not seldom in the rapid vicissitudes of the chase, this natural line, with the maternal end loose, becomes entangled with the hempen one, so that the cub is thereby trapped. Some of the subtlest secrets of the seas seemed divulged to us in this enchanted pond. We saw young Leviathan amours in the deep.[22]

And thus, though surrounded by circle upon circle of consternations and affrights, did these inscrutable creatures at the centre freely and fearlessly indulge in all peaceful concernments; yea, serenely revelled in dalliance and delight. But even so, amid the tornadoed Atlantic of my being, do I myself still for ever centrally disport in mute calm; and while ponderous planets of unwaning woe revolve round me, deep down and deep inland there I still bathe me in eternal mildness of joy.

Meanwhile, as we thus lay entranced, the occasional sudden frantic spectacles in the distance evinced the activity of the other boats, still engaged in drugging the whales on the frontier of the host; or possibly carrying on the war within the first circle, where abundance of room and some convenient retreats were afforded them. But the sight of the enraged drugged whales now and then blindly darting to and fro across the circles, was nothing to what at last met our eyes. It is sometimes the custom when fast to a whale more than commonly powerful and alert, to seek to hamstring him, as it were, by sundering or maiming his gigantic tail-tendon. It is done by darting a short-handled cutting-spade, to which is attached a rope for hauling it back again. A whale wounded (as we afterwards learned) in this part, but not effectually, as it seemed, had broken away from the boat, carrying along with him half of the harpoon line; and in the extraordinary agony of the wound, he was now dashing among the revolving circles like the lone mounted desperado Arnold, at the battle of Saratoga, carrying dismay wherever he went.

But agonizing as was the wound of this whale, and an appalling spectacle enough, any way; yet the peculiar horror with which he seemed to inspire the rest of the herd, was owing to a cause which at first the intervening distance obscured from us. But at length we perceived that by one of the unimaginable accidents of the fishery, this whale had become entangled in the harpoon-line that he towed; he had also run away with the cutting-spade in him; and while the free end of the rope attached to that weapon, had permanently caught in the coils of the harpoon-line round his tail, the cutting-spade itself had worked loose from his flesh. So that tormented to madness, he was now churning through the water, violently flailing with his flexible tail, and tossing the keen spade about him, wounding and murdering his own comrades.

This terrific object seemed to recall the whole herd from their stationary fright. First, the whales forming the margin of our lake began to crowd a little, and tumble against each other, as if lifted by half spent billows from afar; then the lake itself began faintly to heave and swell; the submarine bridal-chambers and nurseries vanished; in more and more contracting orbits the whales in the more central circles began to swim in thickening clusters. Yes, the long calm was departing. A low advancing hum was soon heard; and then like to the tumultuous masses of block-ice when the great river Hudson breaks up in Spring, the entire host of whales came tumbling upon their inner centre, as if to pile themselves up in one common mountain. Instantly Starbuck and Queequeg changed places; Starbuck taking the stern.

"Oars! Oars!" he intensely whispered, seizing the helm— "gripe your oars, and clutch your souls, now! My God, men, stand by! Shove him off, you Queequeg—the whale there!— prick him!—hit him! Stand up—stand up, and stay so! Spring, men—pull, men; never mind their backs—scrape them!—scrape away!"

The boat was now all but jammed between two vast black bulks, leaving a narrow Dardanelles between their long lengths. But by desperate endeavor we at last shot into a temporary opening; then giving way rapidly, and at the same time earnestly watching for another outlet. After many similar hair-breadth escapes, we at last swiftly glided into what had just been one of the outer circles, but now crossed by random whales, all violently making for one centre. This lucky salvation was cheaply purchased by the loss of Queequeg's hat, who, while standing in the bows to prick the fugitive whales, had his hat taken clean from his head by the air-eddy made by the sudden tossing of a pair of broad flukes close by.

Riotous and disordered as the universal commotion now was, it soon resolved itself into what seemed a systematic movement; for having clumped together at last in one dense body, they then renewed their onward flight with augmented fleetness. Further pursuit was useless; but the boats still lingered in their wake to pick up what drugged whales might be dropped astern, and likewise to secure one which Flask had killed and waifed. The waif is a pennoned pole, two or three of which are carried by every boat; and which, when additional game is at hand, are inserted upright into the floating body of a dead whale, both to mark its place on the sea, and also as token of prior possession, should the boats of any other ship draw near.

The result of this lowering was somewhat illustrative of that sagacious saying in the Fishery,—the more whales the less fish. Of all the drugged whales only one was captured. The rest contrived to escape for the time, but only to be taken, as will hereafter be seen, by some other craft than the Pequod.

CHAPTER CXIX

The Candles

Warmest climes but nurse the cruelest fangs: the tiger of Bengal crouches in spiced groves of ceaseless verdure. Skies the most effulgent but basket the deadliest thunders: gorgeous Cuba knows tornadoes that never swept tame northern lands. So, too, it is, that in these resplendent Japanese seas the mariner encounters the direst of all storms, the Typhoon. It will sometimes burst from out that cloudless sky, like an exploding bomb upon a dazed and sleepy town.

Towards evening of that day,[23] the Pequod was torn of her canvas, and bare-poled was left to fight a Typhoon which had struck her directly ahead. When darkness came on, sky and sea roared and split with the thunder, and blazed with the lightning, that showed the disabled masts fluttering here and there with the rags which the first fury of the tempest had left for its after sport.

Holding by a shroud, Starbuck was standing on the quarter-deck; at every flash of the lightning glancing aloft, to see what additional disaster might have befallen the intricate hamper there; while Stubb and Flask were directing the men in the higher hoisting and firmer lashing of the boats. But all their pains seemed naught. Though lifted to the very top of the cranes, the windward quarter boat (Ahab's) did not escape. A great rolling sea, dashing high up against the reeling ship's high tetering side, stove in the boat's bottom at the stern, and left it again, all dripping through like a sieve.

"Bad work, bad work! Mr. Starbuck," said Stubb, regarding the wreck, "but the sea will have its way. Stubb, for one, can't fight it. You see, Mr. Starbuck, a wave has such a great long start before it leaps, all round the world it runs, and then comes the spring! But as for me, all the start I have to meet it, is just across the deck here. But never mind; it's all in fun: so the old song says";—(*sings.*)

> Oh! jolly is the gale,
> And a joker is the whale,
> A flourishin' his tail,—

Such a funny, sporty, gamy, jesty, joky, hoky-poky lad, is the Ocean, oh!

> The scud all a flyin',
> That's his flip only foamin';
> When he stirs in the spicin',—

Such a funny, sporty, gamy, jesty, joky, hoky-poky lad, is the Ocean, oh!

> Thunder splits the ships,
> But he only smacks his lips,
> A tastin' of this flip,—

Such a funny, sporty, gamy, jesty, joky, hoky-poky lad, is the Ocean, oh!

"Avast Stubb," cried Starbuck, "let the Typhoon sing, and strike his harp here in our rigging; but if thou art a brave man thou wilt hold thy peace."

"But I am not a brave man; never said I was a brave man; I am a coward; and I sing to keep up my spirits. And I tell you what it is, Mr. Starbuck, there's no way to stop my singing in this world but to cut my throat. And when that's done, ten to one I sing ye the doxology for a wind-up."

"Madman! look through my eyes if thou hast none of thine own."

"What! how can you see better of a dark night than anybody else, never mind how foolish?"

"Here!" cried Starbuck, seizing Stubb by the shoulder, and pointing his hand towards the weather bow, "markest thou not that the gale comes from the eastward, the very course Ahab is to run for Moby Dick? the very course he swung to this day noon? now mark his boat there; where is that stove? In the stern-sheets, man; where he is wont to stand—his standpoint is stove, man! Now jump overboard, and sing away, if thou must!"

"I don't half understand ye: what's in the wind?"

"Yes, yes, round the Cape of Good Hope is the shortest way to Nantucket," soliloquized Starbuck suddenly, heedless of Stubb's question. "The gale that now hammers at us to stave us, we can turn it into a fair wind that will drive us towards home. Yonder, to windward, all is blackness of doom; but to leeward, homeward—I see it lightens up there; but not with the lightning."

At that moment in one of the intervals of profound darkness, following the flashes, a voice was heard at his side; and almost at the same instant a volley of thunder peals rolled overhead.

"Who's there?"

"Old Thunder!" said Ahab, groping his way along the bulwarks to his pivot-hole; but suddenly finding his path made plain to him by elbowed lances of fire.

Now, as the lightning rod to a spire on shore is intended to carry off the perilous fluid into the soil; so the kindred rod which at sea some ships carry to each mast, is intended to conduct it into the water. But as this conductor must descend to considerable depth, that its end may avoid all contact with the hull; and as moreover, if kept constantly towing there, it would be liable to many mishaps, besides interfering not a little with some of the rigging, and more or less impeding the vessel's way in the water; because of all this, the lower parts of a ship's lightning-rods are not always overboard; but are generally made in long slender links, so as to be the more readily hauled up into the chains outside, or thrown down into the sea, as occasion may require.

"The rods! the rods!" cried Starbuck to the crew, suddenly admonished to vigilance by the vivid lightning that had just been darting flambeaux, to light Ahab to his post. "Are they overboard? drop them over, fore and aft. Quick!"

"Avast!" cried Ahab; "let's have fair play here, though we

be the weaker side. Yet I'll contribute to raise rods on the Himmalehs and Andes, that all the world may be secured; but out on privileges! Let them be, sir."

"Look aloft!" cried Starbuck. "The corpusants! the corpusants!"

All the yard-arms were tipped with a pallid fire; and touched at each tri-pointed lightning-rod-end with three tapering white flames, each of the three tall masts was silently burning in that sulphurous air, like three gigantic wax tapers before an altar.

"Blast the boat! let it go!" cried Stubb at this instant, as a swashing sea heaved up under his own little craft, so that its gunwale violently jammed his hand, as he was passing a lashing. "Blast it!"—but slipping backward on the deck, his uplifted eyes caught the flames; and immediately shifting his tone, he cried—"The corpusants have mercy on us all!"

To sailors, oaths are household words; they will swear in the trance of the calm, and in the teeth of the tempest; they will imprecate curses from the topsail-yard-arms, when most they teter over to a seething sea; but in all my voyagings, seldom have I heard a common oath when God's burning finger has been laid on the ship; when His "Mene, Mene, Tekel Upharsin" has been woven into the shrouds and the cordage.

While this pallidness was burning aloft, few words were heard from the enchanted crew; who in one thick cluster stood on the forecastle, all their eyes gleaming in that pale phosphorescence, like a far away constellation of stars. Relieved against the ghostly light, the gigantic jet negro, Daggoo, loomed up to thrice his real stature, and seemed the black cloud from which the thunder had come. The parted mouth of Tashtego revealed his shark-white teeth, which strangely gleamed as if they too had been tipped by corpusants; while lit up by the preternatural light, Queequeg's tattooing burned like Satanic blue flames on his body.

The tableau all waned at last with the pallidness aloft; and once more the Pequod and every soul on her decks were wrapped in a pall. A moment or two passed, when Starbuck, going forward, pushed against some one. It was Stubb. "What thinkest thou now, man; I heard thy cry; it was not the same in the song."

"No, no, it wasn't; I said the corpusants have mercy on us all; and I hope they will, still. But do they only have mercy on long faces?—have they no bowels for a laugh? And look ye, Mr. Starbuck—but it's too dark to look. Hear me, then: I take that mast-head flame we saw for a sign of good luck; for those masts are rooted in a hold that is going to be chock a' block with sperm-oil, d'ye see; and so, all that sperm will work up into the masts, like sap in a tree. Yes, our three masts will yet be as three spermaceti candles—that's the good promise we saw."

At that moment Starbuck caught sight of Stubb's face slowly beginning to glimmer into sight. Glancing upwards, he cried: "See! see!" and once more the high tapering flames were beheld with what seemed redoubled supernaturalness in their pallor.

"The corpusants have mercy on us all," cried Stubb, again.

At the base of the mainmast, full beneath the doubloon and the flame, the Parsee[24] was kneeling in Ahab's front, but with his head bowed away from him; while near by, from the arched and overhanging rigging, where they had just been engaged securing a spar, a number of the seamen, arrested by the glare, now cohered together, and hung pendulous, like a knot of numbed wasps from a drooping, orchard twig. In various enchanted attitudes, like the standing, or stepping, or running skeletons in Herculaneum, others remained rooted to the deck; but all their eyes upcast.

"Aye, aye, men!" cried Ahab. "Look up at it; mark it well; the white flame but lights the way to the White Whale! Hand me those main-mast links there; I would fain feel this pulse, and let mine beat against it; blood against fire! So."

Then turning—the last link held fast in his left hand, he put his foot upon the Parsee; and with fixed upward eye, and high-flung right arm, he stood erect before the lofty tri-pointed trinity of flames.

"Oh! thou clear spirit of clear fire, whom on these seas I as Persian once did worship, till in the sacramental act so burned by thee, that to this hour I bear the scar; I now know thee, thou clear spirit, and I now know that thy right worship is defiance. To neither love nor reverence wilt thou be kind; and e'en for hate thou canst but kill; and all are killed. No fearless fool now fronts thee. I own thy speechless, placeless power; but to the last gasp of my earthquake life will dispute its unconditional, unintegral mastery in me. In the midst of the personified impersonal, a personality stands here. Though but a point at best; whencesoe'er I came; wheresoe'er I go; yet while I earthly live, the queenly personality lives in me, and feels her royal rights. But war is pain, and hate is woe. Come in thy lowest form of love, and I will kneel and kiss thee; but at thy highest, come as mere supernal power; and though thou launchest navies of full-freighted worlds, there's that in here that still remains indifferent. Oh, thou clear spirit, of thy fire thou madest me, and like a true child of fire, I breathe it back to thee."

[Sudden, repeated flashes of lightning; the nine flames leap lengthwise to thrice their previous height; Ahab, with the rest, closes his eyes, his right hand pressed hard upon them.]

"I own thy speechless, placeless power; said I not so? Nor was it wrung from me; nor do I now drop these links. Thou canst blind; but I can then grope. Thou canst consume; but I can then be ashes. Take the homage of these poor eyes, and shutter-hands. I would not take it. The lightning flashes through my skull; mine eye-balls ache and ache; my whole beaten brain seems as beheaded, and rolling on some stunning ground. Oh, oh! Yet blindfold, yet will I talk to thee. Light though thou be, thou leapest out of darkness; but I am darkness leaping out of light, leaping out of thee! The javelins cease; open eyes; see, or not? There burn the flames! Oh, thou magnanimous! now I do glory in my genealogy. But thou art but my fiery father; my sweet mother, I know not. Oh, cruel! what hast thou done with her? There lies my puzzle; but thine is greater. Thou knowest not how came ye, hence callest thyself unbegotten; certainly knowest not thy beginning, hence callest thyself unbegun. I know that of me, which thou know-

est not of thyself, oh, thou omnipotent. There is some unsuf-
fusing thing beyond thee, thou clear spirit, to whom all thy
eternity is but time, all thy creativeness mechanical. Through
thee, thy flaming self, my scorched eyes do dimly see it. Oh,
thou foundling fire, thou hermit immemorial, thou too hast thy
incommunicable riddle, thy unparticipated grief. Here again
with haughty agony, I read my sire. Leap! leap up, and lick
the sky! I leap with thee; I burn with thee; would fain be welded
with thee; defyingly I worship thee!"

"The boat! the boat!" cried Starbuck, "look at thy boat, old
man!"

Ahab's harpoon, the one forged at Perth's fire, remained
firmly lashed in its conspicuous crotch, so that it projected beyond his whale-boat's bow; but the sea that had stove its bottom
had caused the loose leather sheath to drop off; and from the
keen steel barb there now came a levelled flame of pale, forked
fire. As the silent harpoon burned there like a serpent's tongue,
Starbuck grasped Ahab by the arm—"God, God is against thee,
old man; forbear! 'tis an ill voyage! ill begun, ill continued; let
me square the yards, while we may, old man, and make a fair
wind of it homewards, to go on a better voyage than this."

Overhearing Starbuck, the panic-stricken crew instantly ran
to the braces—though not a sail was left aloft. For the moment
all the aghast mate's thoughts seemed theirs; they raised a half
mutinous cry. But dashing the rattling lightning links to the
deck, and snatching the burning harpoon, Ahab waved it like
a torch among them; swearing to transfix with it the first sailor
that but cast loose a rope's end. Petrified by his aspect, and
still more shrinking from the fiery dart that he held, the men
fell back in dismay, and Ahab again spoke:—

"All your oaths to hunt the White Whale are as binding as
mine; and heart, soul, and body, lungs and life, old Ahab is
bound. And that ye may know to what tune this heart beats:
look ye here; thus I blow out the last fear!" And with one blast
of his breath he extinguished the flame.

As in the hurricane that sweeps the plain, men fly the neighborhood of some lone, gigantic elm, whose very height and

strength but render it so much the more unsafe, because so
much the more a mark for thunderbolts; so at those last words of
Ahab's many of the mariners did run from him in a terror of
dismay.

CHAPTER CXXVIII

The Pequod Meets the Rachel [25]

Next day, a large ship, the Rachel, was descried, bearing
directly down upon the Pequod, all her spars thickly clustering
with men. At the time the Pequod was making good speed
through the water; but as the broad-winged windward stranger
shot nigh to her, the boastful sails all fell together as blank
bladders that are burst, and all life fled from the smitten hull.

"Bad news; she brings bad news," muttered the old Manxman.
But ere her commander, who, with trumpet to mouth, stood up
in his boat; ere he could hopefully hail, Ahab's voice was heard.

"Hast seen the White Whale?"

"Aye, yesterday. Have ye seen a whale-boat adrift?"

Throttling his joy, Ahab negatively answered this unexpected
question; and would then have fain boarded the stranger, when
the stranger captain himself, having stopped his vessel's way,
was seen descending her side. A few keen pulls, and his boat-
hook soon clinched the Pequod's main-chains, and he sprang
to the deck. Immediately he was recognised by Ahab for a
Nantucketer he knew. But no formal salutation was exchanged.

"Where was he?—not killed!—not killed!" cried Ahab, closely
advancing. "How was it?"

It seemed that somewhat late on the afternoon of the day
previous, while three of the stranger's boats were engaged with
a shoal of whales, which had led them some four or five miles
from the ship; and while they were yet in swift chase to windward, the white hump and head of Moby Dick had suddenly
loomed up out of the blue water, not very far to leeward; whereupon, the fourth rigged boat—a reserved one—had been instantly lowered in chase. After a keen sail before the wind, this
fourth boat—the swiftest keeled of all—seemed to have succeeded in fastening—at least, as well as the man at the mast-head

could tell anything about it. In the distance he saw the diminished dotted boat; and then a swift gleam of bubbling white water; and after that nothing more; whence it was concluded that the stricken whale must have indefinitely run away with his pursuers, as often happens. There was some apprehension, but no positive alarm, as yet. The recall signals were placed in the rigging; darkness came on; and forced to pick up her three far to windward boats—ere going in quest of the fourth one in the precisely opposite direction—the ship had not only been necessitated to leave that boat to its fate till near midnight, but, for the time, to increase her distance from it. But the rest of her crew being at last safe aboard, she crowded all sail—stunsail on stunsail—after the missing boat; kindling a fire in her try-pots for a beacon; and every other man aloft on the look-out. But though when she had thus sailed a sufficient distance to gain the presumed place of the absent ones when last seen; though she then paused to lower her spare boats to pull all around her; and not finding anything, had again dashed on; again paused, and lowered her boats; and though she had thus continued doing till daylight; yet not the least glimpse of the missing keel had been seen.

The story told, the stranger Captain immediately went on to reveal his object in boarding the Pequod. He desired that ship to unite with his own in the search; by sailing over the sea some four or five miles apart, on parallel lines, and so sweeping a double horizon, as it were.

"I will wager something now," whispered Stubb to Flask, "that some one in that missing boat wore off that Captain's best coat; mayhap, his watch—he's so cursed anxious to get it back. Who ever heard of two pious whale-ships cruising after one missing whale-boat in the height of the whaling season? See, Flask, only see how pale he looks—pale in the very buttons of his eyes—look—it wasn't the coat—it must have been the—"

"My boy, my own boy is among them. For God's sake—I beg, I conjure"—here exclaimed the stranger Captain to Ahab, who thus far had but icily received his petition. "For eight-and-forty hours let me charter your ship—I will gladly pay for it, and roundly pay for it—if there be no other way—for eight-and-forty hours only—only that—you must, oh, you must, and you *shall* do this thing."

"His son!" cried Stubb, "oh, it's his son he's lost! I take back the coat and watch—what says Ahab? We must save that boy."

"He's drowned with the rest on 'em, last night," said the old Manx sailor standing behind them; "I heard; all of ye heard their spirits."

Now, as it shortly turned out, what made this incident of the Rachel's the more melancholy, was the circumstance, that not only was one of the Captain's sons among the number of the missing boat's crew; but among the number of the other boats' crews, at the same time, but on the other hand, separated from the ship during the dark vicissitudes of the chase, there had been still another son; as that for a time, the wretched father was plunged to the bottom of the cruelest perplexity; which was only solved for him by his chief mate's instinctively adopting the ordinary procedure of a whale-ship in such emergencies, that is, when placed between jeopardized but divided boats, always to pick up the majority first. But the captain, for some unknown constitutional reason, had refrained from mentioning all this, and not till forced to it by Ahab's iciness did he allude to his one yet missing boy; a little lad, but twelve years old, whose father with the earnest but unmisgiving hardihood of a Nantucketer's paternal love, had thus early sought to initiate him in the perils and wonders of a vocation almost immemorially the destiny of all his race. Nor does it unfrequently occur, that Nantucket captains will send a son of such tender age away from them, for a protracted three or four years' voyage in some other ship than their own; so that their first knowledge of a whaleman's career shall be unenervated by any chance display of a father's natural but untimely partiality, or undue apprehensiveness and concern.

Meantime, now the stranger was still beseeching his poor boon of Ahab; and Ahab still stood like an anvil, receiving every shock, but without the least quivering of his own.

"I will not go," said the stranger, "till you say *aye* to me. Do to me as you would have me do to you in the like case. For *you* too have a boy, Captain Ahab—though but a child, and nestling safely at home now—a child of your old age too— Yes, yes, you relent; I see it—run, run, men, now, and stand by to square in the yards."

"Avast," cried Ahab—"touch not a rope-yarn"; then in a voice that prolongingly moulded every word—"Captain Gardiner, I will not do it. Even now I lose time. Good bye, good bye. God bless ye, man, and may I forgive myself, but I must go. Mr. Starbuck, look at the binnacle watch, and in three minutes from this present instant warn off all strangers: then brace forward again, and let the ship sail as before."

Hurriedly turning, with averted face, he descended into his cabin, leaving the strange captain transfixed at this unconditional and utter rejection of his so earnest suit. But starting from his enchantment, Gardiner silently hurried to the side; more fell than stepped into his boat, and returned to his ship.

Soon the two ships diverged their wakes; and long as the strange vessel was in view, she was seen to yaw hither and thither at every dark spot, however small, on the sea. This way and that her yards were swung around; starboard and larboard, she continued to tack; now she beat against a head sea; and again it pushed her before it; while all the while, her masts and yards were thickly clustered with men, as three tall cherry trees, when the boys are cherrying among the boughs.

But by her still halting course and winding, woful way, you plainly saw that this ship that so wept with spray, still remained without comfort. She was Rachel, weeping for her children, because they were not.

CHAPTER CXXXII

The Symphony

It was a clear steel-blue day. The firmaments of air and sea were hardly separable in that all-pervading azure; only, the pensive air was transparently pure and soft, with a woman's look, and the robust and man-like sea heaved with long, strong, lingering swells, as Samson's chest in his sleep.

Hither, and thither, on high, glided the snow-white wings of small, unspeckled birds; these were the gentle thoughts of the feminine air; but to and fro in the deeps, far down in the bottomless blue, rushed mighty leviathans, sword-fish, and sharks; and these were the strong, troubled, murderous thinkings of the masculine sea.

But though thus contrasting within, the contrast was only in shades and shadows without; those two seemed one; it was only the sex, as it were, that distinguished them.

Aloft, like a royal czar and king, the sun seemed giving this gentle air to this bold and rolling sea; even as bride to groom. And at the girdling line of the horizon, a soft and tremulous motion—most seen here at the equator—denoted the fond, throbbing trust, the loving alarms, with which the poor bride gave her bosom away.

Tied up and twisted; gnarled and knotted with wrinkles; haggardly firm and unyielding; his eyes glowing like coals, that still glow in the ashes of ruin; untottering Ahab stood forth in the clearness of the morn; lifting his splintered helmet of a brow to the fair girl's forehead of heaven.

Oh, immortal infancy, and innocency of the azure! Invisible winged creatures that frolic all round us! Sweet childhood of air and sky! how oblivious were ye of old Ahab's close-coiled woe! But so have I seen little Miriam and Martha, laughing-eyed elves, heedlessly gambol around their old sire; sporting with the circle of singed locks which grew on the marge of that burnt-out crater of his brain.

Slowly crossing the deck from the scuttle, Ahab leaned over the side, and watched how his shadow in the water sank and sank to his gaze, the more and the more that he strove to pierce the profundity. But the lovely aromas in that enchanted air did at last seem to dispel, for a moment, the cankerous thing in his soul. That glad, happy air, that winsome sky, did at last stroke and caress him; the step-mother world, so long cruel—forbidding—now threw affectionate arms round his stubborn neck, and did seem to joyously sob over him, as if over one, that however wilful and erring, she could yet find it in her heart to save and to bless. From beneath his slouched hat Ahab dropped a tear into the sea; nor did all the Pacific contain such wealth as that one wee drop.

Starbuck saw the old man; saw him, how he heavily leaned over the side; and he seemed to hear in his own true heart the measureless sobbing that stole out of the centre of the serenity around. Careful not to touch him, or be noticed by him, he yet drew near to him, and stood there.

Ahab turned.

"Starbuck!"

"Sir."

"Oh, Starbuck! it is a mild, mild wind, and a mild looking sky. On such a day—very much such a sweetness as this—I struck my first whale—a boy-harpooneer of eighteen! Forty—forty—forty years ago!—ago! Forty years of continual whaling! forty years of privation, and peril, and storm-time! forty years on the pitiless sea! for forty years has Ahab forsaken the peaceful land, for forty years to make war on the horrors of the deep! Aye and yes, Starbuck, out of those forty years I have not spent three ashore. When I think of this life I have led; the desolation of solitude it has been; the masoned, walled-town of a Captain's exclusiveness, which admits but small entrance to any sympathy from the green country without—oh, weariness! heaviness! Guinea-coast slavery of solitary command!—when I think of all this; only half-suspected, not so keenly known to me before—and how for forty years I have fed upon dry salted fare—fit emblem of the dry nourishment of my soul!—when the poorest landsman has had fresh fruit to his daily hand, and broken the world's fresh bread to my mouldy crusts—away, whole oceans away, from that young girl-wife I wedded past fifty, and sailed for Cape Horn the next day, leaving but one dent in my marriage pillow—wife? wife?—rather a widow with her husband alive! Aye, I widowed that poor girl when I married her, Starbuck; and then, the madness, the frenzy, the boiling blood and the smoking brow, with which, for a thousand lowerings old Ahab has furiously, foamingly chased his prey—more a demon than a man!—aye, aye! what a forty years' fool—fool—old fool, has old Ahab been! Why this strife of the chase? why weary, and palsy the arm at the oar, and the iron, and the lance? how the richer or better is Ahab now? Behold. Oh, Starbuck! is it not hard, that with this weary load I bear, one poor leg should have been snatched from under me? Here, brush this old hair aside; it blinds me, that I seem to weep. Locks so grey did never grow but from out some ashes! But do I look very old, so very, very old, Starbuck? I feel deadly faint, bowed, and humped, as though I were Adam, staggering beneath the piled centuries since Paradise. God! God! God!—crack my heart!—stave my brain!—mockery! mockery! bitter, biting mockery of grey hairs, have I lived enough joy to wear ye; and seem and feel thus intolerably old? Close! stand close to me, Starbuck; let me look into a human eye; it is better than to gaze into sea or sky; better than to gaze upon God. By the green land; by the bright hearth-stone! this is the magic glass, man; I see my wife and my child in thine eye. No, no; stay on board, on board!—lower not when I do; when branded Ahab gives chase to Moby Dick. That hazard shall not be thine. No, no! not with the far away home I see in that eye!"

"Oh, my Captain! my Captain! noble soul! grand old heart, after all! why should any one give chase to that hated fish! Away with me! let us fly these deadly waters! let us home! Wife and child, too, are Starbuck's—wife and child of his brotherly, sisterly, play-fellow youth; even as thine, sir, are the wife and child of thy loving, longing, paternal old age! Away! let us away!—this instant let me alter the course! How cheerily, how hilariously, O my Captain, would we bowl on our way to see old Nantucket again! I think, sir, they have some such mild blue days, even as this, in Nantucket."

"They have, they have. I have seen them—some summer days in the morning. About this time—yes, it is his noon nap now—the boy vivaciously wakes; sits up in bed; and his mother tells him of me, of cannibal old me; how I am abroad upon the deep, but will yet come back to dance him again."

"'Tis my Mary, my Mary herself! She promised that my boy, every morning, should be carried to the hill to catch the first glimpse of his father's sail! Yes, yes! no more! it is done! we head for Nantucket! Come, my Captain, study out the course, and let us away! See, see! the boy's face from the window! the boy's hand on the hill!"

But Ahab's glance was averted; like a blighted fruit tree he shook, and cast his last, cindered apple to the soil.

"What is it, what nameless, inscrutable, unearthly thing is it; what cozening, hidden lord and master, and cruel, remorseless emperor commands me; that against all natural lovings and longings, I so keep pushing, and crowding, and jamming myself on all the time; recklessly making me ready to do what in my own proper, natural heart, I durst not so much as dare? Is Ahab, Ahab? Is it I, God, or who, that lifts this arm? But if the great sun move not of himself; but is as an errand-boy in heaven; nor one single star can revolve, but by some invisible power; how then can this one small heart beat; this one small brain think thoughts; unless God does that beating, does that thinking, does that living, and not I. By heaven, man, we are turned round and round in this world, like yonder windlass, and Fate is the handspike. And all the time, lo! that smiling sky, and this unsounded sea! Look! see yon Albicore! who put it into him to chase and fang that flying-fish? Where do murderers go, man! Who's to doom, when the judge himself is dragged to the bar? But it is a mild, mild wind, and a mild looking sky; and the air smells now, as if it blew from a far-away meadow; they have been making hay somewhere under the slopes of the Andes, Starbuck, and the mowers are sleeping among the new-mown hay. Sleeping? Aye, toil we how we may, we all sleep at last on the field. Sleep? Aye, and rust amid greenness; as last year's scythes flung down, and left in the half-cut swaths—Starbuck!"

But blanched to a corpse's hue with despair, the Mate had stolen away.

Ahab crossed the deck to gaze over on the other side; but started at two reflected, fixed eyes in the water there. Fedallah was motionlessly leaning over the same rail.

CHAPTER CXXXIII

The Chase—First Day

That night, in the mid-watch, when the old man—as his wont at intervals—stepped forth from the scuttle in which he leaned, and went to his pivot-hole, he suddenly thrust out his face fiercely, snuffing up the sea air as a sagacious ship's dog will, in drawing nigh to some barbarous isle. He declared that a whale must be near. Soon that peculiar odor, sometimes to a great distance given forth by the living sperm whale, was palpable to all the watch; nor was any mariner surprised when, after inspecting the compass, and then the dog-vane, and then ascertaining the precise bearing of the odor as nearly as possible, Ahab rapidly ordered the ship's course to be slightly altered, and the sail to be shortened.

The acute policy dictating these movements was sufficiently vindicated at daybreak, by the sight of a long sleek on the sea directly and lengthwise ahead, smooth as oil, and resembling in the pleated watery wrinkles bordering it, the polished metallic-like marks of some swift tide-rip, at the mouth of a deep, rapid stream.

"Man the mast-heads! Call all hands!"

Thundering with the butts of three clubbed handspikes on the forecastle deck, Daggoo roused the sleepers with such judgment claps that they seemed to exhale from the scuttle, so instantaneously did they appear with their clothes in their hands.

"What d'ye see?" cried Ahab, flattening his face to the sky.

"Nothing, nothing, sir!" was the sound hailing down in reply.

"T'gallant sails!—stunsails! alow and aloft, and on both sides!"

All sail being set, he now cast loose the life-line, reserved for swaying him to the main royal-mast head; and in a few moments they were hoisting him thither, when, while but two thirds of the way aloft, and while peering ahead through the horizontal vacancy between the main-top-sail and top-gallant-sail, he raised a gull-like cry in the air, "There she blows!—there she blows! A hump like a snow-hill! It is Moby Dick!"

Fired by the cry which seemed simultaneously taken up by the three look-outs, the men on deck rushed to the rigging to behold the famous whale they had so long been pursuing. Ahab had now gained his final perch, some feet above the other look-outs, Tashtego standing just beneath him on the cap of the top-gallant-mast, so that the Indian's head was almost on a level with Ahab's heel. From this height the whale was now seen some mile or so ahead, at every roll of the sea revealing his high sparkling hump, and regularly jetting his silent spout into the air. To the credulous mariners it seemed the same silent spout they had so long ago beheld in the moonlit Atlantic and Indian Oceans.

"And did none of ye see it before?" cried Ahab, hailing the perched men all around him.

"I saw him almost that same instant, sir, that Captain Ahab did, and I cried out," said Tashtego.

"Not the same instant; not the same—no, the doubloon is mine, Fate reserved the doubloon for me. *I* only; none of ye could have raised the White Whale first. There she blows! there she blows!—there she blows! There again!—there again!" he cried, in long-drawn, lingering, methodic tones, attuned to the gradual prolongings of the whale's visible jets. "He's going to sound! In stunsails! Down top-gallant-sails! Stand by three boats. Mr. Starbuck, remember, stay on board, and keep the ship. Helm there! Luff, luff a point! So; steady, man, steady! There go flukes! No, no; only black water! All ready the boats there? Stand by, stand by! Lower me, Mr. Starbuck; lower, lower,—quick, quicker!" and he slid through the air to the deck.

"He is heading straight to leeward, sir," cried Stubb, "right away from us; cannot have seen the ship yet."

"Be dumb, man! Stand by the braces! Hard down the helm! —brace up! Shiver her!—shiver her!—So; well that! Boats, boats!"

Soon all the boats but Starbuck's were dropped; all the boat-sails set—all the paddles plying; with rippling swiftness, shooting to leeward; and Ahab heading the onset. A pale, death-glimmer lit up Fedallah's sunken eyes; a hideous motion gnawed his mouth.

Like noiseless nautilus shells, their light prows sped through the sea; but only slowly they neared the foe. As they neared him, the ocean grew still more smooth; seemed drawing a carpet over its waves; seemed a noon-meadow, so serenely it spread. At length the breathless hunter came so nigh his seemingly unsuspecting prey, that his entire dazzling hump was distinctly visible, sliding along the sea as if an isolated thing, and continually set in a revolving ring of finest, fleecy, greenish foam. He saw the vast, involved wrinkles of the slightly projecting head beyond. Before it, far out on the soft Turkish-rugged waters, went the glistening white shadow from his broad, milky forehead, a musical rippling playfully accompanying the shade; and behind, the blue waters interchangeably flowed over into the moving valley of his steady wake; and on either hand bright bubbles arose and danced by his side. But these were broken again by the light toes of hundreds of gay fowl softly feathering the sea, alternate with their fitful flight; and like to some flag-staff rising from the painted hull of an argosy, the tall but shattered pole of a recent lance projected from the white whale's back; and at intervals one of the cloud of soft-toed fowls hovering, and to and fro skimming like a canopy over the fish, silently perched and rocked on this pole, the long tail feathers streaming like pennons.

A gentle joyousness—a mighty mildness of repose in swiftness, invested the gliding whale. Not the white bull Jupiter swimming away with ravished Europa clinging to his graceful horns; his lovely, leering eyes sideways intent upon the maid; with smooth bewitching fleetness, rippling straight for the nuptial bower in Crete; not Jove, not that great majesty Supreme!

did surpass the glorified White Whale as he so divinely swam.

On each soft side—coincident with the parted swell, that but once leaving him, then flowed so wide away—on each bright side, the whale shed off enticings. No wonder there had been some among the hunters who namelessly transported and allured by all this serenity, had ventured to assail it; but had fatally found that quietude but the vesture of tornadoes. Yet calm, enticing calm, oh, whale! thou glidest on, to all who for the first time eye thee, no matter how many in that same way thou may'st have bejuggled and destroyed before.

And thus, through the serene tranquillities of the tropical sea, among waves whose hand-clappings were suspended by exceeding rapture, Moby Dick moved on, still withholding from sight the full terrors of his submerged trunk, entirely hiding the wrenched hideousness of his jaw. But soon the fore part of him slowly rose from the water; for an instant his whole marbleized body formed a high arch, like Virginia's Natural Bridge, and warningly waving his bannered flukes in the air, the grand god revealed himself, sounded, and went out of sight. Hoveringly halting, and dipping on the wing, the white sea-fowls longingly lingered over the agitated pool that he left.

With oars apeak, and paddles down, the sheets of their sails adrift, the three boats now stilly floated, awaiting Moby Dick's reappearance.

"An hour," said Ahab, standing rooted in his boat's stern; and he gazed beyond the whale's place, towards the dim blue spaces and wide wooing vacancies to leeward. It was only an instant; for again his eyes seemed whirling round in his head as he swept the watery circle. The breeze now freshened; the sea began to swell.

"The birds!—the birds!" cried Tashtego.

In long Indian file, as when herons take wing, the white birds were now all flying towards Ahab's boat; and when within a few yards began fluttering over the water there, wheeling round and round, with joyous, expectant cries. Their vision was keener than man's; Ahab could discover no sign in the sea.

But suddenly as he peered down and down into its depths, he profoundly saw a white living spot no bigger than a white weasel, with wonderful celerity uprising, and magnifying as it rose, till it turned, and then there were plainly revealed two long crooked rows of white, glistening teeth, floating up from the undiscoverable bottom. It was Moby Dick's open mouth and scrolled jaw; his vast, shadowed bulk still half blending with the blue of the sea. The glittering mouth yawned beneath the boat like an open-doored marble tomb; and giving one sidelong sweep with his steering oar, Ahab whirled the craft aside from this tremendous apparition. Then, calling upon Fedallah to change places with him, went forward to the bows, and seizing Perth's harpoon, commanded his crew to grasp their oars and stand by to stern.

Now, by reason of this timely spinning round the boat upon its axis, its bow, by anticipation, was made to face the whale's head while yet under water. But as if perceiving this stratagem, Moby Dick, with that malicious intelligence ascribed to him, sidelingly transplanted himself, as it were, in an instant, shooting his pleated head lengthwise beneath the boat.

Through and through; through every plank and each rib, it thrilled for an instant, the whale obliquely lying on his back, in the manner of a biting shark, slowly and feelingly taking its bows full within his mouth, so that the long, narrow, scrolled lower jaw curled high up into the open air, and one of the teeth caught in a row-lock. The bluish pearl-white of the inside of the jaw was within six inches of Ahab's head, and reached higher than that. In this attitude the White Whale now shook the slight cedar as a mildly cruel cat her mouse. With un-astonished eyes Fedallah gazed, and crossed his arms; but the tiger-yellow crew were tumbling over each other's heads to gain the uttermost stern.

And now, while both elastic gunwales were springing in and out, as the whale dallied with the doomed craft in this devilish way; and from his body being submerged beneath the boat, he could not be darted at from the bows, for the bows were almost inside of him, as it were; and while the other boats involuntarily paused, as before a quick crisis impossible to withstand, then it was that monomaniac Ahab, furious with this tantalizing vicinity of his foe, which placed him all alive and helpless in the very jaws he hated; frenzied with all this, he seized the long bone with his naked hands, and wildly strove to wrench it from its gripe. As now he thus vainly strove, the jaw slipped from him; the frail gunwales bent in, collapsed, and snapped, as both jaws, like an enormous shears, sliding further aft, bit the craft completely in twain, and locked themselves fast again in the sea, midway between the two floating wrecks. These floated aside, the broken ends drooping, the crew at the stern-wreck clinging to the gunwales, and striving to hold fast to the oars to lash them across.

At that preluding moment, ere the boat was yet snapped, Ahab, the first to perceive the whale's intent, by the crafty upraising of his head, a movement that loosed his hold for the time; at that moment his hand had made one final effort to push the boat out of the bite. But only slipping further into the whale's mouth, and tilting over sideways as it slipped, the boat had shaken off his hold on the jaw; spilled him out of it, as he leaned to the push; and so he fell flat-faced upon the sea.

Ripplingly withdrawing from his prey, Moby Dick now lay at a little distance, vertically thrusting his oblong white head up and down in the billows; and at the same time slowly revolving his whole spindled body; so that when his vast wrinkled forehead rose—some twenty or more feet out of the water—the now rising swells, with all their confluent waves, dazzlingly broke against it; vindictively tossing their shivered spray still higher into the air.[26] So, in a gale, the but half baffled Channel billows only recoil from the base of the Eddystone, triumphantly to overleap its summit with their scud.

But soon resuming his horizontal attitude, Moby Dick swam swiftly round and round the wrecked crew; sideways churning the water in his vengeful wake, as if lashing himself up to still another and more deadly assault. The sight of the splintered boat seemed to madden him, as the blood of grapes and mulberries cast before Antiochus's elephants in the book of Maccabees.[27] Meanwhile Ahab half smothered in the foam of the whale's insolent tail, and too much of a cripple to swim,— though he could still keep afloat, even in the heart of such a whirlpool as that; helpless Ahab's head was seen, like a tossed bubble which the least chance shock might burst. From the boat's fragmentary stern, Fedallah incuriously and mildly eyed him; the clinging crew, at the other drifting end, could not succor him; more than enough was it for them to look to themselves. For so revolvingly appalling was the White Whale's aspect, and so planetarily swift the ever-contracting circles he made, that he seemed horizontally swooping upon them. And though the other boats, unharmed, still hovered hard by; still they dared not pull into the eddy to strike, lest that should be the signal for the instant destruction of the jeopardized castaways, Ahab and all; nor in that case could they themselves hope to escape. With straining eyes, then, they remained on the outer edge of the direful zone, whose centre had now become the old man's head.

Meantime, from the beginning all this had been descried from the ship's mast heads; and squaring her yards, she had borne down upon the scene; and was now so nigh, that Ahab in the water hailed her;—"Sail on the"—but that moment a breaking sea dashed on him from Moby Dick, and whelmed him for the time. But struggling out of it again, and chancing to rise on a towering crest, he shouted,—"Sail on the whale!—Drive him off!"

The Pequod's prows were pointed; and breaking up the charmed circle, she effectually parted the white whale from his victim. As he sullenly swam off, the boats flew to the rescue.

Dragged into Stubb's boat with blood-shot, blinded eyes, the white brine caking in his wrinkles; the long tension of Ahab's bodily strength did crack, and helplessly he yielded to his body's doom: for a time, lying all crushed in the bottom of Stubb's boat, like one trodden under foot of herds of elephants. Far inland, nameless wails came from him, as desolate sounds from out ravines.

But this intensity of his physical prostration did but so much the more abbreviate it. In an instant's compass, great hearts sometimes condense to one deep pang, the sum total of those shallow pains kindly diffused through feebler men's whole lives. And so, such hearts, though summary in each one suffering; still, if the gods decree it, in their life-time aggregate a whole age of woe, wholly made up of instantaneous intensities; for even in their pointless centres, those noble natures contain the entire circumferences of inferior souls.

"The harpoon," said Ahab, half way rising, and draggingly leaning on one bended arm—"is it safe?"

"Aye, sir, for it was not darted; this is it," said Stubb, showing it.

"Lay it before me;—any missing men?"

"One, two, three, four, five;—there were five oars, sir, and here are five men."

"That's good.—Help me, man; I wish to stand. So, so, I see him! there! there! going to leeward still; what a leaping spout!— Hands off from me! The eternal sap runs up in Ahab's bones again! Set the sail; out oars; the helm!"

It is often the case that when a boat is stove, its crew, being picked up by another boat, help to work that second boat; and the chase is thus continued with what is called double-banked oars. It was thus now. But the added power of the boat did not equal the added power of the whale, for he seemed to have treble-banked his every fin; swimming with a velocity which plainly showed, that if now, under these circumstances, pushed on, the chase would prove an indefinitely prolonged, if not a hopeless one; nor could any crew endure for so long a period, such an unintermitted, intense straining at the oar; a thing barely tolerable only in some one brief vicissitude. The ship itself, then, as it sometimes happens, offered the most promising intermediate means of overtaking the chase. Accordingly, the boats now made for her, and were soon swayed up to their cranes— the two parts of the wrecked boat having been previously secured by her—and then hoisting everything to her side, and stacking her canvas high up, and sideways outstretching it with stun-sails, like the double-jointed wings of an albatross; the

Pequod bore down in the leeward wake of Moby Dick. At the well known, methodic intervals, the whale's glittering spout was regularly announced from the manned mast-heads; and when he would be reported as just gone down, Ahab would take the time, and then pacing the deck, binnacle-watch in hand, so soon as the last second of the allotted hour expired, his voice was heard.—"Whose is the doubloon now? D'ye see him?" and if the reply was No, sir! straightway he commanded them to lift him to his perch. In this way the day wore on; Ahab, now aloft and motionless; anon, unrestingly pacing the planks.

As he was thus walking, uttering no sound, except to hail the men aloft, or to bid them hoist a sail still higher, or to spread one to a still greater breadth—thus to and fro pacing, beneath his slouched hat, at every turn he passed his own wrecked boat, which had been dropped upon the quarter-deck, and lay there reversed; broken bow to shattered stern. At last he paused before it; and as in an already over-clouded sky fresh troops of clouds will sometimes sail across, so over the old man's face there now stole some such added gloom as this.

Stubb saw him pause; and perhaps intending, not vainly, though, to evince his own unabated fortitude, and thus keep up a valiant place in his Captain's mind, he advanced, and eyeing the wreck exclaimed—"The thistle the ass refused; it pricked his mouth too keenly, sir, ha! ha!"

"What soulless thing is this that laughs before a wreck? Man, man! did I not know thee brave as fearless fire (and as mechanical) I could swear thou wert a poltroon. Groan nor laugh should be heard before a wreck."

"Aye, sir," said Starbuck drawing near, "'tis a solemn sight; an omen, and an ill one."

"Omen? omen?—the dictionary! If the gods think to speak outright to man, they will honorably speak outright; not shake their heads, and give an old wives' darkling hint.—Begone! Ye two are the opposite poles of one thing; Starbuck is Stubb reversed, and Stubb is Starbuck; and ye two are all mankind; and Ahab stands alone among the millions of the peopled earth, nor gods nor men his neighbors! Cold, cold—I shiver!—How now? Aloft there! D'ye see him? Sing out for every spout, though he spout ten times a second!"

The day was nearly done; only the hem of his golden robe was rustling. Soon it was almost dark, but the look-out men still remained unset.

"Can't see the spout now, sir;—too dark"—cried a voice from the air.

"How heading when last seen?"

"As before, sir,—straight to leeward."

"Good! he will travel slower now 'tis night. Down royals and top-gallant stun-sails, Mr. Starbuck. We must not run over him before morning; he's making a passage now, and may heave-to a while. Helm there! keep her full before the wind! —Aloft! come down!—Mr. Stubb, send a fresh hand to the fore-mast head, and see it manned till morning."—Then advancing towards the doubloon in the main-mast—"Men, this gold is mine, for I earned it; but I shall let it abide here till the White Whale is dead; and then, whosoever of ye first raises him, upon the day he shall be killed, this gold is that man's; and if on that day I shall again raise him, then, ten times its sum shall be divided among all of ye! Away now!—the deck is thine, sir."

And so saying, he placed himself half way within the scuttle, and slouching his hat, stood there till dawn, except when at intervals rousing himself to see how the night wore on.

CHAPTER CXXXIV

The Chase—Second Day

At day-break, the three mast-heads were punctually manned afresh.

"D'ye see him?" cried Ahab, after allowing a little space for the light to spread.

"See nothing, sir."

"Turn up all hands and make sail! he travels faster than I

thought for;—the top-gallant sails!—aye, they should have been kept on her all night. But no matter—'tis but resting for the rush."

Here be it said, that this pertinacious pursuit of one particular whale, continued through day into night, and through night into day, is a thing by no means unprecedented in the South sea fishery. For such is the wonderful skill, prescience of experience, and invincible confidence acquired by some great natural geniuses among the Nantucket commanders; that from the simple observation of a whale when last descried, they will, under certain given circumstances, pretty accurately foretell both the direction in which he will continue to swim for a time, while out of sight, as well as his probable rate of progression during that period. And, in these cases, somewhat as a pilot, when about losing sight of a coast, whose general trending he well knows, and which he desires shortly to return to again, but at some further point; like as this pilot stands by his compass, and takes the precise bearing of the cape at present visible, in order the more certainly to hit aright the remote, unseen headland, eventually to be visited: so does the fisherman, at his compass, with the whale; for after being chased, and diligently marked, through several hours of daylight, then, when night obscures the fish, the creature's future wake through the darkness is almost as established to the sagacious mind of the hunter, as the pilot's coast is to him. So that to this hunter's wondrous skill, the proverbial evanescence of a thing writ in water, a wake, is to all desired purposes well nigh as reliable as the steadfast land. And as the mighty iron Leviathan of the modern railway is so familiarly known in its every pace, that, with watches in their hands, men time his rate as doctors that of a baby's pulse; and lightly say of it, the up train or the down train will reach such or such a spot, at such or such an hour; even so, almost, there are occasions when these Nantucketers time that other Leviathan of the deep, according to the observed humor of his speed; and say to themselves, so many hours hence this whale will have gone two hundred miles, will have about reached this or that degree of latitude or longitude. But to render this acuteness at all successful in the end, the wind and the sea must be the whaleman's allies; for of what present avail to the becalmed or windbound mariner is the skill that assures him he is exactly ninety-three leagues and a quarter from his port? Inferable from these statements, are many collateral subtile matters touching the chase of whales.

The ship tore on; leaving such a furrow in the sea as when a cannon-ball, missent, becomes a plough-share and turns up the level field.

"By salt and hemp!" cried Stubb, "but this swift motion of the deck creeps up one's legs and tingles at the heart. This ship and I are two brave fellows!—Ha! ha! Some one take me up, and launch me, spine-wise, on the sea,—for by live-oaks! my spine's a keel. Ha, ha! we go the gait that leaves no dust behind!"

"There she blows—she blows!—she blows!—right ahead!" was now the mast-head cry.

"Aye, aye!" cried Stubb, "I knew it—ye can't escape—blow on and split your spout, O whale! the mad fiend himself is after ye! blow your trump—blister your lungs!—Ahab will dam off your blood, as a miller shuts his water-gate upon the stream!"

And Stubb did but speak out for well nigh all that crew. The frenzies of the chase had by this time worked them bubblingly up, like old wine worked anew. Whatever pale fears and forebodings some of them might have felt before; these were not only now kept out of sight through the growing awe of Ahab, but they were broken up, and on all sides routed, as timid prairie hares that scatter before the bounding bison. The hand of Fate had snatched all their souls; and by the stirring perils of the previous day; the rack of the past night's suspense; the fixed, unfearing, blind, reckless way in which their wild craft went plunging towards its flying mark; by all these things, their hearts were bowled along. The wind that made great bellies of their sails, and rushed the vessel on by arms invisible as irresistible; this seemed the symbol of that unseen agency which so enslaved them to the race.

They were one man, not thirty. For as the one ship that held

them all; though it was put together of all contrasting things—
oak, and maple, and pine wood; iron, and pitch, and hemp—
yet all these ran into each other in the one concrete hull, which
shot on its way, both balanced and directed by the long central
keel; even so, all the individualities of the crew, this man's
valor, that man's fear; guilt and guiltiness, all varieties were
welded into oneness, and were all directed to that fatal goal
which Ahab their one lord and keel did point to.

The rigging lived. The mast-heads, like the tops of tall palms,
were outspreadingly tufted with arms and legs. Clinging to a
spar with one hand, some reached forth the other with impatient
wavings; others, shading their eyes from the vivid sunlight, sat
far out on the rocking yards; all the spars in full bearing of
mortals, ready and ripe for their fate. Ah! how they still strove
through that infinite blueness to seek out the thing that might
destroy them!

"Why sing ye not out for him, if ye see him?" cried Ahab,
when, after the lapse of some minutes since the first cry, no
more had been heard. "Sway me up, men; ye have been
deceived; not Moby Dick casts one odd jet that way, and then
disappears."

It was even so; in their headlong eagerness, the men had mistaken some other thing for the whale-spout, as the event itself
soon proved; for hardly had Ahab reached his perch; hardly
was the rope belayed to its pin on deck, when he struck the
key-note to an orchestra, that made the air vibrate as with the
combined discharges of rifles. The triumphant halloo of thirty
buckskin lungs was heard, as—much nearer to the ship than
the place of the imaginary jet, less than a mile ahead—Moby
Dick bodily burst into view! For not by any calm and indolent
spoutings; not by the peaceable gush of that mystic fountain
in his head, did the White Whale now reveal his vicinity; but
by the far more wondrous phenomenon of breaching. Rising
with his utmost velocity from the furthest depths, the Sperm
Whale thus booms his entire bulk into the pure element of air,
and piling up a mountain of dazzling foam, shows his place to
the distance of seven miles and more. In those moments, the

torn, enraged waves he shakes off, seem his mane; in some cases, this breaching is his act of defiance.

"There she breaches! there she breaches!" was the cry, as in his immeasurable bravadoes the White Whale tossed himself salmon-like to Heaven. So suddenly seen in the blue plain of the sea, and relieved against the still bluer margin of the sky, the spray that he raised, for the moment, intolerably glittered and glared like a glacier; and stood there gradually fading and fading away from its first sparkling intensity, to the dim mistiness of an advancing shower in a vale.

"Aye, breach your last to the sun, Moby Dick!" cried Ahab, "thy hour and thy harpoon are at hand!—Down! down all of ye, but one man at the fore. The boats!—stand by!"

Unmindful of the tedious rope-ladders of the shrouds, the men, like shooting stars, slid to the deck, by the isolated backstays and halyards; while Ahab, less dartingly, but still rapidly was dropped from his perch.

"Lower away," he cried, so soon as he had reached his boat—a spare one, rigged the afternoon previous. "Mr. Starbuck, the ship is thine—keep away from the boats, but keep near them. Lower, all!"

As if to strike a quick terror into them, by this time being the first assailant himself, Moby Dick had turned, and was now coming for the three crews. Ahab's boat was central; and cheering his men, he told them he would take the whale head-and-head,—that is, pull straight up to his forehead,—a not uncommon thing; for when within a certain limit, such a course excludes the coming onset from the whale's sidelong vision. But ere that close limit was gained, and while yet all three boats were plain as the ship's three masts to his eye; the White Whale churning himself into furious speed, almost in an instant as it were, rushing among the boats with open jaws, and a lashing tail, offered appalling battle on every side; and heedless of the irons darted at him from every boat, seemed only intent on annihilating each separate plank of which those boats were made. But skilfully manœuvred, incessantly wheeling like trained chargers in the field; the boats for a while eluded him;

though, at times, but by a plank's breadth; while all the time, Ahab's unearthly slogan tore every other cry but his to shreds.

But at last in his untraceable evolutions, the White Whale so crossed and recrossed, and in a thousand ways entangled the slack of the three lines now fast to him, that they foreshortened, and, of themselves, warped the devoted boats towards the planted irons in him; though now for a moment the whale drew aside a little, as if to rally for a more tremendous charge. Seizing that opportunity, Ahab first paid out more line: and then was rapidly hauling and jerking in upon it again—hoping that way to disencumber it of some snarls—when lo!—a sight more savage than the embattled teeth of sharks!

Caught and twisted—corkscrewed in the mazes of the line— loose harpoons and lances, with all their bristling barbs and points, came flashing and dripping up to the chocks in the bows of Ahab's boat. Only one thing could be done. Seizing the boat-knife, he critically reached within—through—and then, without—the rays of steel; dragged in the line beyond, passed it, inboard, to the bowsman, and then, twice sundering the rope near the chocks—dropped the intercepted fagot of steel into the sea; and was all fast again. That instant, the White Whale made a sudden rush among the remaining tangles of the other lines; by so doing, irresistibly dragged the more involved boats of Stubb and Flask towards his flukes; dashed them to- gether like two rolling husks on a surf-beaten beach, and then, diving down into the sea, disappeared in a boiling maelstrom, in which, for a space, the odorous cedar chips of the wrecks danced round and round, like the grated nutmeg in a swiftly stirred bowl of punch.

While the two crews were yet circling in the waters, reaching out after the revolving line-tubs, oars, and other floating furni- ture, while aslope little Flask bobbed up and down like an empty vial, twitching his legs upwards to escape the dreaded jaws of sharks; and Stubb was lustily singing out for some one to ladle him up; and while the old man's line—now parting—admitted of his pulling into the creamy pool to rescue whom he could;— in that wild simultaneousness of a thousand concreted perils,

—Ahab's yet unstricken boat seemed drawn up towards Heaven by invisible wires,—as, arrow-like, shooting perpendicularly from the sea, the White Whale dashed his broad forehead against its bottom, and sent it, turning over and over, into the air; till it fell again—gunwale downwards—and Ahab and his men struggled out from under it, like seals from a sea-side cave.

The first uprising momentum of the whale—modifying its direction as he struck the surface—involuntarily launched him along it, to a little distance from the centre of the destruction he had made; and with his back to it, he now lay for a moment slowly feeling with his flukes from side to side; and whenever a stray oar, bit of plank, the least chip or crumb of the boats touched his skin, his tail swiftly drew back, and came sideways smiting the sea. But soon, as if satisfied that his work for that time was done, he pushed his pleated forehead through the ocean, and trailing after him the intertangled lines, continued his leeward way at a traveller's methodic pace.

As before, the attentive ship having descried the whole fight, again came bearing down to the rescue, and dropping a boat, picked up the floating mariners, tubs, oars, and whatever else could be caught at, and safely landed them on her decks. Some sprained shoulders, wrists, and ankles; livid contusions; wrenched harpoons and lances; inextricable intricacies of rope; shattered oars and planks; all these were there; but no fatal or even serious ill seemed to have befallen any one. As with Fedallah the day before, so Ahab was now found grimly clinging to his boat's broken half, which afforded a comparatively easy float; nor did it so exhaust him as the previous day's mishap.

But when he was helped to the deck, all eyes were fastened upon him; as instead of standing by himself he still half-hung upon the shoulder of Starbuck, who had thus far been the foremost to assist him. His ivory leg had been snapped off, leaving but one short sharp splinter.

"Aye aye, Starbuck, 'tis sweet to lean sometimes, be the leaner who he will; and would old Ahab had leaned oftener than he has."

"The ferrule has not stood, sir," said the carpenter, now coming up; "I put good work into that leg."

"But no bones broken, sir, I hope," said Stubb with true concern.

"Aye! and all splintered to pieces, Stubb!—d'ye see it.—But even with a broken bone, old Ahab is untouched; and I account no living bone of mine one jot more me, than this dead one that's lost. Nor white whale, nor man, nor fiend, can so much as graze old Ahab in his own proper and inaccessible being. Can any lead touch yonder floor, any mast scrape yonder roof? —Aloft there! which way?"

"Dead to leeward, sir."

"Up helm, then; pile on the sail again, ship keepers! down the rest of the spare boats and rig them—Mr. Starbuck away, and muster the boat's crews."

"Let me first help thee towards the bulwarks, sir."

"Oh, oh, oh! how this splinter gores me now! Accursed fate! that the unconquerable captain in the soul should have such a craven mate!"

"Sir?"

"My body, man, not thee. Give me something for a cane— there, that shivered lance will do. Muster the men. Surely I have not seen him yet. By heaven it cannot be!—missing?— quick! call them all."

The old man's hinted thought was true. Upon mustering the company, the Parsee was not there.

"The Parsee!" cried Stubb—"he must have been caught in——"

"The black vomit wrench thee!—run all of ye above, alow, cabin, forecastle—find him—not gone—not gone!"

But quickly they returned to him with the tidings that the Parsee was nowhere to be found.

"Aye, sir," said Stubb—"caught among the tangles of your line—I thought I saw him dragging under."

"*My* line! *my* line? Gone?—gone? What means that little word?—What death-knell rings in it, that old Ahab shakes as if he were the belfry. The harpoon, too!—toss over the litter there,—d'ye see it?—the forged iron, men, the white whale's—no, no, no,—blistered fool! this hand did dart it!—'tis in the fish!—Aloft there! Keep him nailed—Quick!—all hands to the rigging of the boats—collect the oars—harpooneers! the irons, the irons!—hoist the royals higher—a pull on all the sheets!—helm there! steady, steady for your life! I'll ten times girdle the unmeasured globe; yea and dive straight through it, but I'll slay him yet!"

"Great God! but for one single instant show thyself," cried Starbuck; "never, never wilt thou capture him, old man—In Jesus' name no more of this, that's worse than devil's madness. Two days chased; twice stove to splinters; thy very leg once more snatched from under thee; thy evil shadow gone—all good angels mobbing thee with warnings:—what more wouldst thou have?—Shall we keep chasing this murderous fish till he swamps the last man? Shall we be dragged by him to the bottom of the sea? Shall we be towed by him to the infernal world? Oh, oh,—Impiety and blasphemy to hunt him more!"

"Starbuck, of late I've felt strangely moved to thee; ever since that hour we both saw—thou know'st what, in one another's eyes. But in this matter of the whale, be the front of thy face to me as the palm of this hand—a lipless, unfeatured blank. Ahab is for ever Ahab, man. This whole act's immutably decreed. 'Twas rehearsed by thee and me a billion years before this ocean rolled. Fool! I am the Fates' lieutenant; I act under orders. Look thou, underling! that thou obeyest mine.—Stand round me, men. Ye see an old man cut down to the stump; leaning on a shivered lance; propped up on a lonely foot. 'Tis Ahab—his body's part; but Ahab's soul's a centipede, that moves upon a hundred legs. I feel strained, half-stranded, as ropes that tow dismasted frigates in a gale; and I may look so. But ere I break, ye'll hear me crack; and till ye hear *that*, know that Ahab's hawser tows his purpose yet. Believe ye, men, in the things called omens? Then laugh aloud, and cry encore! For ere they drown, drowning things will twice rise to the surface; then rise again, to sink for evermore. So with Moby Dick—two days he's floated—to-morrow will

be the third. Aye, men, he'll rise once more,—but only to
spout his last! D'ye feel brave men, brave?"

"As fearless fire," cried Stubb.

"And as mechanical," muttered Ahab. Then as the men
went forward, he muttered on: "The things called omens!
And yesterday I talked the same to Starbuck there, concerning
my broken boat. Oh! how valiantly I seek to drive out of
others' hearts what's clinched so fast in mine!—The Parsee—
the Parsee!—gone, gone? and he was to go before:—but still
was to be seen again ere I could perish—How's that?—There's
a riddle now might baffle all the lawyers backed by the ghosts
of the whole line of judges:—like a hawk's beak it pecks my
brain. *I'll, I'll* solve it, though!"

When dusk descended, the whale was still in sight to leeward.

So once more the sail was shortened, and everything passed
nearly as on the previous night; only, the sound of hammers,
and the hum of the grindstone was heard till nearly daylight,
as the men toiled by lanterns in the complete and careful rigging
of the spare boats and sharpening their fresh weapons for the
morrow. Meantime, of the broken keel of Ahab's wrecked
craft the carpenter made him another leg; while still as on the
night before, slouched Ahab stood fixed within his scuttle;
his hid, heliotrope glance anticipatingly gone backward on its
dial; sat due eastward for the earliest sun.

CHAPTER CXXXV

The Chase—Third Day

The morning of the third day dawned fair and fresh, and
once more the solitary night-man at the fore-mast-head was
relieved by crowds of the daylight look-outs, who dotted every
mast and almost every spar.

"D'ye see him?" cried Ahab; but the whale was not yet in
sight.

"In his infallible wake, though; but follow that wake, that's
all. Helm there; steady, as thou goest, and hast been going.

What a lovely day again! were it a new-made world, and made for a summer-house to the angels, and this morning the first of its throwing open to them, a fairer day could not dawn upon that world. Here's food for thought, had Ahab time to think; but Ahab never thinks; he only feels, feels, feels; *that's* tingling enough for mortal man! to think's audacity. God only has that right and privilege. Thinking is, or ought to be, a coolness and a calmness; and our poor hearts throb, and our poor brains beat too much for that. And yet, I've sometimes thought my brain was very calm—frozen calm, this old skull cracks so, like a glass in which the contents turn to ice, and shiver it. And still this hair is growing now; this moment growing, and heat must breed it; but no, it's like that sort of common grass that will grow anywhere, between the earthy clefts of Greenland ice or in Vesuvius lava. How the wild winds blow it; they whip it about me as the torn shreds of split sails lash the tossed ship they cling to. A vile wind that has no doubt blown ere this through prison corridors and cells, and wards of hospitals, and ventilated them, and now comes blowing hither as innocent as fleeces. Out upon it!—it's tainted. Were I the wind, I'd blow no more on such a wicked, miserable world. I'd crawl somewhere to a cave, and slink there. And yet, 'tis a noble and heroic thing, the wind! who ever conquered it? In every fight it has the last and bitterest blow. Run tilting at it, and you but run through it. Ha! a coward wind that strikes stark naked men, but will not stand to receive a single blow. Even Ahab is a braver thing—a nobler thing than *that*. Would now the wind but had a body; but all the things that most exasperate and outrage mortal man, all these things are bodiless, but only bodiless as objects, not as agents. There's a most special, a most cunning, oh, a most malicious difference! And yet, I say again, and swear it now, that there's something all glorious and gracious in the wind. These warm Trade Winds, at least, that in the clear heavens blow straight on, in strong and steadfast, vigorous mildness; and veer not from their mark, however the baser currents of the sea may turn and tack, and mightiest Mississippies of the land swift and swerve about, uncertain where to go at last. And by the eternal Poles! these same Trades that so directly blow my good ship on; these Trades, or something like them—something so unchangeable, and full as strong, blow my keeled soul along! To it! Aloft there! What d'ye see?"

"Nothing, sir."

"Nothing! and noon at hand! The doubloon goes a-begging! See the sun! Aye, aye, it must be so. I've oversailed him. How, got the start? Aye, he's chasing *me* now; not I, *him*— that's bad; I might have known it, too. Fool! the lines—the harpoons he's towing. Aye, aye, I have run him by last night. About! about! Come down, all of ye, but the regular look outs! Man the braces!"

Steering as she had done, the wind had been somewhat on the Pequod's quarter, so that now being pointed in the reverse direction, the braced ship sailed hard upon the breeze as she rechurned the cream in her own white wake.

"Against the wind he now steers for the open jaw," murmured Starbuck to himself, as he coiled the new-hauled mainbrace upon the rail. "God keep us, but already my bones feel damp within me, and from the inside wet my flesh. I misdoubt me that I disobey my God in obeying him!"

"Stand by to sway me up!" cried Ahab, advancing to the hempen basket. "We should meet him soon."

"Aye, aye, sir," and straightway Starbuck did Ahab's bidding, and once more Ahab swung on high.

A whole hour now passed; gold-beaten out to ages. Time itself now held long breaths with keen suspense. But at last, some three points off the weather bow, Ahab descried the spout again, and instantly from the three mast-heads three shrieks went up as if the tongues of fire had voiced it.

"Forehead to forehead I meet thee, this third time, Moby Dick! On deck there!—brace sharper up; crowd her into the wind's eye. He's too far off to lower yet, Mr. Starbuck. The sails shake! Stand over that helmsman with a top-maul! So, so; he travels fast, and I must down. But let me have one more good round look aloft here at the sea; there's time for that.

An old, old sight, and yet somehow so young; aye, and not changed a wink since I first saw it, a boy, from the sand-hills of Nantucket! The same!—the same!—the same to Noah as to me. There's a soft shower to leeward. Such lovely lee-wardings! They must lead somewhere—to something else than common land, more palmy than the palms. Leeward! the white whale goes that way; look to windward, then; the better if the bitterer quarter. But good bye, good bye, old mast-head! What's this?—green? aye, tiny mosses in these warped cracks. No such green weather stains on Ahab's head! There's the difference now between man's old age and matter's. But aye, old mast, we both grow old together; sound in our hulls, though, are we not, my ship? Aye, minus a leg, that's all. By heaven this dead wood has the better of my live flesh every way. I can't compare with it; and I've known some ships made of dead trees outlast the lives of men made of the most vital stuff of vital fathers. What's that he said? he should still go before me, my pilot; and yet to be seen again? But where? Will I have eyes at the bottom of the sea, supposing I descend those endless stairs? and all night I've been sailing from him, wherever he did sink to. Aye, aye, like many more thou told'st direful truth as touching thyself, O Parsee; but, Ahab, there thy shot fell short. Good bye, mast-head—keep a good eye upon the whale, the while I'm gone. We'll talk to-morrow, nay, to-night, when the white whale lies down there, tied by head and tail."

He gave the word; and still gazing round him, was steadily lowered through the cloven blue air to the deck.

In due time the boats were lowered; but as standing in his shallop's stern, Ahab just hovered upon the point of the descent, he waved to the mate,—who held one of the tackle-ropes on deck—and bade him pause.

"Starbuck!"

"Sir?"

"For the third time my soul's ship starts upon this voyage, Starbuck."

"Aye, sir, thou wilt have it so."

"Some ships sail from their ports, and ever afterwards are missing, Starbuck!"

"Truth, sir: saddest truth."

"Some men die at ebb tide; some at low water; some at the full of the flood;—and I feel now like a billow that's all one crested comb, Starbuck. I am old;—shake hands with me, man."

Their hands met; their eyes fastened; Starbuck's tears the glue.

"Oh, my captain, my captain!—noble heart—go not—go not!—see, it's a brave man that weeps; how great the agony of the persuasion then!"

"Lower away!"—cried Ahab, tossing the mate's arm from him. "Stand by the crew!"

In an instant the boat was pulling round close under the stern.

"The sharks! the sharks!" cried a voice from the low cabin-window there; "O master, my master, come back!"

But Ahab heard nothing; for his own voice was high-lifted then; and the boat leaped on.

Yet the voice spake true; for scarce had he pushed from the ship, when numbers of sharks, seemingly rising from out the dark waters beneath the hull, maliciously snapped at the blades of the oars, every time they dipped in the water; and in this way accompanied the boat with their bites. It is a thing not uncommonly happening to the whale-boats in those swarming seas; the sharks at times apparently following them in the same prescient way that vultures hover over the banners of marching regiments in the east. But these were the first sharks that had been observed by the Pequod since the White Whale had been first descried; and whether it was that Ahab's crew were all such tiger-yellow barbarians, and therefore their flesh more musky to the senses of the sharks—a matter sometimes well known to affect them,—however it was, they seemed to follow that one boat without molesting the others.

"Heart of wrought steel!" murmured Starbuck gazing over the side, and following with his eyes the receding boat— "canst thou yet ring boldly to that sight?—lowering thy keel among ravening sharks, and followed by them, open-mouthed to the chase; and this the critical third day?—For when three days flow together in one continuous intense pursuit; be sure the first is the morning, the second the noon, and the third the evening and the end of that thing—be that end what it may. Oh! my God! what is this that shoots through me, and leaves me so deadly calm, yet expectant,—fixed at the top of a shudder! Future things swim before me, as in empty outlines and skeletons; all the past is somehow grown dim. Mary, girl! thou fadest in pale glories behind me; boy! I seem to see but thy eyes grown wondrous blue. Strangest problems of life seem clearing; but clouds sweep between—Is my journey's end coming? My legs feel faint; like his who has footed it all day. Feel thy heart,—beats it yet? Stir thyself, Starbuck!—stave it off—move, move! speak aloud!—Mast-head there! See ye my boy's hand on the hill?—Crazed;—aloft there!—keep thy keenest eye upon the boats:—mark well the whale!—Ho! again!—drive off that hawk! see! he pecks—he tears the vane"—pointing to the red flag flying at the main-truck—"Ha! he soars away with it!—Where's the old man now? see'st thou that sight, oh Ahab!—shudder, shudder!"

The boats had not gone very far, when by a signal from the mast-heads—a downward pointed arm, Ahab knew that the whale had sounded; but intending to be near him at the next rising, he held on his way a little sideways from the vessel; the becharmed crew maintaining the profoundest silence, as the head-beat waves hammered and hammered against the opposing bow.

"Drive, drive in your nails, oh ye waves! to their uttermost heads drive them in! ye but strike a thing without a lid; and no coffin and no hearse can be mine:—and hemp only can kill me! Ha! ha!"

Suddenly the waters around them slowly swelled in broad circles; then quickly upheaved, as if sideways sliding from a submerged berg of ice, swiftly rising to the surface. A low rumbling sound was heard; a subterraneous hum; and then all held their breaths; as bedraggled with trailing ropes, and harpoons, and lances, a vast form shot lengthwise, but obliquely from the sea. Shrouded in a thin drooping veil of mist, it hovered for a moment in the rainbowed air; and then fell swamping back into the deep. Crushed thirty feet upwards, the waters flashed for an instant like heaps of fountains, then brokenly sank in a shower of flakes, leaving the circling surface creamed like new milk round the marble trunk of the whale.

"Give way!" cried Ahab to the oarsmen, and the boats darted forward to the attack; but maddened by yesterday's fresh irons that corroded in him, Moby Dick seemed combinedly possessed by all the angels that fell from heaven. The wide tiers of welded tendons overspreading his broad white forehead, beneath the transparent skin, looked knitted together; as head on, he came churning his tail among the boats; and once more flailed them apart; spilling out the irons and lances from the two mates' boats, and dashing in one side of the upper part of their bows, but leaving Ahab's almost without a scar.

While Daggoo and Queequeg were stopping the strained planks; and as the whale swimming out from them, turned, and showed one entire flank as he shot by them again; at that moment a quick cry went up. Lashed round and round to the fish's back; pinioned in the turns upon turns in which, during the past night, the whale had reeled the involutions of the lines around him, the half torn body of the Parsee was seen; his sable raiment frayed to shreds; his distended eyes turned full upon old Ahab.

The harpoon dropped from his hand.

"Befooled, befooled!"—drawing in a long lean breath—"Aye, Parsee! I see thee again.—Aye, and thou goest before; and this, *this* then is the hearse that thou didst promise. But I hold thee to the last letter of thy word. Where is the second hearse? Away, mates, to the ship! those boats are useless now; repair them if ye can in time, and return to me; if not, Ahab is enough to die—Down, men! the first thing that but offers to jump from this boat I stand in, that thing I harpoon. Ye are not other men, but my arms and my legs; and so obey me.—Where's the whale? gone down again?"

But he looked too nigh the boat; for as if bent upon escaping with the corpse he bore, and as if the particular place of the last encounter had been but a stage in his leeward voyage, Moby Dick was now again steadily swimming forward; and had almost passed the ship,—which thus far had been sailing in the contrary direction to him, though for the present her headway had been stopped. He seemed swimming with his utmost velocity, and now only intent upon pursuing his own straight path in the sea.

"Oh! Ahab," cried Starbuck, "not too late is it, even now, the third day, to desist. See! Moby Dick seeks thee not. It is thou, thou, that madly seekest him!"

Setting sail to the rising wind, the lonely boat was swiftly impelled to leeward, by both oars and canvas. And at last when Ahab was sliding by the vessel, so near as plainly to distinguish Starbuck's face as he leaned over the rail, he hailed him to turn the vessel about, and follow him, not too swiftly, at a judicious interval. Glancing upwards he saw Tashtego, Queequeg, and Daggoo, eagerly mounting to the three mast-heads; while the oarsmen were rocking in the two staved boats which had just been hoisted to the side, and were busily at work in repairing them. One after the other, through the port-holes, as he sped, he also caught flying glimpses of Stubb and Flask, busying themselves on deck among bundles of new irons and lances. As he saw all this; as he heard the hammers in the broken boats; far other hammers seemed driving a nail into his heart. But he rallied. And now marking that the vane or flag was gone from the main-mast-head, he shouted to Tashtego, who had just gained that perch, to descend again for another flag, and a hammer and nails, and so nail it to the mast.

Whether fagged by the three days' running chase, and the resistance to his swimming in the knotted hamper he bore; or whether it was some latent deceitfulness and malice in him: whichever was true, the White Whale's way now began to abate, as it seemed, from the boat so rapidly nearing him once more; though indeed the whale's last start had not been so long a one as before. And still as Ahab glided over the waves the unpitying sharks accompanied him; and so pertinaciously stuck to the boat; and so continually bit at the plying oars, that the blades became jagged and crunched, and left small splinters in the sea, at almost every dip.

"Heed them not! those teeth but give new rowlocks to your oars. Pull on! 'tis the better rest, the shark's jaw than the yielding water."

"But at every bite, sir, the thin blades grow smaller and smaller!"

"They will last long enough! pull on!—But who can tell"— he muttered—"whether these sharks swim to feast on the whale or on Ahab?—But pull on! Aye, all alive, now—we near him. The helm! take the helm; let me pass,"—and so saying, two of the oarsmen helped him forward to the bows of the still flying boat.

At length as the craft was cast to one side, and ran ranging along with the White Whale's flank, he seemed strangely oblivious of its advance—as the whale sometimes will—and Ahab was fairly within the smoky mountain mist, which, thrown off from the whale's spout, curled round his great, Monadnock [28] hump; he was even thus close to him; when, with body arched back, and both arms lengthwise high-lifted to the poise, he darted his fierce iron, and his far fiercer curse into the hated whale. As both steel and curse sank to the socket, as if sucked into a morass, Moby Dick sideways writhed; spasmodically rolled his nigh flank against the bow, and, without staving a hole in it, so suddenly canted the boat over, that had it not been for the elevated part of the gunwale to which he then clung, Ahab would once more have been tossed into the sea. As it was, three of the oarsmen—who foreknew not the precise instant of the dart, and were therefore unprepared for its effects —these were flung out; but so fell, that, in an instant two of them clutched the gunwale again, and rising to its level on a combing wave, hurled themselves bodily inboard again; the third man helplessly dropping astern, but still afloat and swimming.

Almost simultaneously, with a mighty volition of ungraduated, instantaneous swiftness, the White Whale darted through the weltering sea. But when Ahab cried out to the steersman to take new turns with the line, and hold it so; and commanded the crew to turn round on their seats, and tow the boat up to the mark; the moment the treacherous line felt that double strain and tug, it snapped in the empty air!

"What breaks in me? Some sinew cracks!—'tis whole again; oars! oars! Burst in upon him!"

Hearing the tremendous rush of the sea-crashing boat, the whale wheeled round to present his blank forehead at bay; but in that evolution, catching sight of the nearing black hull of the ship; seemingly seeing in it the source of all his persecutions; bethinking it—it may be—a larger and nobler foe; of a sudden, he bore down upon its advancing prow, smiting his jaws amid fiery showers of foam.

Ahab staggered; his hand smote his forehead. "I grow blind; hands! stretch out before me that I may yet grope my way. Is't night?"

"The whale! The ship!" cried the cringing oarsmen.

"Oars! oars! Slope downwards to thy depths, O sea, that ere it be for ever too late, Ahab may slide this last, last time upon his mark! I see: the ship! the ship! Dash on, my men! will ye not save my ship?"

But as the oarsmen violently forced their boat through the sledge-hammering seas, the before whale-smitten bow-ends of two planks burst through, and in an instant almost, the temporarily disabled boat lay nearly level with the waves; its half-wading, splashing crew, trying hard to stop the gap and bale out the pouring water.

Meantime, for that one beholding instant, Tashtego's mast-head hammer remained suspended in his hand; and the red flag, half-wrapping him as with a plaid, then streamed itself straight out from him, as his own forward-flowing heart; while Starbuck and Stubb, standing upon the bowsprit beneath, caught sight of the down-coming monster just as soon as he.

"The whale, the whale! Up helm, up helm! Oh, all ye sweet powers of air, now hug me close! Let not Starbuck die, if die he must, in a woman's fainting fit. Up helm, I say—ye fools, the jaw! the jaw! Is this the end of all my bursting prayers? all my life-long fidelities? Oh, Ahab, Ahab, lo, thy work. Steady! helmsman, steady. Nay, nay! Up helm again! He turns to meet us! Oh, his unappeasable brow drives on towards one, whose duty tells him he cannot depart. My God, stand by me now!"

"Stand not by me, but stand under me, whoever you are that will now help Stubb; for Stubb, too, sticks here. I grin at thee, thou grinning whale! Who ever helped Stubb, or kept Stubb awake, but Stubb's own unwinking eye? And now poor Stubb goes to bed upon a mattress that is all too soft; would it were stuffed with brushwood! I grin at thee, thou grinning whale! Look ye, sun, moon, and stars! I call ye assassins of as good a fellow as ever spouted up his ghost. For all that, I would yet ring glasses with thee, would ye but hand the cup! Oh, oh! oh, oh! thou grinning whale, but there'll be plenty of gulping soon! Why fly ye not, O Ahab! For me, off shoes and jacket to it; let Stubb die in his drawers! A most mouldy and over salted death, though;—cherries! cherries! cherries! Oh, Flask, for one red cherry ere we die!"

"Cherries? I only wish that we were where they grow. Oh, Stubb, I hope my poor mother's drawn my part-pay ere this; if not, few coppers will now come to her, for the voyage is up."

From the ship's bows, nearly all the seamen now hung inactive; hammers, bits of plank, lances, and harpoons, mechanically retained in their hands, just as they had darted from their various employments; all their enchanted eyes intent upon the whale, which from side to side strangely vibrating his predestinating head, sent a broad band of overspreading semicircular foam before him as he rushed. Retribution, swift vengeance, eternal malice were in his whole aspect, and spite of all that mortal man could do, the solid white buttress of his forehead smote the ship's starboard bow, till men and timbers reeled. Some fell flat upon their faces. Like dislodged trucks, the heads of the harpooneers aloft shook on their bull-like necks. Through the breach, they heard the waters pour, as mountain torrents down a flume.

"The ship! The hearse!—the second hearse!" cried Ahab from the boat; "its wood could only be American!"

Diving beneath the settling ship, the whale ran quivering along its keel; but turning under water, swiftly shot to the surface again, far off the other bow, but within a few yards of Ahab's boat, where, for a time, he lay quiescent.

"I turn my body from the sun. What ho, Tashtego! let me hear thy hammer. Oh! ye three unsurrendered spires of mine; thou uncracked keel; and only god-bullied hull; thou firm deck, and haughty helm, and Pole-pointed prow,—death-glorious ship! must ye then perish, and without me? Am I cut off from the last fond pride of meanest shipwrecked captains? Oh, lonely death on lonely life! Oh, now I feel my topmost greatness lies in my topmost grief. Ho, ho! from all your furthest bounds, pour ye now in, ye bold billows of my whole foregone life, and top this one piled comber of my death! Towards thee I roll, thou all-destroying but unconquering whale; to the last I grapple with thee; from hell's heart I stab at thee; for hate's sake I spit my last breath at thee. Sink all coffins and all hearses to one common pool! and since neither can be mine, let me then tow to pieces, while still chasing thee, though tied to thee, thou damned whale! *Thus*, I give up the spear!"

The harpoon was darted; the stricken whale flew forward; with igniting velocity the line ran through the groove;—ran foul. Ahab stooped to clear it; he did clear it; but the flying turn caught him round the neck, and voicelessly as Turkish mutes bowstring their victim, he was shot out of the boat, ere the crew knew he was gone. Next instant, the heavy eye-splice in the rope's final end flew out of the stark-empty tub, knocked down an oarsman, and smiting the sea, disappeared in its depths.

For an instant, the tranced boat's crew stood still; then turned. "The ship? Great God, where is the ship?" Soon they through dim, bewildering mediums saw her sidelong fading phantom, as in the gaseous Fata Morgana; only the uppermost masts out of water; while fixed by infatuation, or fidelity, or fate, to their once lofty perches, the pagan harpooneers still maintained their sinking lookouts on the sea. And now, concentric circles seized the lone boat itself, and all its crew, and each floating oar, and every lance-pole, and spinning, animate and inanimate, all round and round in one vortex, carried the smallest chip of the Pequod out of sight.

But as the last whelmings intermixingly poured themselves over the sunken head of the Indian at the mainmast, leaving a few inches of the erect spar yet visible, together with long streaming yards of the flag, which calmly undulated, with ironical coincidings, over the destroying billows they almost touched;—at that instant, a red arm and a hammer hovered backwardly uplifted in the open air, in the act of nailing the flag faster and yet faster to the subsiding spar. A sky-hawk that tauntingly had followed the main-truck downwards from its natural home among the stars, pecking at the flag, and incommoding Tashtego there; this bird now chanced to intercept its broad fluttering wing between the hammer and the wood; and simultaneously feeling that etherial thrill, the submerged savage beneath, in his death-gasp, kept his hammer frozen there; and so the bird of heaven, with archangelic shrieks, and his imperial beak thrust upwards, and his whole captive form folded in the flag of Ahab, went down with his ship, which, like Satan, would not sink to hell till she had dragged a living part of heaven along with her, and helmeted herself with it.

Now small fowls flew screaming over the yet yawning gulf; a sullen white surf beat against its steep sides; then all collapsed, and the great shroud of the sea rolled on as it rolled five thousand years ago.

EPILOGUE

"And I only am escaped alone to tell thee."

—Job.

The drama's done. Why then here does any one step forth?—Because one did survive the wreck.

It so chanced, that after the Parsee's disappearance, I was he whom the Fates ordained to take the place of Ahab's bowsman, when that bowsman assumed the vacant post; the same, who, when on the last day the three men were tossed from out the rocking boat, was dropped astern. So, floating on the margin of the ensuing scene, and in full sight of it, when the half-spent suction of the sunk ship reached me, I was then, but slowly, drawn towards the closing vortex. When I reached it, it had subsided to a creamy pool. Round and round, then, and ever contracting towards the button-like black bubble at the axis of that slowly wheeling circle, like another Ixion I did revolve. Till, gaining that vital centre, the black bubble upward burst; and now, liberated by reason of its cunning spring, and, owing to its great buoyancy, rising with great force, the coffin life-buoy[29] shot lengthwise from the sea, fell over, and floated by my side. Buoyed up by that coffin, for almost one whole day and night, I floated on a soft and dirge-like main. The unharming sharks, they glided by as if with padlocks on their mouths; the savage sea-hawks sailed with sheathed beaks. On the second day, a sail drew near, nearer, and picked me up at last. It was the devious-cruising Rachel, that in her retracing search after her missing children, only found another orphan.

[CRITICISM]

From *The Literary World*

(March 6, 1847)

Etchings of a Whaling Cruise, with Notes of a Sojourn on the Island of Zanzibar. To which is appended, a Brief History of the Whale Fishery; its Past and Present Condition. By J. Ross Browne. Illustrated with numerous Engravings on Steel and Wood. Harper & Brothers: 1846. 8vo.

Sailor's Life and Sailor's Yarns. By Captain Ringbolt. New York: C. S. Francis & Co.: 1847. 12mo.

From time immemorial many fine things have been said and sung of the sea. And the days have been, when sailors were considered veritable mermen; and the ocean itself as the peculiar theatre of the romantic and wonderful. But of late years there have been revealed so many plain, matter-of-fact details connected with nautical life, that, at the present day, the poetry of salt water is very much on the wane. The perusal of Dana's "Two Years before the Mast," for instance, somewhat impairs the relish with which we read Byron's spiritual "Address to the Ocean." And when the noble poet raves about laying his hands upon the ocean's mane (in other words manipulating the crest of a wave[1]), the most vivid image suggested is, that of a valetudinarian bather at Rockaway, spluttering and choking in the surf, with his mouth full of brine.

Mr. J. Ross Browne's narrative tends still further to impair the charm with which poetry and fiction have invested the sea. It is a book of unvarnished facts, and with some allowances for the general application of an individual example, unquestionably presents a faithful picture of the life led by the twenty thousand seamen employed in the seven hundred whaling vessels which now pursue their game under the American flag. Indeed, what Mr. Dana has so admirably done in describing the vicissitudes of the merchant-sailor's life, Mr. Browne has very creditably achieved with respect to that of the hardy whaleman's. And the book which possesses this merit, deserves much in the way of commendation. The personal narrative interwoven with it, also, cannot fail to enlist our sympathies for the adventurous author himself. The scenes presented are always graphically and truthfully sketched, and hence fastidious objections may be made to some of them, on the score of their being too coarsely or harshly drawn. But we take it, that as true, unreserved descriptions, they are in no respect faulty; and, doubtless, the author never dreamed of softening down or withholding anything with a view of rendering his sketches the more attractive and pretty. The book is eminently a practical one, and written with the set purpose of accomplishing good by revealing the simple truth. When the brutal tyranny of the Captain of the "Styx" is painted without apology or palliation, it holds up the outrageous abuse to which seamen, in our whaling marine, are actually subjected, or rather, which demands legislation. Mr. Browne himself, it seems, was, to some extent, the victim of the tyranny of which he complains, and, upon this ground, the personal bitterness in which he at times indulges, may be deemed excusable.

As the book professes to embrace a detailed account of all that is interesting in the business of whaling, and essentially possesses this merit, one or two curious errors into which the author has unaccountably fallen, may, without captiousness, be pointed out. We are told, for example, of a whale's *roaring* when wounded by the harpoon. We can imagine the veteran Coffins, and Colemans, and Maceys of old Nantucket, elevating their brows at the bare announcement of such a thing. Now the creature in question is as dumb as a shad, or any other of the finny tribes; and no doubt, if Jonah himself could be summoned to the stand, he would cheerfully testify to his not having heard a single syllable, growl, grunt, or bellow engendered in the ventricle cells of the leviathan, during the irksome period of his incarceration therein.

That in some encounters with the sperm whale a low, indistinct sound *apparently* issues from the monster, is true enough. But all Nantucket and New Bedford are decided as to the causes which produce the phenomenon. Many suppose, however, that it is produced, not by the creature itself, but by the peculiar motion, in the water, of the line which is attached to the harpoon. For, if upon being struck, the whale "sounds" (descends), as is usually the case, and remains below the surface for any length of time, the rope frequently becomes as stiff as the cord of a harp, and the struggles of the animal keep it continually vibrating.

Considering the disenchanting nature of the revelations of sea-life, with which we are presented in Mr. Browne's book, we are inclined to believe that the shipping agents employed in our various cities, by the merchants of New Bedford, will have to present additional inducements to "enterprising and industrious young Americans of good moral character," in order to persuade them to embark in the fishery. In particular, the benevolent old gentleman in Front street[2] (one of the shipping agents of whom our author discourseth), who so politely accosted Browne and his comrade, upon their entering his office for the purpose of seeking further information touching the rate of promotion in the whaling service—this old gentleman, we say, must hereafter infuse into his address still more of the *suaviter in modo*.

As unaffectedly described by Browne, the scene alluded to is irresistibly comic. The agent's business, be it understood, consists in decoying "green hands" to send on to the different whaling ports. A conspicuous placard, without the office, announces to the anxious world, that a few choice vacancies remain to be filled in certain crews of whalemen about to sail, upon the most delightful voyages imaginable (only four years long). To secure a place, of course, instant application should be made.

Our author and his friend, attracted by the placard, hurry up a ladder, to a dark loft above, where the old man lurks like a spider in the midst of his toils. But a single glance at the gentlemanly dress and white hands of his visitors, impresses the wily agent with the idea, that, notwithstanding their calling upon him, they may very possibly have heard disagreeable accounts of the nature of whaling. So, after making a bow, and offering a few legs of a chair, he proceeds to disabuse their minds of any unfavorable impressions. Succeeding in this, he then becomes charmingly facetious and complimentary; assures the youths that they need not be concerned because of their slender waists and silken muscles, for those who employed him were not so particular about weight as beauty. In short, the captains of whaling vessels preferred handsome young fellows who dressed well, and conversed genteelly—in short, those who would reflect credit upon the business of tarring down rigging, and cutting up blubber. Delighted with the agreeable address of the old gentleman, and with many pleasant anticipations of sea-life, the visitors listen with increased attention. Whereupon the agent waxes eloquent, and enlarges upon his animating theme in the style parliamentary. "A whaler, gentlemen," he observes, "is the home of the unfortunate—the asylum of the oppressed," &c., &c., &c.

Duped Browne! Hapless H——! In the end they enter into an engagement with the old gentleman, who subsequently sends them on to New Bedford, consigned to a mercantile house there. From New Bedford the adventurers at length sail in a small whaling barque bound to the Indian Ocean. While yet half dead with sea sickness, the unfortunate H—— is sent by the brutal captain to the mast-head, to stand there his allotted two hours, on the look-out for whale-spouts. He receives a stroke of the sun which, for a time, takes away his reason, and endangers his life. He raves of home and friends, and poor Browne, watching by his side, upbraids himself for having been concerned in bringing his companion to such a state. Ere long the vessel touches at the Azores, where H——, being altogether unfit for duty, is left, to be sent home by the American consul.

He never recovered from the effects of his hardships; for, in the sequel, Browne relates that, after reaching home himself, he visited his old friend in Ohio, and found him still liable to temporary prostrations, directly referable to his sufferings at sea.

With a heavy heart our author, after leaving the Azores, weathers the Cape of Good Hope, and enters upon the Indian Ocean. The ship's company, composed mostly of ignorant, half-civilized Portuguese from the Western Islands, are incessantly quarrelling and fighting; the provisions are of the most wretched kind; their success in the fishery is small; and to crown all, the captain himself is the very incarnation of all that is dastardly, mean, and heartless.

We cannot follow Browne through all his adventures. Suffice it to say, that heartily disgusted with his situation, he at length, with great difficulty, succeeds in leaving the vessel on the coast of Zanzibar. There he tarries for some months, and his residence in this remote region (the eastern coast of Africa, near Madagascar) enables him to make sundry curious observations upon men and things, of which the reader of his work has the benefit. From Zanzibar he ultimately sails for home in a merchant brig, and at last arrives in Boston, thoroughly out of conceit of the ocean.

Give ear, now, all ye shore-disdaining, ocean-enamored youths, who labor under the lamentable delusion that the sea— the "glorious sea" is always, and in reality, "the blue, the fresh, the ever free!" Give ear to Mr. J. Ross Browne, and hearken unto what that experienced young gentleman has to say about the manner in which Barry Cornwall [3] has been humbugging the rising generation on this subject. Alas! Hereafter we shall never look upon an unsophisticated stripling, in flowing "duck" trowsers and a light blue jacket, loitering away the interval which elapses before sailing on his maiden cruise, without mourning over the hard fate in store for him. In a ship's forecastle, alas! he will find no Psyche glass in which to survey his picturesque attire. And the business of making his toilet will be comprised in trying to keep as dry and comfortable as the utter absence of umbrellas, wet decks, and leaky forecastles will admit of. We shudder at all realities of the career they will be entering upon. The long, dark, cold night-watches which, month after month, they must battle out the best way they can; the ship pitching and thumping against the bullying waves—every plank dripping—every jacket soaked— and the captain not at all bland in issuing his order for the poor fellows to mount aloft, in the icy sleet and howling tempest.

"Bless me, Captain, go way up there this excessively disagreeable night?" "Aye, up with you, you lubber—*bare*, I say, or look out for squalls"—a figurative expression, conveying a remote allusion to the hasty application of a sea-bludgeon to the head.

Then the whaling part of the business.—My young friends, just fancy yourselves, for the first time, in an open boat (so slight that three men might walk off with it), some twelve or fifteen miles from your ship, and about a hundred times as far from the nearest land, giving chase to one of the oleaginous monsters. "Pull, pull, you lubberly *hay makers!*" cries the boat-header, jumping up and down in the stern-sheets in a frenzy of professional excitement, while the gasping admirers of Captain Marryat and the sea,[4] tug with might and main at the buckling oars—"Pull, pull, I say; break your lazy backs!" Presently the whale is within "darting distance," and you hear the roar of the waters in his wake. How palpitating the hearts of the frightened oarsmen at this interesting juncture! My young friends, just turn round and snatch a look at that whale. There he goes, surging through the brine, which ripples about his vast head, as if it were the bow of a ship. Believe me, it's quite as terrible as going into battle, to a raw recruit.

"Stand up and give it to him!" shrieks the boat-header at the steering-oar, to the harpooner in the bow. The latter drops his oar, and snatches his "iron." It flies from his hands—and where are we then, my lovelies? It's all a mist, a crash,—a horrible blending of sounds and sights, as the agonized whale lashes the water around him into suds and vapor—dashes the boat aside, and at last rushes madly through the water, towing after him the half-filled craft, which rocks from side to side, while the disordered crew clutch at the gunwale to avoid being tossed out. Meanwhile, all sorts of horrific edged tools, lances, harpoons, and spades, are slipping about; and the imminent line itself—smoking round the logger-head, and passing along the entire length of the boat—is almost death to handle, though it grazes your person.

But all this is nothing to what follows. As yet, you have but simply *fastened* to the whale; he must be fought and killed. But let imagination supply the rest: the monster staving the boat with a single sweep of his ponderous flukes; taking its bows between his jaws (as is frequently the case) and playing with it as a cat with a mouse. Sometimes he bites it in twain, sometimes crunches it into chips, and strews the sea with them.

But we forbear. Enough has been said to convince the uninitiated what sort of a vocation whaling in truth is. If further information is desired, Mr. Browne's book is purchasable, in which they will find the whole matter described in all its interesting details.

After reading the "Etchings of a Whaling Cruise," a perusal of "Sailor's Life and Sailor's Yarns" is, in one respect at least, like hearing "the other side of the question." For, while Browne's is a "Voice from the Forecastle," Captain Ringbolt hails us from the quarter deck, the other end of the ship. Browne gives us a sailor's version of sailors' wrongs, and is not altogether free from prejudices acquired during his little experience on ship-board; Captain Ringbolt almost denies that the sailor has any wrongs, and more than insinuates that sea-captains are not only the best natured fellows in the world, but that they have been sorely maligned. Indeed, he explicitly charges Mr. Dana and Mr. Browne with having presented a decidedly one-sided view of the matter; and he manfully exclaims that the Captain of the Pilgrim—poor fellow!—died too soon to vindicate his character from unjust aspersions. Now, as a class, ship-owners are seldom disposed partially to judge the captains in their employ; and yet we know of a verity, that at least one of the owners of the Pilgrim, an esteemed citizen of the good old town of Boston, will never venture to dispute, that to the extent of his knowledge, at least, Mr. Dana's captain was a most "strict and harsh disciplinarian," which words, so applied by a ship-owner, mean that the man in question was nothing less than what Mr. Dana describes him to have been. But where is Browne's captain? He is alive and hearty, we presume. Let him come forward then, and show why he ought not to be regarded in the decidedly unfavorable light[5] in which he is held up to us in the narrative we have noticed. Now, for aught we know to the contrary, this same Captain of the Styx, who was such a heartless, domineering tyrant at sea, may be quite a different character ashore. In truth, we think this very probable; for the god Janus never had two more decidedly different faces than your sea-captain. Ashore his Nautical Highness has nothing to ruffle him, friends grasp him by the hand, and are overjoyed to see him after his long absence—he is invited out, relates his adventures pleasantly, and everybody thinks what lucky dogs his sailors must have been to have sailed with such a capital fellow. But let poor Jack have a word to say. Why, Sir, he will tell you that when they embarked, his Nautical Highness left behind him all his "quips and cranks and wreathed smiles." Very far, indeed, is the captain from cracking any of his jokes with his crew—that would be altogether too condescending. But then there is no reason why he should bestow a curse every time he gives an order—there is no reason why he should never say a word of sympathy to his men. True, in this respect all sea-captains are not alike; but still, there is enough of truth in both Mr. Dana's and Mr. Browne's statements to justify nearly to the full, the general conclusions to be drawn from what they have said on this subject.

But Captain Ringbolt's book is very far from being a mere plea for the class to which he belongs. What he has to say upon the matter is chiefly contained in one brief sketch under the head of "Sailor's Rights and Sailor's Wrongs." The rest of the book is made up of little stories of the sea, simply and pleasantly told, and withal entertaining.

From *The Literary World*
(August 17 and 24, 1850)

"Hawthorne and His Mosses"
By a Virginian Spending July in Vermont

A papered chamber in a fine old farm-house, a mile from any other dwelling, and dipped to the eaves in foliage—surrounded by mountains, old woods, and Indian ponds,—this, surely, is the place to write of Hawthorne. Some charm is in this northern air, for love and duty seem both impelling to the task. A man of deep and noble nature has seized me in this seclusion. His wild, witch-voice rings through me; or, in softer cadences, I seem to hear it in the songs of the hill-side birds that sing in the larch trees at my window.

Would that all excellent books were foundlings, without father or mother, that so it might be we could glorify them, without including their ostensible authors! Nor would any true man take exception to this; least of all, he who writes, "When the Artist rises high enough to achieve the Beautiful, the symbol by which he makes it perceptible to mortal senses becomes of little value in his eyes, while his spirit possesses itself in the enjoyment of the reality."

But more than this. I know not what would be the right name to put on the title-page of an excellent book; but this I feel, that the names of all fine authors are fictitious ones, far more so than that of Junius; simply standing, as they do, for the mystical, ever-eluding spirit of all beauty, which ubiquitously possesses men of genius. Purely imaginative as this fancy may appear, it nevertheless seems to receive some warranty from the fact, that on a personal interview no great author has ever come up to the idea of his reader. But that dust of which our bodies are composed, how can it fitly express the nobler intelligences among us? With reverence be it spoken, that not even in the case of one deemed more than man, not even in our Saviour, did his visible frame betoken anything of the augustness of the nature within. Else, how could those Jewish eye-witnesses fail to see heaven in his glance!

It is curious how a man may travel along a country road, and yet miss the grandest or sweetest of prospects by reason of an intervening hedge, so like all other hedges, as in no way to hint of the wide landscape beyond. So has it been with me concerning the enchanting landscape in the soul of this Hawthorne, this most excellent Man of Mosses. His "Old Manse" has been written now four years, but I never read it till a day or two since. I had seen it in the book-stores—heard of it often—

even had it recommended to me by a tasteful friend, as a rare,
quiet book, perhaps too deserving of popularity to be popular.
But there are so many books called "excellent," and so much
unpopular merit, that amid the thick stir of other things, the
hint of my tasteful friend was disregarded; and for four years
the Mosses on the Old Manse never refreshed me with their
perennial green. It may be, however, that all this while the
book, like wine, was only improving in flavor and body. At
any rate, it so chanced that this long procrastination eventuated
in a happy result. At breakfast the other day, a mountain girl,
a cousin of mine, who for the last two weeks has every morning
helped me to strawberries and raspberries, which, like the
roses and pearls in the fairy tale, seemed to fall into the saucer
from those strawberry-beds, her cheeks—this delightful creature, this charming Cherry says to me—"I see you spend your
mornings in the hay-mow; and yesterday I found there 'Dwight's
Travels in New England.'[1] Now I have something far better
than that, something more congenial to our summer on these
hills. Take these raspberries, and then I will give you some
moss." "Moss!" said I. "Yes, and you must take it to the
barn with you, and good-bye to 'Dwight.'"

With that she left me, and soon returned with a volume,
verdantly bound, and garnished with a curious frontispiece in
green; nothing less than a fragment of real moss,[2] cunningly
pressed to a fly-leaf. "Why, this," said I, spilling my raspberries, "this is the 'Mosses from an Old Manse.'" "Yes,"
said cousin Cherry, "yes, it is that flowery Hawthorne."
"Hawthorne and Mosses," said I, "no more: it is morning: it
is July in the country: and I am off for the barn."

Stretched on that new mown clover, the hill-side breeze blowing over me through the wide barn-door, and soothed by the
hum of the bees in the meadows around, how magically stole
over me this Mossy Man! and how amply, how bountifully,
did he redeem that delicious promise to his guests in the Old
Manse, of whom it is written—"Others could give them
pleasure, or amusement, or instruction—these could be picked
up anywhere—but it was for me to give them rest. Rest, in a

life of trouble! What better could be done for weary and world-worn spirits? What better could be done for anybody, who came within our magic circle, than to throw the spell of a magic spirit over him?" So all that day, half-buried in the new clover, I watched this Hawthorne's "Assyrian dawn, and Paphian sunset and moonrise, from the summit of our Eastern Hill." [3]

The soft ravishments of the man spun me round about in a web of dreams, and when the book was closed, when the spell was over, this wizard "dismissed me with but misty reminiscences, as if I had been dreaming of him."

What a wild moonlight of contemplative humor bathes that Old Manse! the rich and rare distilment of a spicy and slowly-oozing heart. No rollicking rudeness, no gross fun fed on fat dinners, and bred in the lees of wine,—but a humor so spiritually gentle, so high, so deep, and yet so richly relishable, that it were hardly inappropriate in an angel. It is the very religion of mirth; for nothing so human but it may be advanced to that. The orchard of the Old Manse seems the visible type of the fine mind that has described it—those twisted and contorted old trees, "that stretch out their crooked branches, and take such hold of the imagination, that we remember them as humorists and odd-fellows." And then, as surrounded by these grotesque forms, and hushed in the noon-day repose of this Hawthorne's spell, how aptly might the still fall of his ruddy thoughts into your soul be symbolized by "the thump of a great apple, in the stillest afternoon, falling without a breath of wind, from the mere necessity of perfect ripeness!" For no less ripe than ruddy are the apples of the thoughts and fancies in this sweet Man of Mosses—

"Buds and Bird-voices"—[4]

What a delicious thing is that! "Will the world ever be so decayed, that Spring may not renew its greenness?" And the "Fire-Worship." Was ever the hearth so glorified into an altar before? The mere title of that piece is better than any common work in fifty folio volumes. How exquisite is this:—

"Nor did it lessen the charm of his soft, familiar courtesy and helpfulness, that the mighty spirit, were opportunity offered him, would run riot through the peaceful house, wrap its inmates in his terrible embrace, and leave nothing of them save their whitened bones. This possibility of mad destruction only made his domestic kindness the more beautiful and touching. It was so sweet of him, being endowed with such power, to dwell, day after day, and one long, lonesome night after another, on the dusky hearth, only now and then betraying his wild nature, by thrusting his red tongue out of the chimney-top! True, he had done much mischief in the world, and was pretty certain to do more, but his warm heart atoned for all; He was kindly to the race of man."

But he has still other apples, not quite so ruddy, though full as ripe;—apples, that have been left to wither on the tree, after the pleasant autumn gathering is past. The sketch of "The Old Apple-Dealer" is conceived in the subtlest spirit of sadness; he whose "subdued and nerveless boyhood prefigured his abortive prime, which, likewise, contained within itself the prophecy and image of his lean and torpid age." Such touches as are in this piece cannot proceed from any common heart. They argue such a depth of tenderness, such a boundless sympathy with all forms of being, such an omnipresent love, that we must needs say that this Hawthorne is here almost alone in his generation,—at least, in the artistic manifestation of these things. Still more. Such touches as these,—and many, very many similar ones, all through his chapters—furnish clues whereby we enter a little way into the intricate, profound heart where they originated. And we see that suffering, some time or other and in some shape or other,—this only can enable any man to depict it in others. All over him, Hawthorne's melancholy rests like an Indian-summer, which, though bathing a whole country in one softness, still reveals the distinctive hue of every towering hill and each far-winding vale.

But it is the least part of genius that attracts admiration. Where Hawthorne is known, he seems to be deemed a pleasant writer, with a pleasant style,—a sequestered, harmless man, from whom any deep and weighty thing would hardly be anticipated—a man who means no meanings. But there is no man, in whom humor and love, like mountain peaks, soar to such a rapt height as to receive the irradiations of the upper skies;—there is no man in whom humor and love are developed in that high form called genius; no such man can exist without also possessing, as the indispensable complement of these, a great, deep intellect, which drops down into the universe like a plummet. Or, love and humor are only the eyes through which such an intellect views this world. The great beauty in such a mind is but the product of its strength. What, to all readers, can be more charming than the piece entitled "Monsieur du Miroir"; and to a reader at all capable of fully fathoming it, what, at the same time, can possess more mystical depth of meaning?—yes, there he sits and looks at me,—this "shape of mystery," this "identical Monsieur du Miroir." "Methinks I should tremble now, were his wizard power of gliding through all impediments in search of me, to place him suddenly before my eyes."

How profound, nay appalling, is the moral evolved by the "Earth's Holocaust"; where—beginning with the hollow follies and affectations of the world,—all vanities and empty theories and forms are, one after another, and by an admirably graduated, growing comprehensiveness, thrown into the allegorical fire, till, at length, nothing is left but the all-engendering heart of man; which remaining still unconsumed, the great conflagration is naught.

Of a piece with this, is the "Intelligence Office," a wondrous symbolizing of the secret workings in men's souls. There are other sketches still more charged with ponderous import.

"The Christmas Banquet," and "The Bosom Serpent," would be fine subjects for a curious and elaborate analysis, touching the conjectural parts of the mind that produced them. For spite of all the Indian-summer sunlight on the hither side of Hawthorne's soul, the other side—like the dark half of the physical sphere—is shrouded in a blackness, ten times black. But this darkness but gives more effect to the ever-moving dawn, that for ever advances through it, and circumnavigates his world. Whether Hawthorne has simply availed himself of this mystical blackness as a means to the wondrous effects he makes it to produce in his lights and shades; or whether there really lurks in him, perhaps unknown to himself, a touch of Puritanic gloom,—this, I cannot altogether tell. Certain it is, however, that this great power of blackness in him derives its force from its appeals to that Calvinistic sense of Innate Depravity and Original Sin, from whose visitations, in some shape or other, no deeply thinking mind is always and wholly free. For, in certain moods, no man can weigh this world without throwing in something, somehow like Original Sin, to strike the uneven balance. At all events, perhaps no writer has ever wielded this terrific thought with greater terror than this same harmless Hawthorne. Still more: this black conceit pervades him through and through. You may be witched by his sunlight,—transported by the bright gildings in the skies he builds over you; but there is the blackness of darkness beyond; and even his bright gildings but fringe and play upon the edges of thunderclouds. In one word, the world is mistaken in this Nathaniel Hawthorne. He himself must often have smiled at its absurd misconception of him. He is immeasurably deeper than the plummet of the mere critic. For it is not the brain that can test such a man; it is only the heart. You cannot come to know greatness by inspecting it; there is no glimpse to be caught of it, except by intuition; you need not ring it, you but touch it, and you find it is gold.

Now, it is that blackness in Hawthorne, of which I have spoken, that so fixes and fascinates me. It may be, nevertheless, that it is too largely developed in him. Perhaps he does not give us a ray of his light for every shade of his dark. But however this may be, this blackness it is that furnishes the infinite obscure of his back-ground,—that back-ground, against which Shakspeare plays his grandest conceits, the things that have made for Shakspeare his loftiest but most circumscribed renown, as the profoundest of thinkers. For by philosophers Shakspeare is not adored as the great man of tragedy and

comedy.—"Off with his head; so much for Buckingham!"
This sort of rant, interlined by another hand, brings down the
house,—those mistaken souls, who dream of Shakspeare as a
mere man of Richard-the-Third humps and Macbeth daggers.
But it is those deep far-away things in him; those occasional
flashings-forth of the intuitive Truth in him; those short, quick
probings at the very axis of reality;—these are the things that
make Shakspeare, Shakspeare.   Through the mouths of the
dark characters of Hamlet, Timon, Lear, and Iago, he craftily
says, or sometimes insinuates the things which we feel to be
so terrifically true, that it were all but madness for any good
man, in his own proper character, to utter, or even hint of them.
Tormented into desperation, Lear, the frantic king, tears off the
mask, and speaks the same madness of vital truth.   But, as I
before said, it is the least part of genius that attracts admiration.
And so, much of the blind, unbridled admiration that has been
heaped upon Shakspeare, has been lavished upon the least
part of him.   And few of his endless commentators and critics
seem to have remembered, or even perceived, that the immediate products of a great mind are not so great as that undeveloped
and sometimes undevelopable yet dimly-discernible greatness,
to which those immediate products are but the infallible indices.
In Shakspeare's tomb lies infinitely more than Shakspeare ever
wrote.   And if I magnify Shakspeare, it is not so much for
what he did do as for what he did not do, or refrained from doing.   For in this world of lies, Truth is forced to fly like a
scared white doe in the woodlands; and only by cunning
glimpses will she reveal herself, as in Shakspeare and other
masters of the great Art of Telling the Truth,—even though it
be covertly and by snatches.

But if this view of the all-popular Shakspeare be seldom taken
by his readers, and if very few who extol him have ever read
him deeply, or perhaps, only have seen him on the tricky stage
(which alone made, and is still making him his mere mob renown)—if few men have time, or patience, or palate, for the
spiritual truth as it is in that great genius;—it is then no matter
of surprise, that in a contemporaneous age, Nathaniel Haw-

thorne is a man as yet almost utterly mistaken among men. Here and there, in some quiet arm-chair in the noisy town, or some deep nook among the noiseless mountains, he may be appreciated for something of what he is. But unlike Shakspeare, who was forced to the contrary course by circumstances, Hawthorne (either from simple disinclination, or else from inaptitude) refrains from all the popularizing noise and show of broad farce and blood-besmeared tragedy; content with the still, rich utterance of a great intellect in repose, and which sends few thoughts into circulation, except they be arterialized at his large warm lungs, and expanded in his honest heart.

Nor need you fix upon that blackness in him, if it suit you not. Nor, indeed, will all readers discern it; for it is, mostly, insinuated to those who may best understand it, and account for it; it is not obtruded upon every one alike.

Some may start to read of Shakspeare and Hawthorne on the same page. They may say, that if an illustration were needed, a lesser light might have sufficed to elucidate this Hawthorne, this small man of yesterday. But I am not willingly one of those who, as touching Shakspeare at least, exemplify the maxim of Rochefoucauld, that "we exalt the reputation of some, in order to depress that of others";—who, to teach all noble-souled aspirants that there is no hope for them, pronounce Shakspeare absolutely unapproachable. But Shakspeare has been approached. There are minds that have gone as far as Shakspeare into the universe. And hardly a mortal man, who, at some time or other, has not felt as great thoughts in him as any you will find in Hamlet. We must not inferentially malign mankind for the sake of any one man, whoever he may be. This is too cheap a purchase of contentment for conscious mediocrity to make. Besides, this absolute and unconditional adoration of Shakspeare has grown to be a part of our Anglo-Saxon superstitions. The Thirty-Nine Articles are now Forty. Intolerance has come to exist in this matter. You must believe in Shakspeare's unapproachability, or quit the country. But what sort of a belief is this for an American, a man who is bound to carry republican progressiveness into Literature as well as into Life? Believe me, my friends, that men, not very much inferior to Shakspeare, are this day being born on the banks of the Ohio. And the day will come when you shall say, Who reads a book by an Englishman that is a modern?[5] The great mistake seems to be, that even with those Americans who look forward to the coming of a great literary genius among us, they somehow fancy he will come in the costume of Queen Elizabeth's day; be a writer of dramas founded upon old English history or the tales of Boccaccio. Whereas, great geniuses are parts of the times, they themselves are the times, and possess a correspondent coloring. It is of a piece with the Jews, who, while their Shiloh was meekly walking in their streets, were still praying for his magnificent coming; looking for him in a chariot, who was already among them on an ass. Nor must we forget that, in his own lifetime, Shakspeare was not Shakspeare, but only Master William Shakspeare of the shrewd, thriving business firm of Condell, Shakspeare & Co., proprietors of the Globe Theatre in London; and by a courtly author, of the name of Chettle, was looked at as an "upstart crow," beautified "with other birds' feathers."[6] For, mark it well, imitation is often the first charge brought against real originality. Why this is so, there is not space to set forth here. You must have plenty of sea-room to tell the Truth in; especially when it seems to have an aspect of newness, as America did in 1492, though it was then just as old, and perhaps older than Asia, only those sagacious philosophers, the common sailors, had never seen it before, swearing it was all water and moonshine there.

Now I do not say that Nathaniel of Salem is a greater than William of Avon, or as great. But the difference between the two men is by no means immeasurable. Not a very great deal more, and Nathaniel were verily William.

This, too, I mean, that if Shakspeare has not been equalled, give the world time, and he is sure to be surpassed, in one hemisphere or the other.[7] Nor will it at all do to say, that the world is getting grey and grizzled now, and has lost that fresh charm which she wore of old, and by virtue of which the great poets of past times made themselves what we esteem them to be. Not so. The world is as young to-day as when it was created; and this Vermont morning dew is as wet to my feet, as Eden's dew to Adam's. Nor has nature been all over ransacked by our progenitors, so that no new charms and mysteries remain for this latter generation to find. Far from it. The trillionth part has not yet been said; and all that has been said, but multiplies the avenues to what remains to be said. It is not so much paucity as superabundance of material that seems to incapacitate modern authors.

Let America, then, prize and cherish her writers; yea, let her glorify them. They are not so many in number as to exhaust her good-will. And while she has good kith and kin of her own, to take to her bosom, let her not lavish her embraces upon the household of an alien. For believe it or not, England, after all, is in many things an alien to us. China has more bonds of real love for us than she. But even were there no strong literary individualities among us, as there are some dozens at least, nevertheless, let America first praise mediocrity even, in her own children, before she praises (for everywhere, merit demands acknowledgment from every one) the best excellence in the children of any other land. Let her own authors, I say, have the priority of appreciation. I was much pleased with a hot-headed Carolina cousin of mine, who once said,— "If there were no other American to stand by, in literature, why, then, I would stand by Pop Emmons and his 'Fredoniad,' [8] and till a better epic came along, swear it was not very far behind the Iliad." Take away the words, and in spirit he was sound.

Not that American genius needs patronage in order to expand. For that explosive sort of stuff will expand though screwed up in a vice, and burst it, though it were triple steel. It is for the nation's sake, and not for her authors' sake, that I would have America be heedful of the increasing greatness among her writers. For how great the shame, if other nations should be before her, in crowning her heroes of the pen! But this is almost the case now. American authors have received more just and discriminating praise (however loftily and ridiculously given, in certain cases) even from some Englishmen, than from their own countrymen. There are hardly five critics in America; and several of them are asleep. As for patronage, it is the American author who now patronizes his country, and not his country him. And if at times some among them appeal to the people for more recognition, it is not always with selfish motives, but patriotic ones.

It is true, that but few of them as yet have evinced that decided originality which merits great praise. But that graceful writer, who perhaps of all Americans has received the most plaudits from his own country for his productions,—that very popular and amiable writer, however good and self-reliant in many things, perhaps owes his chief reputation to the self-acknowledged imitation of a foreign model, and to the studied avoidance of all topics but smooth ones.[9] But it is better to fail in originality than to succeed in imitation. He who has never failed somewhere, that man cannot be great. Failure is the true test of greatness. And if it be said, that continual success is a proof that a man wisely knows his powers,—it is only to be added, that, in that case, he knows them to be small. Let us believe it, then, once for all, that there is no hope for us in these smooth, pleasing writers that know their powers. Without malice, but to speak the plain fact, they but furnish an appendix to Goldsmith, and other English authors. And we want no American Goldsmiths: nay, we want no American Miltons. It were the vilest thing you could say of a true American author, that he were an American Tompkins.[10] Call him an American and have done, for you cannot say a nobler thing of him. But it is not meant that all American writers should studiously cleave to nationality in their writings; only this, no American writer should write like an Englishman or a Frenchman; let him write like a man, for then he will be sure to write like an American. Let us away with this leaven of literary flunkeyism towards England. If either must play the flunkey in this thing, let England do it, not us. While we are rapidly preparing for that political supremacy among the nations which prophetically awaits us at the close of the present century, in a literary point of view, we are deplorably unprepared for it; and we seem studious to remain so. Hitherto, reasons might have existed why this should be; but no good reason exists now. And all that is requisite to amendment in this matter, is simply this: that while freely acknowledging all excellence everywhere, we should refrain from unduly lauding foreign writers, and, at the same time, duly recognize meritorious writers that are our own; —those writers who breathe that unshackled, democratic spirit of Christianity in all things, which now takes the practical lead in this world, though at the same time led by ourselves—us Americans. Let us boldly contemn all imitation, though it comes to us graceful and fragrant as the morning; and foster all originality, though at first it be crabbed and ugly as our own pine knots. And if any of our authors fail, or seem to fail, then, in the words of my enthusiastic Carolina cousin, let us clap him on the shoulder, and back him against all Europe for his second round. The truth is, that in one point of view, this matter of a national literature has come to such a pass with us, that in some sense we must turn bullies, else the day is lost, or superiority so far beyond us, that we can hardly say it will ever be ours.

And now, my countrymen, as an excellent author of your own flesh and blood,—an unimitating, and, perhaps, in his way, an inimitable man—whom better can I commend to you, in the first place, than Nathaniel Hawthorne. He is one of the new, and far better generation of your writers. The smell of your beeches and hemlocks is upon him; your own broad prairies are in his soul; and if you travel away inland into his deep and noble nature, you will hear the far roar of his Niagara. Give not over to future generations the glad duty of acknowledging him for what he is. Take that joy to yourself, in your own generation; and so shall he feel those grateful impulses on him, that may possibly prompt him to the full flower of some still greater achievement in your eyes. And by confessing him you thereby confess others; you brace the whole brotherhood. For genius, all over the world, stands hand in hand, and one shock of recognition runs the whole circle round.

In treating of Hawthorne, or rather of Hawthorne in his writings (for I never saw the man; and in the chances of a quiet plantation life, remote from his haunts, perhaps never shall); in treating of his works, I say, I have thus far omitted all mention of his "Twice Told Tales," and "Scarlet Letter." Both are excellent, but full of such manifold, strange, and diffusive beauties, that time would all but fail me to point the half of them out. But there are things in those two books, which, had they been written in England a century ago, Nathaniel Hawthorne had utterly displaced many of the bright names we now revere on authority.[11] But I am content to leave Hawthorne to himself, and to the infallible finding of posterity; and however great may be the praise I have bestowed upon him, I feel that in so doing I have more served and honored myself, than him. For, at bottom, great excellence is praise enough to itself; but the feeling of a sincere and appreciative love and admiration towards it, this is relieved by utterance; and warm, honest praise, ever leaves a pleasant flavor in the mouth; and it is an honorable thing to confess to what is honorable in others.

But I cannot leave my subject yet. No man can ever read a fine author, and relish him to his very bones while he reads, without subsequently fancying to himself some ideal image of the man and his mind. And if you rightly look for it, you will almost always find that the author himself has somewhere furnished you with his own picture. For poets (whether in prose or verse), being painters of nature, are like their brethren of the pencil, the true portrait-painters, who, in the multitude of likenesses to be sketched, do not invariably omit their own; and in all high instances, they paint them without any vanity, though at times with a lurking something, that would take several pages to properly define.

I submit it, then, to those best acquainted with the man personally, whether the following is not Nathaniel Hawthorne; —and to himself, whether something involved in it does not express the temper of his mind,—that lasting temper of all true, candid men—a seeker, not a finder yet:—

"A man now entered, in neglected attire, with the aspect of a thinker, but somewhat too rough-hewn and brawny for a scholar. His face was full of sturdy vigor, with some finer and keener attribute beneath; though harsh at first, it was tempered with the glow of a large, warm heart, which had force enough to heat his powerful intellect through and through. He advanced to the Intelligencer, and looked at him with a glance of such stern sincerity, that perhaps few secrets were beyond its scope.

"'I seek for Truth.' said he."

* * *

Twenty-four hours have elapsed since writing the foregoing. I have just returned from the hay-mow, charged more and more with love and admiration of Hawthorne. For I have just been gleaning through the Mosses, picking up many things here and there that had previously escaped me. And I found that but to glean after this man, is better than to be in at the harvest of others. To be frank (though, perhaps, rather foolish) notwithstanding what I wrote yesterday of these Mosses, I had not then culled them all; but had, nevertheless, been sufficiently sensible of the subtle essence in them, as to write as I did. To what infinite height of loving wonder and admiration I may yet be borne, when by repeatedly banqueting on these Mosses I shall have thoroughly incorporated their whole stuff into my being,—that, I cannot tell. But already I feel that this Hawthorne has dropped germinous seeds into my soul. He expands and deepens down, the more I contemplate him; and further and further, shoots his strong New England roots in the hot soil of my Southern soul.

By careful reference to the "Table of Contents," I now find that I have gone through all the sketches; but that when I yesterday wrote, I had not at all read two particular pieces, to which I now desire to call special attention,—"A Select Party," and "Young Goodman Brown." Here, be it said to all those whom this poor fugitive scrawl of mine may tempt to the perusal of the "Mosses," that they must on no account suffer themselves to be trifled with, disappointed, or deceived by the triviality of many of the titles to these sketches. For in more than one instance, the title utterly belies the piece. It is as if rustic demijohns containing the very best and costliest of Falernian and Tokay, were labelled "Cider," "Perry," and "Elder-berry wine." The truth seems to be, that like many other geniuses, this Man of Mosses takes great delight in hood-winking the world,—at least, with respect to himself. Personally, I doubt not that he rather prefers to be generally esteemed but a so-so sort of author; being willing to reserve the thorough and acute appreciation of what he is, to that party most qualified to judge—that is, to himself. Besides, at the bottom of their natures, men like Hawthorne, in many things, deem the plaudits of the public such strong presumptive evidence of mediocrity in the object of them, that it would in some degree render them doubtful of their own powers, did they hear much and vociferous braying concerning them in the public pastures. True, I have been braying myself (if you please to be witty enough to have it so), but then I claim to be the first that has so brayed in this particular matter; and therefore, while pleading guilty to the charge, still claim all the merit due to originality.

But with whatever motive, playful or profound, Nathaniel Hawthorne has chosen to entitle his pieces in the manner he has, it is certain that some of them are directly calculated to deceive —egregiously deceive, the superficial skimmer of pages. To be downright and candid once more, let me cheerfully say, that two of these titles did dolefully dupe no less an eagle-eyed reader than myself; and that, too, after I had been impressed with a sense of the great depth and breadth of this American man. "Who in the name of thunder" (as the country-people say in this neighborhood), "who in the name of thunder, would anticipate any marvel in a piece entitled 'Young Goodman Brown'?" You would of course suppose that it was a simple little tale, intended as a supplement to "Goody Two Shoes." Whereas, it is deep as Dante; nor can you finish it, without addressing the author in his own words—"It is yours to penetrate, in every bosom, the deep mystery of sin." And with Young

Goodman, too, in allegorical pursuit of his Puritan wife, you cry out in your anguish:

> "'Faith!' shouted Goodman Brown, in a voice of agony and desperation; and the echoes of the forest mocked him, crying, —'Faith! Faith!' as if bewildered wretches were seeking her all through the wilderness."

Now this same piece, entitled "Young Goodman Brown," is one of the two that I had not all read yesterday; and I allude to it now, because it is, in itself, such a strong positive illustration of that blackness in Hawthorne, which I had assumed from the mere occasional shadows of it, as revealed in several of the other sketches. But had I previously perused "Young Goodman Brown," I should have been at no pains to draw the conclusion, which I came to at a time when I was ignorant that the book contained one such direct and unqualified manifestation of it.

The other piece of the two referred to, is entitled "A Select Party," which, in my first simplicity upon originally taking hold of the book, I fancied must treat of some pumpkin-pie party in old Salem, or some chowder-party on Cape Cod. Whereas, by all the gods of Peedee,[12] it is the sweetest and sublimest thing that has been written since Spenser wrote. Nay, there is nothing in Spenser that surpasses[13] it, perhaps nothing that equals it. And the test is this: read any canto in "The Faery Queen," and then read "A Select Party" and decide which pleases you the most,—that is, if you are qualified to judge. Do not be frightened at this; for when Spenser was alive, he was thought of very much as Hawthorne is now,— was generally accounted just such a "gentle" harmless man. It may be, that to common eyes, the sublimity of Hawthorne seems lost in his sweetness,—as perhaps in that same "Select Party" of his; for whom he has builded so august a dome of sunset clouds, and served them on richer plate than Belshazzar's when he banqueted his lords in Babylon.

But my chief business now, is to point out a particular page in this piece, having reference to an honored guest, who under the name of "The Master Genius," but in the guise "of a young man of poor attire, with no insignia of rank or acknowledged eminence," is introduced to the man of Fancy, who is the giver of the feast. Now, the page having reference to this "Master Genius," so happily expresses much of what I yesterday wrote, touching the coming of the literary Shiloh of America, that I cannot but be charmed by the coincidence; especially, when it shows such a parity of ideas, at least in this one point, between a man like Hawthorne and a man like me.[14]

And here, let me throw out another conceit of mine touching this American Shiloh, or "Master Genius," as Hawthorne calls him. May it not be, that this commanding mind has not been, is not, and never will be, individually developed in any one man? And would it, indeed, appear so unreasonable to suppose, that this great fulness and overflowing may be, or may be destined to be, shared by a plurality of men of genius? Surely, to take the very greatest example on record, Shakspeare cannot be regarded as in himself the concretion of all the genius of his time; nor as so immeasurably beyond Marlow, Webster, Ford, Beaumont, Jonson, that those great men can be said to share none of his power? For one, I conceive that there were dramatists in Elizabeth's day, between whom and Shakspeare the distance was by no means great. Let any one, hitherto little acquainted with those neglected old authors, for the first time read them thoroughly, or even read Charles Lamb's Specimens of them, and he will be amazed at the wondrous ability of those Anaks[15] of men, and shocked at this renewed example of the fact, that Fortune has more to do with fame than merit,— though, without merit, lasting fame there can be none.

Nevertheless, it would argue too ill of my country were this maxim to hold good concerning Nathaniel Hawthorne, a man, who already, in some few minds, has shed "such a light, as never illuminates the earth save when a great heart burns as the household fire of a grand intellect."

The words are his,—in the "Select Party"; and they are a magnificent setting to a coincident sentiment of my own, but ramblingly[16] expressed yesterday, in reference to himself. Gainsay it who will, as I now write, I am Posterity speaking by proxy

—and after times will make it more than good, when I declare, that the American, who up to the present day has evinced, in literature, the largest brain with the largest heart, that man is Nathaniel Hawthorne. Moreover, that whatever Nathaniel Hawthorne may hereafter write, "The Mosses from an Old Manse" will be ultimately accounted his masterpiece. For there is a sure, though a secret sign in some works which proves the culmination of the powers (only the developable ones, how-ever) that produced them. But I am by no means desirous of the glory of a prophet. I pray Heaven that Hawthorne may *yet* prove me an impostor in this prediction. Especially, as I somehow cling to the strange fancy, that, in all men, hiddenly reside certain wondrous, occult properties—as in some plants and minerals—which by some happy but very rare accident (as bronze was discovered by the melting of the iron and brass at the burning of Corinth) may chance to be called forth here on earth; not entirely waiting for their better discovery in the more congenial, blessed atmosphere of heaven.

Once more—for it is hard to be finite upon an infinite subject, and all subjects are infinite. By some people this entire scrawl of mine may[17] be esteemed altogether unnecessary, inasmuch "as years ago" (they may say) "we found out the rich and rare stuff in this Hawthorne, whom you now parade forth, as if only *yourself* were the discoverer of this Portuguese diamond in our literature." But even granting all this—and adding to it, the assumption that the books of Hawthorne have sold by the five thousand,—what does that signify? They should be sold by the hundred thousand; and read by the million; and admired by every one who is capable of admiration.

POEMS

TO DANIEL SHEPHERD[1]

Come, Shepherd, come and visit me:
Come, we'll make it A[r]cady:
Come, if but for charity.
Sure, with such a pastoral name,
Thee the city should not claim.
Come, then, Shepherd, come away,
Thy sheep in bordering pastures stray.

Come, Daniel, come and visit me:
I'm lost in many a quandary:
I've dreamed, like Bab'lon's Majesty:[2]   10
Prophet, come expound for me.
—I dreamed I saw a laurel grove,
Claimed for his by the bird of love,
Who, elate with such dominion,
Oft cuffed the boughs with haughty pinion.
Indignantly the trees complain,
Accusing his afflictive reign.
Their plaints the chivalry excite
Of chanticleers, a plucky host:
They battle with the bird of light.   20
Beaten, he wings his northward flight,
No more his laurel realm to boast,
Where now, to crow, the cocks alight,
And—break down all the branches quite!
Such a weight of friendship pure
The grateful trees could not endure.
This dream, it still disturbeth me:
Seer, foreshows it Italy?[3]

346

But other visions stir my head;
No poet-problems, fancy-fed—   30
Domestic prose of board and bed.
I marvel oft how guest *unwined*
Will to this farm-house be resigned.
Not a pint of ruby claret
   Cooleth in our cellar-bin;
And ripening in our sultry garret,
   Otard glows no flask within.
(Claret and otard here I name
Because each is your fav'rite flame:
Placed 'tween the two decanters, you,   40
Like Alexander, your dear charmers view,
And both so fair you find, you neither can eschew:
—That's what they call an Alexandrine; ⎫
Don't you think it very damn'd fine? ⎭
—Brackets serve to fence this prattle,
Pound for episodic cattle.—
I said that me the Fates do cripple
In matter of a wholesome "tipple"—
Now, is it for oft cursing gold,
   For lucre vile,   50
The Hags do thus from me withhold
   Sweet Bacchus' smile?
Smile, that like other smiles as mellow,
Not often greets Truth's simple fellow:—
For why? Not his the magic dollar?
You should know, you Wall-Street scholar!
—Of Bourbon that is rather new
I brag a fat black bottle or two.—
Shepherd, is this such Mountain-Dew
As one might fitly offer you?   60
Yet if cold water will content ye
My word, of that ye shall have plenty.
Thanks to late floods, our spring, it brims,—
Will't mind a crush * of goblet-rims?

    * The MS. may read "a crunch." [*Editor's note.*]

—I've told some doubts that sadly pose me:
Come then now straight resolve me.
Come, these matters sagely read,
Daniel, of the prophet breed.
Daniel Shepherd, come and rove—
    Freely rove the fairy dells;   70
The one the Housatonic[4] clove,
    And that where genial friendship dwells.

Pittsfield July 6th 1859

From *Battle-Pieces*[5]

THE PORTENT

(1859)

Hanging from the beam,
    Slowly swaying (such the law),
Gaunt the shadow on your green,
    Shenandoah!
The cut is on the crown
(Lo, John Brown),
And the stabs shall heal no more.

Hidden in the cap
    Is the anguish none can draw;
So your future veils its face,   10
    Shenandoah!
But the streaming beard is shown
(Weird John Brown),
The meteor of the war.

LYON[6]

Battle of Springfield, Missouri

(August 1861)

Some hearts there are of deeper sort,
    Prophetic, sad,
Which yet for cause are trebly clad;

Known death they fly on:
This wizard-heart and heart-of-oak had Lyon.

"They are more than twenty thousand strong,
 We less than five,
Too few with such a host to strive."
 "Such counsel, fie on!
'Tis battle, or 'tis shame"; and firm stood Lyon.   10

"For help at need in vain we wait—
 Retreat or fight:
Retreat the foe would take for flight,
 And each proud scion
Feel more elate; the end must come," said Lyon.

By candlelight he wrote the will,
 And left his all
To Her for whom 'twas not enough to fall;
 Loud neighed Orion
Without the tent; drums beat; we marched with Lyon.   20

The night-tramp done, we spied the Vale
 With guard-fires lit;
Day broke, but trooping clouds made gloom of it:
 "A field to die on,"
Presaged in his unfaltering heart, brave Lyon.

We fought on the grass, we bled in the corn—
 Fate seemed malign;
His horse the Leader led along the line—
 Star-browed Orion;
Bitterly fearless, he rallied us there, brave Lyon.   30

There came a sound like the slitting of air
 By a swift sharp sword—
A rush of the sound; and the sleek chest broad
 Of black Orion
Heaved, and was fixed; the dead mane waved toward Lyon.

"General, you're hurt—this sleet of balls!"
    He seemed half spent;
With moody and bloody brow, he lowly bent:
    "The field to die on;
But not—not yet; the day is long," breathed Lyon.   40

For a time becharmed there fell a lull
    In the heart of the fight;
The tree-tops nod, the slain sleep light;
    Warm noon-winds sigh on,
And thoughts which he never spake had Lyon.

Texans and Indians trim for a charge:
    "Stand ready, men!
Let them come close, right up, and then
    After the lead, the iron;
Fire, and charge back!" So strength returned to Lyon. 50

The Iowa men who held the van,
    Half drilled, were new
To battle: "Some one lead us, then we'll do,"
    Said Corporal Tryon:
"Men! *I* will lead," and a light glared in Lyon.

On they came: they yelped, and fired;
    His spirit sped;
We levelled right in, and the half-breeds fled,
    Nor stayed the iron,
Nor captured the crimson corse of Lyon.   60

This seer foresaw his soldier-doom,
    Yet willed the fight.
He never turned; his only flight
    Was up to Zion,
Where prophets now and armies greet brave Lyon.

A UTILITARIAN VIEW OF THE MONITOR'S FIGHT[7]

Plain be the phrase, yet apt the verse,
  More ponderous than nimble;
For since grimed War here laid aside
His Orient pomp, 'twould ill befit
    Overmuch to ply
  The rhyme's barbaric cymbal.

Hail to victory without the gaud
  Of glory; zeal that needs no fans
Of banners; plain mechanic power
Plied cogently in War now placed—   10
    Where War belongs—
  Among the trades and artisans.

Yet this was battle, and intense—
  Beyond the strife of fleets heroic;
Deadlier, closer, calm 'mid storm;
No passion; all went on by crank,
    Pivot, and screw,
  And calculations of caloric.

Needless to dwell; the story's known.
  The ringing of those plates on plates   20
Still ringeth round the world—
The clangor of that blacksmiths' fray.
    The anvil-din
  Resounds this message from the Fates:

War shall yet be, and to the end;
  But war-paint shows the streaks of weather;
War yet shall be, but warriors
Are now but operatives; War's made
    Less grand than Peace,
  And a singe runs through lace and feather.   30

MALVERN HILL[8]
(July, 1862)

Ye elms that wave on Malvern Hill
  In prime of morn and May,
Recall ye how McClellan's men
    Here stood at bay?
While deep within yon forest dim
  Our rigid comrades lay—
Some with the cartridge in their mouth,
Others with fixed arms lifted South—
    Invoking so
The cypress glades? Ah wilds of woe!   10

The spires of Richmond, late beheld
  Through rifts in musket-haze,
Were closed from view in clouds of dust
    On leaf-walled ways,
Where streamed our wagons in caravan;
  And the Seven Nights and Days
Of march and fast, retreat and fight,
Pinched our grimed faces to ghastly plight—
    Does the elm wood
Recall the haggard beards of blood?   20

The battle-smoked flag, with stars eclipsed,
  We followed (it never fell!)—
In silence husbanded our strength—
    Received their yell;
Till on this slope we patient turned
  With cannon ordered well;
Reverse we proved was not defeat;
But ah, the sod what thousands meet!—
    Does Malvern Wood
Bethink itself, and muse and brood?   30

    We elms of Malvern Hill
    Remember everything;

> But sap the twig will fill:
> Wag the world how it will,
>   Leaves must be green in Spring.

SHERIDAN AT CEDAR CREEK[9]
(October, 1864)

Shoe the steed with silver
    That bore him to the fray,
When he heard the guns at dawning—
    Miles away;
When he heard them calling, calling—
    Mount! nor stay:
        Quick, or all is lost;
        They've surprised and stormed the post,
        They push your routed host—
    Gallop! retrieve the day.   10

House the horse in ermine—
    For the foam-flake blew
White through the red October;
    He thundered into view;
They cheered him in the looming,
    Horseman and horse they knew.
        The turn of the tide began,[10]
        The rally of bugles ran,
        He swung his hat in the van;
    The electric hoof-spark flew.   20

Wreathe the steed and lead him—
    For the charge he led
Touched and turned the cypress
    Into amaranths for the head
Of Philip, king of riders,
    Who raised them from the dead.

The camp (at dawning lost),
    By eve, recovered—forced,
Rang with laughter of the host
    At belated Early fled.   30

Shroud the horse in sable—
    For the mounds they heap!
There is firing in the Valley,
    And yet no strife they keep;
It is the parting volley,
    It is the pathos deep.
        There is glory for the brave
        Who lead, and nobly save,
        But no knowledge in the grave
    Where the nameless followers sleep.   40

From *Verses Inscriptive and Memorial*

ON THE GRAVE OF A YOUNG CAVALRY
OFFICER KILLED IN THE VALLEY OF
VIRGINIA

Beauty and youth, with manners sweet, and friends—
    Gold, yet a mind not unenriched had he
Whom here low violets veil from eyes.
    But all these gifts transcended be:
His happier fortune in this mound you see.

A REQUIEM

for Soldiers lost in Ocean Transports

When, after storms that woodlands rue,
    To valleys comes atoning dawn,
The robins blithe their orchard-sports renew;
    And meadow-larks, no more withdrawn,

Caroling fly in the languid blue;
The while, from many a hid recess,
Alert to partake the blessedness,
The pouring mites their airy dance pursue.
  So, after ocean's ghastly gales,
When laughing light of hoyden morning breaks,   10
    Every finny hider wakes—
  From vaults profound swims up with glittering scales;
  Through the delightsome sea he sails,
With shoals of shining tiny things
Frolic on every wave that flings
  Against the prow its showery spray;
All creatures joying in the morn,
Save them forever from joyance torn,
  Whose bark was lost where now the dolphins play;
Save them that by the fabled shore,   20
  Down the pale stream are washed away,
Far to the reef of bones are borne;
  And never revisits them the light,
Nor sight of long-sought land and pilot more;
  Nor heed they now the lone bird's flight
Round the lone spar where mid-sea surges pour.

A MEDITATION

Attributed to a Northerner after attending the last of two
  funerals from the same homestead—those of a National
  and a Confederate officer (brothers), his kinsmen, who had
  died from the effects of wounds received in the closing
  battles.

          How often in the years that close,
              When truce had stilled the sieging gun,
          The soldiers, mounting on their works,
              With mutual curious glance have run
          From face to face along the fronting show,
          And kinsman spied, or friend—even in a foe.

What thoughts conflicting then were shared,
    While sacred tenderness perforce
Welled from the heart and wet the eye;
    And something of a strange remorse   10
Rebelled against the sanctioned sin of blood,
And Christian wars of natural brotherhood.

Then stirred the god within the breast—
    The witness that is man's at birth;
A deep misgiving undermined
    Each plea and subterfuge of earth;
They felt in that rapt pause, with warning rife,
Horror and anguish for the civil strife.

Of North or South they recked not then,
    Warm passion cursed the cause of war: 20
Can Africa pay back this blood
    Spilt on Potomac's shore?
Yet doubts, as pangs, were vain the strife to stay,
And hands that fain had clasped again could slay.

How frequent in the camp was seen
    The herald from the hostile one,
A guest and frank companion there
    When the proud formal talk was done;
The pipe of peace was smoked even 'mid the war,
And fields in Mexico again fought o'er.   30

In Western battle long they lay
    So near opposed in trench or pit,
That foeman unto foeman called
    As men who screened in tavern sit:
"You bravely fight" each to the other said—
"Toss us a biscuit!" o'er the wall it sped.

And pale on those same slopes, a boy—
    A stormer, bled in noon-day glare;

No aid the Blue-coats then could bring,
   He cried to them who nearest were,   40
And out there came 'mid howling shot and shell
A daring foe who him befriended well.

Mark the great Captains on both sides,
   The soldiers with the broad renown—
They all were messmates on the Hudson's marge,
   Beneath one roof they laid them down;
And, free from hate in many an after pass,
Strove as in school-boy rivalry of the class.

A darker side there is; but doubt
   In Nature's charity hovers there: 50
If men for new agreement yearn,
   Then old upbraiding best forbear:
"*The South's the sinner!*" Well, so let it be;
But shall the North sin worse, and stand the Pharisee?

O, now that brave men yield the sword,
   Mine be the manful soldier-view;
By how much more they boldly warred,
   By so much more is mercy due:
When Vicksburg fell, and the moody files marched out,
Silent the victors stood, scorning to raise a shout.   60

From *John Marr and Other Sailors*[11]

JOHN MARR[12]

Since as in night's deck-watch ye show,
Why, lads, so silent here to me,
Your watchmate of times long ago?

Once, for all the darkling sea,
You your voices raised how clearly,
Striking in when tempest sung;
Hoisting up the storm-sail cheerly,
Life is storm—let storm! you rung.

Taking things as fated merely,
Child-like though the world ye spanned;   10
Nor holding unto life too dearly,
Ye who held your lives in hand—
Skimmers, who on oceans four
Petrels were, and larks ashore.

O, not from memory lightly flung,
Forgot, like strains no more availing,
The heart to music haughtier strung;
Nay, frequent near me, never staling,
Whose good feeling kept ye young.
Like tides that enter creek or stream,   20
Ye come, ye visit me, or seem
Swimming out from seas of faces,
Alien myriads memory traces,
To enfold me in a dream!

I yearn as ye. But rafts that strain,
Parted, shall they lock again?
Twined we were, entwined, then riven,
Ever to new embracements driven,
Shifting gulf-weed of the main!
And how if one here shift no more,   30
Lodged by the flinging surge ashore?
Nor less, as now, in eve's decline,
Your shadowy fellowship is mine.
Ye float around me, form and feature:—
Tattooings, ear-rings, love-locks curled;
Barbarians of man's simpler nature,
Unworldly servers of the world.
Yea, present all, and dear to me,
    Though shades, or scouring China's sea.

Whither, whither, merchant-sailors,   40
Whitherward now in roaring gales?

Competing still, ye huntsman-whalers,
In leviathan's wake what boat prevails?
And man-of-war's men, whereaway?
If now no dinned drum beat to quarters
On the wilds of midnight waters—
Foemen looming through the spray;
Do yet your gangway lanterns, streaming,
Vainly strive to pierce below,
When, tilted from the slant plank gleaming,   50
A brother you see to darkness go?

But, gunmates lashed in shotted canvas,
If where long watch-below ye keep,
Never the shrill *"All hands up hammocks!"*
Breaks the spell that charms your sleep,
And summoning trumps might vainly call,
And booming guns implore—
A beat, a heart-beat musters all,
One heart-beat at heart-core.
It musters. But to clasp, retain;   60
To see you at the halyards main—
To hear your chorus once again!

FAR OFF-SHORE

Look, the raft, a signal flying,
    Thin—a shred;
None upon the lashed spars lying,
    Quick or dead.

Cries the sea-fowl, hovering over,
    "Crew, the crew?"
And the billow, reckless rover,
    Sweeps anew!

THE ENVIABLE ISLES [13]
(From "Rammon")

Through storms you reach them and from storms are free.
    Afar descried, the foremost drear in hue,
But, nearer, green; and, on the marge, the sea
    Makes thunder low and mist of rainbowed dew.

But, inland, where the sleep that folds the hills
A dreamier sleep, the trance of God, instills—
    On uplands hazed, in wandering airs aswoon,
Slow-swaying palms salute love's cypress tree
    Adown in vale where pebbly runlets croon
A song to lull all sorrow and all glee.   10

Sweet-fern and moss in many a glade are here,
    Where, strown in flocks, what cheek-flushed myriads lie
Dimpling in dream—unconscious slumberers mere,
    While billows endless round the beaches die.

From *Timoleon* [14]

AFTER THE PLEASURE PARTY [15]

Lines Traced
Under an Image of
Amor Threatening

Fear me, virgin whosoever
Taking pride from love exempt,
    Fear me, slighted. Never, never
Brave me, nor my fury tempt:
Downy wings, but wroth they beat
Tempest even in reason's seat.

Behind the house the upland falls
With many an odorous tree—
White marbles gleaming through green halls,
Terrace by terrace, down and down,   10
And meets the starlit Mediterranean Sea.

'Tis Paradise.   In such an hour
Some pangs that rend might take release.
Nor less perturbed who keeps this bower
Of balm, nor finds balsamic peace?
From whom the passionate words in vent
After long revery's discontent?

    Tired of the homeless deep,
Look how their flight yon hurrying billows urge,
Hitherward but to reap   20
Passive repulse from the iron-bound verge!
Insensate, can they never know
'Tis mad to wreck the impulsion so?

    An art of memory is, they tell:
But to forget! forget the glade
Wherein Fate sprung Love's ambuscade,
To flout pale years of cloistral life
And flush me in this sensuous strife.
'Tis Vesta struck with Sappho's smart.
No fable her delirious leap: 30
With more of cause in desperate heart,
Myself could take it—but to sleep!

    Now first I feel, what all may ween,
That soon or late, if faded e'en,
One's sex asserts itself.   Desire,
The dear desire through love to sway,
Is like the Geysers that aspire—
Through cold obstruction win their fervid way.
But baffled here—to take disdain,
To feel rule's instinct, yet not rein;   40
To dote, to come to this drear shame—
Hence the winged blaze that sweeps my soul
Like prairie fires that spurn control,
Where withering weeds incense the flame.

And kept I long heaven's watch for this,
Contemning love, for this, even this?
O terrace chill in Northern air,
O reaching ranging tube I placed
Against yon skies, and fable chased
Till, fool, I hailed for sister there   50
Starred Cassiopeia in Golden Chair.
In dream I throned me, nor I saw
In cell the idiot crowned with straw.

And yet, ah yet scarce ill I reigned,
Through self-illusion self-sustained,
When now—enlightened, undeceived—
What gain I barrenly bereaved!
Than this can be yet lower decline—
Envy and spleen, can these be mine?

The peasant girl demure that trod   60
Beside our wheels that climbed the way,
And bore along a blossoming rod
That looked the sceptre of May-Day—
On her—to fire this petty hell,
His softened glance how moistly fell!
The cheat! on briars her buds were strung;
And wiles peeped forth from mien how meek.
The innocent bare-foot! young, so young!
To girls, strong man's a novice weak.
To tell such beads!   And more remain,   70
Sad rosary of belittling pain.

When after lunch and sallies gay,
Like the Decameron folk we lay
In sylvan groups; and I—let be!
O, dreams he, can he dream that one
Because not roseate feels no sun?
The plain lone bramble thrills with Spring
As much as vines that grapes shall bring.

Me now fair studies charm no more.
Shall great thoughts writ, or high themes sung   80
Damask wan cheeks—unlock his arm
About some radiant ninny flung?
How glad with all my starry lore,
I'd buy the veriest wanton's rose
Would but my bee therein repose.

Could I remake me! or set free
This sexless bound in sex, then plunge
Deeper than Sappho, in a lunge
Piercing Pan's paramount mystery!
For, Nature, in no shallow surge   90
Against thee either sex may urge,
Why hast thou made us but in halves—
Co-relatives? This makes us slaves.
If these co-relatives never meet
Self-hood itself seems incomplete.
And such the dicing of blind fate
Few matching halves here meet and mate.
What Cosmic jest or Anarch blunder
The human integral clove asunder
And shied the fractions through life's gate?   100

Ye stars that long your votary knew
Rapt in her vigil, see me here!
Whither is gone the spell ye threw
When rose before me Cassiopeia?
Usurped on by love's stronger reign—
But lo, your very selves do wane:
Light breaks—truth breaks! Silvered no more,
But chilled by dawn that brings the gale
Shivers yon bramble above the vale,
And disillusion opens all the shore.   110

One knows not if Urania yet
The pleasure-party may forget;

Or whether she lived down the strain
Of turbulent heart and rebel brain;
For Amor so resents a slight,
And her's had been such haught disdain,
He long may wreak his boyish spite,
And boy-like, little reck the pain.

One knows not, no. But late in Rome
(For queens discrowned a congruous home)   120
Entering Albani's porch [16] she stood
Fixed by an antique pagan stone
Colossal carved. No anchorite seer,
Not Thomas à Kempis, monk austere,
Religious more are in their tone;
Yet far, how far from Christian heart
That form august of heathen Art.
Swayed by its influence, long she stood,
Till surged emotion seething down,
She rallied and this mood she won: 130

Languid in frame for me,
To-day by Mary's convent shrine,
Touched by her picture's moving plea
In that poor nerveless hour of mine,
I mused—A wanderer still must grieve.
Half I resolved to kneel and believe,
Believe and submit, the veil take on.
But thee, armed Virgin! [17] less benign,
Thee now I invoke, thou mightier one.
Helmeted woman—if such term   140
Befit thee, far from strife
Of that which makes the sexual feud
And clogs the aspirant life—
O self-reliant, strong and free,
Thou in whom power and peace unite,
Transcender! raise me up to thee,
Raise me and arm me!

Fond appeal.
For never passion peace shall bring,
Nor Art inanimate for long
Inspire. Nothing may help or heal   150
While Amor incensed remembers wrong.
Vindictive, not himself he'll spare;
For scope to give his vengeance play
Himself he'll blaspheme and betray.

   Then for Urania, virgins everywhere,
O pray! Example take too, and have care.

LONE FOUNTS

Though fast youth's glorious fable flies,
View not the world with worldling's eyes;
Nor turn with weather of the time.
Foreclose the coming of surprise:
Stand where Posterity shall stand;
Stand where the Ancients stood before,
And, dipping in lone founts thy hand,
Drink of the never-varying lore:
Wise once, and wise thence evermore.

ART [18]

In placid hours well-pleased we dream
Of many a brave unbodied scheme.
But form to lend, pulsed life create,
What unlike things must meet and mate:
A flame to melt—a wind to freeze;
Sad patience—joyous energies;
Humility—yet pride and scorn;
Instinct and study; love and hate;
Audacity—reverence. These must mate
And fuse with Jacob's mystic heart,   10
To wrestle with the angel—Art.

THE AGE OF THE ANTONINES [19]

While faith forecasts millennial years
   Spite Europe's embattled lines,
Back to the Past one glance be cast—
   The Age of the Antonines!
O summit of fate, O zenith of time
When a pagan gentleman reigned,
And the olive was nailed to the inn of the world
Nor the peace of the just was feigned.
   A halcyon Age, afar it shines,
Solstice of Man and the Antonines.   10

Hymns to the nations' friendly gods
Went up from the fellowly shrines,
No demagogue beat the pulpit-drum
   In the Age of the Antonines!
The sting was not dreamed to be taken from death,
No Paradise pledged or sought,
But they reasoned of fate at the flowing feast,
Nor stifled the fluent thought.
   We sham, we shuffle while faith declines—
They were frank in the Age of the Antonines.   20

Orders and ranks they kept degree,
Few felt how the parvenu pines,
No law-maker took the lawless one's fee
   In the Age of the Antonines!
Under law made will the world reposed
And the ruler's right confessed,
For the heavens elected the Emperor then,
The foremost of men the best.
   Ah, might we read in America's signs
The Age restored of the Antonines.   30

THE GREAT PYRAMID [20]

   Your masonry—and is it man's?
   More like some Cosmic artisan's.

Your courses as in strata rise,
Beget you do a blind surmise
        Like Grampians.

Far slanting up your sweeping flank
Arabs with Alpine goats may rank,
And there they find a choice of passes
Even like to dwarfs that climb the masses
        Of glaciers blank.   10

Shall lichen in your crevice fit?
Nay, sterile all and granite-knit:
Weather nor weather-stain ye rue,
But aridly you cleave the blue
        As lording it.

Morn's vapor floats beneath your peak,
Kites skim your side with pinion weak;
To sand-storms battering, blow on blow,
Raging to work your overthrow,
        You—turn the cheek.   20

All elements unmoved you stem,
Foursquare you stand and suffer them:
Time's future infinite you dare,
While, for the past, 'tis you that wear
        Eld's diadem.

Slant from your inmost lead the caves
And labyrinths rumored.   These who braves
And penetrates (old palmers said)
Comes out afar on deserts dead
        And, dying, raves.   30

Craftsmen, in dateless quarries dim,
Stones formless into form did trim,
Usurped on Nature's self with Art,
And bade this dumb I AM to start,
        Imposing him.

LETTERS

[TO EVERT DUYCKINCK]

Lansingburgh[1] July 3ᵈ 1846

There was a spice of civil scepticism in your manner, my dear Sir, when we were conversing together the other day about "Typee"—What will the politely incredulous Mr Duyckinck now say to the true Toby's[2] having turned up in Buffalo, and written a letter to the Commercial Advertiser of that place, vouching for the truth of all that part (what has been considered the most extraordinary part) of the narrative, where he is made to figure.—

Give ear then, oh ye of little faith—especially thou man of the Evangelist—and hear what Toby has to say for himself.—

Seriously, my dear Sir, this resurection [*sic*] of Toby from the dead—this strange bringing together of two such places as Typee & Buffalo, is really very curious.—It can not but settle the question of the book's genuineness. The article in the C. A. with the letter of Toby can not possibly be gainsaid in any conceivable way—therefore I think it ought to be pushed into circulation. I doubt not but that many papers will copy it— Mr Duyckinck might say a word or two on the subject which would tell.—The paper I allude to is of the 1st Inst. I have written Toby a letter & expect to see him soon & hear the sequel of the book I have written (How strangely that sounds!)

Bye the bye, since people have always manifested so much concern for "poor Toby," what do you think of writing an account of what befell him in escaping from the island—should the adventure prove to be of sufficient interest?—I should value your opinion very highly on this subject.—

I began with the intention of tracing a short note—I have come near writing a long letter.

Believe me, my Dear Sir
Very Truly Yours
HERMAN MELVILLE

Pardon me, if I have unintentionally translated your patronymick into the Sancrit [*sic*] or some other tongue—"What's in a name?" says Juliet—a strange combination of vowels & consonants, at least in Mr Duyckinck's, Miss, is my reply.

H M

P.S. No 2. Possibly the letter of Toby might by some silly ones be regarded as a hoax—to set you right on that point, altho' I only saw the letter last night for the first—I will tell you that it alludes to things that no human being could ever have heard of except Toby. Besides the Editor seems to have seen him.

[TO EVERT DUYCKINCK]

[New York, November 14, 1848]
Tuesday Morning

What the deuce does it mean?—Here's a book[1] positively turned wrong side out, the title page on the cover, an index to the whole in more ways than one.—I open at the beginning, & find myself in the middle of the Blue Laws & Dr O'Callaghan. Then proceeding, find several extracts from the Log Book of Noah's Ark—Still further, take a hand at three or four bull fights, & then I'm set down to a digest of all the commentators on Shakespeare, who, according "to our author" was a dunce & a blackguard—Vide passim.

Finally the book—so far as this copy goes—winds up with a dissertation on Duff Gordon Sherry & St Anthony's Nose, North River.—

You have been horribly imposed upon, my Dear Sir. The book is no book, but a compact bundle of wrapping paper. And as for Mr Hart, pen & ink, should certainly be taken away from that infatuate man, upon the same principle that pistols are withdrawn from the wight bent on suicide.

—Prayer should be offered up for him among the congregations, and Thanksgiving Day postponed untill long after his "book" is published. What great national sin have we committed to deserve this infliction?

—Seriously, Mr Duyckinck, on my bended knees, & with tears
in my eyes, deliver me from writing ought upon this crucifying
Romance of Yachting
—What has Mr Hart done that I should publicly devour him?
—I bear that hapless man no malice.   Then why smite him?
—And as for glossing over his book with a few common-
places,—*That* I can not do.—The book deserves to be burnt
in a fire of asafetida, & by the hand that wrote it.

Seriously again, & on my conscience, the book is an abortion,
the mere trunk of a book, minus head arm or leg.—Take it
back, I beseech, & get some one to cart it back to the author

Yours Sincerely

H.M.

[TO EVERT DUYCKINCK]

[Boston] Feb 24th [1849]

DEAR DUYCKINCK

Thank you for satisfying my curiosity.   Mr Butler's[1] a
genius, but between you & me, I have a presentment that he
never will surprise me more.—I have been passing my time
very pleasantly here.   But chiefly in lounging on a sofa (a la
the poet Gray) & reading Shakespeare.   It is an edition[2] in
glorious great type, every letter whereof is a soldier, & the top
of every "t" like a musket barrel.   Dolt & ass that I am I have
lived more than 29 years, & until a few days ago, never made
close acquaintance with the divine William.   Ah, he's full of
sermons-on-the-mount, and gentle, aye, almost as Jesus.   I
take such men to be inspired.   I fancy that this mount [?]
Shakespeare in heaven ranks with Gabriel Raphael and Michael.
And if another Messiah ever comes twill be in Shakespeare's
person.—I am mad to think how minute a cause has prevented me hitherto from reading Shakespeare.   But until now,
any copy that was come-at-able to me, happened to be in a vile
small print unendurable to my eyes which are tender as young
sparrows.   But chancing to fall in with this glorious edition, I
now exult over it, page after page.—

I have heard Emerson since I have been here. Say what they will, he's a great man. Mrs Butler[3] too I have heard at her Readings. She makes a glorious Lady Macbeth, but her Desdemona seems like a boarding school miss.—She's so unfemininely masculine that had she not, on unimpeachable authority, borne children, I should be curious to learn the result of a surgical examination of her person in private. The Lord help Butler—not the poet—I marvel not he seeks being amputated off from his maternal half.

My respects to Mrs Duyckinck & your brother

Yours

Evert A Duyckinck Esq   H MELVILLE

[TO EVERT DUYCKINCK]

Mount Vernon Street [Boston]
Saturday, 3d. [March 1849]

Nay, I do not oscillate in Emerson's rainbow, but prefer rather to hang myself in mine own halter than swing in any other man's swing. Yet I think Emerson is more than a brilliant fellow. Be his stuff begged, borrowed, or stolen, or of his own domestic manufacture he is an uncommon man. Swear he is a humbug—then is he no common humbug. Lay it down that had not Sir Thomas Browne lived, Emerson would not have mystified—I will answer that had not old Zack's[1] father begot him, Old Zack would never have been the hero of Palo Alto. The truth is that we are all sons, grandsons, or nephews or great-nephews of those who go before us. No one is his own sire.—I was very agreeably disappointed in Mr Emerson. I had heard of him as full of transcendentalisms, myths & oracular gibberish; I had only glanced at a book of his once in Putnam's store—that was all I knew of him, till I heard him lecture.—To my surprise, I found him quite intelligible, tho' to say truth, they told me that that night he was unusually plain.—Now, there is a something about every man elevated above mediocrity, which is, for the most part, instinctively perceptible. This I see in Mr Emerson. And, frankly, for the sake of the argument, let us call him a fool;—Then had I rather be a fool than a wise man.—I love all men who *dive*. Any fish can swim near the surface, but it takes a great whale to go down stairs five miles or more; & if he dont attain the bottom, why, all the lead in Galena can't fashion the plummet that will. I'm not talking of Mr Emerson now—but of the whole corps of thought-divers, that have been diving & coming up again with blood-shot eyes since the world began.

I could readily see in Emerson, notwithstanding his merit, a gaping flaw. It was, the insinuation, that had he lived in those days when the world was made, he might have offered some valuable suggestions. These men are all cracked right across the brow. And never will the pullers-down be able to cope with the builders-up. And this pulling down is easy enough— a keg of powder blew up Block's Monument—but the man who applied the match, could not, alone, build such a pile to save his soul from the shark-maw of the Devil. But enough of this Plato who talks thro' his nose. To one of your habits of thought, I confess that in my last, I seemed, but only *seemed* irreverent. And do not think, my boy, that because I, impulsively broke forth in jubilations over Shakespeare, that, therefore, I am of the number of the *snobs* who burn their tuns of rancid fat at his shrine. No, I would stand afar off & alone, & burn some pure Palm oil, the product of some overtopping trunk.

—I would to God Shakespeare had lived later, & promenaded in Broadway. Not that I might have had the pleasure of leaving my card for him at the Astor, or made merry with him over a bowl of the fine Duyckinck punch; but that the muzzle which all men wore on their souls in the Elizabethan day, might not have intercepted Shakespeare from articulation. Now I hold it a verity, that even Shakespeare, was not a frank man to the uttermost. And, indeed, who in this intolerant universe is, or can be? But the Declaration of Independence makes a difference.—There, I have driven my horse so hard that I have made my inn before sundown. I was going to say some-

thing more—It was this.—You complain that Emerson tho'
a denizen of the land of gingerbread, is above munching a plain
cake in company of jolly fellows, & swiging [*sic*] off his ale
like you & me. Ah, my dear sir, that's his misfortune, not his
fault. His belly, sir, is in his chest, & his brains descend down
into his neck, & offer an obstacle to a draught of ale or a
mouthful of cake. But here I am. Good bye—

H.M.

[TO EVERT DUYCKINCK]

March 28th [1849] Boston

Dear Duyckinck—When last in New York, you expressed a
desire to be supplied in advance with the sheets of that new
work of mine. Yesterday in a note to Cliff Street[1] I requested
them to furnish you with the sheets, as ere this they must have
been printed. They are for your private eye. I suppose the
book will be published now in two or three weeks. Mr Bentley
is the man in London.—Rain, Rain, Rain—an interminable rain
that to seek elsewhere than in Boston would be utterly vain—
Rhyme by Jove, and spontaneous as heart-beating.—This is the
Fourth Day of the Great Boston Rain, & how much longer it
is to last the ghost of the last man drowned by the Deluge only
knows. I have a continual dripping sensation; and feel like
an ill-wrung towel—my soul is damp, & by spreading itself out
upon paper seeks to get dry.

Your well saturated
H MELVILLE

[TO EVERT DUYCKINCK]

Boston April 5th 1849

DEAR DUYCKINCK—

Thank you for your note, & the paper which came duly to
hand. By the way, that "Smoking Spiritualized"[1] is not bad.
Doubtless it has improved by age. The quaint old lines lie in
coils like a sailor's pigtail in its keg.

—Ah this sovereign virtue of age—how can we living men attain
unto it. We may spice up our dishes with all the condiments of
the Spice Islands & Moluccas, & our dishes may be all venison
& wild boar—yet how the deuce can we make them a century or
two old?—My Dear Sir, the two great things yet to be discovered are these—The Art of rejuvenating old age in men,
& oldageifying youth in books.—Who in the name of the
trunk-makers would think of reading *old* Burton were his book
published for the first to day?—All ambitious authors should
have ghosts capable of revisiting the world to snuff up the steam
of adulation, which begins to rise straightway as the Sexton
throws his last shovelfull on him.—Down goes his body & up
flies his name.

Poor Hoffman[2]—I remember the shock I had when I first
saw the mention of his madness.—But he was just the man to
go mad—imaginative, voluptuously [?] inclined, poor, un-
employed, in the race of life distanced by his inferiors, un-
married—without a port or haven in the universe to make.
His present misfortune—rather blessing—is but the sequel to a
long experience of unwhole [?] habits of thought.—This going
mad of a friend or acquaintance comes straight home to every
man who feels his soul in him,—which but few men do. For
in all of us lodges the same fuel to light the same fire. And
he who has never felt, momentarily, what madness is has but
a mouthful of brains. What sort of sensation permanent madness is may be very well imagined—just as we imagine how we
felt when we were infants, tho' we can not recall it. In both
conditions we are irresponsible & riot like gods without fear
of fate.—It is the climax of a mad night of revelry when the
blood has been transmuted into brandy.—But if we prate much
of this thing we shall be illustrating our own proposition.—

I am glad you like that affair of mine.[3] But it seems so long
now since I wrote it, & my mood has so changed, that I dread
to look into it, & have purposely abstained from so doing
since I thanked God it was off my hands.—Would that a man
could do something & then say—It is finished.—not that one
thing only, but all others—that he has reached his uttermost,

& can never exceed it. But live & push—tho' we put one leg forward ten miles—its no reason the other must lag behind— no, *that* must again distance the other—& so we go till we get the cramp & die.—I bought a set of Bayle's Dictionary the other day, & on my return to New York intend to lay the great old folios side by side & go to sleep on them thro' the summer, with the Phaedon in one hand & Tom Brown[4] in the other.— Good bye I'm called.—I shall be in New York next week— early part.

H MELVILLE

[TO EVERT DUYCKINCK]

Paris Dec 2d 1849

MY DEAR MR DUYCKINCK,

I could almost whip myself that after receiving your most kind & friendly letter, I should suffer so long an interval to go by without answering it. But what can you expect of me? I have served persons the nearest to me in like manner. Traveling takes the wit out of one's pen as well as the cash out of one's purse.—Thank you for the papers you sent me.

—The other evening I went to see Rachel—& having taken my place in the "*que*" (how the devil do you spell it?) or tail—& having waited there for full an hour—upon at last arriving at the ticket-box—the woman there closed her little wicket in my face—& so the "tail" was cut off.

—Now my traveling "tail" has been cut off in like manner, by the confounded state of the Copyright Question[1] in England. It has prevented me from receiving an unmerited [?] supply of cash—I am going home within three weeks or so.— But I have not failed to enjoy myself & learn somewhat, notwithstanding.

Give my best remembrances to your brother.[2] Tell him I stumbled upon an acquaintance of his—a book dealer in the Strand. Tell him that Davidson[3] proved a good fellow, & that we took some punch together at the Blue Posts.—Mr Delf I was not so happy as to see when I called there.

But I may see him on my return.

My compliments to Mrs Duyckinck & all your pleasant family, & Believe me Sincerely yours

H Melville.

London, Dec 14, 49.

My Dear Duyckinck—I meant to send this to you by a Havre packet—but learning more about her—did not. So I have kept the note by me, & send it to you now with a supplement, a sequel, & my "last convictions," which as an author, you will duly value.—I sail hence on the 21st Inst:—and am only detained now by reason of some business. Yesterday being at Mr Bentley's I enquired for his copies of the last "Literary Worlds"—but they had been sent on to Brighton—so I did not see your say about the book Redburn, which to my surprise (somewhat) seems to have been favorably received. I am glad of it—for it puts money into an empty purse. But I hope I shall never write such a book again—tho' when a poor devil writes with duns all round him, & looking over the back of his chair—& perching on his pen & diving in his inkstand— like the devils about St: Anthony—what can you expect of that poor devil?—What but a beggarly "Redburn!" And when he attempts anything higher—God help him & save him! for it is not with a hollow purse as with a hollow balloon—for a hollow purse makes the poet *sink*—witness "Mardi." But we that write & print have all our books predestinated—& for me, I shall write such things as the Great Publisher of Mankind ordained ages before he published "The World"—this planet, I mean—not the Literary Globe.—What a madness & anguish it is, that an author can never—under no conceivable circumstances—be at all frank with his readers.—Could I, for one, be frank with them—how would they cease their railing—those at least who have railed.—In a little notice of "The Oregon Trail" [4] I once said something "critical" about another's [*sic*] man's book—I shall never do it again. Hereafter I shall no more stab at a book (in print, I mean) than I would stab at a man.—

I am but a poor mortal, & I admit that I learn by experience & not by divine intuitions. Had I not written & published "Mardi," in all likelihood, I would not be as wise as I am now, or may be. For that thing was stabbed *at* (I do not say *through*) —& therefore, I am the wiser for it.—But a bit of note paper is not large enough for this sort of writing—so no more of it. Pardon it, & know me to be yours.

H MELVILLE.

I this morning did myself the pleasure of calling on Mrs: Daniel [5] for the first. I saw her, & also two very attractive young ladies. Had you seen these young ladies, you would have never told Mrs: Duyckinck of it. You must on no account tell Mrs. Welford of this; for those nymphs were her sisters.

H.M.

[TO EVERT DUYCKINCK]

[New York] Saturday Evening, Feb 2d. [1850]

MY DEAR DUYCKINCK—

Tho' somewhat unusual for a donor, I must beg to apologize for making you the accompanying present of "Mardi." But no one who knows your library[1] can doubt, that such a choice conservatory of exotics & other rare things in literature, after being long enjoyed by yourself, must, to a late posterity, be preserved intact by your descendants. How natural then—tho' vain—in your friend to desire a place in it for a plant, which tho' now unblown (emblematically, the leaves, you perceive, are uncut) may possibly—by some miracle, that is—flower like the aloe, a hundred years hence—or not flower at all, which is more likely by far, for some aloes never flower.

Again: (as the divines say) political republics should be the asylum for the persecuted of all nations; so, if Mardi be admitted to your shelves, your bibliographical Republic of Letters may find some contentment in the thought, that it has afforded refuge to a work, which almost everywhere else has been driven forth like a wild, mystic Mormon into shelterless exile.

—The leaves, I repeat, are uncut—let them remain so—and let me supplementaryly hint, that a bit of old parchment (from some old Arabic M.S.S. on Astrology) tied round each volume, & sealed on the back with a Sphynx, & never to be broken till the aloe flowers—would not be an unsuitable device for the bookbinders of "Mardi."—That book is a sort of dose, if you please—(tho', in the present case, charitably administered in three parts, instead of two) and by way of killing the flavor of it, I hurry to follow it up with a fine old spicy duodecimo mouthful in the shape of "Hudibras" which I got particularly for yourself at Stribbs's in the Strand—& a little marvel that your brother George overlooked so enticing a little volume during his rummagings in the same shop.—Pray, glance at the title page, & tell me, if you can, what "Black Boy" that was in Paternoster Row. My curiosity is excited, and indeed aggravated & exacerbated about that young negro. Did the late Mr Baker have a small *live* Nubian standing at his shop door, like the moccasined Indian of our Bowery tobacconist? I readily see the propriety of the Indian—but in that "Black Boy" I perceive no possible affinity to books—unless, by the way, Mr Baker dealt altogether in black-letter,—Thomas the Rhymer, Lydgate, & Battle Abbey Directories.—Are they not delicious, & full flavored with suggestiveness, these old fashioned London imprints?

So much for No: 1 & No: 2.—No: 3 is a bronze medal which I mean for your brother George, if he will gratify me by accepting such a trifling token of my sense of his kindness in giving me an "outfit" of guide-books. It comes from a mountainous defile of a narrow street in the Latin Quarter of Paris, where I disinterred it from an old antiquary's cellar, which I doubt not connected, somehow, with the Catacombs & the palace of Thermes.

Numbers 4 & 5 are two medals (warranted *not* silver) which I wish little Evert & George * to keep by way of remembrances that I remembered them, even while thirty feet under water. They come from the Thames Tunnel.[3]

* Erratum: for "George" read "Henry."[2]

No: 6 (which brings up the rear of this valuable collection) is a bottle-stopper from Cologne, for yourself. Do not despise it—there is a sermon in it. Shut yourself up in a closet, insert the stopper into a bottle of Sour Claret, & then study that face.

Wishing you a merry Saturday night, & a serene Sunday morrow, I am, my Dear Duyckinck

Truly Yours
H MELVILLE.

I return, with my best thanks, to your brother, *three* of the books he loaned me. I can not account for "Cruchley's" [4] accident in the back.—The Guide books for Northern & Central Italy are neither stolen, lost, sold, or mislaid. I will, I think, satisfactorily account for them when I see your brother. They are safe.

[TO EVERT DUYCKINCK]

[New York] Thursday Morning [March 7, 1850]

MY DEAR DUYCKINCK

I hasten to return you the tickets which you were so good as to send last evening. I should have gone—as I love music —were it not that having been shut up all day, I could not stand being shut up all the evening—so I mounted my *green* jacket[1] & strolled down to the Battery to study the stars.

Yours
H MELVILLE

[TO EVERT DUYCKINCK]

Banian Hall [Pittsfield] Aug 16th 1850

I call it Banian Hall,[1] My Dear Duyckinck because it seems the old original Hall of all this neighborhood—besides, it is a wide-spreading house, and the various outhouses seem shoots from it, that have taken root all round.

—I write you this from the *garret-way*, seated at that little embrasure of a window (you must remember it) which commands so noble a view of Saddleback.—My desk is an odd one—an old thing of my Uncle the Major's, which for twelve years back has been packed away in the corn-loft over the carriage house. Upon dragging it out to the day light, I found that it now was covered with the marks of fowls—quite white with them— eggs had been laid in it—think of that!—Is it not typical of those other eggs that authors may be said to lay in their desks,— especially those with pigeon-holes?

Day before yesterday—Wednesday—I received your letter of the 13th, also Mathews',[2] and was delighted & softened by both. But I could not avoid a real feeling of grief, to think of you, once more in those dreary regions which are Trans-Taconic to me.—What are you doing there, My Beloved, among the bricks & cobble-stone *boulders?* Are you making mortar? Surely, My Beloved, you are not carrying a hod? —That were a quizzical sight, to see any godly man, with a pen behind his ear, and a hod on his shoulder.—I have a horrible presentment that you are even now hanging round the City-Hall, trying to get a contract from the Corporation to pave Broadway between Clinton Place[3] & Union-Square. For heaven's sake, come out from among the Hittites & Hodites— give up mortar forever.—There is one thing certain, that, chemically speaking, mortar was the *preciptate* of the Fall; & with a brickbat, or a cobble-stone *boulder*, Cain killed Abel.— Do you drink Lime-water in the morning by way of a sto-machic? Do you use brick-bats for paper-weights in the office? Do you & Mathews pitch paving-stones, & play ball that way in the cool of the evening, opposite the Astor-House?—How do they sell mortar by the quart now? Cheaper than ice-cream, I suppose.—A horrible something in me tells me that you are about dipping your head in plaster at Fowler's for your bust.[4]— But enough—the visions come too thick for me to master them.

Twelve more beautiful babies than you sent me in that wicker cradle by Express, I have never seen. Uncommon intelligence was in their aspect, and they seem full of animation & hilarity. I have no doubt, if they were let alone awhile, they would all grow to be demijohns. In a word, my Dear Fellow, they were but too well thought of you,—because so much more than I deserved.

—Let me now tell you how that precious basket was carried in state to the farm—something like the Flitch of Bacon.

—A gentleman & a lady arrived here as boarders yesterday morning. In the afternoon in four carriages a party of us went to Leabanon⁵ [*sic*]. Returning, we stopped at the Express office in the village; and then, with the basket borne before me at my feet, I drove off full speed followed by the whole galloping procession. Today, at dinner, we cracked the Champagne, & our first glass (all round the table) was Mr Duyckinck & Mr Mathews.

But the cigars!—The oriental looking box! and the Antilles smell of them! And the four different thrones & dominations of bundles, all harmonizing together like the Iroquois. Had there been two more bundles, I should have called them the Six Nations.

I received the "Literary World." Under the circumstances the printing is far more correct, than I expected; but there are one or two ugly errors.⁶ However, no one sees them, I suppose, but myself.—Send me the other proof, if you can; but don't, if it will be the least inconvenience. If it is a fair day, I shall drive to Hawthorne's to morrow, & deliver his parcels.— Mrs H. Melville & others too numerous to enumerate send their best remembrances to you.—When you write, tell me that you are coming on for a second visit. Don't forget it.— Good bye

H MELVILLE

[TO EVERT DUYCKINCK]

Tuesday Evening [December 12, 1850]
Pittsfield.

MY DEAR DUYCKINCK,

If you overhaul your old diaries you will see that a long period ago you were acquainted with one Herman Melville; that he then resided in New York; but removing after a time into a remote region called Berkshire, and failing to answer what letters you sent him, you but reasonably supposed him dead; at any rate did not hear anything of him again, & so by degrees you thought no more about him.

I now write to inform you that this man has turned up—in short, my Dear Fellow in spite of my incivility I am alive & well, & would fain be remembered.

Before I go further let me say here that I am writing this by candle light—an uncommon thing with me—& therefore my writing wont be very legible, because I am keeping one eye shut & wink at the paper with the other.

If you expect a letter from a man who lives in the country you must make up your mind to receive an egotistical one—for he has no gossip nor news of any kind, unless his neighbor's cow has calved or the hen has laid a silver egg.—By the way, this reminds me that one of my neighbors has has [*sic*] really met with a bad accident in the loss of a fine young colt. That neighbor is our friend Mrs Morewood.[1] Mr Doolittle—my cousin—was crossing the R.R. track yesterday (where it runs thro the wooded part of the farm.) in his slay—*sleigh* I mean—and was followed by all three of Mrs Morewood's horses (they running at large for the sake of the air & exercise). Well: just as Doolittle got on the track with his vehicle, along comes the Locomotive—whereupon Doolittle whips up like mad & steers clear; but the frightened horses following him, they scamper off full before the engine, which hitting them right & left, tumbles one into a ditch, pitches another into a snow-bank, & chases the luckless third so hard as to come into direct contact with him, & break his leg clean into two pieces.—With his leg "in splints" that is done up by the surgeon, the poor colt now lies in his straw, & the prayers of all good Christians are earnestly solicited in his behalf. Certainly, considering the bounding spirit and full-blooded life in that colt—how it might for many a summer have sported in pastures of red clover & gone cantering merrily along the "Gulf Road" with a sprightly Mrs Morewood on his back, patting his neck & lovingly talking to him—considering all this, I say, I really think that a broken leg for him is not one jot less bad than it would be for me—tho'

I grant you, even as it is with him, he has one more leg than I have now.

I have a sort of sea-feeling here in the country, now that the ground is all covered with snow. I look out of my window in the morning when I rise as I would out of a port-hole of a ship in the Atlantic. My room seems a ship's cabin; & at nights when I wake up & hear the wind shrieking, I almost fancy there is too much sail on the house, & I had better go on the roof & rig in the chimney.

Do you want to know how I pass my time?—I rise at eight—thereabouts—& go to my barn—say good-morning to the horse, & give him his breakfast. (It goes to my heart to give him a cold one, but it can't be helped) Then, pay a visit to my cow—cut up a pumpkin or two for her, & stand by to see her eat it—for its a pleasant sight to see a cow move her jaws—she does it so mildly & with such a sanctity.—My own breakfast over, I go to my work-room & light my fire—then spread my M.S.S. on the table—take one business squint at it, & fall to with a will. At $2\frac{1}{2}$ P.M. I hear a preconcerted knock at my door, which (by request) continues till I rise & go to the door, which serves to wean me effectively from my writing, however interested I may be. My friends the horse & cow now demand their dinner—& I go & give it them. My own dinner over, I rig my sleigh & with my mother or sisters start off for the village—& if it be a Literary World day, great is the satisfaction thereof.—My evenings I spend in a sort of mesmeric state in my room—not being able to read—only now & then skimming over some large-printed book.—Can you send me about fifty fast-writing youths, with an easy style & not averse to polishing their labors? If you can, I wish you would, because since I have been here I have planned about that number of future works & cant find enough time to think about them separately. —But I dont know but a book [2] in a man's brain is better off than a book bound in calf—at any rate it is safer from criticism. And taking a book off the brain, is akin to the ticklish & dangerous business of taking an old painting off a panel—you have to scrape off the whole brain in order to get at it with due safety—

& even then, the painting may not be worth the trouble.—I
meant to have left more room for something else besides my
own concerns. But I cant help it.—I see Adler[3] is at work—or
has already achieved a German translation. I am glad to hear it.
Remember me to him.—In the country here, I begin to appreciate the Literary World. I read it as a sort of private letter
from you to me.

Remember me to your brother. My respects to Mrs Duyckinck & all your family. The "sad" young lady sends her
regards.

                                                             H MELVILLE.

Mrs Melville with Malcolm is in Boston—or that lady would
send her particular regards.

[TO EVERT DUYCKINCK]

Trade mark
of 'Carson's
Dalton MS.'   about 5 miles
from here, North East. I went
there & got a sleigh-load of
this paper. A great neighborhood for authors, you see, is
Pittsfield.

                         Pittsfield, Wednesday [February 12], 1851.
MY DEAR DUYCKINCK,

"A dash of salt spray"!—where am I to get salt spray here in
inland Pittsfield? I shall have to import it from foreign parts.
All I now have to do with salt, is when I salt my horse & cow—
not *salt them down*—I dont mean that (tho' indeed I have before
now dined on "salt-horse") but when I give them their weekly
salt, by way of seasoning all their week's meals in one prospective lump.

How shall a man go about refusing a man?[1]—Best be roundabout, or plump on the mark?—I can not write the thing
you want. I am in the humor to lend a hand to a friend, if I

can;—but I am not in the humor to write the kind of thing you need—and I am not in the humor to write for Holden's Magazine. If I were to go on to give you all my reasons— you would pronounce me a bore, so I will not do that. You must be content to believe that I *have* reasons, or else I would not refuse so small a thing.—As for the Daguerreotype (I spell the word right from your sheet) that's what I can not send you, because I have none. And if I had, I would not send it for such a purpose, even to you.—Pshaw! you cry—& so cry I.— "This is intensified vanity, not true modesty or anything of that sort!"—Again, I say so too. But if it be so, how can I help it. The fact is, almost everybody is having his "mug" engraved nowadays; so that this test of distinction is getting to be re-versed; and therefore, to see one's "mug" in a magazine, is presumptive evidence that he's a nobody. So being as vain a man as ever lived; & believing that my illustrious name is famous through[?] the world—I respectfully decline being *ob-livionated* by a Daguerreotype (what a devil of an unspellable word!)

We are all queer customers, Mr Duyckinck, you, I, & every body else in the world. So if I here seem queer to you, be sure, I am not alone in my queerness, tho' it present itself at a different port [?], perhaps, from other people, since every one has his own distinct peculiarity. But I trust you take me aright. If you don't I shall be sorry—that's all.

After a long procrastination, I drove down to see Mr Haw-thorne a couple of weeks ago. I found him, of course, buried in snow; & the delightful scenery about him, all wrapped up & tucked away under a napkin, as it were. He was to have made me a day's visit, & I had promised myself much pleasure in getting him up in my snug room here, & discussing the Uni-verse with a bottle of brandy & cigars. But he has not been able to come, owing to sickness in his family—or else, he's up to the lips in the *Universe* again.

By the way, I have recently read his "Twice Told Tales" (I had not read but a few of them before) I think they far exceed the "Mosses"—they are, I fancy, an earlier vintage from

his vine. Some of those sketches are wonderfully subtle. Their
deeper meanings are worthy of a Brahmin. Still there is something lacking—a good deal lacking—to the plump sphericity
of the man. What is that?

—He doesn't patronize the butcher—he needs roast-beef, done
rare.—Nevertheless, for one, I regard Hawthorne (in his books)
as evincing a quality of genius, immensely loftier, & more profound, too, than any other American has shown hitherto in the
printed form. Irving is a grasshopper to him—putting the
souls of the two men together, I mean.—But I must close.
Enclosed is a note from the "Sad One."

>   With remembrances to your brother, I am
>   Truly Yours
>   H Melville.

>   5. P.M. Wednesday.

I am just on the point of starting a'foot for the village, and
have glanced over the previous letter, before sealing.—I thought
there seemed an unkindness in it—& that had I, under the
circumstances, rec'd such a letter from you, in reply to such a
letter as yours to me—I would deem it not well of you.—Still,
I can't help it—and I may yet be of some better service to you
than merely jotting a paragraph for Holden's.—

My respects to Mrs Duyckinck. Jog Adler's[2] memory about
me now & then.—The society here is very much pleased
with Leigh Hunt's magazine.—What a quizzical thing that
is of the Duel—the man who was wounded in certain *important* parts.[3]

>   Adieu again,
>   H.M.

[TO NATHANIEL HAWTHORNE]

>   Pittsfield, Wednesday morning.
>   [March [?], 1851]

My dear Hawthorne,—

Concerning the young gentleman's shoes, I desire to say
that a pair to fit him, of the desired pattern, cannot be had in all

Pittsfield,—a fact which sadly impairs that metropolitan pride I formerly took in the capital of Berkshire. Henceforth Pittsfield must hide its head. However, if a pair of *bootees* will at all answer, Pittsfield will be very happy to provide them. Pray mention all this to Mrs. Hawthorne, and command me.

"The House of the Seven Gables: A Romance. By Nathaniel Hawthorne. One vol. 16mo, pp. 344." The contents of this book do not belie its rich, clustering, romantic title. With great enjoyment we spent almost an hour in each separate gable. This book is like a fine old chamber, abundantly, but still judiciously, furnished with precisely that sort of furniture best fitted to furnish it. There are rich hangings, wherein are braided scenes from tragedies! There is old china with rare devices, set out on the carved buffet; there are long and indolent lounges to throw yourself upon; there is an admirable sideboard, plentifully stored with good viands; there is a smell as of old wine in the pantry; and finally, in one corner, there is a dark little black-letter volume in golden clasps, entitled "Hawthorne: A Problem." It has delighted us; it has piqued a re-perusal; it has robbed us of a day, and made us a present of a whole year of thoughtfulness; it has bred great exhilaration and exultation with the remembrance that the architect of the Gables resides only six miles off, and not three thousand miles away, in England, say. We think the book, for pleasantness of running interest, surpasses the other works of the author. The curtains are more drawn; the sun comes in more; genialities peep out more. Were we to particularize what most struck us in the deeper passages, we would point out the scene where Clifford, for a moment, would fain throw himself forth from the window to join the procession; or the scene where the judge is left seated in his ancestral chair. Clifford is full of an awful truth throughout. He is conceived in the finest, truest spirit. He is no caricature. He is Clifford. And here we would say that, did circumstances permit, we should like nothing better than to devote an elaborate and careful paper to the full consideration and analysis of the purport and significance of what so strongly characterizes all of this author's writings. There is a certain tragic phase of humanity which, in our opinion, was never more powerfully embodied than by Hawthorne. We mean the tragedies of human thought in its own unbiassed, native, and profounder workings. We think that into no recorded mind has the intense feeling of the usable truth ever entered more deeply than into this man's. By usable truth, we mean the apprehension of the absolute condition of present things as they strike the eye of the man who fears them not, though they do their worst to him,—the man who, like Russia or the British Empire, declares himself a sovereign nature (in himself) amid the powers of heaven, hell, and earth. He may perish; but so long as he exists he insists upon treating with all Powers upon an equal basis. If any of those other Powers choose to withhold certain secrets, let them; that does not impair my sovereignty in myself; that does not make me tributary. And perhaps, after all, there is *no* secret. We incline to think that the Problem of the Universe is like the Freemason's mighty secret, so terrible to all children. It turns out, at last, to consist in a triangle, a mallet, and an apron,—nothing more! We incline to think that God cannot explain His own secrets, and that He would like a little information upon certain points Himself. We mortals astonish Him as much as He us. But it is this *Being* of the matter; there lies the knot with which we choke ourselves. As soon as you say *Me*, a *God*, a *Nature*, so soon you jump off from your stool and hang from the beam. Yes, that word is the hangman. Take God out of the dictionary, and you would have Him in the street.

There is the grand truth about Nathaniel Hawthorne. He says No! in thunder; but the Devil himself cannot make him say *yes*. For all men who say *yes*, lie; and all men who say *no*,— why, they are in the happy condition of judicious, unincumbered travellers in Europe; they cross the frontiers into Eternity with nothing but a carpet-bag,—that is to say, the Ego. Whereas those *yes*-gentry, they travel with heaps of baggage, and, damn them! they will never get through the Custom House. What's the reason, Mr. Hawthorne, that in the last stages of metaphysics a fellow always falls to *swearing* so? I could rip an hour. You see, I began with a little criticism extracted for your benefit from the "Pittsfield Secret Review," and here I have landed in Africa.

Walk down one of these mornings and see me. No nonsense; come. Remember me to Mrs. Hawthorne and the children.

H. MELVILLE.

P.S. The marriage of Phoebe with the daguerreotypist is a fine stroke, because of his turning out to be a *Maule*. If you pass Hepzibah's cent-shop, buy me a Jim Crow (fresh) and send it to me by Ned Higgins.[1]

[TO NATHANIEL HAWTHORNE]

[Pittsfield June [?] 1851]

My DEAR HAWTHORNE,—

I should have been rumbling down to you in my pine-board chariot a long time ago, were it not that for some weeks past I have been more busy than you can well imagine,—out of doors, —building and patching and tinkering away in all directions. Besides, I had my crops to get in,—corn and potatoes (I hope to show you some famous ones by and by),—and many other things to attend to, all accumulating upon this one particular season. I work myself; and at night my bodily sensations are akin to those I have so often felt before, when a hired man, doing my day's work from sun to sun. But I mean to continue visiting you until you tell me that my visits are both super-erogatory and superfluous. With no son of man do I stand upon any etiquette or ceremony, except the Christian ones of charity and honesty. I am told, my fellow-man, that there is an aristocracy of the brain. Some men have boldly advocated and asserted it. Schiller seems to have done so, though I don't know much about him. At any rate, it is true that there have been those who, while earnest in behalf of political equality, still accept the intellectual estates. And I can well perceive, I think, how a man of superior mind can, by its intense cultivation, bring himself, as it were, into a certain spontaneous aristocracy of feeling,—exceedingly nice and fastidious,—similar to that which, in an English Howard, conveys a torpedo-fish thrill at the slightest contact with a social plebian. So, when you see or hear of my ruthless democracy on all sides, you may possibly feel a touch of a shrink, or something of that sort. It is but nature to be shy of a mortal who boldly declares that a thief in jail is as honorable a personage as Gen. George Washington. This is ludicrous. But Truth is the silliest thing under the sun. Try to get a living by the Truth—and go to the Soup Societies. Heavens! Let any clergyman try to preach the Truth from its very stronghold, the pulpit, and they would ride him out of his church on his own pulpit bannister. It can hardly be doubted that all Reformers are bottomed upon the truth, more or less; and to the world at large are not reformers almost universally laughing-stocks? Why so? Truth is ridiculous to men. Thus easily in my room here do I, conceited and garrulous, revere the test of my Lord Shaftesbury.[1]

It seems an inconsistency to assert unconditional democracy in all things, and yet confess a dislike to all mankind—in the mass. But not so.—But it's an endless sermon,—no more of it. I began by saying that the reason I have not been to Lenox is this,—in the evening I feel completely done up, as the phrase is, and incapable of the long jolting to get to your house and back. In a week or so, I go to New York, to bury myself in a third-story room, and work and slave on my "Whale" while it is driving through the press. *That* is the only way I can finish it now,—I am so pulled hither and thither by circumstances. The calm, the coolness, the silent grass-growing mood in which a man *ought* always to compose,—that, I fear, can seldom be mine. Dollars damn me; and the malicious Devil is forever grinning in upon me, holding the door ajar. My dear Sir, a presentiment is on me,—I shall at last be worn out and perish, like an old nutmeg-grater, grated to pieces by the constant attrition of the wood, that is, the nutmeg. What I feel most moved to write, that is banned,—it will not pay. Yet, altogether, write the *other* way I cannot. So the product is a final hash, and all my books are botches. I'm rather sore, perhaps, in this letter; but see my hand!—four blisters on this palm, made by hoes and hammers within the last few days. It is a rainy morning; so I am indoors, and all work suspended. I feel cheerfully disposed, and therefore I write a little bluely. Would the Gin[2] were here! If ever, my dear Hawthorne, in the eternal times that are to come, you and I shall sit down in Paradise, in some little shady corner by ourselves; and if we shall by any means be able to smuggle a basket of champagne there (I won't believe in a Temperance Heaven), and if we shall then cross our celestial legs in the celestial grass that is forever tropical, and strike our glasses and our heads together, till both musically ring in concert,—then, O my dear fellow-mortal, how shall we pleasantly discourse of all the things manifold which now so distress us,—when all the earth shall be but a reminiscence, yea, its final dissolution an antiquity. Then shall songs be composed as when wars are over; humorous, comic songs,—"Oh, when I lived in that queer little hole called the world," or, "Oh, when I toiled and sweated below," or, "Oh, when I knocked and was knocked in the fight"—yes, let us look forward to such things. Let us swear that, though now we sweat, yet it is because of the dry heat which is indispensable to the nourishment of the vine which is to bear the grapes that are to give us the champagne hereafter.

But I was talking about the "Whale." As the fishermen say, "he's in his flurry" when I left him some three weeks ago. I'm going to take him by his jaw, however, before long, and finish him up in some fashion or other. What's the use of elaborating what, in its very essence, is so short-lived as a modern book? Though I wrote the Gospels in this century, I should die in the gutter.—I talk all about myself, and this is selfishness and egotism. Granted. But how help it? I am writing to you; I know little about you, but something about myself. So I write about myself,—at least, to you. Don't trouble yourself, though, about writing; and don't trouble yourself about visiting; and when you *do* visit, don't trouble yourself about talking. I will do all the writing and visiting and talking myself.—By the way, in the last "Dollar Magazine" I read "The Unpardonable

Sin."[3] He was a sad fellow, that Ethan Brand. I have no
doubt you are by this time responsible for many a shake and
tremor of the tribe of "general readers." It is a frightful
poetical creed that the cultivation of the brain eats out the heart.
But it's my *prose* opinion that in most cases, in those men who
have fine brains and work them well, the heart extends down to
hams. And though you smoke them with the fire of tribulation,
yet, like veritable hams, the head only gives the richer and the
better flavor. I stand for the heart. To the dogs with the head!
I had rather be a fool with a heart, than Jupiter Olympus with
his head. The reason the mass of men fear God, and *at bottom
dislike* Him, is because they rather distrust His heart, and fancy
Him all brain like a watch. (You perceive I employ a capital
initial in the pronoun refering to the Deity; don't you think
there is a slight dash of flunkeyism in that usage?) Another
thing. I was in New York for four-and-twenty hours the other
day, and saw a portrait of N.H. And I have seen and heard
many flattering (in a publisher's point of view) allusions to the
"Seven Gables." And I have seen "Tales," and "A New
Volume"[4] announced, by N.H. So upon the whole, I say to
myself, this N.H. is in the ascendant. My dear Sir, they begin
to patronize. All Fame is patronage. Let me be infamous:
there is no patronage in *that*. What "reputation" H.M. has is
horrible. Think of it! To go down to posterity is bad enough,
any way; but to go down as a "man who lived among the
cannibals!" When I speak of posterity, in reference to myself,
I only mean the babies who will probably be born in the
moment immediately ensuing upon my giving up the ghost.
I shall go down to some of them, in all likelihood. "Typee"
will be given to them, perhaps, with their gingerbread. I have
come to regard this matter of Fame as the most transparent of
all vanities. I read Solomon more and more, and every time
see deeper and deeper and unspeakable meanings in him. I did
not think of Fame, a year ago, as I do now. My development
has been all within a few years past. I am like one of those
seeds taken out of the Egyptian Pyramids, which, after being
three thousand years a seed and nothing but a seed, being

planted in English soil, it developed itself, grew to greenness, and then fell to mould. So I. Until I was twenty-five, I had no development at all. From my twenty-fifth year I date my life. Three weeks have scarcely passed, at any time between then and now, that I have not unfolded within myself. But I feel that I am now come to the inmost leaf of the bulb, and that shortly the flower must fall to the mould. It seems to me now that Solomon was the truest man who ever spoke, and yet that he a little *managed* the truth with a view to popular conservatism; or else there have been many corruptions and interpolations of the text.—In reading some of Goethe's sayings, so worshipped by his votaries, I came across this, "*Live in the all.*" That is to say, your separate identity is but a wretched one,—good; but get out of yourself, spread and expand yourself, and bring to yourself the tinglings of life that are felt in the flowers and the woods, that are felt in the planets Saturn and Venus, and the Fixed Stars. What nonsense! Here is a fellow with a raging toothache. "My dear boy," Goethe says to him, "you are sorely afflicted with that tooth; but you must *live in the all*, and then you will be happy!" As with all great genius, there is an immense deal of flummery in Goethe, and in proportion to my own contact with him, a monstrous deal of it in me.

H. MELVILLE.

P.S. "Amen!" saith Hawthorne.

N.B. This "all" feeling, though, there is some truth in. You must often have felt it, lying on the grass on a warm summer's day. Your legs seem to send out shoots into the earth. Your hair feels like leaves upon your head. This is the *all* feeling. But what plays the mischief with the truth is that men will insist upon the universal application of a temporary feeling or opinion.

P.S. You must not fail to admire my discretion in paying the postage on this letter.

[TO NATHANIEL HAWTHORNE]

Pittsfield, Monday afternoon.
[November [?], 1851]

MY DEAR HAWTHORNE,—

People think that if a man has undergone any hardship, he should have a reward; but for my part, if I have done the hardest possible day's work, and then come to sit down in a corner and eat my supper comfortably—why, then I don't think I deserve any reward for my hard day's work—for am I not now at peace? Is not my supper good? My peace and my supper are my reward, my dear Hawthorne. So your joy-giving and exultation-breeding letter[1] is not my reward for my ditcher's work with that book, but is the good goddess's bonus over and above what was stipulated for—for not one man in five cycles, who is wise, will expect appreciative recognition from his fellows, or any one of them. Appreciation! Recognition! Is love appreciated? Why, ever since Adam, who has got to the meaning of his great allegory—the world? Then we pygmies must be content to have our paper allegories but ill comprehended. I say your appreciation is my glorious gratuity. In my proud, humble way,—a shepherd-king,—I was lord of a little vale in the solitary Crimea; but you have now given me the crown of India. But on trying it on my head, I found it fell down on my ears, notwithstanding their asinine length— for it's only such ears that sustain such crowns.

Your letter was handed me last night on the road going to Mr. Morewood's, and I read it there. Had I been at home, I would have sat down at once and answered it. In me divine magnanimities are spontaneous and instantaneous—catch them while you can. The world goes round, and the other side comes up. So now I can't write what I felt. But I felt pantheis-tic then—your heart beat in my ribs and mine in yours, and both in God's. A sense of unspeakable security is in me this moment, on account of your having understood the book. I have written a wicked book, and feel spotless as the lamb. Ineffable socialities are in me. I would sit down and dine with you and all the gods in old Rome's Pantheon. It is a strange feeling—no hopefulness is in it, no despair. Content—that is it; and irresponsibility; but without licentious inclination. I speak now of my profoundest sense of being, not of an incidental feeling.

Whence come you, Hawthorne? By what right do you drink from my flagon of life? And when I put it to my lips—lo, they are yours and not mine. I feel that the Godhead is broken up like the bread at the Supper, and that we are the pieces. Hence this infinite fraternity of feeling. Now, sympathizing with the paper, my angel turns over another page. You did not care a penny for the book. But, now and then as you read, you understood the pervading thought that impelled the book— and that you praised. Was it not so? You were archangel enough to despise the imperfect body, and embrace the soul. Once you hugged the ugly Socrates because you saw the flame in the mouth, and heard the rushing of the demon,—the familiar,—and recognized the sound; for you have heard it in your own solitudes.

My dear Hawthorne, the atmospheric skepticisms steal into me now, and make me doubtful of my sanity in writing you thus. But, believe me, I am not mad, most noble Festus! But truth is ever incoherent, and when the big hearts strike together, the concussion is a little stunning. Farewell. Don't write a word about the book. That would be robbing me of my miserly delight. I am heartily sorry I ever wrote anything about you —it was paltry.[2] Lord, when shall we be done growing? As long as we have anything more to do, we have done nothing. So, now, let us add Moby Dick to our blessing, and step from that. Leviathan is not the biggest fish;—I have heard of Krakens.

This is a long letter, but you are not at all bound to answer it. Possibly, if you do answer it, and direct it to Herman Melville, you will missend it—for the very fingers that now guide this pen are not precisely the same that just took it up and put it on this paper. Lord, when shall we be done changing? Ah! it's a long stage, and no inn in sight, and night coming, and the body cold. But with you for a passenger, I am content and can be happy. I shall leave the world, I feel, with more satisfaction for having come to know you. Knowing you persuades me more than the Bible of our immortality.

What a pity, that, for your plain, bluff letter, you should get such gibberish! Mention me to Mrs. Hawthorne and to the children, and so, good-by to you, with my blessing.

                                                        HERMAN.

P.S. I can't stop yet. If the world was entirely made up of Magians, I'll tell you what I should do. I should have a paper-mill established at one end of the house, and so have an endless riband of foolscap rolling in upon my desk; and upon that endless riband I should write a thousand—a million—billion thoughts, all under the form of a letter to you. The divine magnet is on you, and my magnet responds. Which is the biggest? A foolish question—they are *One*.

                                                        H.

P.P.S. Don't think that by writing me a letter, you shall always be bored with an immediate reply to it—and so keep both of us delving over a writing-desk eternally. No such thing! I sha'n't always answer your letters, and you may do just as you please.

[TO GEORGE DUYCKINCK]

                              Pittsfield Dec. 20th—Monday [1858]

MY DEAR DUYCKINCK—

Your note (received on Saturday) is unaccountably among the missing.—Some one must have pilfered it for the autograph. I can't otherwise account for its mysterious disappearance.

But, as I remember, you have named Feb. 7th for my day, and deprecate any change.—Well and good. Let that be the day—only, is it certain that I can get to Baltimore the day following in time to immortalize myself there also? But I suppose I can.

Touching Mr. Davidson[1] and Jersey City, I am sure I am much obliged to you for your good offices in speaking to him.

I don't know that I can do anything about it at present, further at least than to let the matter alone, and dispose myself according to the event.—I should be glad to lecture there—or anywhere. If they will pay expenses, and give a reasonable fee, I am ready to lecture in Labrador or on the Isle of Desolation off Patagonia.

Bear with mine infirmity of jocularity (which I am aware, should hardly intrude into a semi-business letter like this) and Believe me

Sincerely yours
H MELVILLE

George Duyckinck Esq
    New York

[TO MALCOLM MELVILLE]

Pacific Ocean
(Off the coast of South America
On the Tropic of Capricorn)
Saturday September 1st 1860

MY DEAR MALCOLM:

It is now three months exactly since the ship "Meteor" sailed from Boston—a quarter of a year. During this long period, she has been continually moving, and has only seen land on two days. I suppose you have followed out on the map (or my *globe* were better—so you get Mama to clean it off for you) the route from Boston to San Francisco. The distance, by the straight track, is about 16000 miles; but the ship will have sailed before she gets there nearer 18 or 20000 miles. So you see it is further than from the apple-tree to the big rock. When we crossed the Line in the Atlantic Ocean it was very warm; & we had warm weather for some weeks; but as we kept getting to the Southward it began to grow less warm, and then coolish, and cold and colder, till at last it was winter. I wore two flannel shirts, and big mittens & overcoat, and a great Russia cap, a very thick leather cap, so called by sailors. At last we came in sight of land all covered with snow—uninhabited land, where no one ever lived, and no one ever will live—it is so barren, cold and desolate. This was Staten Land—an island. Near it, is the big island of Terra del Fuego. We passed through between these islands, and had a good view of both. There are some "wild people" living on Terra del Fuego; but it being the depth of winter there, I suppose they kept in their caves. At any rate we saw none of them. The next day we were off Cape Horn, the Southernmost point of all America. Now it was very bad weather, and was dark at about three o'clock in the afternoon. The wind blew terribly. We had hail-storms, and snow and sleet, and often the spray froze as it touched the deck. The ship rolled, and sometimes took in so much water on the deck as to wash people off their legs. Several sailors were washed along the deck this way, and came near getting washed overboard. And this reminds me of a very sad thing that happened the very morning we were off the Cape—I mean the very *pitch* of the Cape.—It was just about day-light; it was blowing a gale of wind; and Uncle Tom ordered the topsails (big sails) to be furled. Whilst the sailors were aloft on one of the yards, the ship rolled and plunged terribly; and it blew with sleet and hail, and was very cold & biting. Well, all at once, Uncle Tom saw something falling through the air, and then heard a thump, and then,—looking before him, saw a poor sailor lying dead on the deck. He had fallen from the yard, and was killed instantly.—His shipmates picked him up, and carried him under cover. By and by, when time could be spared, the sailmakers sewed up the body in a piece of sail-cloth, putting some iron balls—cannon balls—at the foot of it. And, when all was ready, the body was put on a plank, and carried to the ship's side in the presence of all hands. Then Uncle Tom, as Captain, read a prayer out of the prayer-book, and at a given word, the sailors who held the plank tipped it up, and immediately the body slipped into the stormy ocean, and we saw it no more.— Such is the way a poor sailor is buried at sea. This sailor's name was Ray. He had a friend among the crew; and they were both going to California, and thought of living there; but you see what happened.

We were in this stormy weather about forty or fifty days, dating from the beginning. But now at last we are in fine weather again, and the sun shines warm. (See page 5th)

Pacific Ocean
On the Line, Sep. 16th 1860

My Dear Malcolm: Since coming to the end of the fourth page, we have been sailing in fine weather, and it has continued quite warm.—The other day we saw a whale-ship; and I got into a boat and sailed over the ocean in it to the whale-ship, and stayed there about an hour. They had eight or ten of the "wild people" aboard. The Captain of the whale-ship had hired them at one of the islands called Rarotonga. He wanted them to help pull in the whale-boat when they hunt the whale.—Uncle Tom's crew are now very busy making the ship look smart for San Francisco. They are tarring the rigging, and are going to paint the ship, & the masts and yards. She looks very rusty now, oweing [*sic*] to so much bad weather that we have been in.— When we get to San-Francisco, I shall put this letter in the post office there, and you will get it in about 25 days afterwards. It will go in a steamer to a place called Panama, on the Isthmus of Darien (get out your map, & find it) then it will cross the Isthmus by railroad to Aspinwall or Chagres on the Gulf of Mexico; then, another steamer will take it, which steamer, after touching at Havanna in Cuba for coals, will go direct to New York; and there, it will go to the Post Office, and so, get to Pittsfield.

I hope that, when it arrives, it will find you well, and all the family. And I hope that you have called to mind what I said to you about your behaviour previous to my going away. I hope that you have been obedient to your mother, and helped her all you could, & saved her trouble. Now is the time to show what you are—whether you are a good, honorable boy, or a good-for-nothing one. Any boy, of your age, who disobeys his mother, or worries her, or is disrespectful to her— such a boy is a poor shabby fellow; and if you know any such boys, you ought to cut their acquaintance.

[Continued from 6th page.]

Now my Dear Malcolm, I must finish my letter to you.
I think of you, and Stanwix & Bessie and Fanny very often;
and often long to be with you. But it can not be, at present.
The picture which I have of you & the rest, I look at sometimes,
till the faces almost seem real.—Now, my Dear Boy, good bye,
& God bless you

Your affectionate father
H MELVILLE

I enclose a little baby flying-fish's wing for Fanny

[TO HIS WIFE]

[March 24, 1861]

MY DEAREST LIZZIE:

Sunday afternoon
Washington

I wrote you the other day from here, and now for another
note. In the first place I must say that as yet I have been able
to accomplish nothing in the matter of the counsulship—have
not in fact been able as yet so much as even to *see* any one on
the subject. I called last night at Senator's [*sic*] Sumner's, but
he was at a dinner somewhere. I shall call again to-morrow
After leaving Sumner's I went with Dr. Nourse [?] to a little
sort of a party given by the wife of a man connected with one
of the Departments. Had quite a pleasant evening. Several
Senators were there with wives, daughters etc. The Vice
President also & wife. Mrs. Hamlin is in appearance something
like you—so she struck me at least. I need not add that she
was very pleasing in her manner.—The night previous to this
I was at the second levee at the White House. There was a
great crowd, & a brilliant scene. Ladies in full dress by the
hundred. A steady stream of two-&-twos wound thro' the
apartments shaking hands with "Old Abe" and immediately
passing on. This continued without cessation for an hour &
a half. Of course I was one of the shakers. Old Abe is much
better looking that [*sic*] I expected & younger looking. He
shook hands like a good fellow—working hard at it like a man

sawing wood at so much per cord. Mrs. Lincoln is rather good-looking I thought. The scene was very fine altogether. Superb furniture—flood of light—magnificent flowers—full band of music etc.

I have attended the Senate twice; but nothing very interesting. The new wings of the Capitol are noble buildings, by far the richest in marble of any on the continent. I allude more particularly to the marble of the interior—staircases etc. They are in short palatial. The whole structure taken together is truly immense. It would astonish you to get lost among the labyrinths of halls, passages & splendid corridors.

This morning I spent in the park opposite the White House, sunning myself on a seat. The grass is bright & beautiful, & the shrubbery trying to bud. It is just cool enough to make an overcoat comfortable sitting out of doors. The wind is high however, & except in the parks, all is dust. I am boarding in a plain home—plain fare plain people—in fact all plain but the road to Florence. But if nothing else comes of it, I will at least derive good from the trip at this season. Though, to tell the truth, I feel home-sick at times, strange as it may seem. How long I shall remain is uncertain. I am expecting letters every day, & can do little or nothing till they arrive.

This afternoon I visited the Washington Monument. Huge tower some 160 feet high of white marble. Could not get inside. Nothing been done to it for long time.

Dr. Nourse is as facetious as ever. I went with him to the White House at the levee. But he is the greater part of the time engaged prosecuting his application for office. I venture to say, he will not succeed, & he begins to think so himself, I judge, from what he tells me of his experiences thus far. He leaves here probably on Tuesday.

Monday Morning.

Dearest Lizzie: Feel rather overdone this morning—overwalked yesterday. But the trip will do me good. Kisses to the children. Hope to get a letter from you today.

Thine, My Dearest Lizzie,

HERMAN

[TO SAMUEL SHAW]

Pittsfield Dec. 10th 1862

MY DEAR SAM[1]:

I remember that some days after my mishap,[2] when I was able to give the necessary attention, Lizzie read to me the letter you wrote her on that occasion.—I can not help telling you how sensible I am of the kindness you showed, and write you this that you may have the ocular evidence of my recovery. To be sure, I shall carry my arm (the left one, happily) in a sling, and the neuralgia gives me a love-pinch in the cheek now and then. But upon the whole I am now in a fair way of being completely restored to what I was before the accident.—This recovery is flattering to my vanity. I begin to indulge in the pleasing idea that my life must needs be of some value. Probably I consume a certain amount of oxygen, which unconsumed might create some subtle disturbance in Nature. Be that as it may, I am going to try and stick to the conviction named above. For I have observed that such an idea, once well bedded in a man, is a wonderful conservator of health and almost a prophecy of long life. I once, like other spoonies, cherished a loose sort of notion that I did not care to live very long. But I will frankly own that I have now no serious, no insuperable objections to a respectable longevity. I don't like the idea of being left out night after night in a cold church-yard.—In warm and genial countries, death is much less of a bugbear than in our frozen latitudes. A native of Hindostan takes easily and kindly to his latter end. It is but as a stepping round the corner to him. He knows he will sleep warm.—Pretty topics these [drawing of a death's-head] for a friendly note, you say. (By the way, Death, in my skull, seems to tip a knowing sort of wink out of his left eye. What does that mean, I wonder?)

But my page is more than half gone, so I must stop this trifling.

Lizzie is quite well, though a little jaded by her manifold cares, we not yet being quite in order yet. The children are flourishing as usual. Tomorrow we expect the gratification of

a visit from my mother, whom we hope to be able to keep
some time with us.—My best remembrances to your mother,
Lemuel, and the rest of the family.

Adieu

H.M.

[TO THE HON. PETER GANSEVOORT]

New York, Aug. 26 '75

MY DEAR UNCLE PETER[1]:

Last evening I received through a note from Mr. Lansing[2]
a check for $1200, which he says you requested him to send me.
—I shall at once deposit the money in a Savings Bank, there to
remain till needed for the purpose designed.

And now, my Dear Uncle, in receiving this generous gift
from you, so much enhanced by the circumstances, I feel the
same sentiments which I expressed to you in person at Albany
when you so kindly made known your intention. I will not
repeat them here; but only pray God to bless you, and have
you in His keeping.

With respect and true affection,

Your nephew

HERMAN MELVILLE

[TO JAMES BILLSON]

104, East 26th Street, New York.

The last day of 1888.

MY DEAR SIR,—

I have your letter, and thank you for it, and not the less for
the book[1] accompanying it. You could hardly have sent me
anything more welcome. All the contents are highly interesting; but I agree with you in thinking the Essay on Blake the
most so. I learned much from it. But "The City of Dreadful
Night," one can hardly over-estimate it, massive and mighty as
it is—its gloom is its sublimity. The confronting Sphinx and
Angel, where shall we go to match them? Thomson's criticisms

in general are very refreshing in their ignoring of the conventional in criticism. But I must rein up. My eyes have been annoying me for some days past; and I know of hardly anything more disconcerting. But let me think of those lines on Patti,[2] and forget that.

You did well in giving your superfluous volume of "John Marr" to Mr. Barrs,[3] to whom I am indebted for "A Voice from the Nile," etc., an appreciated gift. May the Powers long keep snug your *Bird's Nest!* [4]

NOTES

Melville wrote *Typee* at his mother's house in Lansingburgh. When it was nearly completed, his brother Gansevoort was appointed Secretary to the American Legation at the Court of St. James as a reward for his campaign services to the Democratic party in 1844. At the suggestion of a friend, Thomas L. Nichols, who dropped into Gansevoort's law office in Wall Street one day, it was decided that Gansevoort should find a publisher in London so that if an English reputation were secured for the book its publication in America would have a better chance of success (Adkins, "A Note on Melville's *Typee*," *New England Quarterly*, V, 348–351). Gansevoort drove a good bargain with Murray, who gave £100 for the right to print a thousand copies in the "Colonial and Home Library" under the title *Narrative of a Four Months' Residence among the Natives of a Valley of the Marquesas Islands*. He also arranged with Mr. Putnam of the American firm of Wiley and Putnam to bring out the book immediately in America (Weaver, *Herman Melville*, 252–255). Gansevoort saw the book through the press and loyally advertised its virtues to his friends, among whom were some men of great influence in English literary circles. The Chevalier Bunsen, for example, wrote to him after reading *Typee*: "Let me first wish you joy for this most interesting brother and his book: he must be a young man of uncommon energy and fine intellect . . ." (Duyckinck Collection, New York Public Library). V. H. Paltsits intends to publish the London journal of Gansevoort Melville which contains valuable data concerning his devoted efforts to launch his brother as a writer.

When Melville finished the *Sequel* to *Typee*, after his reunion with Toby in July, 1846 (see letter, p. 368 above), it was incorporated in the revised edition late in that year. Several changes in the text were also made at this time in order to cool the colors of his Earthly Paradise and soften his libellous remarks on the missionaries. Bernard De Voto has shown, however, that alterations in the text for the purpose of bowdlerization were made between the first issue and the revised edition ("Editions of *Typee*," *Saturday Review of Literature*, V, 406).

1. After escaping from the ship, Melville and Toby had made a perilous descent into one of the interior valleys of the island. One of the valleys was known to be inhabited by the cannibal Typees.

2. Melville had been afflicted by a painful swelling in one leg.

3. Taioa. Melville betrays his New England ancestry by his phonetic spelling of South Sea names. R. L. Stevenson wrote to E. L. Burlingame in February, 1890: "Our admirable friend Herman Melville, of whom, since I could judge, I have thought more than ever, had no ear for languages whatever: his Hapar tribe should be Hapaa [Happa], etc." (*Letters*, New York, 1911, III, 185.)

4. The word "Kannaka" is at the present day universally used in the South Seas by Europeans to designate the Islanders. In the various dialects of the principal groups it is simply a sexual designation applied to the males; but it is now used by the natives in their intercourse with foreigners in the same sense in which the latter employ it.

A "Tabooed Kannaka" is an islander whose person has been made to a certain extent sacred by the operation of a singular custom. . . . [*Melville's note.*]

5. Admiral A. du Petit-Thouars hoisted the French flag at Nukuhiva on June 2, 1842.

6. The Typees, in spite of their great friendliness, made it plain to Toby and Melville that they were determined to keep them in the valley. Toby contrived, however, to escape, promising to bring help to effect the rescue of Melville who was in too weakened a condition to think of trying to accompany him.

7. A servant-companion who carried Melville on his back while he was lame.

8. A lounging pavilion for the men. See p. 34 ff.

9. In some copies of the "first" edition of *Typee* this passage in brackets is lacking.

10. The strict honesty which the inhabitants of nearly all the Polynesian Islands manifest towards each other, is in striking contrast with the thieving propensities some of them evince in their intercourse with foreigners. It would almost seem that, according to their peculiar code of morals, the pilfering of a hatchet or a wrought nail from a European, is looked upon as a praiseworthy action. Or rather, it may be presumed, that bearing in mind the wholesale forays made upon them by their nautical visitors, they consider the property of the latter as a fair object of reprisal. This consideration, while it serves to reconcile an apparent contradiction in the moral character of the islanders, should in some measure alter that low opinion of it which the reader of South Sea voyages is too apt to form. [*Melville's note.*]

11. Orientalist (1746–1794).

12. A stranger, from another tribe, who could speak English.

13. External evidence shows that Melville actually spent not more than a month in the valley. See Introduction, p. xlvii.

14. Toby had done his best to persuade the perfidious sailor who

helped him escape to go back with him after Melville. Thwarted in this attempt, he had to rely on the sailor's false promises to bring Melville down to the coast. Before anything further could be done, the vessel on which Toby had shipped weighed anchor and put out to sea.

15. The ship in which Melville had come to the Marquesas. Actually the *Acushnet*.

OMOO (67–136)

Omoo was completed late in 1846. On December 10 Melville sent Evert Duyckinck the remaining chapters which he had not yet seen, noting in his letter three (Nos. 5, 7 and 17) which were to be rejected. This unpublished letter ends with the significant paragraph: "I beg you to pay particular attention to the following chapters—chapters *33.34*—and *45.46.47.48.49.50*—They all refer more or less to the missions and the condition of the natives" (Duyckinck Collection, New York Public Library). Duyckinck, though asked to act the part of conscience for Melville, was evidently not disturbed by the prospect of missionary wrath. Writing his brother George on December 15 he gives him this information about the book: "Melville is in town with new MSS agitating the conscience of John Wiley and tempting the pockets of the Harpers. I have read it. His further adventures in the south seas after leaving Typee. He owes a sailor's grudge to the Missionaries and pays it off at Tahiti. His account of the church building there is very much in the spirit of Dickens' humorous handling of sacred things in Italy" (Duyckinck Collection, New York Public Library).

Duyckinck's reference to Wiley and Putnam's conscientious scruples about *Omoo's* plain-speaking suggests that their timidity made it possible for the house of Harper to acquire the book, for they were the publishers. Murray gave £150 for the English rights. The English publication was in March, 1847. On April 24 the *Literary World* published two extracts.

1. Melville escaped from the Marquesas Islands aboard the ship *Lucy Ann*, the *Julia* of *Omoo*.

2. With her cowardly captain sick and her crew mutinous, the ship had made sail for Papeetee, the harbor of the island of Tahiti. Against the command of the acting consul there, who ordered them to prepare to put to sea again in a few days, Melville and his companions brought her into the harbor. For this insubordination they were imprisoned, first on the frigate *Reine Blanche* and later in the local jail.

3. The Newtonian theory concerning the tides does not hold good at Tahiti; where, throughout the year, the waters uniformly commence ebbing at noon and midnight, and flow about sunset and

daybreak. Hence the term Tooerar-Po is used alike to express high-water and midnight. [*Melville's note.*]

4. Pritchard was the British missionary consul, then absent in England.

5. Signed by the crew and petitioning for a redress of their grievances.

6. Concerning the singular ignorance of the natives respecting their own country, it may be here observed, that a considerable inland lake—Whaiherea by name—is known to exist, although their accounts of it strangely vary. Some told me it had no bottom, no outlet, and no inlet; others, that it fed all the streams on the island. A sailor of my acquaintance said, that he once visited this marvellous lake, as one of an exploring party from an English sloop-of-war. It was found to be a great curiosity: very small, deep, and green; a choice well of water bottled up among the mountains, and abounding with delicious fish. [*Melville's note.*]

7. When Lieutenant Wise, U.S.N., visited Tahiti, he found Dr. Johnson still wrathful over Melville's portrait of him and meditating a suit for libel against the publishers. He allowed Wise to examine his dose-book and declared to him that the "embrocation" so relished by Long Ghost was "a villanous preparation, having the least taste of gin in the world, and made up from laudanum, turpentine, and soap linament!" Wise also learned that at the time of his visit Long Ghost was supposed to be in Sydney or in California prospecting for gold. He says of other characters in *Omoo*, some of whom have not appeared at this point in the story: "Captain Bob, of the Calaboosa, was 'muckee-moi,' so was Father Murphy, all under the sod. Charming Mrs. Bell had taken to drink, *before* Mr. Melville's rencontre, and may have been slightly elevated on that occasion. H.M. *cidevant* Consul, Mr. Wilson, was in the like vinous state, and occupied his leisure in the pursuit of shells at the Navigator Islands. Shorty was still devoting his talents to the culture of potatoes at Aimeo, and strongly suspected of shooting his neighbour's cattle" (Wise, *Los Gringos*, 357).

The discoveries of J. W. Earnshaw (see Bibliography under Simon, "Recherches australiennes sur Hermann [*sic*] Melville") have added many facts concerning the persons and circumstances described in *Omoo*, particularly about the *Lucy Ann* (Melville's *Julia*) and Dr. Long Ghost. He finds that Long Ghost was a member of the party of the missionary John Williams, massacred at Erromango in 1839. It is probable that he was W. C. Cunningham, nephew of a navy surgeon and son of the poet Allan Cunningham, and that he was made a vice-consul after the affair at Erromango. At the time Melville encountered him, he had been degraded. In 1856 he was married and settled at Concepción in Chile.

8. An old shipmate of Jermin, long supposed dead but now resident on the island.

9. An English trader named Lucett who, in his *Rovings in the Pacific* (1851), attacked Melville as a rogue and a liar, declares that the *Lucy Ann* was seen lying at Annatam in June, 1848, and that Melville had grossly maligned her seaworthy qualities (*op. cit.* I, 294).

10. *Polynesia: or an Historical Account of the Principal Islands of the South Sea:* By the Right Rev. M. Russell, LL.D. (Harpers' Family Library Edition), p. 96. [*Melville's note.*]

11. *A New Voyage Round the World in the Years 1823-24-25-26:* By Otto Von Kotzebue, Post Captain in the Russian Imperial Service (London, 1830; 2 vols. 8vo.), vol. i, p. 168. [*Melville's note.*]

12. The author of a *Voyage Round the World, in the Years 1800-1804* (3 vols. 8vo. London), 1805. [*Melville's note.*]

13. *Narrative of a Voyage to the Pacific and Bherring's* [sic] *Straits, under the Command of Captain F. W. Beechey, R.N.* (London, 1831), vol. i., p. 287. [*Melville's note.*]

14. *Memoirs of the Life and Gospel Labors of the late Daniel Wheeler, a minister of the Society of Friends* (London, 1842, 8vo.), p. 757. [*Melville's note.*]

15. *A Missionary Voyage to the South Pacific Ocean*, Appendix, pp. 336, 342. [*Melville's note.*]

16. See *Vancouver's Voyages*, 4to. edition, vol. i, p. 172. [*Melville's note.*]

17. *Beechey's Narrative*, p. 269. [*Melville's note.*]

18. After their release from the Calabooza Melville and Dr. Long Ghost had obtained jobs on the neighboring island of Eimeo with two planters, a Yankee and a Cockney named Zeke and Shorty. These jobs they soon gave up because they found weeding the potato-patch too irksome and were eager to get on with their explorations.

19. A decayed fisherman-chief of the island.

20. White men.

21. Where there was a mission.

22. Long Ghost and Melville were known to their employers as Peter and Paul.

23. At the village of Partoowye the wanderers were most civilly entertained by Po-Po, his wife Arfretee, and their mischievous daughter Loo.

24. Melville actually came home in a U.S. man-of-war sailing from Honolulu.

MARDI (137–170)

Mardi is a satirical allegory, veiling the institutions and occupations of modern life, with which is interwoven a symbolic theme of a quest, among islands which resemble the nations of the western world, for a mysterious maiden named Yillah who may symbolize "heavenly love" or the spiritual life. The story begins realistically with the escape from a whaling vessel of the hero and his companion, Jarl. They come eventually on a native boat from which they capture the beautiful, blue-eyed Yillah, killing a priest who guards her, to effect her rescue. They now sail westward and land on the island of Odo where the hero of the book is received as Taji, a demi-god. King Media is delighted to have him as a companion. When Taji sets forth in search of Yillah who has disappeared, King Media goes with him to explore the Mardian world. The other members of their party are Mohi, or Braid-beard, one of the keepers of the Chronicles of the Kings of Mardi; Babbalanja, a philosopher; and Yoomy, the poet. The remainder of the book is concerned with their visits to one Mardian island after another, in each of which Taji searches in vain for Yillah and is himself pursued by another mysterious phantom, Hautia.

The book was published by Richard Bentley of London in March, 1849; by Harper and Brothers of New York in April. Evert Duyckinck had requested Melville to allow him to publish extracts in the *Literary World*. The eighty-fourth chapter, "Taji sits down to dinner with five-and-twenty kings" was printed, with flattering remarks about the book's showing "an onward development," in the issue of April 7, 1849. Duyckinck genuinely admired *Mardi*, for he wrote his brother, March 9, 1848: "Melville the other night brought me a few chapters of his new book which in the poetry and wildness of the thing will be ahead of Typee and Omoo" (Duyckinck Collection, New York Public Library).

Writing to his father-in-law, April 23, 1849, Melville said: "I see that *Mardi* has been cut into by the *London Atheneum* [*sic*], and also burnt by the common hangman in the *Boston Post*. However, the *London Examiner* & *Literary Gazette* & other papers this side of the water have done differently. These attacks are matters of course, and are essential to the building up of any permanent reputation— if such should ever prove to be mine—'There's nothing in it!' cried the dunce when he threw down the 47th problem of the 1st Book of Euclid—'There's nothing in it!'—Thus with the posed critic. But Time, which is the solver of all riddles, will solve *Mardi*" (quoted by Weaver, *Herman Melville*, 274).

Melville did not exaggerate in the case of the *Athenaeum* which thought *Mardi* a "most frantic romance" and the key to its allegory irretrievably buried. The *Examiner's* critic parted from "Mr. Melville in as good humour as his former books have always left us in." The *Literary Gazette* was puzzled but thought the adventures "superb." On the whole the reviewers were favorable, though amazed at the sight of a teller of traveler's tales metamorphosed into a satirist. The *United States Magazine and Democratic Review* noticed that the critics had failed to see that *Mardi* is "an allegory that mirrors the world."

1. Dominora is England. The hump on King Bello's back is her national debt. Melville particularly satirizes in this chapter England's imperialism, her arrogance in diplomacy, and her wars of conquest.

2. The Mardian god.

3. The continent of Europe. Franko is France; Ibeereea is Spain; Luzianna, Portugal; Latianna, Italy; Vatikanna, the Papal States; Hapzaboro, Austria; Tutoni, the German States; Muzkovi, Russia.

4. The Balance of Power, since the time of Henry VIII the object of England's foreign policy.

5. The United States of America.

6. The impressing of American seamen, which was a contributing cause of the War of 1812.

7. A glance at England's preoccupation with the Napoleonic wars.

8. The herald. He sat in the prow of the first canoe which terminated in a large, open shark's mouth.

9. Dr. Sangrado is a quack in *Gil Blas* whose only cure is to bleed his patients and give them hot water to drink.

10. Teeth were the coin of the realm in Mardi.

11. A portly, pleasant, old monarch whose state had earlier been visited by the travelers.

12. In this passage Melville is satirizing the evils of enclosure and the factory system.

13. The Chartists who, in April, 1848, marched on London in an abortive attempt to force Parliament to act on their six-point petition.

14. The capitol at Washington.

15. Texas and Florida, admitted to the Union in 1845; Iowa, in 1846; Wisconsin, in 1848.

16. A negro slave.

17. The Senate at that time met in the semi-circular chamber which was later, until 1935, occupied by the Supreme Court.

18. Probably Daniel Webster. Carlyle in a letter to Emerson (*Correspondence*, 1883, I, 247–248) described: "The tanned complexion, that amorphous crag-like face; the dull black eyes under their precipice of brows, like dull anthracite furnaces, needing only to be *blown*."

19. Phrenologists.

20. Daniel Lambert (1770–1809) was the fattest man of whom record exists.

21. Senator William Allen of Ohio, an eloquent advocate of expansion into the Oregon territory where England asserted her

claims.   Melville's anti-imperialism, which made him an anti-expansionist in domestic politics, is evident in this passage.

22. The Revolutions of 1848 in Europe.

23. That Melville's parable deals with the Roman kings of the Tarquin dynasty and Rome's subsequent history, hardly needs to be pointed out.

24. England's Charles I.

25. The Mexican War of 1846.

26. Without waiting four or five hundred centuries, we shall be willing to risk the comment that Taji-Melville wrote this scroll.

27. Calhoun, whose *South Carolina Exposition*, written in 1828, was the first full exposition of the idea of nullification.   The *Southern Quarterly Review* (XVI, 260–261) objected to this "loathsome picture of Mr. Calhoun, in the character of a slave driver."

28. The realm of the High Pontiff of a group of Mardian isles. To Melville it symbolized the shallowness and hypocrisy of ecclesiasticism.   The name he probably derived from Dante's Maremma, a malarial swamp along the Tuscan coast.

WHITE-JACKET (171–216)

When Melville journeyed to London in November, 1849, he had with him the proof-sheets of *White-Jacket* which was to be issued by Harper and Brothers in America.   In London Murray refused it, but Bentley was willing to pay Melville well for the rights (see p. xxix above).   The book was published in England in January, 1850. Evert Duyckinck had what was perhaps the first American copy. Allan Melville wrote him on March 6, 1850: "I am assured from a 'source that is undoubted' as the editors say, that when you have placed the accompanying sheets with those you got at the Harpers yesterday you will have a complete copy of 'White Jacket'" (Duyckinck Collection, New York Public Library).   According to a note under "Literary Items" in the *Home Journal* for April 6, 1850, "The first edition of Melville's new work, the 'White Jacket,' was sold as soon as published."

White-Jacket mingles autobiography, fiction, and propaganda in a fashion more disconcerting to the critic, perhaps, than to the general reader.   We happen to know a good deal about this particular voyage of the frigate *United States*, called by Melville the *Neversink*, so it is possible to separate what he invented from what he saw or actually experienced.

Melville had, on June 1, 1843, signed an indenture with one Isaac Montgomery of Honolulu to be clerk in his business for one year, the employment to begin on July 1 (Forsythe, "Herman Melville in Honolulu," *New England Quarterly*, VIII, 99–105).   The muster-roll of the *United States* shows that he enlisted at Honolulu on August 17.

Did the presence in the vicinity of the *Acushnet*, from which he had deserted a year before, make him think he might be safer on board an American warship?

Several of the officers and men whom Melville describes with such pitiless or admiring completeness, can easily be identified from the frigate's muster-roll. A comparison of the book and the roll has been made by Albert Mordell, from whose " Melville and ' White-Jacket'" (*Saturday Review of Literature*, VII, 946) many of the notes below have been drawn.

An unsubstantiated inference has been transformed into the traditional statement that *White-Jacket* was instrumental in causing, in 1850, the abolition of flogging in the navy. The origin of this myth can be traced to S. R. Franklin's *Memories of a Rear-Admiral Who Has Served for More than Half a Century in the Navy of the U.S.* (1898). This officer, who had been a midshipman on the *United States* when Melville was aboard, dimly remembered the novelist. In speaking of *White-Jacket*, he asserts that: "This book was placed on the desk of every member of Congress, and was a most eloquent appeal to the humane sentiment of the country" (*op. cit.*, p. 64). Actually there is no mention of Melville in the Congressional Debates of the session of 1849–1850 in which the controversy over flogging was at its height (C. R. Anderson, "A Reply to Herman Melville's *White-Jacket*," *American Literature*, VII, 142). His book appeared at the moment when long-continued agitation for the abolition of corporal punishment in the navy, well epitomized by the series of articles entitled "Flogging in the Navy" which ran in the *Democratic Review* from August through December, 1849, was about to eventuate in action. Melville was aware that his chapters of propaganda in the cause were by no means the first attack on the evil, for he mentions earlier writers on the subject. He rejoiced when, in September, 1850, the barbarous punishment was done away with. He refers to the act of Congress in a letter to Evert Duyckinck dated "Sunday Evening 1850": "I am offering up devout jubilations for the abolition of the flogging law" (Duyckinck Collection, New York Public Library).

1. John H. Chase was the actual name of this sailor whom Melville held to be the paragon of all seamen. He was number 513 in the muster-roll of the *United States*. The impression of Jack's manliness and good-nature stayed green in Melville's memory. He dedicated his (posthumous) *Billy Budd* to "Jack Chase, Englishman, wherever that great heart may now be here on earth or harbored in Paradise."

2. The dandiacal hero of Bulwer Lytton's novel of the same name.

3. Camoens' *Lusiads* is the Portuguese national epic, published in 1572.

4. Admiral Franklin's remarks on Jack Chase (*op. cit.*, pp. 64–65) bear out what Melville says of him.

5. "A cant name for a man-of-war, and also for government and government authorities" (*The Sailor's Word-Book*, 1867).

6. The "over-lop," the lowest deck.

7. On the island of Minorca, off eastern Spain.

8. In the angle of the bows of the ship.

9. Small tackle with two or three pulleys.

10. The hero of the book had made himself a white jacket of duck in lieu of a proper *grego* or sailor's surtout. It made him notorious in the ship and brought him many a misfortune as well as his nickname.

11. According to C. R. Anderson (*op. cit.*, p. 128) this chapter is based on fact. It was not Jack Chase's personal worth, however, but the desire of the Commodore to make a diplomatic gesture, which secured Chase exemption from punishment for what he had done.

12. *Le Droit des Gens* of Emmerich de Vattel, published first in 1758.

13. The frigate *United States* was commanded by Captain James Armstrong until June 3, 1844, but from Callao to Boston, on Melville's home voyage, by Captain Cornelius Stribling. Armstrong was noted, however, for his fondness for claret-wine, and Melville saw fit to satirize him rather than the actual commander during the months covered by *White-Jacket* (Anderson, *op. cit.*, p. 126).

14. The previous chapter tells how "a raw-boned, crack-pated" Down Easter had been robbed of his "dunderfunk," and scolded by the lieutenant who had never heard of this choice dish of hard biscuit, beef fat, molasses, and water.

15. George Bancroft, who was Secretary of the Navy from 1845 to 1846, was instrumental in founding the Naval Academy.

16. St. Paul, who said when he was to be examined by scourging, "Is it lawful for you to scourge a man that is a Roman, and uncondemned?" (Acts 22 : 25.)

17. The Surgeon of the Fleet, William Johnson, was probably not the original of Cadwallader Cuticle (Anderson, *op. cit.*, p. 129).

18. While attempting to swim ashore he had been fired at by a sentry and wounded in the right thigh.

19. A Roman physician of the time of Augustus.

20. John Bell and Sir Benjamin Brodie were nineteenth century English surgeons. One suspects that Cuticle invented Lally.

21. Cuticle probably meant John Hennen, an English army surgeon who published *Observations on Military Surgery* in 1818.

22. George James Guthrie performed several unusual surgical operations at Waterloo. He actually did write treatises on gunshot wounds.

23. In the preceding chapter Melville mentions the flogging of a mulatto called Rose-Water.

24. The episode related in this chapter is possibly fictitious.

25. This exciting chapter which has all the marks of autobiographical truth, was constructed by Melville out of an episode described in Nathaniel Ames's *A Mariner's Sketches, Originally Published in the Manufacturers and Farmers Journal* . . . (Providence, 1830), pp. 227–230. As an example of Melville's ability in transforming mediocre stuff into a work of art, this chapter in *White-Jacket* is unsurpassed. For purposes of comparison, the pertinent sections from Ames follow.

"I was going aloft and had got as far as the futtock shrouds, when a ratlin broke under my feet, and I fell backwards. My first sensation was surprise; I could not imagine where I was, but soon ascertained from the rushing of the air by my ears that I was falling and that headforemost.

"Dr. Johnson says that the near approach of death wonderfully concentrates a man's ideas. I am sure it did mine for I never thought so *fast* before or since, as I did during the few seconds that I was tumbling.

"In an instant the recollection came into my head that one of the quarter deck guns (No. 20) was directly under me, and I should in all human probability, be dashed to pieces upon it. I would have given the world to vent my feelings in cries, I tried to gather my limbs together, to contract my muscles, to shrink my body into as small a compass as possible, and with unspeakable terror awaited the 'death shock.'

"All this while there was a blood red light before my eyes, through which a thousand horrible forms were constantly gliding. Then I thought of home, and the forms of all I hold dear on earth, and many others, 'strangers of distinction,' beside, floated before me. Then the recollection of the infernal gun and the consequent smash across the breech of it, put all these phantoms to flight, and I felt that peculiar sickness and distress at the stomach, which it is said one experiences when on the point of undergoing a sudden and violent and painful death, and I thought to myself 'surely it *must* be almost time for the shock.'

"A shock I certainly did receive, and that no very gentle one across the back of the head, neck and left shoulder, and in an instant all was dark and still. 'It is all over,' thought I, 'this is the state between death and resurrection.' I really thought I had passed the first and awaited with increased terror for the second, when to my utter dismay, I felt myself falling a second time, but the sensation was different; the blow that I had received turned me, and I was descending feet foremost.

"But no words can express my delight, my extacy, at finding myself *overboard*, instead of on the gun. I kept going down, down, till it appeared to me that the seven fathoms and a half, (the depth of water at our anchorage,) had more than doubled since we let go our anchor.

"After a while I became stationary and soon began slowly to ascend. When I looked up, I saw high, very high above me, a dim greenish light, which became brighter and brighter till at last I bounded on the surface like a cork.

"I immediately swam to the accommodation ladder and went on board. My shoulder and neck were much bruised by striking against a spare maintopsail yard, that was stowed over the starboard quarter, and my head felt 'sort o' queer,' from sundry thumps and knocks and thumps it had received in the fall, which however were mere 'cakes and gingerbread.'"

C. R. Anderson noted Melville's use of Ames, of which this is not the only instance (*op. cit.*, p. 131). He also discovered that there is no mention in the Log Book of the *United States* of any such accident to Melville as this fictitious one he invented.

26. Harpoons with two or more prongs.

MOBY-DICK (217–319)

Moby-Dick, dedicated to Hawthorne, "In Token of my Admiration for his Genius," was published October 18, 1851, by Bentley in England, under the title of *The Whale*. Harper and Brothers issued it in America in November. The English text is a revision of the proof-sheets of the American edition. A number of passages were excised to remove what the English might consider objectionable references to religion, sex, and the deity. (See Ament, "Bowdler and the Whale," *American Literature*, IV, 39–46.)

We know more of the state of mind of Melville and the circumstances under which he wrote *Moby-Dick* than we do in the case of any of his other works. When Evert Duyckinck visited him at "Broadhall" in Pittsfield during August, 1850, Melville had made good progress with the book. At least so we judge from Duyckinck's probably exaggerated remark, in a letter to his brother, that it is "mostly done." (See pp. 432–433 below.) In October Melville moved into his own house nearby. His eyes troubled him badly so that he was not able to write in the evening. (See p. 383 above.) His working hours, in the short New England winter day, covered the time from the completion of his morning farm chores to 2:30 in the afternoon. Inspiration flowed into him at this time and his brain was teeming with ideas for future works. In the early summer, for three weeks he abandoned the book while his days went to getting the crops into the ground and tending to the innumerable farm chores. In a week, he writes Hawthorne, he will go to New York to bury himself in a third-story room and slave on the *Whale* while it is driving through the press—the only way he can finish it now, he is "so pulled hither and thither by circumstances." (See p. 390 above.)

When the book was finished Hawthorne was one of the first to see it. His admiration, which was sincere and warm, prompted him to suggest to Melville that he might review it. (See p. 395 above.) Melville rejected this proposal though he exults that Hawthorne has appreciated what a book he has written. We know from the ecstatic letter he wrote in reply to Hawthorne's letter (which has disappeared) that he felt himself to have arrived at the fullness of his powers. "Lord, when shall we be done growing? As long as we have anything more to do, we have done nothing. So, now, let us add Moby Dick to our blessing, and step from that. Leviathan is not the biggest fish;—I have heard of Krakens."

1. A South Sea island head-hunter who had been the bed-fellow of "Ishmael," the teller of the story, at the Spouter Inn in New Bedford before embarking on the voyage.

2. The Persian King in the Book of Esther.

3. A Prussian in Paris at the time of the Revolution. He appeared before the Assembly in 1790 as the leader of a pretended foreign delegation.

4. When Ishmael and Queequeg signed on for a voyage on the *Pequod*, they were accosted one day by a mysterious man named Elijah who hinted to them of dire things that would happen under Captain Ahab's command.

5. Ahab had thrown his pipe overboard, symbolizing that he had put behind him all serene and contented living.

6. Melville used familiar sailor-lore in his account of Moby Dick. His exploits were recounted by J. N. Reynolds in the *Knickerbocker Magazine* for May, 1839 (pp. 377–392), in an article entitled "Mocha Dick: or the White Whale of the Pacific: a Leaf from a Manuscript Journal." Knowing how carefully Melville documented his stories while writing them, we can be certain that he had seen this article, though one finds little evidence of its having influenced him. According to Reynolds, Mocha Dick was finally conquered by the first mate of an American vessel. "He measured more than seventy feet from his noddle to the tips of his flukes. . . . It may emphatically be said, that 'the scars of his old wounds were near his new,' for not less than twenty harpoons did we draw from his back; the rusted mementos of many a desperate rencounter" (*op. cit.*, p. 390).

Another famous story of a ferocious whale, which attacked the ship *Essex* on November 20, 1819, and assaulted it again as it was sinking, was also current and known to Melville, since he mentions, in his list of extracts at the beginning of *Moby-Dick*, the book which relates it.

Just at the time when *Moby-Dick* appeared the papers were re-printing from the *Panama Herald* an account of the ramming and sinking of the *Ann Alexander* by a whale, which took place in August, 1851. The review of *Moby-Dick* in the *Literary World* (November 15,

1851) opens with a long notice of the incident. Melville was excited by the report. He wrote to Evert Duyckinck as soon as he heard the story from him:

"Your letter received last night had a sort of stunning effect on me. For some days past being engaged in the woods with axe, wedge, and beetle, the Whale had almost completely slipped me for the time (and I was the merrier for it) when Crash! comes Moby Dick himself (as you justly say) and reminds me of what I have been about for part of the last year or two. It is really and truly a surprising coincidence—to say the least. I make no doubt it *is* Moby Dick himself, for there is no account of his capture after the sad fate of the Pequod about fourteen years ago. Ye Gods! What a Commentator is this Ann Alexander whale. What he has to say is short and pithy but very much to the point. I wonder if my evil art has raised this monster" (Duyckinck Collection, New York Public Library).

7. A gnostic sect of the second century who worshipped a serpent god.

8. The fifteenth-century Hôtel de Cluny in Paris is built upon the ruins of a Roman palace which contained extensive baths. When Melville visited Paris in 1849 he thought the Hôtel "just the house I'd like to live in."

9. Job, chapter 41.

10. Northwest of Siam.

11. The Revelation of St. John the Divine 4 : 4 and 1 : 14.

12. With reference to the Polar bear, it may possibly be urged by him who would fain go still deeper into this matter, that it is not the whiteness, separately regarded, which heightens the intolerable hideousness of that brute; for, analysed, that heightened hideousness, it might be said, only arises from the circumstance, that the irresponsible ferociousness of the creature stands invested in the fleece of celestial innocence and love; and hence, by bringing together two such opposite emotions in our minds, the Polar bear frightens us with so unnatural a contrast. But even assuming all this to be true; yet, were it not for the whiteness, you would not have that intensified terror.

As for the white shark, the white gliding ghostliness of repose in that creature, when beheld in his ordinary moods, strangely tallies with the same quality in the Polar quadruped. This peculiarity is most vividly hit by the French in the name they bestow upon that fish. The Romish mass for the dead begins with "Requiem eternam" (eternal rest), whence *Requiem* denominating the mass itself, and any other funeral music. Now, in allusion to the white, silent stillness of death in this shark, and the mild deadliness of his habits, the French call him *Requin*. [*Melville's note.*]

13. I remember the first albatross I ever saw. It was during a prolonged gale, in waters hard upon the Antarctic seas. From my forenoon watch below, I ascended to the overclouded deck; and there, dashed upon the main hatches, I saw a regal, feathery thing of unspotted whiteness, and with a hooked, Roman bill sublime. At intervals, it arched forth its vast archangel wings, as if to embrace some holy ark. Wondrous flutterings and throbbings shook it. Though bodily unharmed, it uttered cries, as some king's ghost in supernatural distress. Through its inexpressible, strange eyes, methought I peeped to secrets which took hold of God. As Abraham before the angels, I bowed myself; the white thing was so white, its wings so wide, and in those for ever exiled waters, I had lost the miserable warping memories of traditions and of towns. Long I gazed at that prodigy of plumage. I cannot tell, can only hint, the things that darted through me then. But at last I awoke; and turning, asked a sailor what bird was this. A goney, he replied. Goney! I never had heard that name before; is it conceivable that this glorious thing is utterly unknown to men ashore! never! But some time after, I learned that goney was some seaman's name for albatross. So that by no possibility could Coleridge's wild Rhyme have had aught to do with those mystical impressions which were mine, when I saw that bird upon our deck. For neither had I then read the Rhyme, nor knew the bird to be an albatross. Yet, in saying this, I do but indirectly burnish a little brighter the noble merit of the poem and the poet.

I assert, then, that in the wondrous bodily whiteness of the bird chiefly lurks the secret of the spell; a truth the more evinced in this, that by a solecism of terms there are birds called grey albatrosses; and these I have frequently seen, but never with such emotions as when I beheld the Antarctic fowl.

But how had the mystic thing been caught? Whisper it not, and I will tell; with a treacherous hook and line, as the fowl floated on the sea. At last the Captain made a postman of it; tying a lettered, leathern tally round its neck, with the ship's time and place; and then letting it escape. But I doubt not, that leathern tally, meant for man, was taken off in Heaven, when the white fowl flew to join the wing-folding, the invoking, and adoring cherubim! [*Melville's note.*]

14. See chapter CCCL of Lord Berners' translation of Froissart's *Chronicles of England, France and Spain.*

15. St. John, in his Revelation, 6:8, saw "a pale horse: and his name that sat on him was Death, and Hell followed with him."

16. One of the mountains of the Harz. Tradition makes it the meeting place of the witches on St. Walpurgis' Night. The Specter of the Brocken (Blocksberg) is seen on rare occasions.

17. Stubb had killed a whale, and the business of cutting it up now begins.

18. The supposed apparition at 33 Cock Lane, Smithfield, drew crowds to the house. Dr. Johnson was interested and made a private investigation of his own.

19. Pig-iron ballast set into the frame of the ship.

20. Wet sails are taut and give greater resistance to the wind.

21. The stampede of King Porus' elephants helped Alexander win the fight.

22. The sperm whale, as with all other species of the Leviathan, but unlike most other fish, breeds indifferently at all seasons; after a gestation which may probably be set down at nine months, producing but one at a time; though in some few known instances giving birth to an Esau and Jacob:—a contingency provided for in suckling by two teats, curiously situated, one on each side of the anus; but the breasts themselves extend upwards from that. When by chance these precious parts in a nursing whale are cut by the hunter's lance, the mother's pouring milk and blood rivallingly discolor the sea for rods. The milk is very sweet and rich; it has been tasted by man; it might do well with strawberries. When overflowing with mutual esteem, the whales salute *more hominum*. [*Melville's note.*]

23. The frantic Ahab had thrown down and trampled upon his quadrant at high-noon of "that day."

24. The mysterious Fedallah whom Ahab had stowed away to be a member of his own boat-crew. He exercised a strange power over his master. A secret, potent spell seemed to join them. "At times, for longest hours, without a single hail, they stood far parted in the starlight; Ahab in his scuttle, the Parsee by the mainmast; but still fixedly gazing upon each other; as if in the Parsee Ahab saw his forethrown shadow, in Ahab the Parsee his abandoned substance" (chapter CXXX).

25. The *Pequod* meets several ships in the course of her doomed voyage. These encounters have symbolical significance in the allegory. On the *Jeroboam* a malignant disease has broken out which is half-believed to be the work of a crazed seaman who holds the crew in awe. A letter which Ahab carries for one of her officers cannot be delivered. He is dead. Shortly before the episode of the corposants, they sight the *Bachelor*, full of oil and pennants flying, on her homeward voyage. The gay commander tries to entice Ahab aboard, but he repulses the offer to join their revelry. Their ways are to opposite poles. One more ship the *Pequod* will meet, after this encounter with the *Rachel*. It is miserably named the *Delight*, for it had met the White Whale and lost five brave men in fighting him.

26. This motion is peculiar to the sperm whale. It receives its designation (pitchpoling) from its being likened to that preliminary

up-and-down poise of the whale-lance, in the exercise called pitch-poling, previously described. By this motion the whale must best and most comprehensively view whatever objects may be encircling him. [*Melville's note.*]

27. I Maccabees 6 : 34. The wine was apparently meant to represent blood to the elephants.

28. A mountain in southern New Hampshire.

29. When Queequeg was ailing he had had a coffin made for himself by the ship's carpenter. As soon as it was finished, he began to recover. The coffin he henceforth used as a sea-chest. When the ship's life-buoy, a cask which filled and sank, had to be replaced, the coffin was made to serve.

CRITICISM

Etchings of a Whaling Cruise (320–327)

This review is, it would seem, the first piece of criticism written by Melville. The holograph MS. I was lucky enough to come upon in a file of unsigned contributions to the *Literary World* in the Duyckinck Collection in the New York Public Library. The MS. has been placed with the other Melville papers in that collection.

The text printed here reproduces that of the first publication, in the *Literary World* for March 6, 1847, pp. 105–106. The copy which Melville furnished the printer was fairly "clean" so the errors are few. These have been corrected from the MS. No attempt has been made, however, to change the punctuation to accord with Melville's style. The usage of the *Literary World* required as many commas as a schoolmaster, but one is, at that, safer in following it than Melville's careless and inconsistent style. The changes in phraseology which Melville made in the review as he was writing it are almost entirely in the direction of a smoother flowing sentence. In this respect it differs decidedly from "Hawthorne and His Mosses," where Melville wrestled with his thought as he wrote.

We know at present of five critical articles by Melville, all of which were contributed to the *Literary World*. There are probably more which remain to be identified as his. In the order of their appearance these reviews are: "Etchings of a Whaling Cruise" and "Sailor's Life and Sailor's Yarns," March 6, 1847, pp. 105–106; "Mr. Parkman's Tour" (*The California and Oregon Trail*), March 31, 1849, pp. 291–293; "Cooper's New Novel" (*The Sea Lions*), April 28, 1849, p. 370; "A Thought on Book-Binding" (Cooper's *The Red Rover*), March 16, 1850, pp. 276–277; "Hawthorne and His Mosses," August 17, 1850, pp. 125–127 and August 24, pp. 145–147. The notice of *The Red Rover* J. H. Birss identified from the holograph MS. in the Duyckinck Collection and printed in the *New England Quarterly*, V, 346–348.

1. This parenthesis replaces Melville's first phrase: "dabbling in its bubbles."

2. Front Street, New York, runs north from the Battery, one block from the East River.

3. B. W. Procter ("Barry Cornwall") is not referred to by Browne but one can imagine what he would have thought of the poetic excesses of Cornwall's "The Sea," which begins:

The Sea! the Sea! the open Sea!
The blue, the fresh, the ever free!

4. Cf. *Typee*, chapter IV: "Some long-haired, bare-necked youths who, forced by the united influences of Captain Marryat and hard times, embark at Nantucket for a pleasure excursion to the Pacific . . . oftentimes return very respectable middle-aged gentlemen."

5. "Regarded in the decidedly unfavorable light" was substituted for "held a scoundrel."

"Hawthorne and His Mosses" (327–345)

The MS. of this review, written in two hands, one of which is Melville's, is now among the Melville MSS. and letters in the Duyckinck Collection in the New York Public Library. I discovered it in a file of unsigned contributions which had been published in the *Literary World* and which Evert Duyckinck had saved. Melville evidently took great pains with the article, rewriting a number of passages entirely, adding new material and altering many words and phrases to better the writing or modify the tone of what he had originally put down. Some of these changes are listed in the notes.

The text here printed reproduces that of the first publication of the article, in the *Literary World*, August 17 and 24, 1850. Typographical errors are silently corrected. Wherever the printer has misread Melville's copy, the correct reading has been substituted from the MS.

Among Melville's books is a copy of the first edition of the *Mosses* with the inscription "From Aunt Mary, July 18, 1850." Pasted on the inside cover is a patch of sea-moss with the remark, in Melville's hand: "This moss was gathered in Salem, and therefore I place it here for a frontispiece. P.S. It may be objected that this is sea-moss;—but then, it only went to sea—like many young mortals—in its youth, and to my certain knowledge has been ashore ever since." Several passages of the text were marked by Melville—as he lay in the hay-mow reading?—with such rapturous exclamations as "The moral here is wonderfully fine"; "Exquisite"; "What a revelation." Clearly his ecstatic reading of the *Mosses* took place, as he says in his title, in July, 1850. But the barn was in Pittsfield, not in Vermont.

The pleasantest of ironic circumstances attended the writing of the review. Hawthorne and Melville were living six miles apart at the moment, and were to meet in a few days, that is, on August 5 (see p. 434 below). When the review appeared in the *Literary World* they were on the way to friendship, but the Hawthornes had no idea who this great admirer of Mr. Hawthorne could be. They wrote letters to Evert Duyckinck on the same day, August 29, betraying their delight. To add to the irony both of them mention the pleasure Melville's books are giving them, and we learn that Hawthorne is reading the work of *his* new friend also, oddly enough, in the hay barn.

Mrs. Hawthorne's letter, after some remarks about Flaxman, continues:

"But, my dear Mr. Duyckinck, I cannot speak or think of anything now but the extraordinary review of Mr. Hawthorne in the Literary World. The Virginian is the first person who has ever in *print* apprehended Mr. Hawthorne. I keep constantly reading over and over the inspired utterances, and marvel more and more that the word has at last been said which I have so long hoped to hear, and so well said. There is such a generous, noble enthusiasm as I have not before found in any critic of any writer. While bringing out the glory of his subject, (excuse me, but I am speaking as an indifferent person) he surrounds himself with a glory. The freshness of primeval nature is in that man, and the true Promethean fire is in him. Who can he be, so fearless, so rich in heart, of such fine intuition? Is his name altogether hidden?

"We have been very much interested in Mr. Melville's books, and we are very much obliged to you for them. Mr. Hawthorne has read them all on the new hay in the barn, which is a delightful place for the perusal of worthy books" (Duyckinck Collection, New York Public Library).

Hawthorne's letter is as follows:

"I have read Melville's works with a progressive appreciation of the author. No writer ever put the reality before his reader more unflinchingly than he does in 'Redburn,' and 'White Jacket.' 'Mardi' is a rich book, with depths here and there that compel a man to swim for his life. It is so good that one scarcely pardons the writer for not having brooded long over it, so as to make it a great deal better.

"You will see by my wife's note that I have all along had one staunch admirer; and with her to back me, I really believe I should do very well without any other. Nevertheless, I must own that I have read the articles in the Literary World with very great pleasure. The writer has a truly generous heart; nor do I think it necessary to appropriate the whole significance of his encomium, any more than to devour everything on the table, when a host of noble hospitality spreads a banquet before me. But he is no common man; and, next to deserving his praise, it is good to have beguiled or bewitched such a man into praising me and more than I deserve" (Duyckinck Collection, New York Public Library).

1. Published in four volumes, 1821–1822. Timothy Dwight was President of Yale College and an epicist.

2. See above.

3. In the first sketch in the volume, "The Old Manse," Hawthorne says that it was in this same house, now his, that Emerson wrote "Nature" and used to watch "the Assyrian dawn," etc.

4. The title of the eighth sketch in the *Mosses*.

5. An echo of Sydney Smith's famous challenge: "In the four quarters of the globe, who reads an American book?"

6. Melville is unwittingly unfair to Chettle. It was Robert Greene who, in *A Groatsworth of Wit*, thus maligned Shakespeare.

7. Melville here crossed out six lines which are important in showing how vehement were his first impulses as regards the subject of America's literary future. The paragraph originally began: "This, too, I mean, that if Shakespeare has not been equalled, he is sure to be surpassed, and surpassed by an American born now or yet to be born. For it will never do for us who in most other things out-do as well as out-brag the world, it will not do for us to fold our hands and say in the highest department advance there is none."

8. Among epics which the new national consciousness evoked, none equals the bathetic *Fredoniad; or Independence Preserved—an Epic Poem of the War of 1812*, written by Richard Emmons, M.D. His poem, dedicated to Lafayette, begins with a convocation in Hades.

9. Probably Washington Irving.

10. Melville originally wrote "Milton" instead of "Tompkins." This vehement passage was even more downright in its first draft. Some of the changes are revealing. The "leaven of literary flunkeyism" had the adjective "Bostonian" before it. After the next sentence Melville added, and then crossed out, the threat: "and the time is not far off when circumstances may force her to it."

11. Melville originally made the sentence end: "displaced Oliver Goldsmith and many another brighter name than that."

12. Melville first wrote "Greece."

13. "Equals" was crossed out, "surpasses" substituted, and the rest of the sentence added.

14. "Man like me" was substituted for "a mere person."

15. "Anaks" was substituted for "now half-forgotten men."

16. "Ramblingly" was substituted for "feebly."

17. "Scrawl of mine" was substituted for "dissertation."

POEMS (346–367)

1. This poem has not previously been published. I am allowed to print it here through the kindness of Mrs. Eleanor Melville Metcalf, in whose possession it now is.

Shepherd was a New York lawyer. He was educated at Union College and began the practice of law in Saratoga, where he returned in 1861. From 1845 to 1861 he lived in New York, maintaining an office at 7 Wall Street. Allan Melville seems to have introduced him to Herman and to the Duyckincks. Evert Duyckinck noted in his diary under October 8, 1856: "In the evening home: Allan Melville brought his friend Daniel Shepherd whose novel just published 'Saratoga a Tale of 1787' he had sent me in the afternoon." The next day he set down the following: "In the evening at Mr. Shepherd's, in 14th str. [his residence, at 124 W. 14] with Herman and Allan Melville and Tomes. Good talk. Herman warming like an old sailor over the supper...." (Duyckinck Collection, New York Public Library). Shepherd wrote two other novels: *The Bride of the Old Frontier*, 1859, and *A Crusade of the Forest*, 1860. He died in 1870 of softening of the brain.

2. Nebuchadnezzar "dreamed dreams, wherewith his spirit was troubled, and his sleep brake from him" (Daniel 2 : 1).

3. If Melville is jestingly referring to the contemporary political situation in Italy, then the reign of the bird of love must signify the Austrians whom the French (the chanticleers) had just defeated, in the war for the liberation of Italy, at Magenta (June 4) and Malegnano (June 8).

4. The river near Melville's Pittsfield home.

5. *Battle-Pieces* was published by Harper and Brothers in 1866. The firm had already, during 1866, printed in its periodical, *Harper's New Monthly Magazine*, five of the poems in the book: "The March to the Sea" (February, p. 366); "The Cumberland" (March, p. 474); "Sheridan at Cedar Creek"—under the title "Philip" (April, p. 640); "Chattanooga" (June, p. 44); "Gettysburg" (July, p. 209). For a discussion of the impulse which caused Melville to write these war poems and of his method of composing them, see Introduction, p. lxxxvii ff.

6. Melville extemporized on the reports of the battle which he found in the *Rebellion Record* (II, 511–519). For the sake of the rhymes he ingeniously named the valiant horse Orion and the corporal Tryon. In the report from the *Missouri Democrat* the following caught his eye: "Gen. Lyon now desired the Iowa boys, whom he had found so brave, to prepare to meet the next onset of the enemy with the bayonet immediately after firing. They said, 'Give us a leader and we will follow to the death.'" (*Rebellion Record*, p. 513). From the *New York Tribune's* account he took the general's dappled gray horse, changing his color to black; the reluctance of his officers to fight; the "unnatural glare in his eyes" as he placed himself in the van of the Iowans.

7. The battle between the *Monitor* and the *Merrimac*, which to a

naval man would forcibly suggest the end of the old order of sea-fighting in wooden ships, impelled Melville to write two other poems on the event: "In the Turret" and "The Temeraire."

8. McClellan's pickets were within sight of Richmond before he decided to shift his base to the James. On the two sides 36,000 men were lost in the following seven days of fighting which culminated in the battle of Malvern Hill, July 1, 1862.

9. Sheridan had spent the night at Winchester, Virginia, twenty miles from Cedar Creek where the Confederates attacked at dawn on October 19, 1864. After their defeat here they could never again menace Washington.

Thomas Buchanan Read's "Sheridan's Ride" might well be displaced in anthologies by this poem of Melville's on the same theme. It was reprinted in the *New York Leader*, December 8, 1866; in the *Pittsfield Sun*, January 17, 1867; and elsewhere.

10. As the poem was printed in *Harper's New Monthly Magazine* lines 17 and 18 were given as follows:

> They faced about, each man;
> Faint hearts were strong again;

11. The MS. and proof-sheets of this volume, which was issued privately by Melville in 1888 in an edition of twenty-five copies, are now in the Harvard College Library.

12. In a prose introduction to this poem Melville pictures John Marr as a mariner who had made his final port on the frontier-prairie. His efforts to be convivial with the solemn, work-driven pioneers were obstructed. When he attempted to speak of the scenes of his roving life, he was gently rebuked, on one occasion, by an evangelical blacksmith who said: "Friend, we know nothing of that here." For a time he had kept up a little correspondence with his former shipmates, but that solace was finally gone. He could do nothing as the sense of his isolation grew upon him but indulge more and more in retrospective musings. The phantoms of his companions became "lit by that aureola circling over any object of the affections in the past for reunion with which an imaginative heart passionately yearns."

13. There exists in the Melville MSS. a carefully worked-over poem entitled "Rammon the Enviable Isles."

14. The MS. of *Timoleon* has been placed in the Harvard College Library. The book was printed privately, in an edition of twenty-five copies, in 1891.

15. This obscure poem seems, on the surface at least, to relate the inner conflict of a virginal woman, called appropriately Urania, whose life has been given over to study, and the sudden awakening of love within her at the "pleasure party." In despair whether to

yield or maintain the austerity of her existence, she considers for a moment entering the church and taking the veil. This impulse is succeeded by a calm determination to devote herself to Minerva, the armed Virgin. But Amor incensed remembers wrong and he will yet exact his vengeance.

The poem can be entirely explained in this objective manner, although the theme and the frank way it is treated are unique in Melville's writing. Lewis Mumford in his *Herman Melville* (pp. 274–281), reading its details as thinly-veiled biography, makes it bear the weight of his conjecture about Melville's failure to find satisfaction in his marriage and the injurious repressions of his sexual life. To do this he has been forced to twist the narrative rather badly.

16. Melville twice visited the Villa Albani, on February 28 and March 14, 1857. See *Journal up the Straits*, pp. 130–131, 141.

17. Minerva.

18. The writing of this poem gave Melville a great deal of trouble. The MS. is so much written over as to be almost undecipherable. Three slips of paper on which corrections or fresh beginnings have been made are pinned to the first sheet. An attempt is made below to reproduce these rewritings. The lowest sheet reads:

Art

In him who would evoke—create
extremes
Contraries must meet and mate
Flames that burn, and winds that freeze
to

This is crossed out and over it is pinned:

Art

well pleased we
In placid hours ~~we easy~~ ∧ dream
brave   unbodied
Of many a ~~bright~~ unborn [?] scheme
lend   ~~tru~~ pulsed
But form to ~~give,~~ & life create,
What unlike things must meet and mate
A flame to melt

A second slip pinned on reads:

Sad patience,—joyous energies;
yet
Humility—~~and~~ pride, and scorn;
~~Reverence; love and hate twin-born;~~
~~Instinct and culture; ere meet~~
~~Audacity—reverence [?]; love and hate~~
~~Instinct and culture; These must mate~~
~~With more than~~ [*erasure*]

A third slip pinned on top reads:

> Audacity—reverence; love and hate
> Instinct and culture.) These must mate—
> With more than even Jacob's heart
>   the
>   To wrestle with that Angel—Art
>   and fuse with Jacob's heart

19. Melville wrote to his brother-in-law John C. Hoadley on Saturday in Easter Week, 1877: "In return for your M.S. yarns I send you something I found the other day—came across in a lot of papers. I remember that the lines were suggested by a passage in Gibbon (Decline & Fall) Have you a copy? Turn to "*Antonine*" &c. in index. What the deuce the thing means I dont know; but here it is" (Paltsits, *Family Correspondence of Herman Melville*, 48). The copy of the poem which he enclosed differs from the final version, printed here, in which Melville has the American scene in mind throughout.

20. From the group of poems in *Timoleon* headed "Fruit of Travel Long Ago." See the Introduction, p. lxxxv, for the suggestion that these poems, inspired by scenes of his travels in 1856–1857, made up the volume of verse which Melville tried, unsuccessfully, to publish in 1860.

The desert and the pyramids affected him profoundly. The passages describing his feeling of awe and terror are among the most remarkable in the *Journal up the Straits* (pp. 56–59, 63–64). Many close parallels to this poem and "In the Desert" can be found in the *Journal*.

LETTERS (368–404)

To Evert Duyckinck, July 3, 1846.

Printed in part in Minnigerode, *Some Personal Letters of Herman Melville*, 14–15. This and the other letters to the Duyckinck brothers, here printed, are in the Duyckinck Collection, New York Public Library.

1. Melville's mother was living at Lansingburgh near Albany.

2. Richard Tobias Greene ("Toby") saw a notice of *Typee* in the New York *Evangelist* (April 9, 1846). He communicated the fact of his existence to the Buffalo *Commercial Advertiser* and confirmed the accuracy of Melville's account of their sequestration in the Typee valley. In July Melville visited Toby, as is shown by an unpublished letter (Duyckinck Collection, New York Public Library) of Allan Melville to Evert Duyckinck, written July 22: "Dr. Sir: My brother desires me . . . to say that he has reached home after having seen 'Toby,' and that he will be in town on Monday with the sequel."

To Evert Duyckinck, November 14, 1848.

Printed in part in Minnigerode, 30–31.

1. Although Melville refused to review Joseph C. Hart's *Romance of Yachting*—the subject of this letter—his entertaining remarks on the book's absurdities were used by the author of the review which was published in the *Literary World* for December 2, 1848. The following extract from the second paragraph of the review shows the debt to Melville: "Mr. Hart has in the early pages of his work instructive selections from the Connecticut Blue Laws and the Dutch Antiquarianism of Dr. O'Callaghan, followed by several extracts from a nautical log which is in a high mood of animal spirits and composition, with sundry specimens of the vernacular. We are next called to take a hand at a bullfight in old Spain and then—set down to a digest of the thrice sodden commentators on Shakespeare, who, according to Mr. Hart, is an author fast passing into oblivion, and who once owed his success to his indecency! There is something after this on Duff Gordon Sherry and Anthony's nose."

Hart's earlier effort, *Miriam Coffin, or The Whale Fishermen* (1834), is a readable yarn. Melville knew the book and may have made slight use of it in writing *Moby-Dick*. See Leon Howard, "A Predecessor of *Moby-Dick*," *Modern Language Notes*, XLIX, 310–311.

To Evert Duyckinck, February 24, 1849.

Unpublished. Seven lines quoted in Mumford, *Herman Melville*, 138.

1. Probably W. A. Butler, a contributor to the *Literary World*.

2. This set of Shakespeare, containing notes in Melville's hand, is still in existence, deposited in the Harvard College Library.

3. Fanny Kemble Butler, daughter of the English actor Charles Kemble, gained a phenomenal reputation as a Shakespearian actress in 1829, though Leigh Hunt thought her "an entirely artificial performer." In 1832 she visited America and married here Pierce Butler, a wealthy plantation owner living in Philadelphia. They were divorced in 1849. She was a favorite in the literary circles of the Berkshire region, though her use of strong language and her boldness in wearing trousers when she went fishing, scandalized the graver sort. Her Shakespeare readings were the fashionable diversion of the moment. It is asserted that she first appeared as a reader before Catherine Sedgwick, Melville, Longfellow, and Hawthorne (L. S. Driver, *Fanny Kemble* [Chapel Hill, N.C., 1933], p. 163).

To Evert Duyckinck, March 3, 1849.

Printed in part in Minnigerode, 32–34.

1. "Old Zack" is, of course, Zachary Taylor, hero of the Mexican War. In May, 1846, he defeated the enemy at Palo Alto, one of the

early engagements of the war. As the Whig candidate, he became
President of the United States in 1848. Melville contributed seven
hilarious articles entitled "Authentic Anecdotes of 'Old Zack'" to
the humorous magazine *Yankee Doodle*, the series running from
July 24 to Sept. 11, 1847 (Mansfield, "Melville's Comic Articles on
Zachary Taylor," *American Literature*, ix, 411).

To Evert Duyckinck, March 28, 1849.
    Unpublished.
    1. The office of Harper & Brothers was at 82 Cliff Street. The
book soon to be published is *Mardi*. A notice of it, with long extracts, appeared in the *Literary World* for April 7, 1849, pp. 309–310;
April 14, pp. 333–336; and April 21, pp. 351–353.

To Evert Duyckinck, April 5, 1849.
    Printed in part in Minnigerode, 8–9.
    1. The *Literary World* for March 31, 1849 (p. 295) contained a re-
view under the title "Theological Poems," of *Gospel Sonnets; or,
Spiritual Songs* by the late Rev. Mr. Ralph Erskine (d. 1752).
The reviewer quotes a specimen of the author's style entitled "Smoking Spiritualized." To prove the aptness of Melville's description of
the verses, as lying "in coils like a sailor's pigtail in its keg," the first
stanza is cited here:

> "This Indian weed, now wither'd quite,
>   Though green at noon, cut down at night,
>   Shows thy decay;
>   All flesh is hay.
> Thus think, and smoke tobacco."

    2. Charles Fenno Hoffman (1806–1884) edited the *Literary World*
from May 8, 1847 through September 1848, Nos. 14–87. As critic,
poet, novelist, and editor, he was one of the best known of New
York literary men in the mid-century. He recovered temporarily
from his insanity, but was eventually confined in the State Hospital
at Harrisburg for over thirty years.
    3. "That affair of mine" must be *Mardi* which Duyckinck was
reading in proof.
    4. Sir Thomas Browne, in two volumes, Melville had borrowed
from Evert Duyckinck in 1847 or 1848. The 1686 folio of Browne's
works is one of the books Melville bought in London in December
1849. "Old Burton" he had bought in April, 1847, discovering subsequently that the copy had once belonged to his father.

To Evert Duyckinck, December 2, 1849.
    Brief portions printed in Minnigerode, 51–52.
    Generous extracts from the journal which Melville kept on this
trip abroad are published in Weaver's *Herman Melville*, pp. 284–304.

In London his negotiations with Bentley, who had published *Mardi* and *Redburn*, secured him an offer of £200 for the first thousand copies of *White-Jacket*.

On November 27 he crossed to France, leaving Paris on December 6 to make a hasty trip to Brussels, Cologne, and Coblenz. He was again in London on December 13. During his stay he saw something of English literary society, explored the city, indulged his passion for the theater and book-collecting. He sailed on Christmas Day, from Portsmouth.

We get an intimate glimpse of Melville's state of mind while in Paris from a letter of G. J. Adler to Evert Duyckinck (February 16, 1850). Adler, a professor of German who contributed to the *Literary World*, crossed the ocean with Melville and was with him frequently during his stay abroad.

"Our friend Mr. Melville has, I hope, long ago reached his home again safely, and you will have gained from him an account of our voyage and peregrination in England and London. I regretted his departure very much; but all that I could do to check and fix his restless mind for a while at least was of no avail. His loyalty to his friends at home and the instinctive impulse of his imagination to assimilate and perhaps to work up into some beautiful chimaeras . . . the materials he had already gathered in his travels, would not allow him to prolong his stay."

1. In spite of Bentley's liberality, it would seem, from this remark, that there had been some delay in the payment of advance royalties on *White-Jacket*.

The rights of foreign authors were not fully protected in America until 1891, and our failure to enter into any international copyright agreement made it doubtful until then whether American authors could be protected in the English market. In spite of this uncertainty both Bentley and Murray paid writers like Irving and Melville respectable sums for the privilege of publishing their works.

2. George Duyckinck had traveled in Europe in the late 1840's, and passed Melville on to his London acquaintances. Melville had gone to England well equipped with letters of introduction. At the request of Judge Shaw, Edward Everett had written to Samuel Rogers asking him to help Melville to meet a "few of those choicest spirits, who even at the present day increase the pride which we feel in speaking the language of Shakespeare and Milton" (P. W. Clayden, *Rogers and his Contemporaries*, London, 1889, II, 342–343). Rogers responded by inviting Melville to his breakfast parties.

3. Possibly the Davidson who was connected with the business affairs of the *Literary World*.

4. It appeared in the *Literary World* for March 31, 1849 under the title "Mr. Parkman's Tour."

5. Melville called again the next day (Weaver, *Herman Melville*, 300).

To Evert Duyckinck, February 2, 1850.
    Printed in part in Minnigerode, 41–43.
    1. The 17,000 books in Duyckinck's library form one of the chief collections of the New York Public Library.
    2. Evert Duyckinck's sons.
    3. Connecting Wapping and Rotherhithe. It was completed in 1843.
    4. George Frederick Cruchley's *Picture of London* was a standard guidebook of the day.

To Evert Duyckinck, March 7, 1850.
    Unpublished.
    1. This green jacket attracted attention in the London streets and "played the devil" with his respectability there. See Weaver, *Herman Melville*, 292 and 299.

To Evert Duyckinck, August 16, 1850.
    Printed in part in Minnigerode, 66–68.
    1. After the War of 1812, Melville's uncle Thomas, a major in the United States army, settled on a farm in Pittsfield to which the name "Broadhall" was given in 1851. (It is now the country-club.) Here, as a boy and young man, Herman spent many pleasant months as "an active assistant on the farm." After the Major's death the house was turned into a kind of private hotel where such distinguished guests as Longfellow and ex-President Tyler boarded. Here in 1850 Melville brought his family until he could find a permanent home in the neighborhood. He soon secured the piece of property which adjoined "Broadhall" to the east. The house, with its enormous central chimney, had been a tavern in the late eighteenth century. Melville named it "Arrowhead." In a sketch called "I and my Chimney"—one of the *Piazza Tales*—he describes its labyrinthine interior with humorous realism. When he returned to New York to live, in 1863, he sold "Arrowhead" to his brother Allan, in whose family it remained until 1927.
    The first visit (August 2–12, 1850) which Duyckinck made to Melville impressed him enormously. He described the excursions and parties in five letters to his wife and in two to his brother George. These are in the Duyckinck Collection of the New York Public Library. All except the second letter to George are printed in L. S. Mansfield's "Glimpses of Herman Melville's Life in Pittsfield, 1850–1851," *American Literature*, IX, 26–48. The conclusion of the first letter to George (August 7) alludes to *Moby-Dick:* "We are in a fine old country mansion on the best site I have seen in the region.

Melville has a new book mostly done—a romantic, fanciful and literal and most enjoyable presentment of the Whale Fishery—something quite new."

2. Cornelius Mathews (1817–1889), a poet, playwright, and critic, was one of the chief contributors to the *Literary World*. With Evert Duyckinck he founded, in 1840, *Arcturus, a Journal of Books and Opinion*. He accompanied Duyckinck on this visit to Pittsfield. In a series of three articles in the *Literary World* (August 24 and 31; September 7, 1850), entitled "Several Days in Berkshire," Mathews described their sojourn with the Melvilles.

3. The Duyckinck offices were at 20 Clinton Place. This street is now the section of 8th Street between Sixth Avenue and Broadway. Melville passed many hilarious evenings there over the Duyckinck punch-bowl.

4. So that it might be displayed in the Phrenological Museum of Fowler and Wells.

5. The Shaker village there, eight miles from Pittsfield, was a favorite excursion of Melville's.

6. The proof errors to which Melville objects—they were excessive—are in his article "Hawthorne and His Mosses" which ran in two installments in the *Literary World*, August 17 and August 24, 1850. See pp. 327–345 above.

To Evert Duyckinck, December 12, 1850.
Printed in part in Minnigerode, 69–71.

1. The family of J. R. Morewood had settled at "Broadhall." Mrs. Morewood wrote to Evert Duyckinck, December 28, 1851: "Mr. Herman . . . is a pleasant companion at all times and I like him very much. Mr. Morewood now that he knows him better likes him the more—still he dislikes many of Mr. Herman's opinions and religious views" (Duyckinck Collection, New York Public Library). An amusing picture of Mrs. Morewood, who was an indefatigable organizer of picnic excursions, emerges from Evert Duyckinck's letters to his wife during his second visit to Pittsfield, in August, 1851 (Mansfield, "Glimpses of Herman Melville's Life in Pittsfield, 1850–1851," 39–47). The Morewoods' son William married a daughter of Allan Melville.

2. The book was, of course, *Moby-Dick*.

3. See p. 431 above.

4. Elizabeth Shaw Melville, Herman's wife.

To Evert Duyckinck, February 12, 1851.
Printed as two letters in Minnigerode, 72–73, 55–56.

1. See Introduction, p. xliii.

2. See p. 431 above.

3. This is possibly a reference to "The Murdered Pump," a quizzical sketch by Leigh Hunt in *Leigh Hunt's Journal*, December 28, 1850, pp. 59–61. It tells in dialogue how a drunken gentleman fights a duel with an old pump under the impression that he is exacting satisfaction for an insult.

To Nathaniel Hawthorne, March [?], 1851.

Printed in Julian Hawthorne, *Nathaniel Hawthorne and His Wife*, I, 385–389; also in Weaver, *Herman Melville*, 315–317.

The Hawthornes moved to Lenox, Mass., six miles from Pittsfield in the early summer of 1850. The Melvilles came to "Broadhall" to board during the same summer. In October they moved into "Arrowhead" a half-mile away. J. E. A. Smith in his novel *Taghconic, The Romance and Beauty of the Hills* (Boston, 1879, p. 318), mentions that the two authors met for the first time on a picnic excursion during which "the two were compelled by a thunder shower to take shelter in a narrow recess of the rocks of Monument Mountain." Evert Duyckinck alludes to the circumstances of this first meeting (August 5, 1850) in a letter to his brother George, August 7, 1850. He was visiting the Melvilles at the time. "Dudley D. Field who met us going up in the cars . . . slaughtered for us not only turkeys and beeves but got up a battle of lions on Monument Mountain. He had Dr. Holmes whose grounds adjoin this Melville land and Hawthorne from Lenox and J. T. Fields from Boston and Headley (in the afternoon) and our full party all came out strong—as you may imagine. We had a thunder shower on the mountain and a visit to the Icy Glen etc. etc.—a brilliant day" (Duyckinck Collection, New York Public Library). Duyckinck also sent a vivid account of this party to his wife. It is quoted by Mansfield, "Glimpses of Herman Melville's Life in Pittsfield, 1850–1851," 29–31. Hawthorne mentions the picnic in his journal.

1. Ned Higgins, it will be remembered, is the small boy in the novel who has an insatiable fondness for Miss Hepzibah's gingerbread Jim Crows.

To Nathaniel Hawthorne, June [?], 1851.

Printed in Julian Hawthorne, *Nathaniel Hawthorne and His Wife*, I, 400–407; also in Weaver, *Herman Melville*, 320–324.

1. "Truth, 'tis suppos'd, may bear *all* Lights: and *one* of those principal Lights or natural Mediums, by which Things are to be view'd in order to a thorow Recognition, is *Ridicule* it-self, or that Manner of Proof by which we discern whatever is liable to just Raillery in any Subject. So much, at least, is allow'd by all, who at any time appeal to this *Criterion*" (Shaftesbury, *Characteristicks*, 1727, I, 61).

2. Jinn—demons who exercise supernatural influence over men.

3. Hawthorne's short story, "Ethan Brand." Brand describes his sin as "the sin of an intellect that triumphed over the sense of brotherhood with man and reverence for God, and sacrificed everything to its own mighty claims."

4. *A Wonder Book for Girls and Boys.*

To Nathaniel Hawthorne, November [?], 1851.

Printed in Lathrop, *Memories of Hawthorne*, 156–160; also, inaccurately, in Weaver, *Herman Melville*, 327–329.

1. Hawthorne did genuinely admire *Moby-Dick*. In a letter to Evert Duyckinck, written from West Newton, Mass., December 1, 1851, he said of it: "What a book Melville has written! It gives me an idea of much greater power than his preceding ones. It hardly seemed to me that the review of it, in the Literary World, did justice to its best points" (Duyckinck Collection, New York Public Library).

2. "Hawthorne and His Mosses," in the *Literary World*, August 17 and 24, 1850. See pp. 327–345.

To George Duyckinck, December 20, 1858.

Unpublished.

In the years from 1857–1860 Melville contrived to supplement his income by lecturing on the three subjects "Statuary in Rome," "The South Seas," "Travelling." His engagements carried him as far afield as Chicago and Montreal. His engagement-book is preserved and has been partially published in Weaver, *Herman Melville*, 369–370.

The *New-York Daily Tribune* of Saturday, February 5, 1859, carried the following advertisement: "New-York Historical Society Lecture. Herman Melville esq. author of 'Typee,' 'Omoo,' &c. will deliver the Fourth lecture of the series in the Hall of the Library, 2d av. corner of 11th st. on Monday Evening, February 7, at $7\frac{1}{2}$. Subject: South Sea Islands. Tickets, 50 cents, may be obtained of E. J. Brown & Co., no. 145 Broadway . . . and at the Library. The number of tickets to be sold is limited to 500. E. J. Brown, Chairman Lecture Committee." The series of five lectures was given in January and February, 1859, for the benefit of the Historical Society and was arranged for by a committee of the Society of which George Duyckinck was a member. The other lectures were delivered by the Rev. George W. Bethune, D.D., on "Lectures and Lecturers"; J. G. Holland, of the *Springfield Republican*, on "American Social Life"; David Paul Brown, on "Stratford-on-Avon"; and the Rev. E. H. Chapin, on "Columbus." The *Tribune* of February 8 carried, under "City Items," an account of Melville's lecture (p. 7, col. 4): "Mr. Herman Melville (the author of 'Typee,' etc.) delivered the fourth of the series of lectures before the New-York Historical

Society last evening, giving a description of the South Sea Islands, their extent, geographical position, and natural beauties, together with some notice of the curious and rare fishes which inhabit those waters, and the many beautiful as well as strange, birds which are so numerous in those islands. These islands, occupying so large a space in the Pacific waters, offer rare attractions to the traveler seeking after unknown and untried scenes of interest. New beauties present themselves continually, and nature seems to have decorated their hills and valleys with a most lavish hand. Mr. Melville also gave a slight sketch of the manners, customs and religious belief of the inhabitants of the different groups of islands, relating many interesting incidents concerning them. He was listened to with great attention by a fair audience."

A fuller account of this lecture, as delivered by Melville at Tremont Temple in Boston on January 30, is given in Weaver, *Herman Melville*, pp. 373–375.

1. Apparently Davidson could not secure him another engagement. His next appearance was in Baltimore on February 8.

To Malcolm Melville, September 1, 1860.

Printed in part in the *Horn Book*, III, 9–10. This and the next two letters are in the Harvard College Library.

When Melville sailed round the Horn in 1860 with his brother Captain Thomas, he kept a brief journal of the voyage. This was published in the *New England Quarterly*, II, 120–125, but is much less vivid than this letter to his eleven-year-old son.

To his wife, March 24, 1861.

A few sentences quoted in Weaver, *Herman Melville*, 375–376.

Melville hoped to get a consular appointment, possibly at Florence, under the new administration.

To Samuel Shaw, December 10, 1862.

Unpublished.

1. Samuel Shaw, Melville's brother-in-law.

To the Hon. Peter Gansevoort, August 26, 1875.

Unpublished.

1. The Hon. Peter Gansevoort (1788–1876), the brother of Melville's mother, was a man of eminence in the affairs of Albany and New York State. His fondness for his nephew is particularly shown in his desire to pay the costs of publishing Melville's long poem *Clarel*. He died on January 4, 1876, before the book, which is dedicated to him, appeared.

2. Mr. Lansing was the husband of the Hon. Peter Gansevoort's daughter Catherine. Mrs. Lansing showed herself, in many generous

but unobtrusive acts, a most devoted cousin of the Melvilles. The Gansevoort-Lansing papers, of great importance not only to students of Melville but to American historians, are now in the New York Public Library.

To James Billson, December 31, 1888.

Printed in the *Nation and Athenaeum*, XXIX, 713. In the 1880's in Leicester, England, a group of young secularists, to whom James Thomson was introduced by his friend John Barrs, met congenially to discuss literary and social problems. They became interested in Melville through Thomson's enthusiasm. *Typee* and *Omoo* and *Mardi* they could easily procure, but they wished more. One of their number, Mr. James Billson, wrote to Melville to secure the titles of all the books he had written. The ardent appreciation of this English group, conveyed to Melville through Mr. Billson, led him to do what he seldom did in these late years, open a correspondence. The eight delightful letters which he wrote Mr. Billson were published by him in the *Nation and Athenaeum*. The letter printed here is the last of the series.

1. Melville read the poems and essays of James Thomson with a sense of having found a kindred spirit.

2. Thomson's lines on Patti's singing, a little *jeu d'esprit* which Melville wishes to "think of" to forget the condition of his eyes is printed in *The Poetical Works of James Thomson*, London, 1895, I, 313. The first of the four stanzas runs as follows:

> Who is this appealing, with archly tender feeling,
>> To that sturdy rustic as sullen as a boar?
> Sweet Zerlina Patti singing *Batti, batti;*
>> Rustical Masetto sulking sulking more and more.

3. Mr. Barrs' copy of *John Marr* is now in the British Museum.

4. "Bird's Nest Farm" was Billson's home.